Mer[illegible]as 1986
We [illegible]osé
from
Mom + Dad

The Illustrated Encyclopedia and
ATLAS OF THE EARTH

NEW YORK

Academic Advisors:
Doctor Ray Hall,
Lecturer in Geography,
Queen Mary College,
University of London.

Doctor P. F. Rawson, B.Sc., Ph.D., F.G.S.,
Lecturer in Geology,
Queen Mary College,
University of London.

Editors:
Michael Bisacre
Richard Carlisle
Deborah Robertson
John Ruck

First published in the USA
1984 by Exeter Books

Distributed by Bookthrift
Exeter is a trademark of Simon & Schuster, Inc.
Bookthrift is a registered trademark of
Simon & Schuster, Inc.
New York, New York

Printed and bound in Italy by New Interlitho SpA.

ISBN 0-671-07045-2

This volume is not to be sold in Australia
or New Zealand

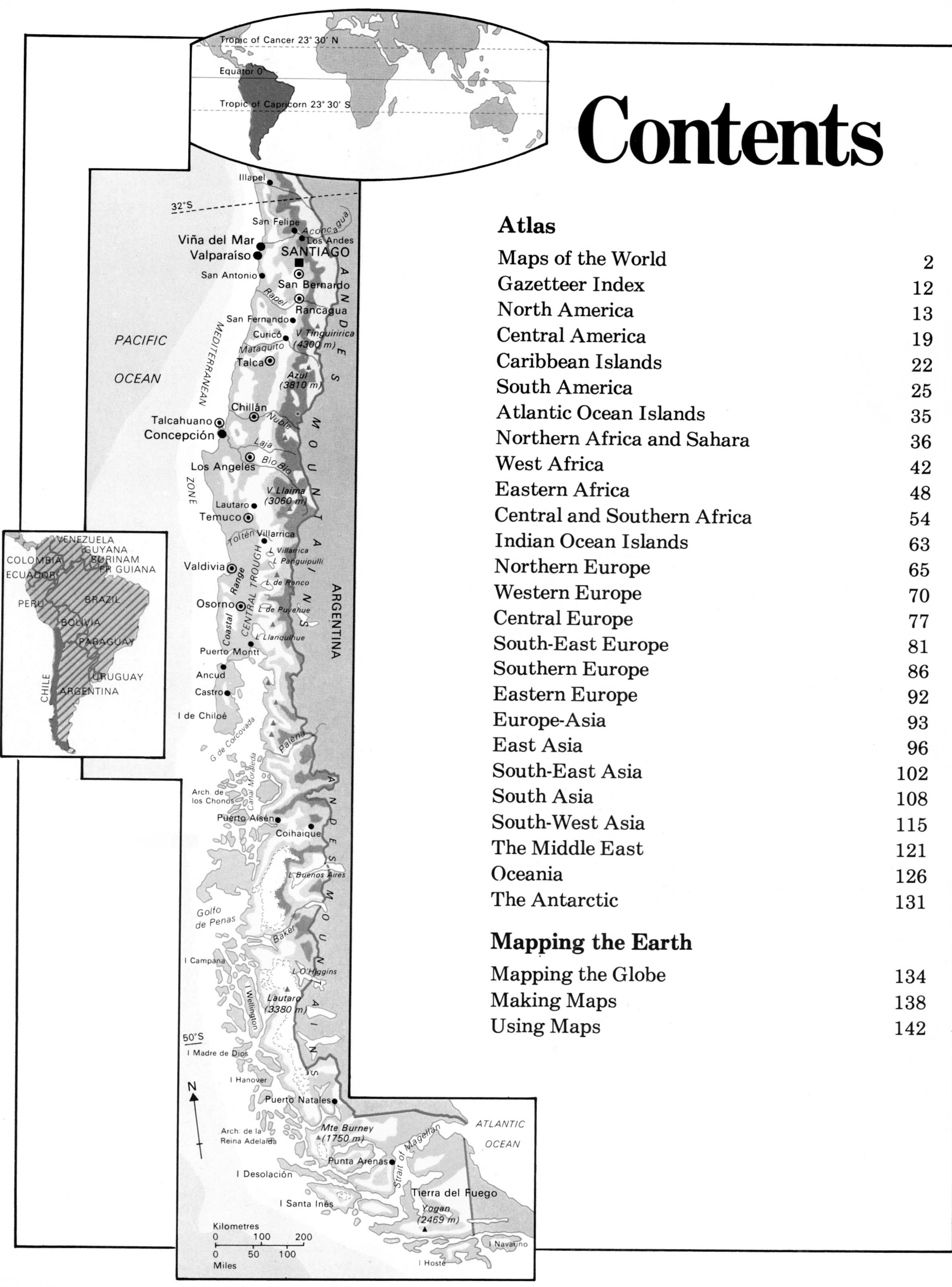

Contents

Atlas

Mapping the Earth

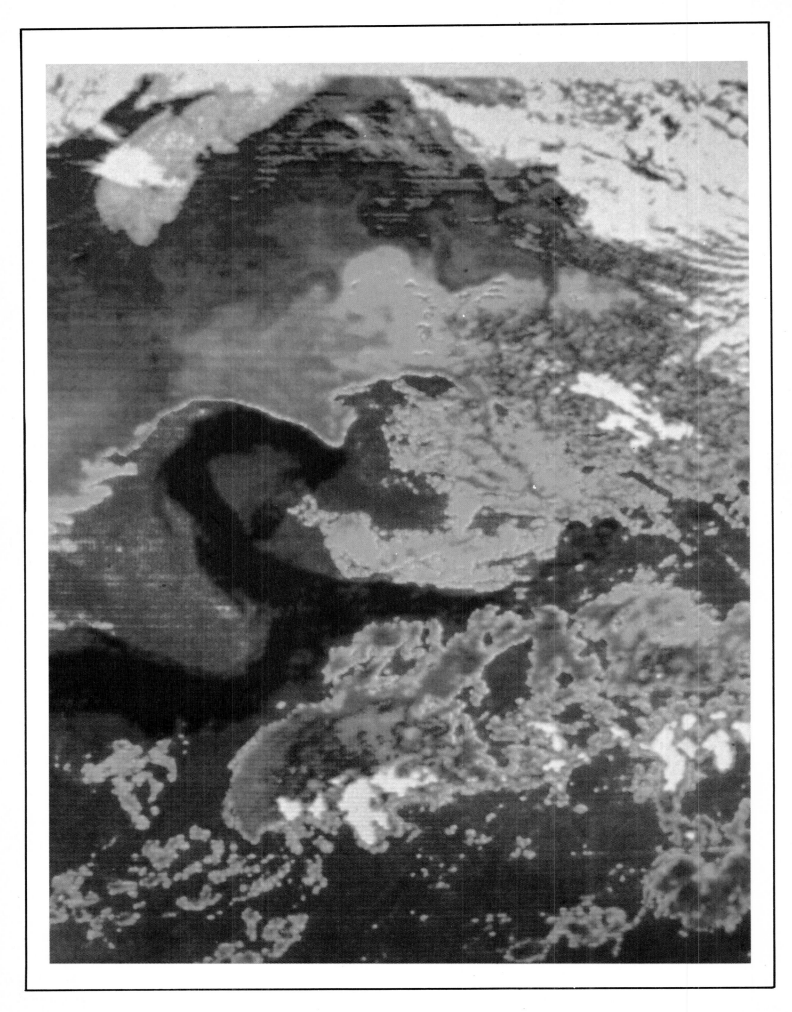

Atlas

The World in Hemispheres
Physical and Astronomical Geography

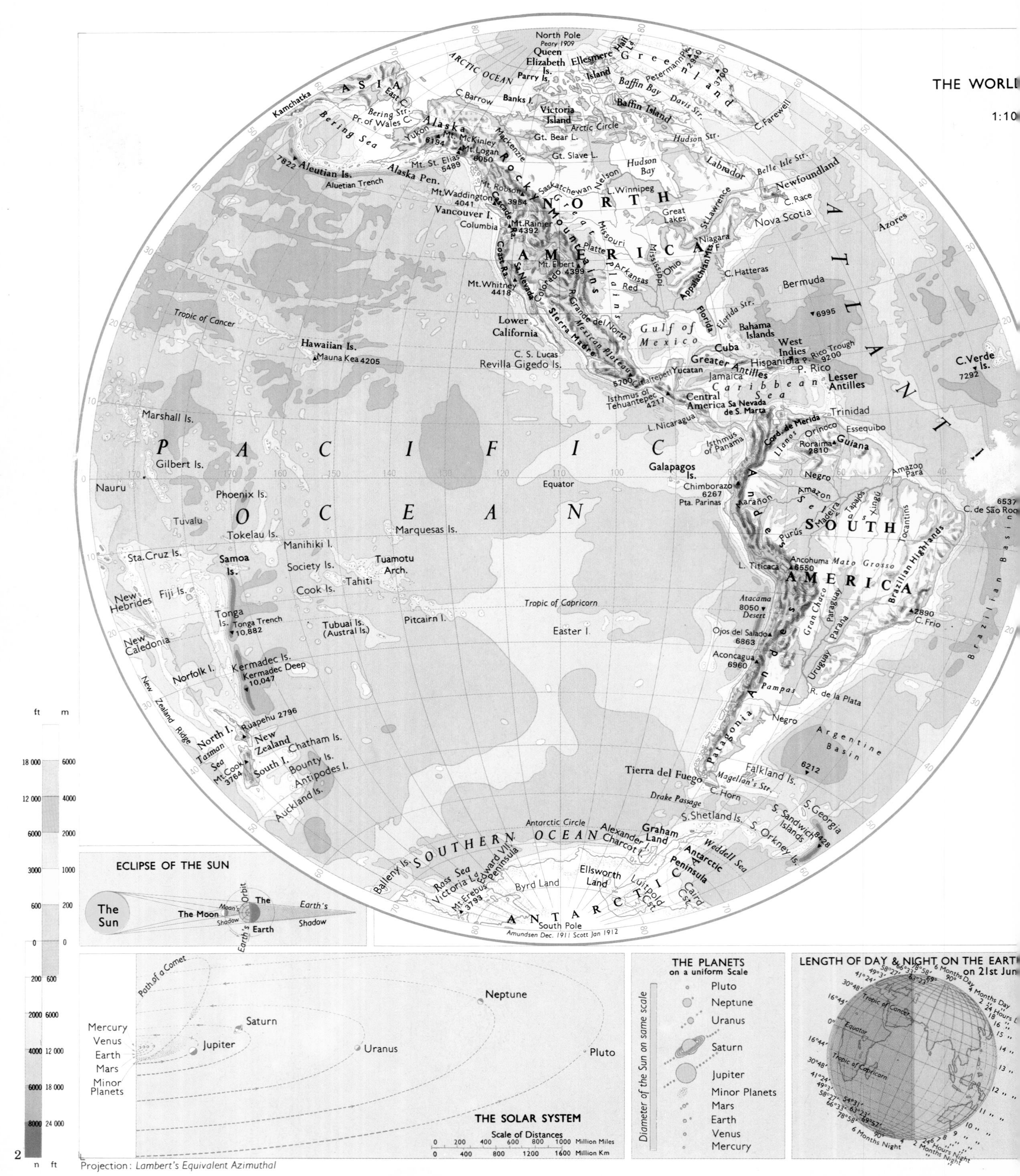

Projection: *Lambert's Equivalent Azimuthal*

PHYSICAL

00 000

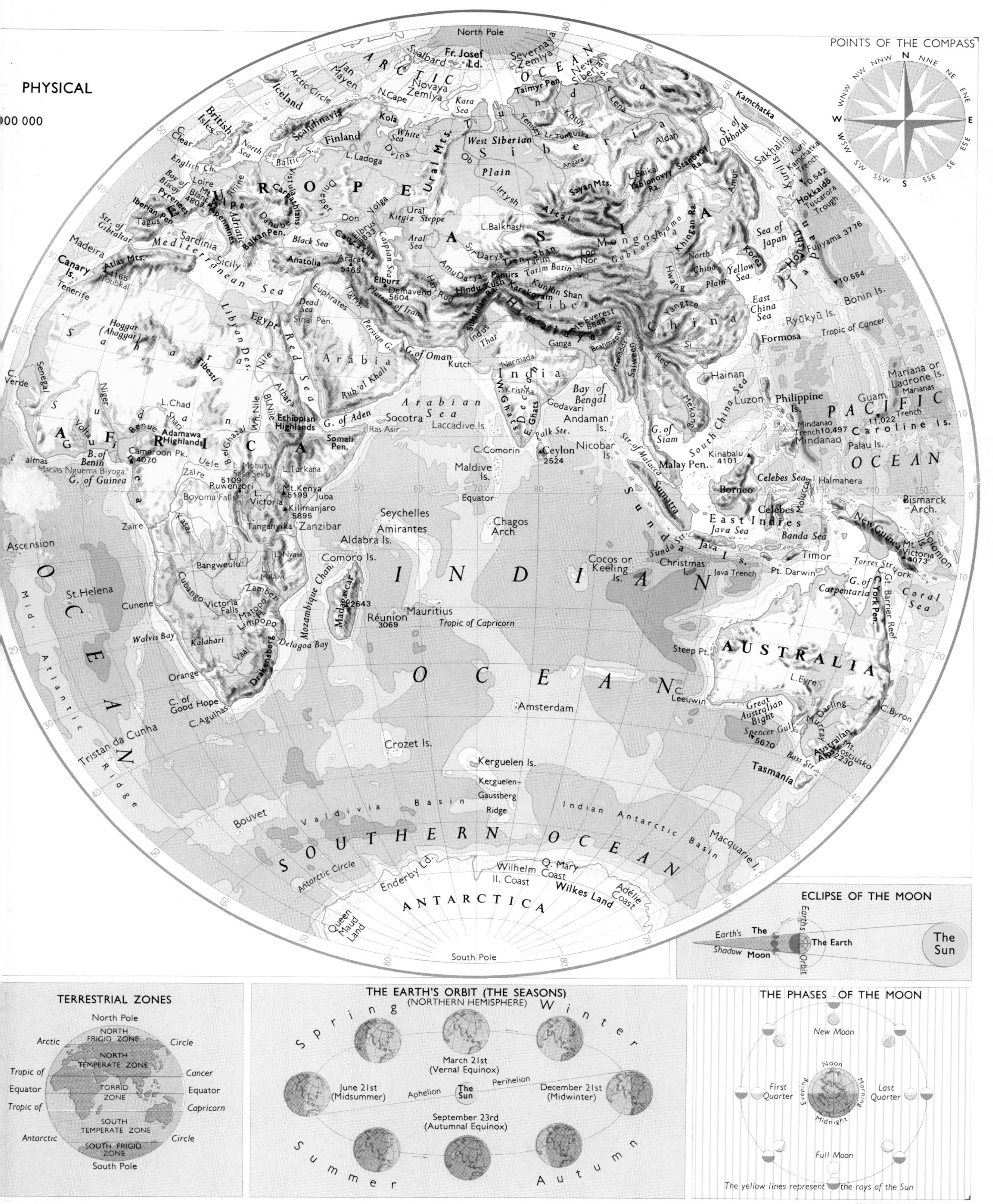

North America: Physical

O C E A N
Clarion Fracture Zone
Revilla Gigedo Is.
Gulf of California
California
C. San Lucas
C. Corrientes
Western Sierra Madre
Mexican Plateau
Eastern Sierra Madre
Monterrey
Guadalajara
México
Puebla
Popocatepetl 5452
Citlaltepetl 5700
Isthmus of Tehuantepec
G. of Tehuantepec
Guatemala Trench
6662
Guatemala
Rio Grande del Norte
Houston
Mississippi Delta
New Orleans
Gulf of Mexico
Gulf of Campeche
Yucatán Peninsula
C. Catoche
Yucatán Strait
Yucatán Basin
Gulf of Honduras
Coco
C. Gracias a Dios
L. Nicaragua
3837
Panama Canal
G. of Panama
G. of Darién
Florida Strait
C. Sable
La Habana
Cuba
Bahama Islands
Tropic of Cancer
Greater Antilles
Cayman Trough 7680
Jamaica
Port-au-Prince
Hispaniola
Milwaukee Deep 9200
Puerto Rico
Caribbean Sea
Colombian Basin
Venezuelan Basin
G. of Venezuela
Maracaibo
Sa. Nevada de Sta. Marta 5800
Sierra de Mérida
Andes
Magdalena
Orinoco
ANNUAL RAINFALL
1:70 000 000
mm
3000
2000
1000
500
250
Arctic Circle
Tropic of Cancer
Projection: Bonne
West from 90 Greenwich
m
8000
6000
4000
2000
200
0
200
400
1000
1500
2000
3000
4000
m
1:30 000 000
200 0 200 400 600 800 1000 km
UNITED STATES ADMINISTRATIVE
1:40 000 000
Montgomery : State Capital
Washington : National Capital
The two states not depicted above are
Alaska (capital Juneau) and Hawaii (capital Honolulu)
C. CONNECTICUT
D. DELAWARE
M. MARYLAND
MASS. MASSACHUSETTS
D.C. DISTRICT OF COLUMBIA
N.H. NEW HAMPSHIRE
N.J. NEW JERSEY
R.I. RHODE ISLAND
VER. VERMONT
CANADA
BRITISH COLUMBIA
ALBERTA
SASKATCHEWAN
MANITOBA
ONTARIO
QUÉBEC
NEWFOUNDLAND
NEW BRUNSWICK
NOVA SCOTIA
PR. EDWARD I.
MEXICO
CUBA
BAHAMAS
WASHINGTON
OREGON
CALIFORNIA
NEVADA
IDAHO
MONTANA
WYOMING
UTAH
ARIZONA
COLORADO
NEW MEXICO
N. DAKOTA
S. DAKOTA
NEBRASKA
KANSAS
OKLAHOMA
TEXAS
MINNESOTA
IOWA
MISSOURI
ARKANSAS
LOUISIANA
WISCONSIN
ILLINOIS
MICHIGAN
INDIANA
OHIO
KENTUCKY
TENNESSEE
MISSISSIPPI
ALABAMA
GEORGIA
FLORIDA
SOUTH CAROLINA
NORTH CAROLINA
VIRGINIA
WEST VIRGINIA
PENNSYLVANIA
NEW YORK
MAINE
Tropic of Cancer
West from Greenwich
COPYRIGHT GEORGE PHILIP & SON LTD

North America: Natural Vegetation

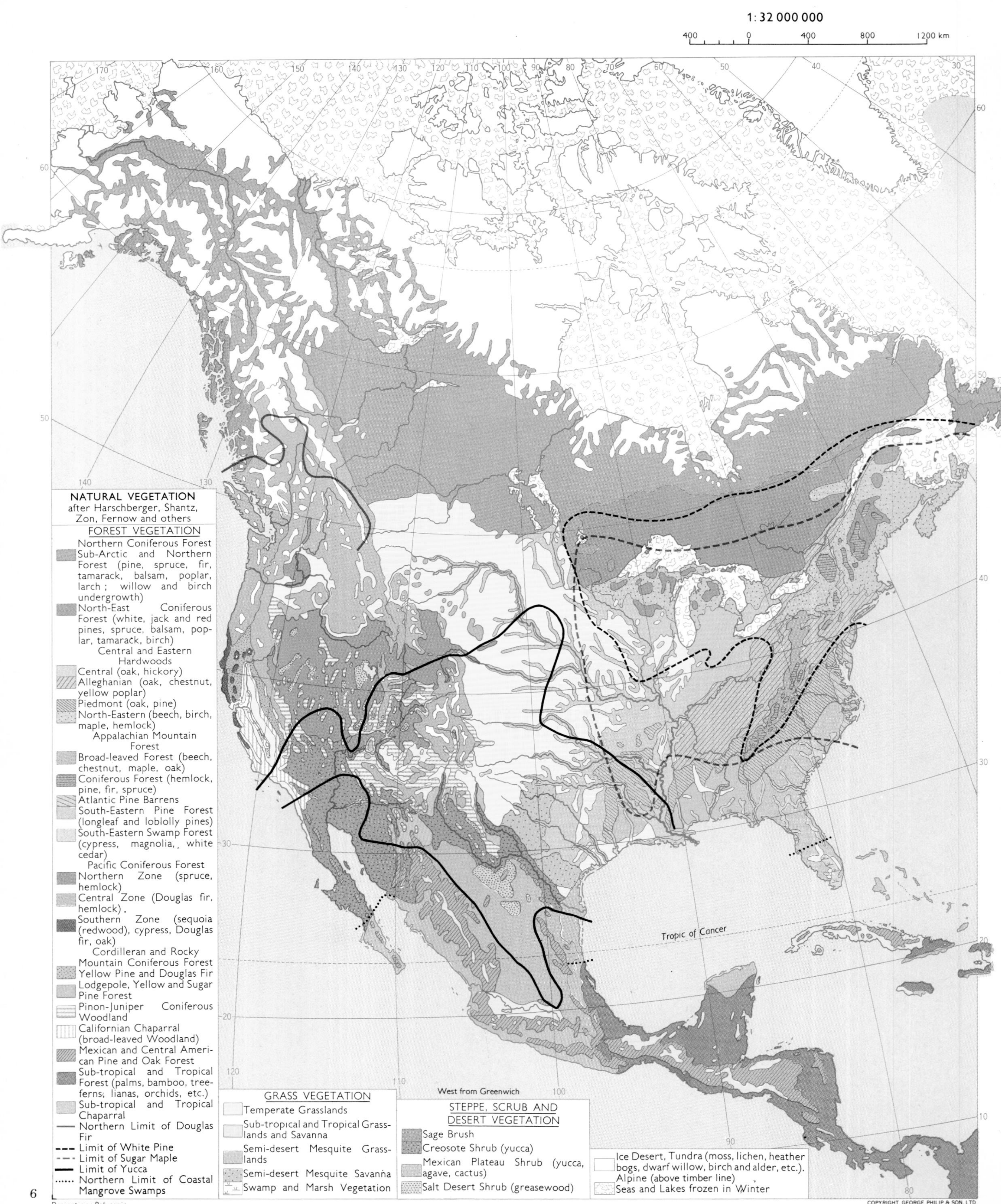

1: 32 000 000
400 0 400 800 1200 km
NATURAL VEGETATION
after Harschberger, Shantz, Zon, Fernow and others
FOREST VEGETATION
Northern Coniferous Forest
Sub-Arctic and Northern Forest (pine, spruce, fir, tamarack, balsam, poplar, larch; willow and birch undergrowth)
North-East Coniferous Forest (white, jack and red pines, spruce, balsam, poplar, tamarack, birch)
Central and Eastern Hardwoods
Central (oak, hickory)
Alleghanian (oak, chestnut, yellow poplar)
Piedmont (oak, pine)
North-Eastern (beech, birch, maple, hemlock)
Appalachian Mountain Forest
Broad-leaved Forest (beech, chestnut, maple, oak)
Coniferous Forest (hemlock, pine, fir, spruce)
Atlantic Pine Barrens
South-Eastern Pine Forest (longleaf and loblolly pines)
South-Eastern Swamp Forest (cypress, magnolia, white cedar)
Pacific Coniferous Forest
Northern Zone (spruce, hemlock)
Central Zone (Douglas fir, hemlock)
Southern Zone (sequoia (redwood), cypress, Douglas fir, oak)
Cordilleran and Rocky Mountain Coniferous Forest
Yellow Pine and Douglas Fir
Lodgepole, Yellow and Sugar Pine Forest
Pinon-Juniper Coniferous Woodland
Californian Chaparral (broad-leaved Woodland)
Mexican and Central American Pine and Oak Forest
Sub-tropical and Tropical Forest (palms, bamboo, tree-ferns, lianas, orchids, etc.)
Sub-tropical and Tropical Chaparral
Northern Limit of Douglas Fir
Limit of White Pine
Limit of Sugar Maple
Limit of Yucca
Northern Limit of Coastal Mangrove Swamps
GRASS VEGETATION
Temperate Grasslands
Sub-tropical and Tropical Grasslands and Savanna
Semi-desert Mesquite Grasslands
Semi-desert Mesquite Savanna
Swamp and Marsh Vegetation
STEPPE, SCRUB AND DESERT VEGETATION
Sage Brush
Creosote Shrub (yucca)
Mexican Plateau Shrub (yucca, agave, cactus)
Salt Desert Shrub (greasewood)
Ice Desert, Tundra (moss, lichen, heather bogs, dwarf willow, birch and alder, etc.).
Alpine (above timber line)
Seas and Lakes frozen in Winter
Tropic of Cancer
West from Greenwich

Projection: Polyconic

South America: Physical

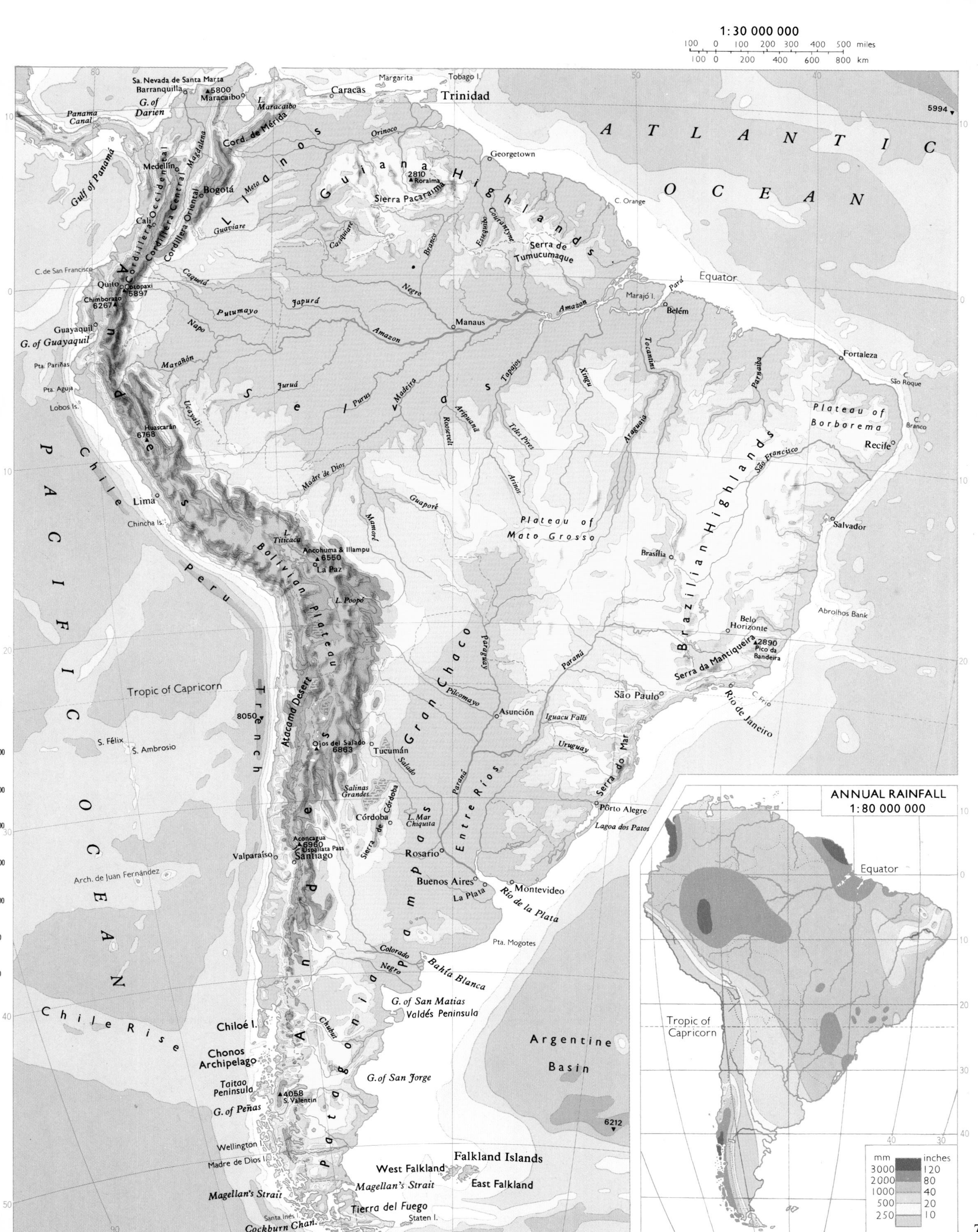

Europe: Physical

ANNUAL RAINFALL
1: 40 000 000
mm inches
1500 60
1000 40
750 30
500 20
250 10
Arctic Circle
Iceland
Reykjavik
Hekla 1491
Öræfajökull 2119
NORWEGIAN SEA
Faroe Is.
Shetland Is.
Orkney Is.
Rockall
St. Kilda
Hebrides
British Isles
Ben Nevis 1343
Edinburgh
NORTH SEA
Belfast
Irish Sea
Ireland
Dublin
Great Britain
St. George's Channel
Snowdon 1085
Cardiff
London
Thames
Amsterdam
Netherlands
Frisian Is.
Lands End
Scilly Is.
English Channel
Str. of Dover
Channel Is.
Brussel
Rhine
Westerwald
Eifel
Ardennes
Taunus
Hunsrück
Meuse
Vosges
Black Forest
Brittany
Paris
Seine
Loire
Saône
Zürich
Jura
Massif Central
Mt. Dore 1886
Mt. Blanc 4807
Cevennes
Garonne
Rhône
Po
Gironde
Bay of Biscay
4861
ATLANTIC OCEAN
C. Clear
Flores
Terceira
Pico
Azores
São Miguel
C. Finisterre
Cantabrian Mts.
Old Castile
Iberian Peninsula
Douro
Madrid
Ebro
Pyrenees
Maladetta 3404
G. of Lion
Riviera
Ligurian Sea
Corsica
Lisboa
C. da Roca
Tagus
New Castile
Guadiana
Sierra Morena
C. St. Vincent
Sardinia
Str. of Bonifacio
Balearic Is.
6293
Madeira
Guadalquivir
Andalusia
Mulhacen 3478
Sa. Nevada
C. Trafalgar
Str. of Gibraltar
Gibraltar
MEDITERRANEAN
Er Rif
Casablanca
Alger
Maritime Atlas
Tunis
Plateau of the Shotts
Saharan Atlas
Great Atlas
Toubkal 4165
Palma
Tenerife
Canary Is.
Gran Canaria
Fuerteventura
Gulf of Gabes
Tropic of Cancer
Sahara
3734
Lindesnes
ft m
12,000 4000
6000 2000
3000 1000
1200 400
600 200
0 0
200 600
2000 6000
4000 12,000
m ft
Projection: Bonne.
West from Greenwich
East from Greenwich

1:17 500 000
100 0 100 200 300 400 500 miles
100 0 200 400 600 800 km
Nordkapp
Nordkinn
Lofoten
L. Inari
Kebnekaise 2123
Torne älv
Lappland
Kola Peninsula
Kanin Peninsula
Tundra
Pechora
Narodnaya 1894
Telpos Iz. 1617
Ural Mountains
West Siberian Plain
Ob
Irtysh
Tobol
White Sea
Mezen
N. Dvina
Onega
L. Onega
Scandinavia
Umeälv
Indalsälven
Gulf of Bothnia
Finland
Lake Ladoga
Svir
Åland Is.
Helsinki
Gulf of Finland
Neva
Leningrad
Rybinsk Res.
Kama
Oslo
Stockholm
Mälaren
Vänern
Vättern
Skaw
Kattegat
Gotland
BALTIC SEA
København
L. Chudskoye
Valdai Hills
Volga
Moskva
Oka
Gorkiy
Dvina
European Plain
Central Russian Uplands
Volga Heights
Obshchi Syrt
Ural
Kirgiz Steppe
Neman
North European Plain
Berlin
Oder
Vistula
Warszawa
Pripet
Pripet Marshes
Kiyevo
Dnieper
Ukraine
Tsimlyansk Res.
Don
Ore Mts.
Praha
Sudetes
Bohemian Forest
Moravian Hts.
Danube
Inn
Wien
Tatra 2655
Carpathians
Bug
Dniester
Prut
Budapest
Bakony Forest
Plain of Hungary
Drava
Mureş
Tisza
Sava
Transylvanian Alps
Bucureşti
Wallachia
Beograd
Morava
Odessa
Mouths of the Danube
Crimea
Sea of Azov
Kuban
Strait of Kerch
Black Sea
2211
Terek
Elbrus 5633
Caucasus
Transcaucasia
Kura
Baku
Caspian Sea
-28
Ust Urt Plateau
Karagiye Depression -132
Kara Bogaz
Dinaric Alps
Dalmatia
Adriatic Sea
Apennines
Roma
Gran Sasso 2914
Balkans
Sofiya
Rhodope
Balkan Peninsula
Istanbul
Bosporus
Sea of Marmara
Pontine Mts.
Ararat 5165
Araks
L. Van
L. Urmia
Elburz Mts.
Tehrān
Str. of Otranto
Pindus
Dardanelles
Aegean Sea
Ankara
Kizil
Anatolia
Kurdistan
L. Tuz
Erciyas 3770
Taurus Mts.
Strait of Messina
Calabria
Ionian Sea
Ionian Is.
Etna 3263
Sicily
C. Spartivento
Athinai
Morea
5121
C. Matapan
Halab
Euphrates
Tigris
Mesopotamia
Baghdād
Malta
Rhodes
Crete
Cyprus
Bayrūt
Levant
Syrian Desert
MEDITERRANEAN SEA
Persian Gulf
Tripoli
Gulf of Sidra
Nile Delta
Tel Aviv-Yafo
Dead Sea -395
COPYRIGHT, GEORGE PHILIP & SON, LTD.

Africa: Physical

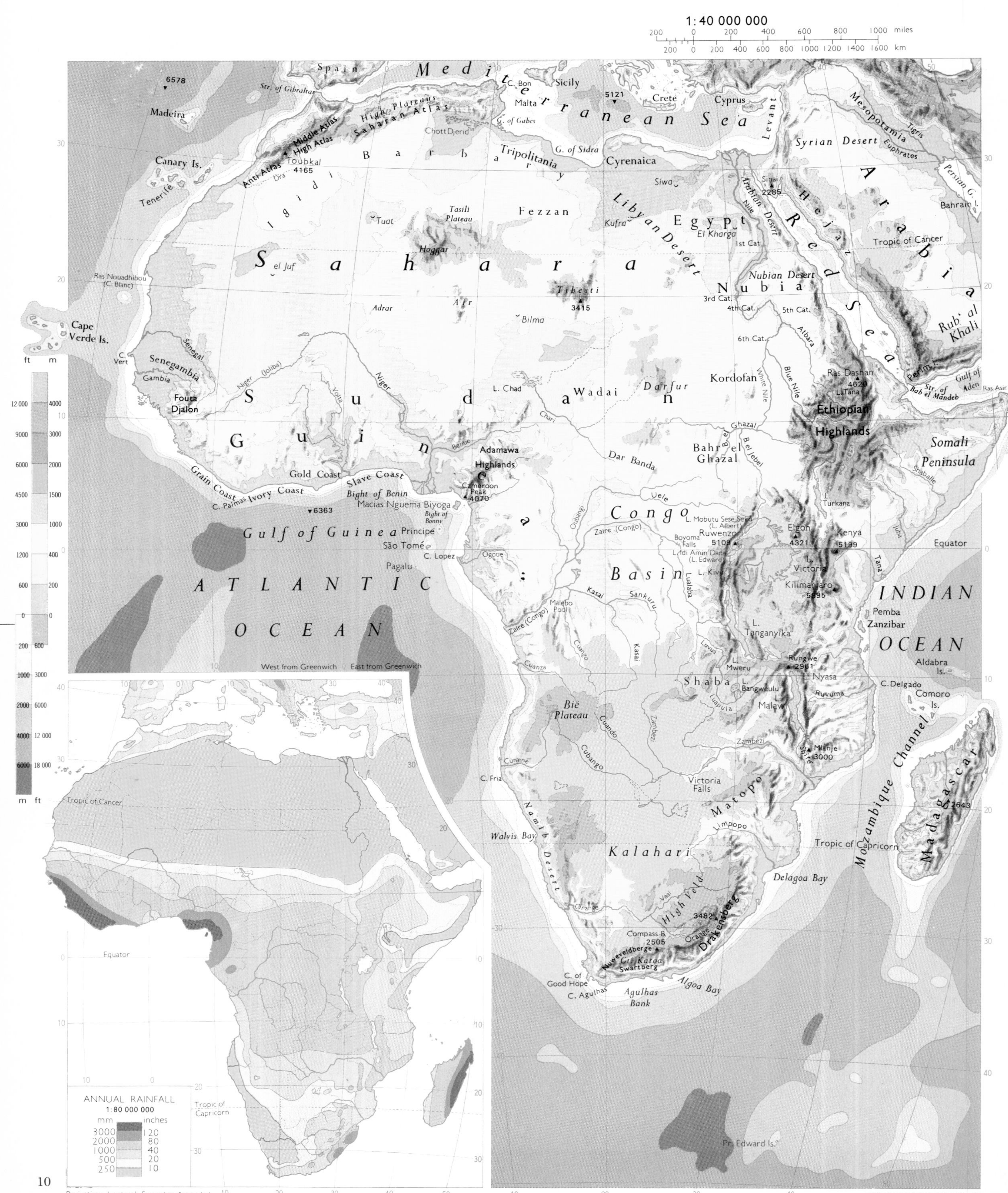

1:40 000 000
miles
km
Mediterranean Sea
Spain
Str. of Gibraltar
Madeira
Canary Is.
Tenerife
Anti Atlas
High Atlas
Middle Atlas
Toubkal
4165
High Plateaus
Saharan Atlas
Chott Djerid
C. Bon
Sicily
Malta
G. of Gabes
Tripolitania
G. of Sidra
Cyrenaica
Crete
Cyprus
Levant
Syrian Desert
Mesopotamia
Tigris
Euphrates
Persian G.
Bahrain
Arabia
Hejaz
Red Sea
Sinai
2285
Egypt
El Kharga
Siwa
Kufra
Libyan Desert
Arabian Desert
Nile
1st Cat.
Nubian Desert
Nubia
3rd Cat.
4th Cat.
5th Cat.
6th Cat.
Atbara
Tropic of Cancer
Rub' al Khali
Barbary
Igidi
Tuat
Tasili Plateau
Fezzan
Hoggar
Sahara
el Juf
Tibesti
3415
Adrar
Aïr
Bilma
Ras Nouadhibou (C. Blanc)
Cape Verde Is.
C. Vert
Senegal
Senegambia
Gambia
Fouta Djalon
Niger (Joliba)
Niger
Volta
Benue
Sudan
L. Chad
Wadai
Darfur
Kordofan
White Nile
Blue Nile
Ras Dashan
4620
L. Tana
Perim
Str. of Bab el Mandeb
Gulf of Aden
Ras Asir
Ethiopian Highlands
Somali Peninsula
Shaballe
Guinea
Grain Coast
C. Palmas
Ivory Coast
Gold Coast
Slave Coast
Bight of Benin
Macias Nguema Biyoga
Bight of Bonny
Adamawa Highlands
Cameroon Peak
4070
6363
Gulf of Guinea
Principe
São Tomé
Pagalu
C. Lopez
Ogooué
ATLANTIC OCEAN
West from Greenwich
East from Greenwich
Chari
Dar Banda
Bahr el Ghazal
Bahr el Jebel
Uele
Oubangi
Congo Basin
Zaire (Congo)
L. Mobutu Sese Seko (L. Albert)
Ruwenzori
5109
Boyoma Falls
L. Idi Amin Dada (L. Edward)
L. Kivu
Lualaba
Elgon
4321
Kenya
5199
L. Turkana
Juba
Equator
Tana
Victoria
Kilimanjaro
5895
INDIAN OCEAN
Pemba
Zanzibar
Kasai
Sankuru
Malebo Pool
Zaire (Congo)
Cuango
Kasai
Cuanza
L. Tanganyika
Luvua
L. Mweru
Rungwe
2961
Shaba
L. Bangweulu
Luapula
L. Nyasa
L. Malawi
Ruvuma
C. Delgado
Aldabra Is.
Comoro Is.
Bié Plateau
Cuando
Zambezi
Cubango
Cunene
C. Fria
Victoria Falls
Matopo
Mlanje
3000
Shire
Mozambique Channel
Madagascar
2643
Namib Desert
Walvis Bay
Kalahari
Limpopo
Tropic of Capricorn
Delagoa Bay
Vaal
High Veld
Orange
3482
Drakensberg
Compass B.
2505
Nuweveldberge
Gt. Karoo
Swartberg
C. of Good Hope
C. Agulhas
Agulhas Bank
Algoa Bay
Pr. Edward Is.
ft
m
ANNUAL RAINFALL
1:80 000 000
mm
inches
Tropic of Cancer
Equator
Tropic of Capricorn
Projection: Lambert's Equivalent Azimuthal
COPYRIGHT: GEORGE PHILIP & SON LTD

Asia: Physical

1: 50 000 000

250 0 250 500 750 1000 miles

250 0 500 1000 1500 km

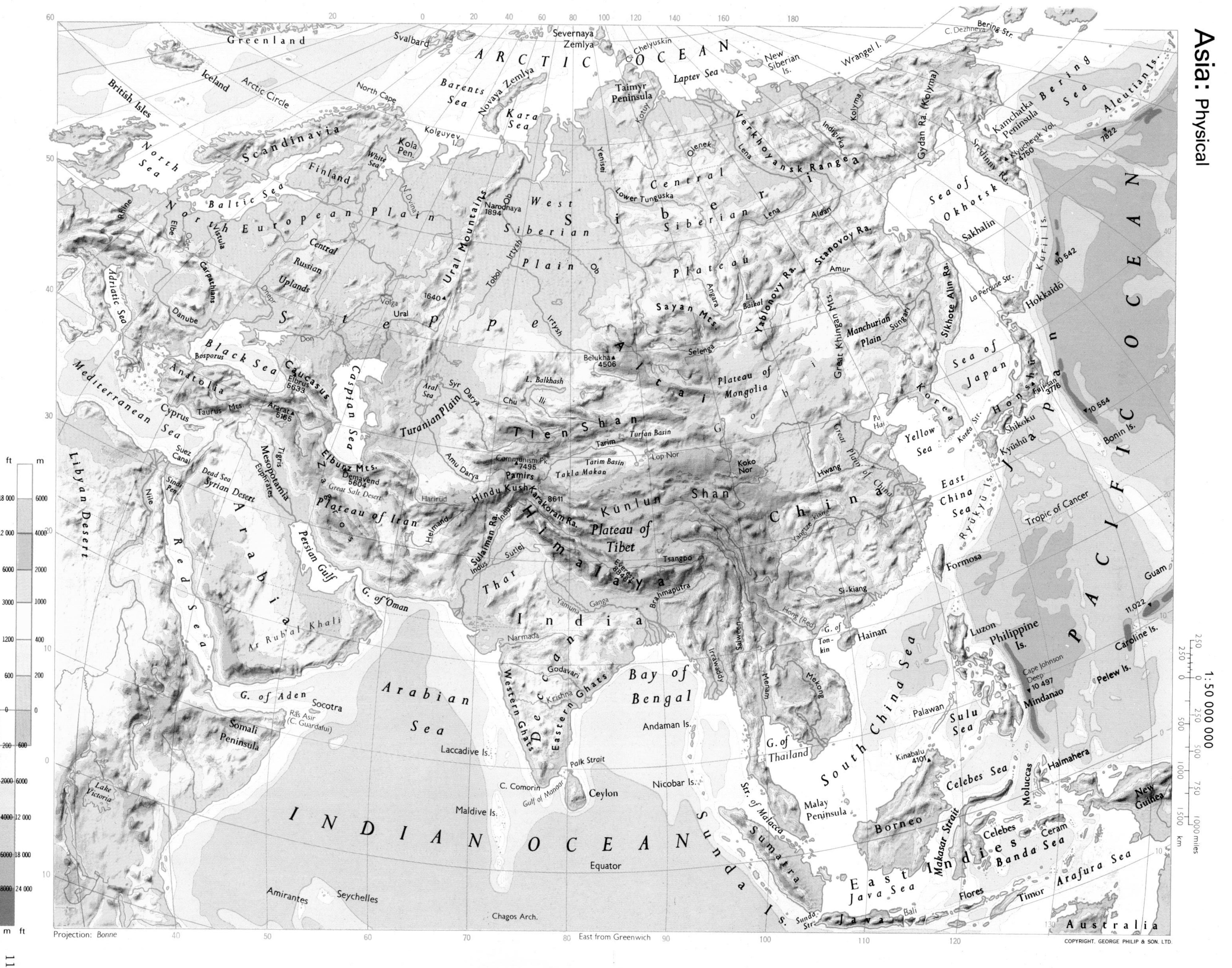

ft	18 000	12 000	6000	3000	1200	600	0	600	6000	12 000	18 000	24 000
m	6000	4000	2000	1000	400	200	0	200	2000	4000	6000	8000

The Gazetteer

The Gazetteer is a collection of maps of the countries of the world, arranged regionally. As well as providing topographical information each map contains details of population, industry, climate and language. The countries are listed below.

North America

United States 1

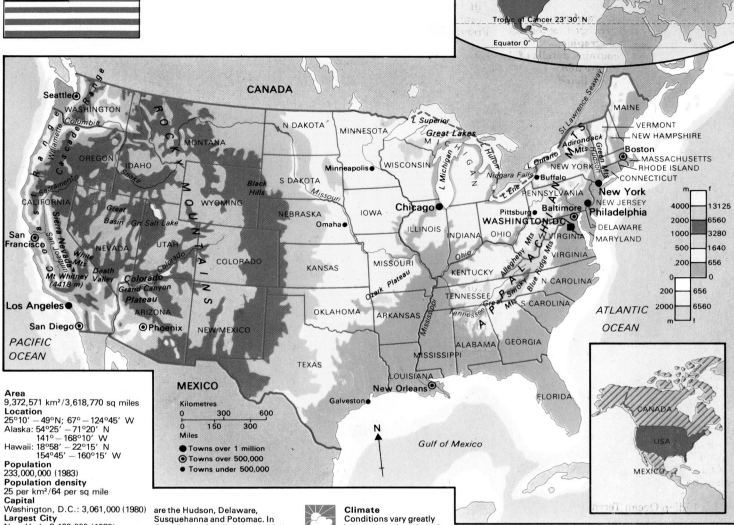

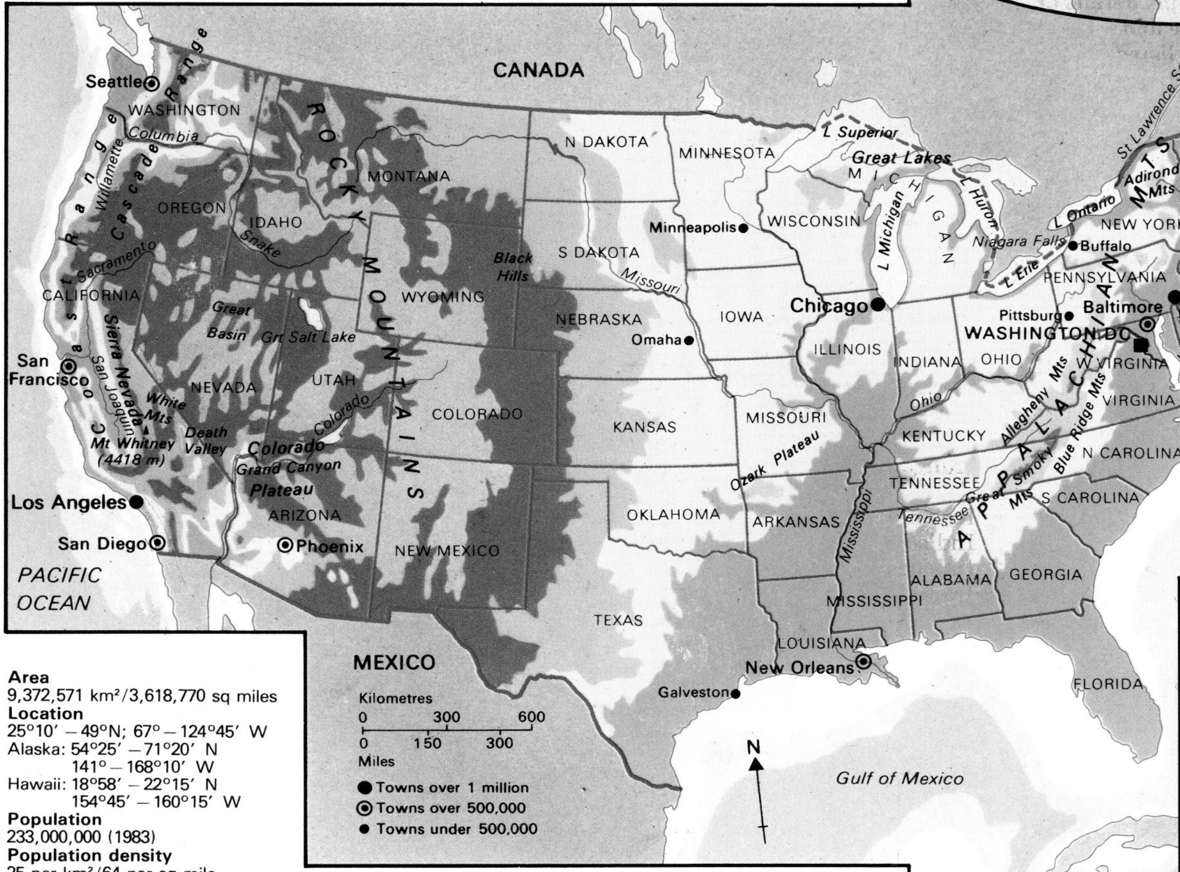

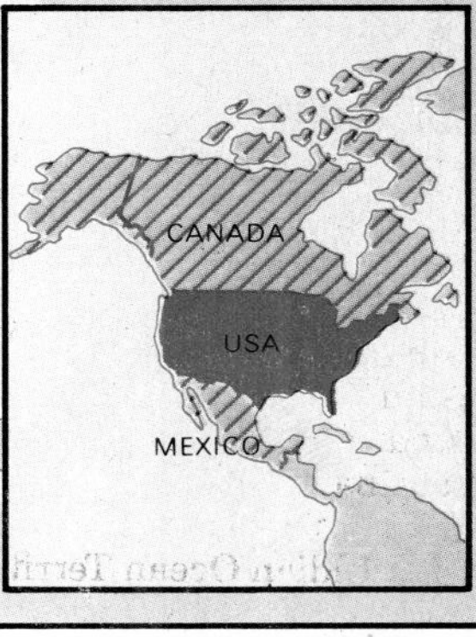

Area
9,372,571 km²/3,618,770 sq miles
Location
25°10′ – 49°N; 67° – 124°45′ W
Alaska: 54°25′ – 71°20′ N
141° – 168°10′ W
Hawaii: 18°58′ – 22°15′ N
154°45′ – 160°15′ W
Population
233,000,000 (1983)
Population density
25 per km²/64 per sq mile
Capital
Washington, D.C.: 3,061,000 (1980)
Largest City
New York: 9,120,000 (1980)
Language
English
Major imports
machinery, transport equipment, petroleum, foods, textiles, electrical goods
Major exports
machinery, vehicles and aircraft, chemical manufactures, wheat and other foods
Currency
dollar (1 dollar = 100 cents)
Gross National Product
2,946,020 million US dollars (1981)
Status
federal republic

The US consists of 50 states and the District of Columbia (the site of the federal capital). The above facts relate to the whole territory.

Physical features

The US, the world's fourth largest nation both in area and in population, can be roughly divided into three regions: a hilly east, a flat centre and a mountainous west. The principal feature of the eastern sector is the Appalachian system, a mountain chain extending southwestwards from Canada to Alabama. This chain includes the White, Green and Adirondack mountains in the north and, further south, the Allegheny, Blue Ridge and Great Smoky ranges. Although some peaks rise to almost 2,000 m, most are under 900 m. The main rivers penetrating the Appalachian block are the Hudson, Delaware, Susquehanna and Potomac. In Georgia and Carolina the land falls away to a coastal plain over 300 km wide. The Atlantic coast is rocky in the north but consists of marshes, dunes, lagoons and sandbars south of Maine. The central plains are broken by a few upland blocks, such as the Black Hills of South Dakota and the Ozark Plateau but the main feature is the Mississippi-Missouri river system (6,212 km), the third longest in the world. Every minute the Mississippi deposits a further 200 tonnes of silt in the delta which is slowly expanding into the Gulf. The Ohio is the major eastern tributary of the Mississippi. To the north lie the Great Lakes. In the west, the Rockies, running from Alaska to Mexico, climb to over 4,000 m. These rugged mountains contain some of North America's most spectacular scenery with snowy peaks, waterfalls, gorges, geysers, lakes and forests. West of the Rockies lies a region of tablelands, basins, canyons and deserts. It includes the Colorado Plateau (mostly over 2,000 m high,) the Grand Canyon, the arid Great Basin of Nevada, the Great Salt Lake and California's Death Valley (85 m below sea level). This region is bordered by the high Sierra Nevada and Cascade ranges whose highest point is Mt Whitney (4,418 m). Between these and the Coast Ranges lie a series of sheltered valleys including the Willamette, Sacramento and San Joaquin valleys which are important agriculturally. The chief rivers in the west are the Snake, Columbia, Sacramento and Colorado.

Climate

Conditions vary greatly between north and south, coast and interior, in a country the size of the US. Summers are generally hot and, in coastal areas, humid. July averages 24°C in New York, 28°C in New Orleans, 32°C in Phoenix but only 17°C in San Francisco (because of cool currents and sea breezes). Winters are mild on the west coast but colder east of the Rockies: January averages 12°C in San Francisco,— 7°C in Omaha, —1°C in New York but 15°C in Florida. In the east, annual rainfall is over 100 cm and occurs throughout the year; the central plains receive under 50 cm, mostly in summer. On the west coast, winters are wettest but the amounts range from 180 cm in the north to less than 20 cm in the desert south.

Flora and fauna

A third of the country is forested. Conifers (spruce, pine, fir, hemlock, redwood) cover the western mountains; mixed forest (pine, hemlock, fir, spruce, birch, maple, beech) predominates in the east but gives way to deciduous (oak, beech, hickory) in the southeast. Pine, cypress, palm and mangrove grow on the Gulf coast and in southern Florida. Grasslands characterize the centre while desert scrub and cactus occur in southern California and Arizona. Wildlife includes the Rocky Mountain goat and marmot in the west; buffalo and prairie dog on the plains; bear, deer, racoon and beaver in the north-east; and alligators in Florida.

Transport

Life in the US is car-dominated with almost one car for every two Americans. The 6,000,000 km road network (the world's longest) is densest along the eastern seaboard, the Mississippi and Ohio valleys and the Pacific coast. Although the US has a quarter of the world's railway track, rail transport is in decline: in the mid 1970s, 90% of passenger travel was by car, and only 1% by train; transcontinental passenger services have been discontinued. But railways are still important for goods transport and carry about 40% of the country's freight. Chicago is a major terminus and ranks as the world's largest railway centre. Other freight movements are by road, pipeline (oil, gas, acids) and water. The principal inland waterways are the Mississippi-Missouri-Ohio system extending to Omaha, Minneapolis and Pittsburg; the Great Lakes-St Lawrence Seaway which brings ocean-going vessels as far inland as Duluth; and the New York State Barge canal which links New York to Buffalo and the Great Lakes. The leading ports in terms of tonnage are New Orleans, New York and Houston. Other major ports include Valdez (Alaska), Norfolk, Baltimore and (inland) Chicago. Railways have also lost traffic to buses and planes; there is a comprehensive network of internal air routes, with some 4,000 public airports served by 50 airlines.

Energy

The US, using 33% of the world's energy, ranks as the largest energy-consuming nation; it also leads in energy production, accounting for 27% of the world total. Petroleum (25% imported) and natural gas provide about 65% of the nation's energy needs. The main oil and gas producing states are Texas, Louisiana, California, Oklahoma, New Mexico, Wyoming and Kansas. The pipeline network, totalling 282,000 km, is densest between the southern fields and the industrial Great Lakes region; oil from the Gulf Coast fields is transported to the northeast by tanker. Coal is also a major source of power and 70% of output comes from the Appalachian fields, especially in West Virginia, Kentucky and Pennsylvania. Appalachian coal (providing 25% of world output) is one of the main reasons why 75% of American industry is concentrated in the northeast. The Indiana-Illinois field is the other chief coal-producing area and lignite occurs in the Rockies. Over 80% of the country's electricity is generated in thermal stations by oil, gas or coal but other sources of electricity are water and nuclear power. Major hydro schemes are located on the rivers Columbia (producing 25% of all US hydro-power), Tennessee, Colorado and Sacramento and at Niagara Falls. The US produces over 50% of the world's nuclear power, using uranium from the Rockies.

North America

United States 2

(Eastern)

Mining

Although the US leads the world in mineral production, imports are vital, especially of tin, nickel, asbestos, bauxite, industrial diamonds, platinum, manganese and tungsten. Most of America's minerals are located in the west except for iron ore, sulphur and phosphates. Over 80% of iron ore comes from the Lake Superior fields of Minnesota (Mesabi range), Michigan and Wisconsin; some iron ore is mined in the Adirondacks and Alabama. The US is the world's largest producer of phosphates and sulphur; both occur on the Gulf Coast, sulphur in Louisiana and Texas, phosphates in Florida and Tennessee. The western Ozark mountains are important for lead and zinc.

Iron and steel

The US makes a quarter of the world's steel and 78% of national output comes from the Pennsylvania—Great Lakes region. Factors behind the industry's growth are Lake Superior iron ore, coal from the Appalachians, limestone near Lake Huron and a navigable waterway (the Great Lakes) linking these reserves. Ore is also imported from Canada, Venezuela and Liberia. Major iron and steel centres include Philadelphia, Baltimore, Pittsburg, Cleveland, Lorain, Toledo, Detroit, Gary, Chicago, Milwaukee and Duluth. Outside the northeast, the main steel-making region is at Birmingham and Bessemer (Alabama). Local ore, coal and limestone are used and steel goods are shipped via the Black Warrior river and the Gulf port of Mobile.

Other industry

Around 75% of US manufacturing is concentrated in the area between Minneapolis, St Louis, Baltimore and Boston. In addition to iron and steel, the northeast is also the centre of the engineering, electrical, chemical and textile industries. About ten million motor vehicles (25% of the world total) are made each year in the Detroit district.
Other engineering products coming principally from the northeast are agricultural machinery (Chicago), ships (Philadelphia, Camden, Baltimore), machine tools (New England) and industrial machinery. Pittsburg, Boston and Springfield are major centres of electrical and electronic equipment. Chemical plants are mostly located in northeastern seaports, steel towns, along the Kanawha (W Virginia) and Tennessee valleys and the Gulf coast. The textile industry has spread from its original New England base; in particular, cotton textiles have moved south to the Carolinas and Georgia. Food processing is widespread and is mainly centred on producing areas.

Forest industries

The US produces a large share of the world's timber products, providing 20% of its lumber, 35% of pulp, 11% of newsprint and 44% of all other paper. The eastern forests are important, especially in New York, South Carolina, Mississippi and Minnesota, which together account for 85% of paper output, 78% of pulp and 33% of its lumber.

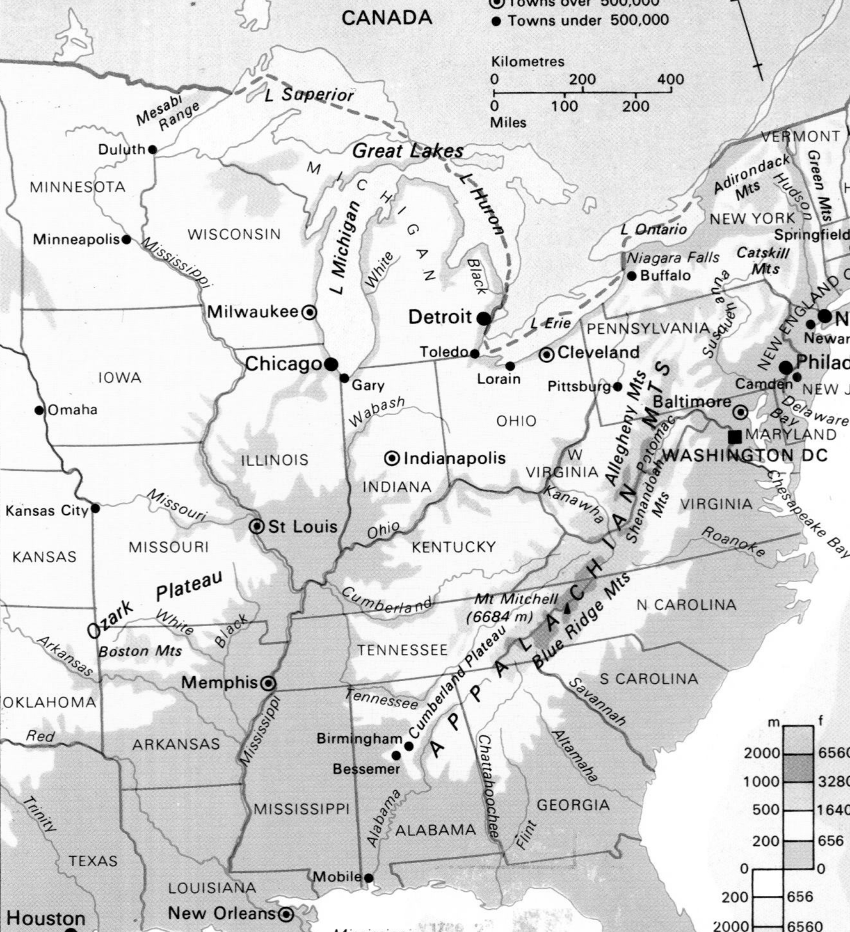

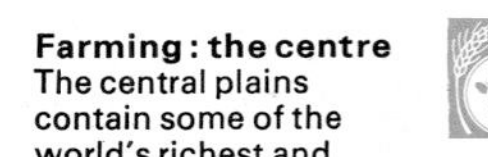

Farming: the centre

The central plains contain some of the world's richest and most extensive farmlands. Dairying predominates in the north; Wisconsin alone produces 15% of America's milk and 50% of its cheese and butter. South of the dairy belt lies the corn belt, stretching across Iowa, Illinois, Indiana and Ohio. Corn (maize) covers 30% of arable land in this area; other crops are wheat, oats, hay and soybeans. The corn belt is also a major meat-producing zone and 85% of corn is used as stockfeed for cattle and pigs. Southwards lies a mixed farming region, followed by the cotton belt in the lower Mississippi basin. The name 'cotton belt' now belongs to history as cotton production has moved west, mainly to Texas. Traditional sources such as Mississippi, Arkansas, Louisiana and Alabama provide only 45% of the national total. In place of cotton, the South is growing soybeans, peanuts, vegetables and fodder. Rice and sugarcane grow on the Gulf coast.

Farming: the east

The urbanized east coast, particularly from Boston to Washington, offers a big market for fresh fruit and vegetables; consequently, truck farming (market gardening) is highly developed in the northeast. This region, especially New England, is also important for dairying and poultry. In Virginia, the Carolinas and Georgia, tobacco is a major cash crop. Other crops are: peanuts and soybeans on the coastal plain, maize and cotton inland and, further south, fruit. Florida is noted for citrus.

Fishing

Fishing is important and supplies a highly developed processing industry. The catch from the Atlantic and Gulf is very varied and includes lobsters and cod off New England, oysters and crabs off Delaware and in Chesapeake Bay, shellfish and menhaden (herring-like fish used for fertiliizer and oil) from the Gulf. Boston is the main fishing port.

Peoples

The first European settlers were Spaniards, moving up from Mexico, followed by English colonists who came to Virginia and Massachusetts. Since then, over 50 million people have migrated to the US. Some of the non-European groups are concentrated in certain areas: most Mexican immigrants live in Texas and California, Japanese in San Francisco, Chinese in San Francisco and New York, and Puerto Ricans in New York.
During the first centuries of settlement, frequent wars between white colonists and native Indians threatened the Indian population with extinction. Protection measures have, however, contributed to an increase in numbers (1.4 million: 1980). Many live on reservations in the mid- and far west. Black Americans (265 million: 1970) are the descendants of slaves brought in to work the southern plantations. In 1900, 90% lived in the south but, with the decline in southern agriculture, 40% have since moved north.

Urban growth

Initially, the US was a rural country: in 1790, only 5% lived in towns and there were no centres with more than 50,000 inhabitants. Today, 75% of Americans are urbanized and 35 metropolitan areas have populations of over one million. A recent trend is suburban growth coupled with inner-city decline: for every one person moving into a city, five move to the suburbs. As the middle classes escape to the less crowded, less polluted and less expensive suburbs, city centres are left to the rich and the poor; the latter are often black migrants from the south in search of employment.

Cities

One American in two lives in the industrial northeast. New York started as a trading post in 1624 on Manhattan Island and is now the world's second largest city. Manhattan is still the heart of New York and the country's financial and commercial centre although the port, factory and residential districts have spread far beyond the island. About 10% of US industrial output comes from New York while the port handles 20% of the country's trade. Chicago (7.1 m) leads the world in steel production and has important food-processing industries based on produce from the hinterland. Other major urban centres in the east are Philadelphia (4.7 m), Detroit (4.4 m), Washington DC, Boston (2.8 m), St Louis (2.4 m), Pittsburg (2.3 m), Baltimore (2.2 m), Newark (2.0 m) and Buffalo (1.2 m).

United States 3
(Western)

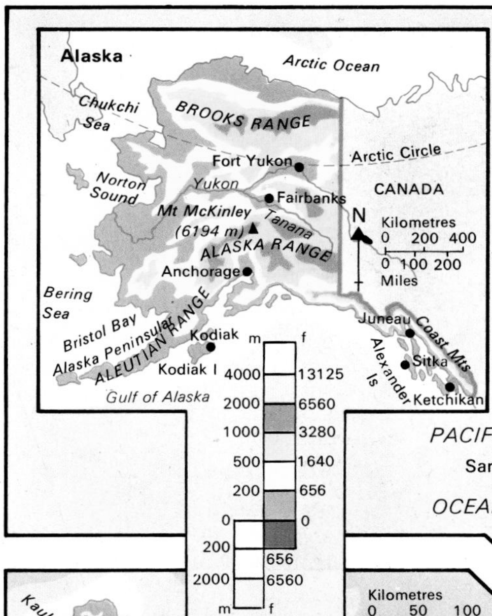

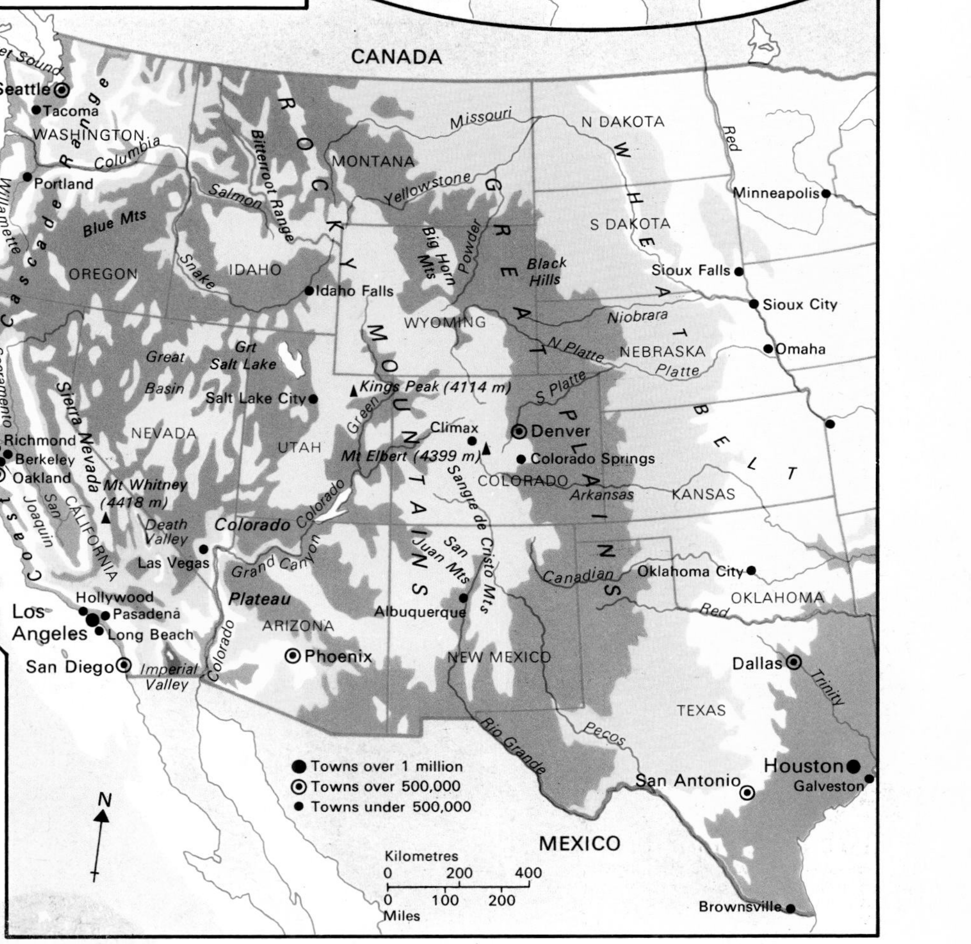

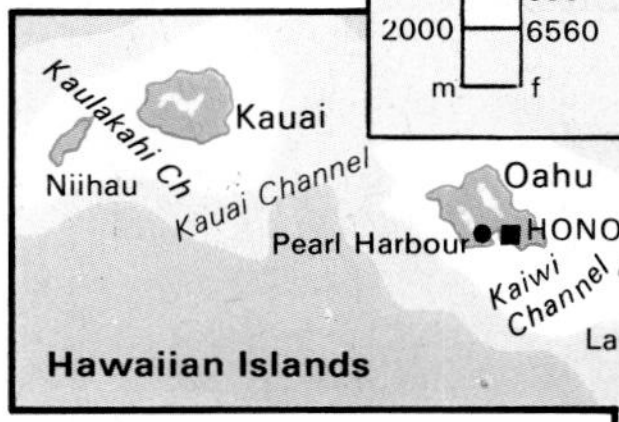

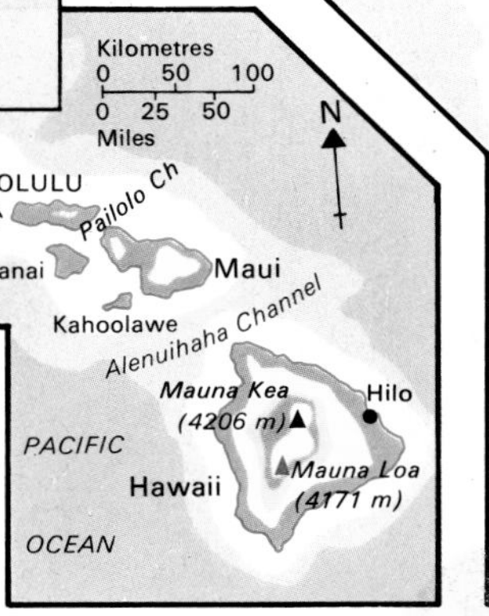

Crop farming
East of the Rockies lie the Great Plains. The eastern sector of this low rainfall zone corresponds to the wheat belt: winter wheat is grown in Nebraska, Kansas, Texas and Oklahoma; spring wheat in the Dakotas. West of the Rockies, cultivation is limited to areas where water is available: alfalfa, sugarbeet and wheat are grown in the Columbia and Snake valleys and near Great Salt Lake; cotton, fruit and vegetables along the Salt and Rio Grande rivers and in Imperial Valley. The main cash crop of the Pacific Coast is fruit: apples and pears in the northwest and grapes, citrus, peaches, apricots, plums and nuts from the California central valley and Los Angeles region. Cotton, sugar beet, rice and alfalfa are also grown in the central valley.

Livestock
The Great Plains and some arid zones of the western plateau are used for grazing cattle. Except in the south (Arizona and Texas) the cattle winter in sheltered valleys and feed on alfalfa and other fodder grown under irrigation. Animals are mostly fattened on the plains of the Midwest or in lowland California. Sheep are kept for wool. Dairying is important along the Pacific coast and well developed in the Willamette valley and near Seattle.

Fishing
Fishing is an important west coast activity, providing 25% of the total US catch. Tuna and halibut are caught in the Pacific, salmon in Puget Sound, the Columbia and Sacramento. Fishing ports, all with canning and freezing plants, include San Diego, San Francisco and Seattle.

Mining & industry
The US is the world's largest producer of copper, uranium and molybdenum. Copper comes mai from Arizona, Montana and Utah, uranium occurs in Wyoming and New Mexico; Climax (Colorado) is the world's chief source of molybdenum. Northwest Montana has important lead-zinc deposits. In the 19th century, thousands of adventurers went west in search of gold and silver. Gold is still produced in South Dakota, Utah, Nevada and California; silver in Idaho and Utah. Industry in the Great Plains and Rockies is basically concerned with primary products (flour milling, meat packing, metal refining and timber processing). The port of Houston is important for oil refining, metallurgy, engineering, food processing, chemicals and textiles. Dallas has oil refining, engineering and leatherwork. A wide range of manufacturing exists on the Pacific coast (Seattle, Portland, the San Francisco Bay towns, Los Angeles and San Diego). The leading sector, engineering, specializes in aircraft and missile construction; other branches are motor vehicles, ships, machinery and electrical equipment. Food processing is next in importance and includes dried fruit, wine, canned fish and fruit juices. The other major industry is timber. Tourism, chemicals and textiles (wool in the northwest and cotton in California) are well established.

Forestry
The coniferous forests that cover 75% of Washington and 50% of [illegible]n and California are a [illegible]source. In Washington and Oregon, the timber industries employ 50% of the industrial workforce and, although the eastern US leads in pulp and paper manufacture, over half the country's softwood lumber comes from the west. Seattle, Tacoma, and Portland are timber centres.

Cities
While the Great Plains and western mountains are thinly populated, pa[illegible] Pacific coast, espe[illegible]n California, are highly urbanized. About 90% of Californians live in urban areas and 40% of these in the Los Angeles district where the main industries are aerospace, tourism and fruit processing. The Los Angeles conurbation (7.5 m) covers 600 km² and over 100 municipalities including Long Beach, Pasadena and Hollywood. The San Francisco conurbation (3.3 m) includes bay towns such as Richmond, Berkeley and Oakland. San Francisco's industrial growth has been stimulated by its port activity and by the rich agriculture of the central valley. Other major cities in California are San Jose and San Diego. Outside California, the two leading west coast cities are Seattle (1.6 m) in Washington and Portland (1.2 m) in Oregon.

Alaska: the land
Alaska (1,518,776 km²), situated partly within the Arctic circle, is a desolate, mountainous territory. The Alaska and Aleutian ranges, which terminate in the Aleutian islands, are part of the Pacific mountain system, while the northern Brooks range is a continuation of the Rockies; Mt McKinley (6,194 m) is North America's highest peak. A region of low hills, drained by Alaska's longest river, the Yukon, lies between the southern and northern highlands. Beyond the Brooks massif a flat coastal plain extends to the Arctic Ocean. Winters are cold (—40°C), summers are cool (6°C).

Alaska: the economy
Fishing, forestry and mining are the chief activities. Alaska ranks as the world's leading supplier of salmon, caught offshore and in the Yukon. Juneau, Ketchikan, Sitka and Kodiak have big canneries. Other species taken are halibut, herring, crab and shrimp. In the southeast, coniferous forests provide large volumes of lumber and pulp; there are pulp mills at Ketchikan, Sitka and Juneau. Mineral production includes petroleum, natural gas, gold and coal. There is a little arable and dairy farming in the Anchorage region. Anchorage, Fairbanks, Ketchikan and Juneau account for 60% of the total population (438,000).

Hawaii: the land
Hawaii, the only non-mainland US state, consists of 312 islands lying about 4,000 km southwest of San Francisco. The islands rise from a submerged mountain ridge and form a 3,000 km-long chain across the north Pacific. At the eastern end, the 8 main islands (Hawaii, Maui, Oahu, Kauai, Molokai, Lanai, Niihau and uninhabited Kahoolawe) make up all but 7 km² of the state's total area of 16,705 km². Hawaii is the largest (10,458 km²) and has the groups highest mountain, Mauna Kea (4,206 m), and an active volcano, Mauna Loa. The other islands are just volcanic stacks, coral reefs and shoals. The climate is warm (23°C) with heavy winter rainfall.

Hawaii: the economy
The activity generated by the US naval base at Pearl Harbor (Oahu) is the state's chief source of income. Next in importance is tourism with 3 million visitors a year. Farming is highly commercialized: the two main crops, sugar cane and pineapples, occupy 90% of cultivated land. Skipjack tuna accounts for half of the fish catch. Food-processing industries are important with sugar, canned pineapple and juice, canned tuna, tropical fruits and flowers sent to the US mainland. About 75% of the 994,000 inhabitants live on Oahu which has the state capital, Honolulu (365,000).

The Arctic and Greenland

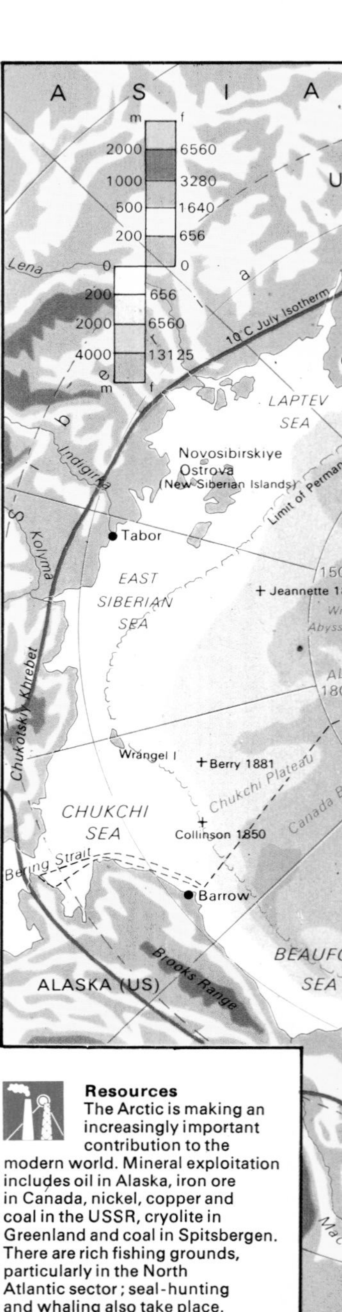

The Arctic
The Arctic, the vast northern polar region, consists of an immense central ocean fringed by innumerable islands and the shores of Asia, Europe and North America. Its southern limit lies along an astronomically determined line, the Arctic Circle (66°32′ N); above this latitude the sun never rises in midwinter nor sets in midsummer. For geographical purposes, however, the polar boundary is often defined by the 10°C July isotherm: an imaginary line passing through all places with an average July temperature of 10°C. This line roughly coincides with the northern limit of trees and brings within the Arctic the whole of Greenland, most of Iceland and a broad belt, up to 500 km wide, along the north coast of the American and Eurasian continents.

Physical features
The Arctic's dominant feature is its great ocean, 3,000 m deep and covering 14,200,000 km². Much of the surface of this huge ocean is permanently frozen, but in summer some melting occurs along the southern margins and navigation is possible. The Arctic lands bordering the ocean are partly mountainous and in some places are liable to earthquakes; Jan Mayen island has the world's most northerly volcano. With the exception of Greenland and neighbouring islands, most land is free of ice and snow in summer. Several major rivers drain into the ocean, including the Mackenzie (Canada), Lena, Yenisey and Ob (USSR).

Climate
Over most of the Arctic, mean temperatures for the warmest and coldest months are about —1°C and —35°C. On the continental land masses, temperatures are more extreme, rising to 9°C in summer but falling to —46°C in winter. Winters are generally milder on the islands: Spitsbergen averages —20°C in February. Much of the Arctic is basically desert as precipitation (in the form of snow blizzards) seldom exceeds 20 cm.

Vegetation
Between the tree line and the shores of the Arctic Ocean lies the *tundra*—a forlorn monotonous plain, littered with swamps and lakes, which early explorers called 'the barrens'. During the short summer, when temperatures remain above freezing, the tundra bursts into life: mosses, lichens, grasses, low shrubs and small flowering plants form a dense, colourful carpet. The vegetation draws its moisture from the thawed surface of the permanently frozen subsoil (permafrost), a feature of all Arctic lands.

Wildlife
The Arctic Ocean, with its rocky shores, freezing waters and pack-ice, is the home of polar bears, walruses, seals and whales. Many land animals, such as caribou, wolves, wolverines and grizzly bears, migrate in winter; others, including the musk-ox, lemming and Arctic fox, are permanent tundra residents.

Resources
The Arctic is making an increasingly important contribution to the modern world. Mineral exploitation includes oil in Alaska, iron ore in Canada, nickel, copper and coal in the USSR, cryolite in Greenland and coal in Spitsbergen. There are rich fishing grounds, particularly in the North Atlantic sector; seal-hunting and whaling also take place. Large herds of reindeer are kept for their meat and skins on the Eurasian mainland and in Canada, the breeding of musk oxen is being developed as the animals produce a very valuable fine wool.

Peoples
The Arctic has a total population of about half a million; the majority are Americans, Canadians, Danes and Russians who have moved into the area to develop its economic, scientific and strategic potential. The indigenous peoples are: Eskimos in North America, Greenlanders (mixed Eskimos and Europeans), Lapps in the Kola peninsula and north Scandinavia, Samoyeds, Yakuts, Tungus and other tribes in Siberia. Although these groups are spread over a vast area, their cultures are similar and their traditional activities of hunting and fishing provide them with food, clothes and oil (for heat and light).

Greenland
Area
2,175,600 km²/840,000 sq miles
Location
59°45′—83°40′ N
12°—73° W
Population
51,000 (1982)
Population density
1 person per 43 km²/16 sq miles
Capital and largest town
Nuuk (Godthåb): 9,500
Languages
Greenlandic, Danish
Major imports
fuels, foods, machinery, vehicles
Major exports
fish, cryolite, skins
Currency
Danish kroner
Gross National Product
550 million US dollars
Status
island territory of Denmark

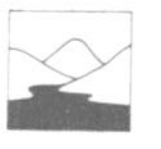

The land
Most of Greenland, the world's largest island, lies within the Arctic Circle. The low-lying interior is covered by a giant ice-sheet (1,833,900 km²) some 2,000 m thick. The surrounding coastal zone, seasonally free of ice and snow, features mountain ranges rising to 3,700 m and deep fjords. The island's polar climate is harshest in the north: July and February in Upernavik are 5°C and —23°C, in Ivigtut, 10°C and —8°C; temperatures on the ice-cap are always below freezing. Rainfall decreases from 110 cm in the south to 20cm in the north.

The economy
Greenlanders, of mixed Eskimo and Danish origin, mostly live on the southwest coast where they work in fishing (cod, halibut, shrimp) and associated industries; Godthåb, Frederikshåb and Holsteinsborg are the principal centres. Other activities include sheep-farming in the south, seal-hunting in the north and some mining (marble, coal, lead, zinc and cryolite). Deposits near Ivigtut are the world's only commercial source of cryolite, used in making ceramic glazes and aluminium. There are important meteorological and radio stations on the island.

Canada

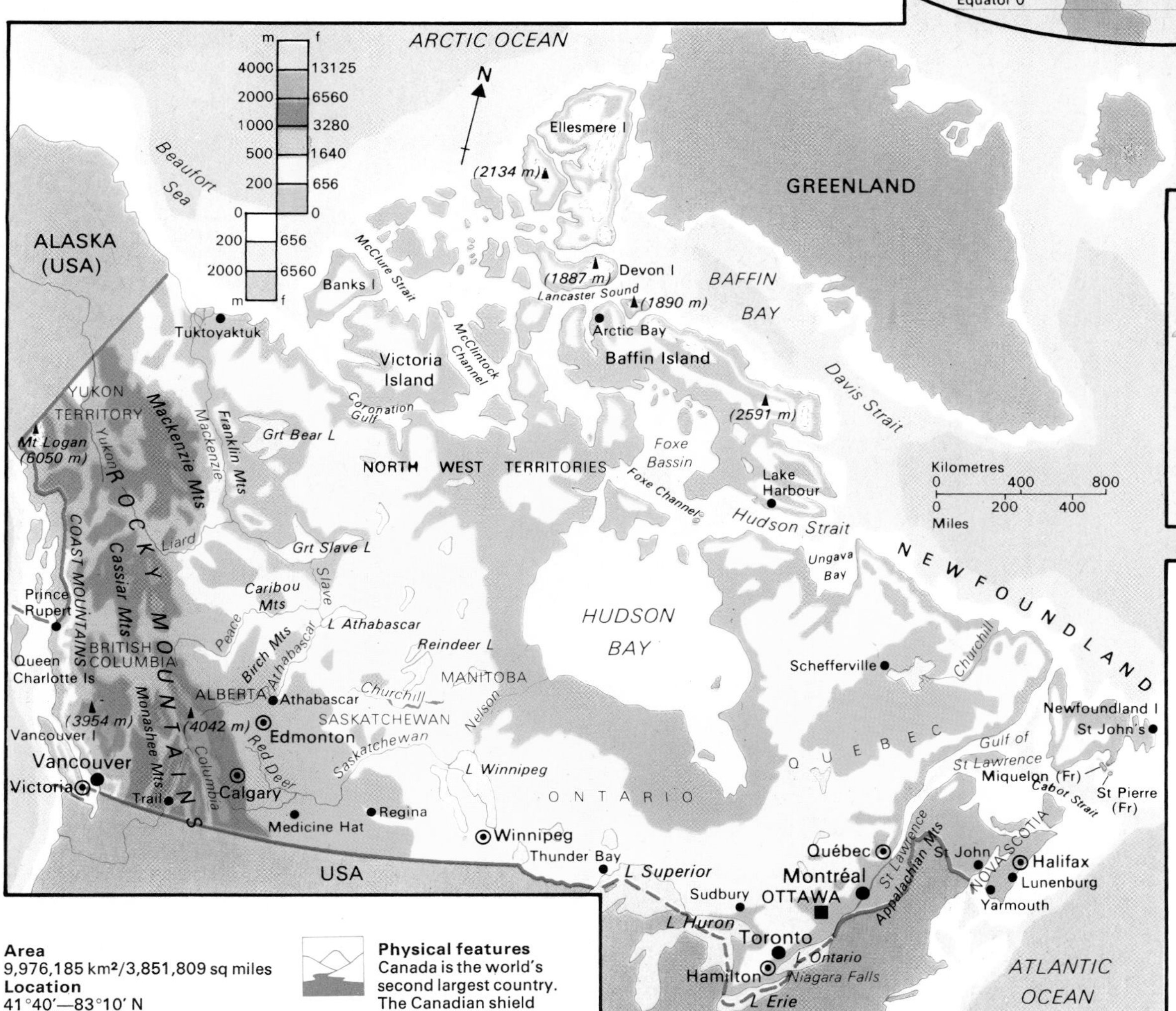

Area
9,976,185 km²/3,851,809 sq miles
Location
41°40′—83°10′ N
52°40′—141° W
Population
24,231,000 (1982)
Population density
2 per km²/6 per sq mile
Capital
Ottowa: 695,000 (1981)
Largest City
Montréal: 2,828,000 (1982)
Languages
English, French
Major imports
vehicles, machinery, foods, metal manufactures, chemicals, textiles
Major exports
vehicles, machinery, ores and metals, wheat, other edible products, lumber, petroleum, newsprint, pulp
Currency
dollar (1 dollar = 100 cents)
Gross National Product
276,220 million US dollars (1981)
Status
independent federal state

Forestry

Canada's forests, which cover a third of the country, stretch from the Atlantic to the Pacific. About 80% are coniferous (spruce, fir, pine, cedar, hemlock) but some mixed forest occurs near the southeastern border. Forestry and allied industries are most important in British Columbia, Québec and Ontario. Forest products provide 12% of total exports and Canada ranks as the world's leading producer of newsprint and the second largest producer of wood.

Physical features

Canada is the world's second largest country. The Canadian shield underlies half the territory; this core of very old, hard rock spreads from the Arctic Ocean and the Mackenzie river, down to Lakes Superior and Huron and the St Lawrence and up into Newfoundland. Glacial action has left the area thin-soiled and badly drained with many lakes and swamps. Flat plains stretch between the shield's western rim and the Rockies. To the southeast lie peninsular Ontario and the St Lawrence valley—both fertile and densely populated regions. Uplands west of the river are an extension of the Appalachians. Western Canada consists of a central plateau flanked by the Rockies, which rise to over 3,000 m, and by the Coast Mts, which climb steeply from the sea and reach 6,050 m at Mt Logan. There are three main river systems: the Great Lakes/St Lawrence river to the Atlantic; the Saskatchewan/Nelson system draining into Hudson Bay and Canada's longest river, the Mackenzie (4,241 km), flowing into the Arctic Ocean.

Climate

Canada has a continental climate with mountain barriers limiting ocean influences. Winters are cold: January averages —31°C at Arctic Bay, —20°C at Winnipeg. Summers are cool in the north warm in the south (6°C at Arctic Bay in July, 19°C at Winnipeg). Most areas have 75-130 cm of rain; the Coast Mts have over 250 cm.

Agriculture

Although Canada is basically an industrial country, agriculture is still important and accounts for 12% of total exports. Farmland, covering less than 8% of the country, lies mostly south of 55°N and is concentrated on the west. Canada's main crop, spring wheat, is grown on the Prairies (southern Alberta, Saskatchewan and Manitoba) and 75% is exported. Other Prairie crops are oats, barley and oilseeds. British Columbia is noted for fruit, particularly apples. Southern Ontario and Québec specialize in maize, tobacco, fruit and dairying (73% of Canada's milk comes from this region). Meat animals are reared in Ontario, Quebec, the Prairies and northern British Columbia.

Fishing

Canada is the world's fourth largest fish exporter with 65% of the catch exported. About 85% of the catch comes from the Atlantic where the main species are cod (off Newfoundland), herring, halibut and lobster. Salmon is caught off the west coast. The Great Lakes yield eel, whitefish and pickerel. St John, Lunenburg, Yarmouth and Halifax in the east, and Vancouver and Prince Rupert in the west are fishing ports.

Mining

Canada has immense mineral wealth and leads the world in output of nickel, zinc and asbestos. It holds second place for uranium, sulphur and molybdenum, exports more iron ore than any other country and produces a large share of the world's gold, lead, potash, silver and copper. The chief mining regions are west Newfoundland (iron ore), south Québec (asbestos, copper, gold), southeast Ontario (copper, zinc, nickel, lead, uranium, gold and silver) and southeast British Columbia (zinc). Sudbury (Ontario) and Trail (British Columbia) are important mining centres. About 65% of minerals are exported, accounting for 25% of total exports.

Energy

Canada is self-sufficient in energy resources with petroleum its leading mineral. Alberta produces 85% of petroleum requirements, 40% of the coal and some natural gas. Further vast reserves of oil and natural gas occur in the Athabasca tar sands and there are valuable coal fields in British Columbia, Saskatchewan and Nova Scotia. Hydro-electric stations generate 75% of electricity with major plants located on the Churchill, St Lawrence, Niagara, Peace and Columbia rivers.

Industry

Industry is highly developed with motor vehicles, pulp and paper, processed meat, petroleum products, wood, iron and steel, dairy goods, machinery and chemicals as the leading manufactures. Industry is mainly concentrated in Ontario and Quebec, especially Toronto and Montréal, but other centres are located on the Newfoundland iron ore deposits, the Alberta oil and gas fields and at Vancouver and Victoria.

Transport

Transport plays a vital role in a country as large as Canada. Passenger traffic is mainly by road and air, while freight moves by road, rail and water. The 829,300 km road network includes the Trans-Canada Highway (7,776 km), the world's longest paved road. There are also two trans-continental railways. The St Lawrence Seaway/Great Lakes system is one of the world's main commercial waterways: the chief cargoes are wheat (downbound) and iron ore (upbound). Increased trade with Japan has made Vancouver the leading port with Montréal second; other major ports are Halifax, St John, Québec, Toronto, Hamilton and Thunder Bay.

Towns

About 75% of Canadians live in urban areas, mainly in the south. Ontario and Québec account for two-thirds of the population. In particular, peninsular Ontario and the St Lawrence valley are highly urbanized and include Montréal, Toronto (2,800,000), Ottawa, Hamilton and Québec. Other centres are Winnipeg, Edmonton and Calgary in the Prairies, and Vancouver (1,100,000) in the west.

St Pierre & Miquelon

The French Overseas Territory of St Pierre and Miquelon, lying 25 km off the south coast of Newfoundland, consists of 8 small rocky islands with a total area of 242 km² and 5,200 inhabitants. The chief economic activity is cod-fishing with salted, frozen, smoked and canned fish as the main exports.

Mexico

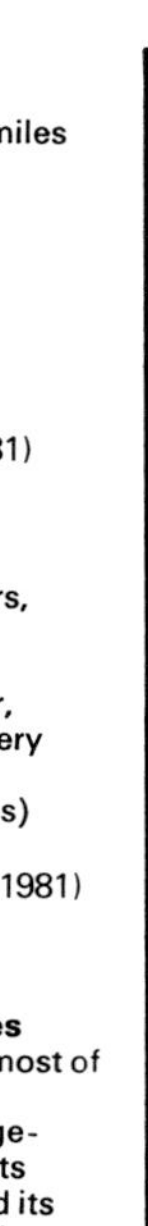

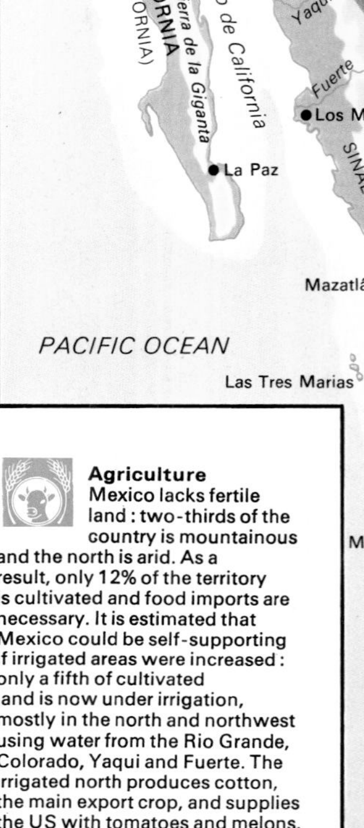

Area
1,972,547 km²/761,601 sq miles
Location
14°30′—32°40′ N
86°50′—117°10′ W
Population
71,215,000 (1981)
Population density
36 per km²/94 per sq mile
Capital and largest city
Mexico City: 8,942,000 (1981)
Language
Spanish
Major imports
machinery, vehicles, fertilizers, food, steel, paper
Major exports
cotton, coffee, oil, zinc, silver, shrimps, vegetables, machinery
Currency
peso (1 peso = 100 centavos)
Gross National Product
160,230 million US dollars (1981)
Status
federal republic

Physical features

Mountains cover most of Mexico. The chief feature is the wedge-shaped central plateau with its base along the US border and its apex south of Mexico City. The northern part of the plateau, averaging 1,200 m altitude, contains wide shallow basins and isolated upland blocks. It is an arid region with only two permanent rivers, the Rio Grande and its tributary, the Conchos. Southwards, the plateau becomes higher (2,500 m) and more mountainous—ending in a belt of snow-capped volcanoes including the still active Popocatepetl (5,452 m). The central plateau is bounded on the west and east by the steep and rugged Sierra Madre ranges, the western chain rising to over 3,000 m. Beyond the volcanic zone, the southern part of the country consists of a high, mountainous plateau crossed by deep river valleys. In the south-east are the Chiapas uplands. Lowland Mexico is limited to the narrow Pacific coast, the wide swampy plain bordering the Gulf, the Tehuantepec isthmus and the Yucatán peninsula. The Santiago, Pánuco and Balsas are major rivers.

Climate

Altitude has a major influence on Mexico's climate with temperatures of 27°C on the lowlands, 21°C on the central plateau and 15°C in the mountains. Rainfall, occurring mostly in summer, varies greatly from one region to another. The eastern lowlands and the south are the wettest parts (100 to 300 cm of rain a year), being in the path of the trade winds. The central plateau, sheltered by the Sierra, is dry (60 cm near Mexico City to under 10 cm in the north). The northern Pacific coast and lower California are also arid, but in the south-west, the Sierra and Chiapas highlands receive up to 200 cm.

Flora & fauna

Lowland vegetation consists of rainforest in wet areas, savanna and scrub in drier parts. In the mountains, mixed forest occurs up to 1,800 m with pine and fir on higher slopes. Grasslands cover the central plateau giving way northwards to scrub, cacti and desert. Wildlife includes jaguars, pumas, monkeys, iguanas, toucans and parrots.

Agriculture

Mexico lacks fertile land: two-thirds of the country is mountainous and the north is arid. As a result, only 12% of the territory is cultivated and food imports are necessary. It is estimated that Mexico could be self-supporting if irrigated areas were increased: only a fifth of cultivated land is now under irrigation, mostly in the north and northwest using water from the Rio Grande, Colorado, Yaqui and Fuerte. The irrigated north produces cotton, the main export crop, and supplies the US with tomatoes and melons. Other cash crops (sugarcane, coffee, citrus) are grown on the Gulf lowlands and half the world's sisal comes from the Yucatán peninsula. Subsistence farming predominates on the central plateau and in the south. Maize, grown on 50% of all arable land, is the basic food crop followed by wheat, beans and rice. Beef cattle are reared on large ranches in the semi-arid north. There is some small-scale dairying in the centre and south.

Mining

Mining, the main industry, plays a significant part in the economy. Mexico has considerable energy resources. Oilfields, mostly on the Gulf lowlands (Tamaulipas, Veracruz, Campeche, Tabasco, Chiapas), supply all the country's petroleum and natural gas. There are also big reserves of coal: Sabinas is the main producing area. Mexico leads the world in silver production with the principal mines (many worked for centuries) on the central plateau. These same mines yield lead, zinc and copper. Mexico is also a major world producer of sulphur, found in the Veracruz region. Other important minerals are iron ore (mined at Durango) and manganese. Large deposits of uranium and phosphates exist.

Forestry & fishing

About 20% of Mexico is forested. Commercial forestry occurs on the Sierra Madre Occidental (pine) and along the southern coasts (mahogany, ebony, dye-woods). Chicle, used in the US as a chewing-gum base, comes from the forests of the Yucatán peninsula. Fishing is important off the 9,660 km-long coast, particularly in the Pacific. The catch includes sardine, tuna and shrimp.

Industry

The past few decades have seen considerable industrial growth. The main sectors are textiles, steel and petrochemicals. The textile industry, based on cotton from the north, is located at Mexico City, Puebla, León, Guadalajara and Veracruz. Steel manufacture, using Durango ore and Sabinas coal, is centred on Monterrey and Monclova. Fruit, meat and fish canning and other food-processing is widespread. The Mexico City area is the chief industrial region, accounting for over 50% of all manufactures. Monterrey is the hub of the second manufacturing zone.

Tourism

Tourism accounts for 40% of foreign earnings. Visitors, 80% from the US and Canada, are attracted by the beaches (Acapulco is world famous), mountain scenery and the remains of the Mayan and Aztec civilizations.

Transport

Transport systems have been improved to meet the growing demands of tourism and economic development. Hard-surfaced roads, totalling 85,000 km, carry 70% of the country's passenger traffic and 60% of its freight. The 25,000 km rail network is densest on the central plateau. In places mountains make road and rail traffic difficult but this is overcome by an extensive internal air service. There are 50 seaports of which the most important are Veracruz, Tampico and Manzanillo.

People & cities

About 70% of Mexicans are *mestizo* (of mixed white and American Indian descent), 20% are white and 10% Indian. Half the population lives in towns and 25% of these in Mexico City where densities exceed 5,000 per km². Mexico City, built on the site of Tenochtitlan (the ancient Aztec capital), is expanding rapidly and has doubled its population since 1960. Consequently, over-crowding and shanty-town growth are major problems. Its central position has stimulated its development as the chief commercial and manufacturing centre and as the focus of national transport systems. The capital's industry is powered by hydro-electricity from installations in the nearby mountains and by oil and gas piped from the Gulf fields. Other major cities are Guadalajara (2 m) and Monterrey (1.5 m).

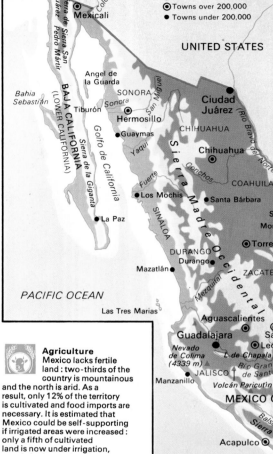

Honduras

Nicaragua

Honduras and Nicaragua

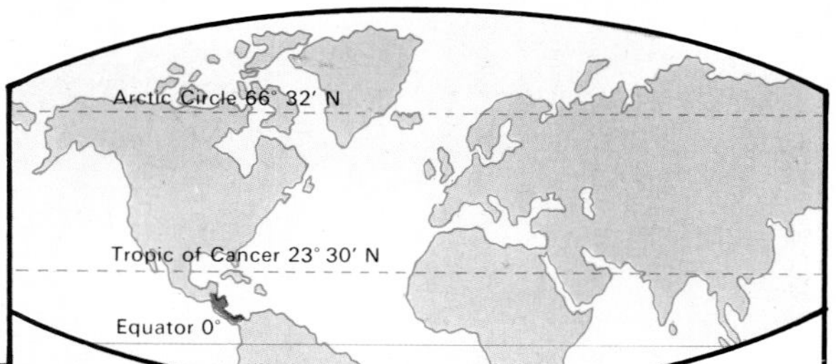

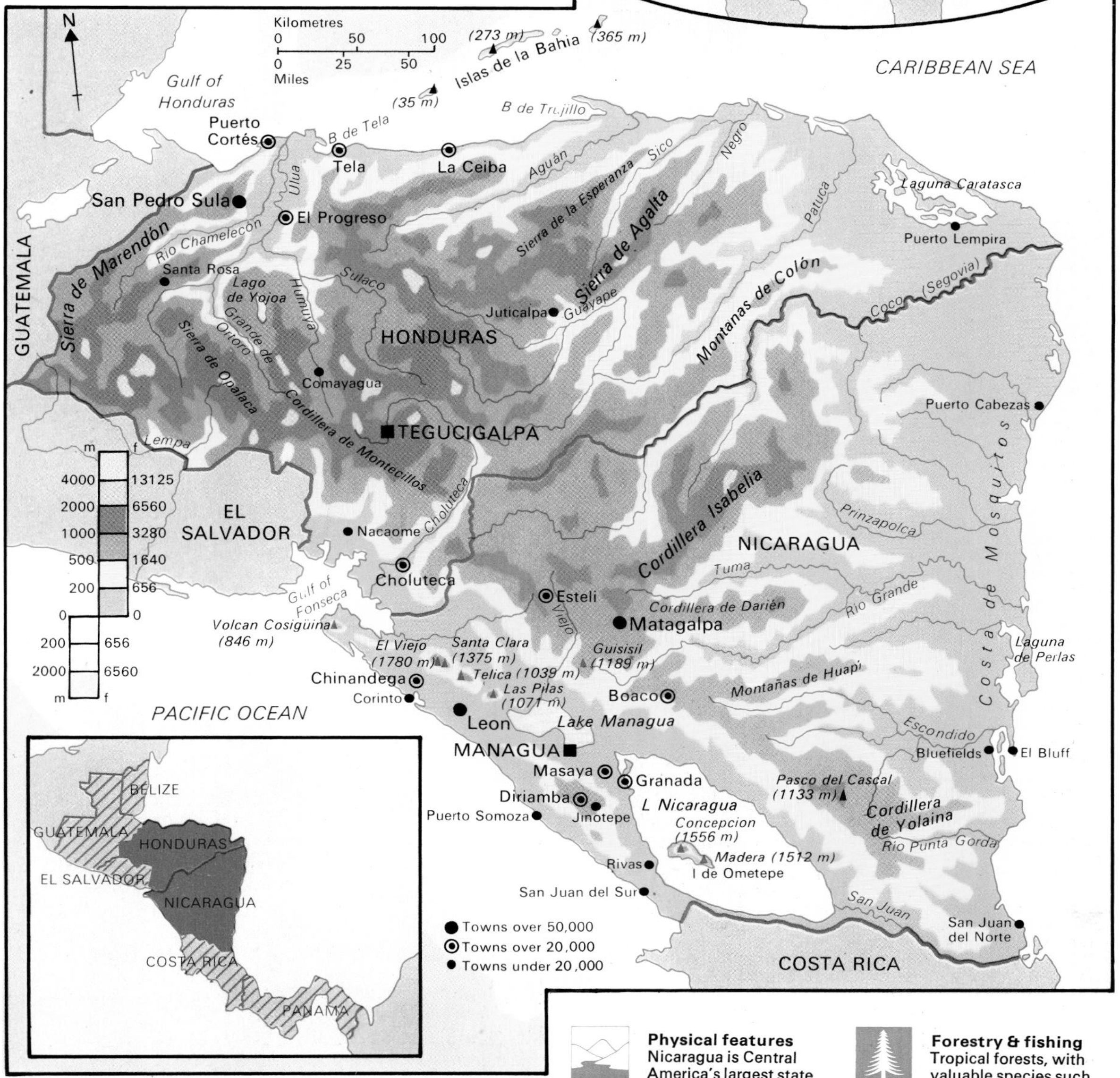

Honduras
Area
112,088 km²/43,227 sq miles
Location
13°—16°30′ N
83°15′—89°30′ W
Population
3,818,000 (1981)
Population density
34 per km²/88 per sq mile
Capital and largest city
Tegucigalpa: 472,700 (1980)
Language
Spanish
Major imports
machinery and transport equipment, fuels, chemicals, foods
Major exports
bananas, coffee, timber, lead and zinc, meat, sugar, tobacco
Currency
lempira (1 lempira = 100 centavos)
Gross National Product
2,270 million US dollars (1981)
Status
republic

Physical features
Honduras is a mountainous country. Ranges, lying east-west, cover most of the territory and are highest in the south where rugged peaks rise to 2,500 m. The mountains enclose numerous basins with fertile volcanic soils. Lowland areas are limited to the small Pacific coastal plain and the alluvial valleys formed by rivers draining into the Caribbean Sea.

Climate
The Caribbean coast is hot and humid with average temperatures of 27°C and 250 cm of rain. Inland, the tropical climate is modified by altitude: at 2,000 m temperatures average 15°C and, in central areas, rainfall seldom exceeds 100 cm. The country is exposed to hurricanes and was devastated by one in 1974.

Flora & fauna
Dense tropical rain-forest occurs along the Caribbean coast and the northern margin of the highlands; inland, savanna grasslands and pine forests predominate. The varied wildlife includes jaguars, pumas, wild pigs, deer, crocodiles, alligators and many exotic birds.

Forestry & fishing
Forests, covering almost 70% of the land, are a valuable source of income. Softwood production (pine) is centred on the interior while hardwoods (notably mahogany, walnut and rosewood) come from the Northeast. Shrimp and lobster fishing, mainly on the Caribbean, is being developed.

Agriculture
Honduras is the poorest Central American state and its backward economy depends largely on agriculture. Bananas, the chief export, are grown on plantations along the northern coast and Honduras ranks as a leading world producer. Coffee, from upland zones, is the second important cash crop. Some sugar, cotton and plantains are also exported. Food crops include maize, beans and rice. Livestock is important, particularly in the southern highlands. Less than a quarter of the country is under cultivation.

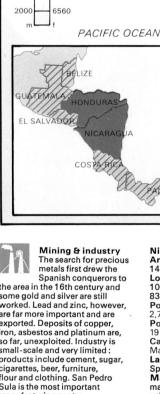

Mining & industry
The search for precious metals first drew the Spanish conquerors to the area in the 16th century and some gold and silver are still worked. Lead and zinc, however, are far more important and are exported. Deposits of copper, iron, asbestos and platinum are, so far, unexploited. Industry is small-scale and very limited: products include cement, sugar, cigarettes, beer, furniture, flour and clothing. San Pedro Sula is the most important manufacturing centre.

Transport
Communications are inadequate. Most of the roads, totalling 6,200 km, are unpaved and the 1,000 km rail network primarily serves the banana plantations in the north. As road and rail systems are so poor, internal air services (linking some 40 centres) are of vital importance. The main ports, Puerto Cortés, Tela, La Ceiba and Trujillo, are all on the Caribbean, but a new port is under construction on the Pacific.

Nicaragua
Area
148,000 km²/57,143 sq miles
Location
10°45′—15°10′ N
83°15′—87°40′ W
Population
2,777,000 (1981)
Population density
19 per km²/49 per sq mile
Capital and largest city
Managua: 553,000 (1980)
Language
Spanish
Major imports
manufactured goods, machinery, vehicles, chemicals, food
Major exports
coffee, cotton, meat, sugar, timber, bananas
Currency
córdoba (1 córdoba = 100 centavos)
Gross National Product
2,400 million US dollars (1981)
Status
republic

Climate
Temperatures vary from 26°C on the lowlands to 18°C in the mountains. Rainfall is heavy (over 350 cm) on the east coast.

Physical features
Nicaragua is Central America's largest state. To the east lies a wide, swampy plain dissected by river valleys. The central region consists of a mountain block, 1,500 to 2,000 m high, which extends southwards like a wedge with its base on the Honduran border. West of the highlands is a depression which contains Lakes Managua and Nicaragua as well as several active volcanoes. A chain of hills separates the depression from the forested Pacific coastlands.

Agriculture
Although agriculture employs 65% of the workforce and provides 75% of exports, farmland occupies only 15% of the total area—mostly in the western half of the country. The principal cash crops are coffee (from the lower mountain slopes) and cotton, sugar and bananas from the Pacific coastlands. Some cocoa, tobacco and sesame seed are also exported. Maize, rice, sorghum, beans, oranges, pineapples and sweet potatoes are grown for domestic consumption. About 50% of agricultural land, mostly in the southern highlands, is pasture and beef is a leading export.

Forestry & fishing
Tropical forests, with valuable species such as mahogany, cedar and rosewood, cover 36% of the country. Production is centred on the Pacific plain and the eastern river valleys. Fishing is important off both coasts; shrimp and lobster are exported.

Mining & industry
Various minerals occur in northern Nicaragua but, so far, gold, silver and copper are the only ones mined. The manufacturing sector is expanding; products include soluble coffee, canned meat, cocoa powder, plywood, cigarettes, textiles, cement, flour, dairy foods and shoes.

Transport
Economic development is hampered by poor communications. Roads are mostly unpaved; the rail network, linking major towns in the west, totals only 350 km; air services are limited. Corinto, handling 60% of all trade, is the main seaport followed by Puerto Somoza, San Juan del Sur, Puerto Cabezas and El Bluff. The state airline, LANCIA, operates overseas and internal flights from Managua airport.

Guatemala, Belize and El Salvador

Above: **El Salvador**
Above left: **Guatemala**
Left: **Belize**

Guatemala
Area
108,889 km²/42,042 sq miles
Location
13°40′—17°50′ N
88°15′—92°15′ W
Population
7,477,000 (1981)
Population density
69 per km²/178 per sq mile
Capital and largest city
Guatemala City: 1,300,000 (1981)
Language
Spanish
Major imports
machinery, vehicles, chemicals, fuels, foods
Major exports
coffee, cotton, bananas, sugar, meat
Currency
quetzal (1 quetzal = 100 centavos)
Gross National Product
8,510 million US dollars (1981)
Status
republic

The land
The Sierra Madre range dominates southern Guatemala and includes a chain of volcanic peaks rising to over 3,500 m; dormant Tajumulco (4,210 m) is the country's highest point. In the south, the highlands fall sharply to the narrow Pacific plain but northwards they drop gently to a low limestone plateau covered with tropical forest. The main river, the Motagua, drains into the Caribbean. Temperatures decrease from 28°C on the lowlands to 20°C in the mountains; rain occurs in summer on the Pacific coast but all year round on the Caribbean side. The Pacific coast is most densely populated.

Farming & forestry
Agriculture is the basis of the economy. The leading export crops are coffee (grown on the fertile mountain soils), cotton and sugar (on the Pacific coastal plain) and bananas (in the Motagua valley). Guatemala is also a major world supplier of chicle (a chewing-gum base) and essential oils (citronella and lemon grass). Maize, beans and rice are cultivated for food. Livestock farming, mostly beef cattle, is important. As the northern forests are largely inaccessible, valuable hardwoods remain underexploited.

Mining & industry
Various minerals occur but production is limited to nickel, zinc and lead; oil deposits on the northern plateau are being developed. The manufacturing sector includes food-processing, textiles, chemicals and electrical goods, but expansion is checked by inadequate power supplies. Tourism is being encouraged: the main assets are the spectacular mountain scenery and vestiges of Mayan and pre-Mayan civilization.

Transport
The 13,000 km road network, densest in the south, is being improved and expanded. Railways, which total 1,000 km, link the Pacific and Caribbean coasts and connect Guatemala with neighbouring Mexico and El Salvador. Puerto Barrios and Champerico are the chief ports. There is an international airport.

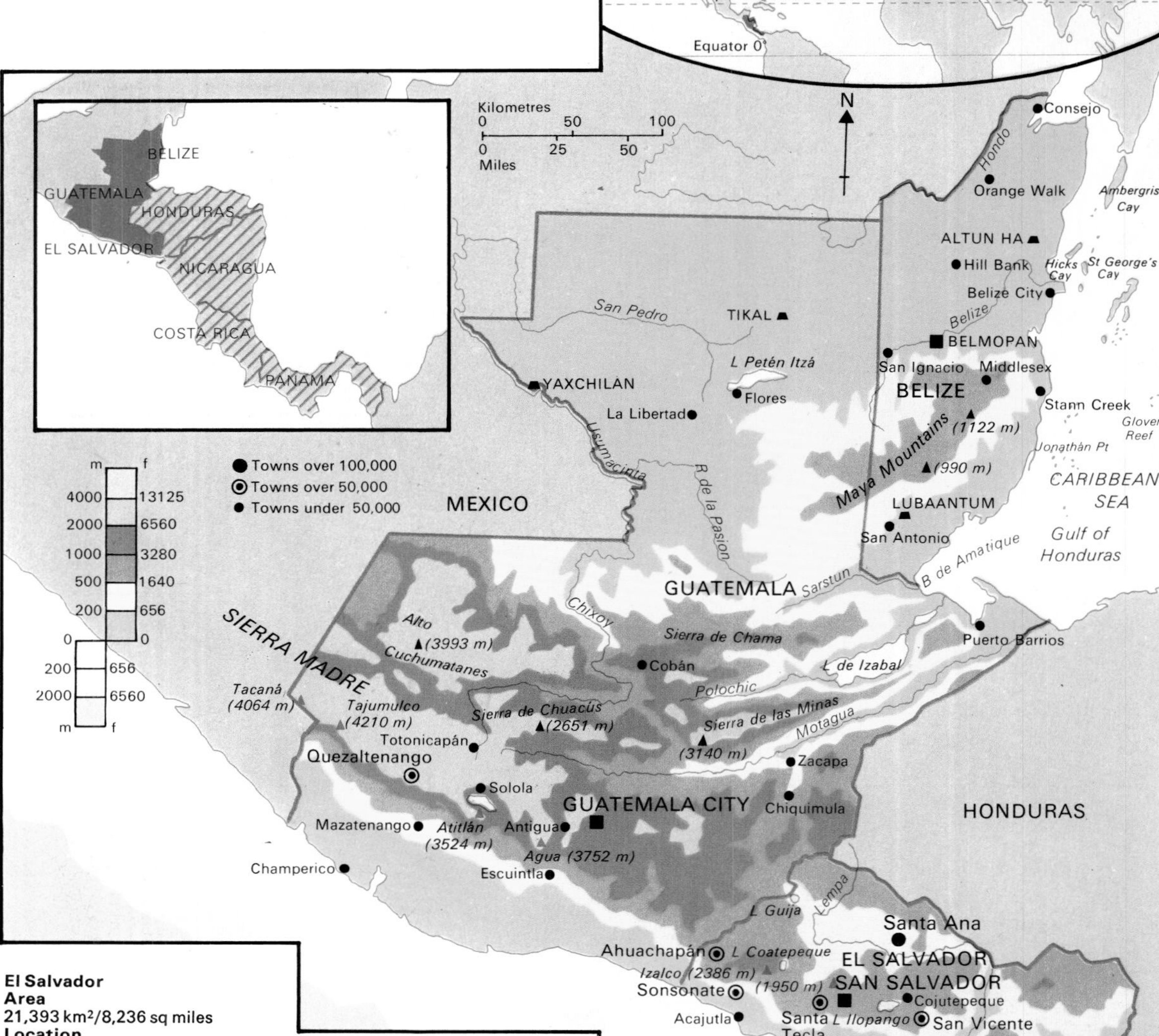

El Salvador
Area
21,393 km²/8,236 sq miles
Location
13°10′—14°25′ N
87°40′—90°10′ W
Population
4,671,000 (1981)
Population density
218 per km²/567 per sq mile
Capital and largest city
San Salvador: 400,000 (1981)
Language
Spanish
Major imports
chemicals, machinery, transport equipment, fuels, food
Major exports
coffee, cotton, sugar, shrimps
Currency
colón (1 colón = 100 centavos)
Gross National Product
3,040 million US dollars (1981)
Status
republic

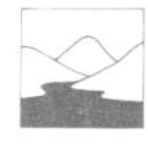

The land
El Salvador, the smallest and most densely populated of the Central American republics, is a highland country. Behind the Pacific coast, two parallel chains of volcanoes rise to over 1,500 m; Izalco still shows signs of activity. The ranges enclose a central plateau some 600 m high where most of the population dwell. Lowland areas comprise the narrow coastal plain and the valley of the Lempa, the main river. The coast is hot but temperatures decrease inland with altitude: San Salvador (670 m) averages 23°C. The wet season, with up to 170 cm of rain lasts from May to October.

Farming & forestry
El Salvador is primarily agricultural: about 30% of the land is used for crops and 30% for pasture. The main cash crop, coffee, provides 50% of all exports and is grown on the rich volcanic soils of the plateau and lower slopes. Cotton, another major export, is cultivated on the coastal plain. Sugar production is increasing. Rice and maize are the basic food crops. Forests cover a third of the country from which cedar and walnut lumber, mahogany and balsam are produced. El Salvador is the world's chief source of balsam—a medicinal gum.

Industry
El Salvador is the most industrialized state in Central America. Many industries are based on agriculture and include sugar refining, flour milling and cotton spinning; others, such as chemicals and engineering, rely on imported materials. Fishing is important and frozen shrimps are exported. Industrial development owes much to good transport systems and to the development of hydro-power resources. The main ports are Acajutla, La Libertad and La Union and there is a rail link to the Caribbean port of Puerto Barrios in Guatemala. Mountain scenery, Mayan remains and surf beaches are tourist attractions.

Belize
Area
22,966 km²/8,867 sq miles
Location
15°55′—18°30′ N
88°10′—89°10′ W
Population
149,000 (1981)
Population density
6 per km²/17 per sq mile
Capital
Belmopan: 4,000 (1975)
Largest City
Belize City: 40,000 (1980)
Language
English
Major imports
machinery, vehicles, foods
Major exports
sugar, citrus, timber, lobsters
Currency
dollar (1 dollar = 100 cents)
Gross National Product
76 million US dollars (1972)
Status
UK dependent territory

Transport
Although swamp, jungle and mountain hamper communications, there is a good all-weather road network. Belize City and Stann Creek are the main ports.

The land
Swamps, lakes and sluggish rivers characterize the low-lying north. In contrast, southern Belize is dominated by the Maya Mountains which rise steeply from the coastal plain to over 1,000 m. Offshore, a chain of coral cays forms a long barrier reef. The climate is hot (26°C) with rainfall increasing from 125 cm in the north to 460 cm in the south. Hurricanes occasionally ravage the coast.

The economy
Belize's weak economy is largely based on farming and forestry. Cultivated land, accounting for 25% of the total area, is concentrated along the coast and in forest clearings. The chief cash crops are sugar, citrus (mainly grapefruit) and bananas. Forests, covering 60% of the country, are a valuable resource: mahogany, rosewood and cedar are the principal species exported. Fishing is important and lobsters are supplied to the US. Industry, confined to processing primary products, is very limited.

Costa Rica and Panama

Costa Rica

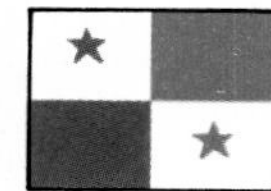
Panama

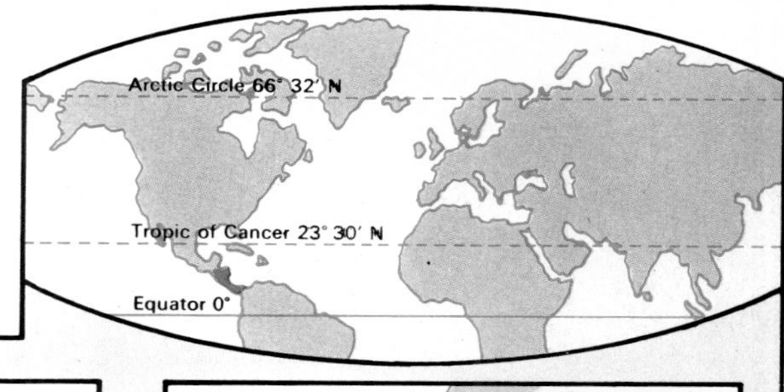

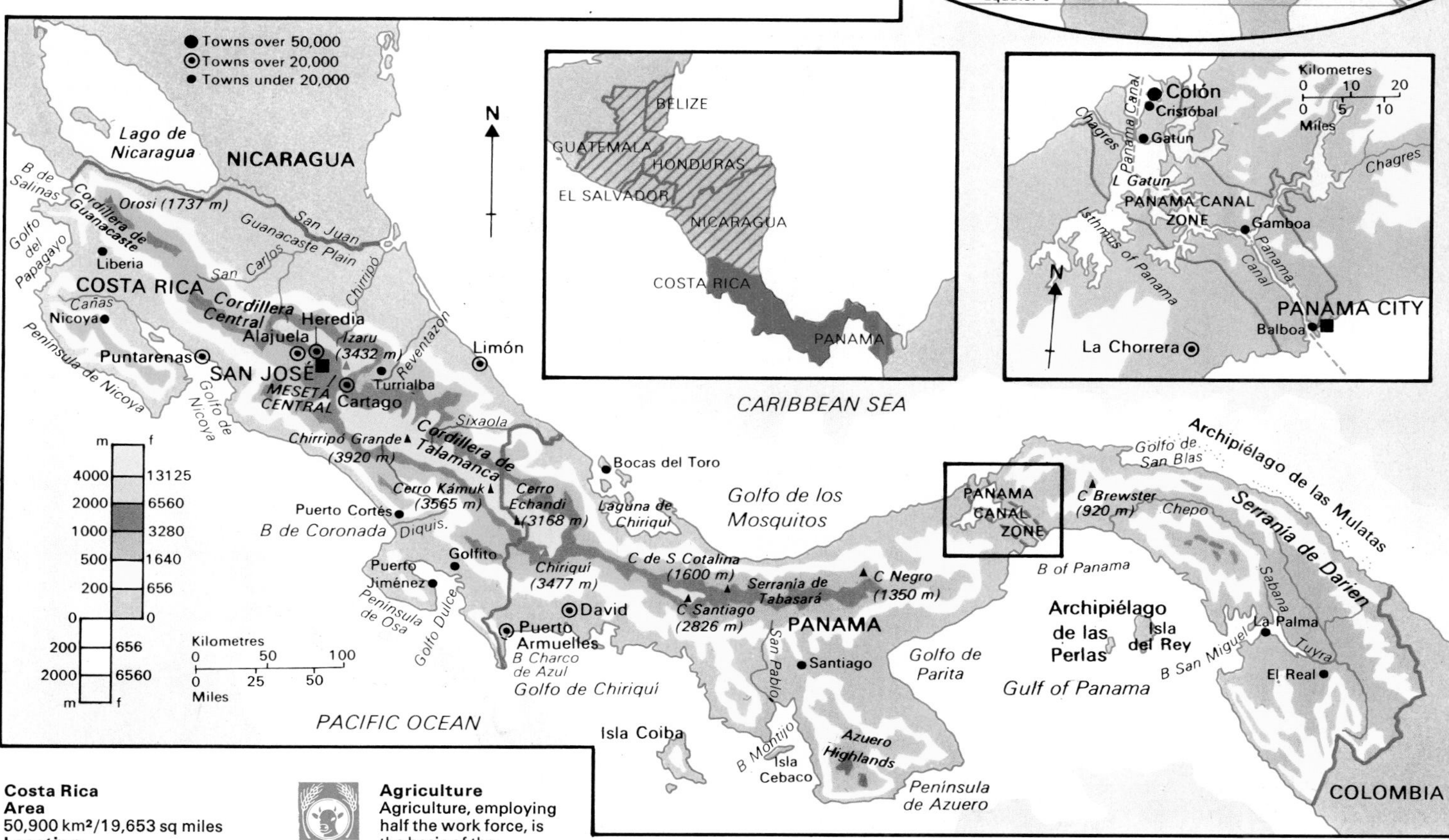

Costa Rica
Area
50,900 km²/19,653 sq miles
Location
8°—11°15′ N
82°35′—85°55′ W
Population
2,340,000 (1981)
Population density
46 per km²/119 per sq mile
Capital and largest city
San José: 865,000 (1982)
Language
Spanish
Major imports
manufactures, machinery, chemicals
Major exports
coffee, bananas, sugar, live animals and meat, cocoa
Currency
colón (1 colón = 100 centimos)
Gross National Product
3,340 million US dollars (1981)
Status
republic

Physical features
Mountains (1,000 to 3,600 m high) cover most of Costa Rica. The three principal blocks, lying northwest-southeast, are the Guanacaste, Central and Talamanca ranges. The Guanacaste and Central Mountains contain active volcanoes including Izaru (3,432 m). The Cordillera Central flanks the Meseta Central, a tableland 1,000 to 1,500m above sea level, which is the country's economic hub. Lowland Costa Rica consists of the narrow Pacific seaboard, the Caribbean coastland (a swampy forested area, widest in the north) and the Guanacaste plain (between the mountains and the Nicoya peninsula).

Climate
The lowlands have a hot, humid tropical climate, but more temperate conditions characterize the Meseta Central. Rainfall is heaviest on the Caribbean coast.

Agriculture
Agriculture, employing half the work force, is the basis of the economy. The Meseta Central, the chief farming region, provides most of the country's coffee, sugar and dairy produce plus a large share of food such as maize, beans and potatoes. Coffee accounts for 50% of all exports. Bananas, the second main cash crop, are grown on the coastal lowlands with the Caribbean zone also producing hemp and cocoa. Stock-raising is important on the Guanacaste plain. Forestry and fishing are both underdeveloped.

Mining & industry
Mineral output is limited to gold, limestone and salt (extracted from the sea). Bauxite and manganese also occur. Manufacturing is small-scale: products include textiles, foodstuffs, fertilizers, furniture, pharmaceuticals, cement and tyres. Most industry is located on the Meseta and at Limón and Puntarenas. The exploitation of hydro-power resources in the Cordillera Central is aiding industrial development.

Transport
The Meseta Central, home of 65% of the population, is the focal point of Costa Rica's transport systems. Roads connect San José to the principal towns: Alajuela, Heredia, Cartago, Turrialba—all on the Meseta. The capital is also linked by the Pan-American Highway to Nicaragua and Panama and by rail to the ports of Limón and Puntarenas. Golfito is the third major port. The state airline, LACSA, provides overseas and domestic services.

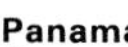

Panama
Area
75,650 km²/29,201 sq miles (excluding the Canal Zone)
Location
7°15′—9°40′ N
77°15′—83° W
Population
1,877,000 (1981)
Population density
25 per km²/64 per sq mile
Capital and largest city
Panama City: 655,000 (1981)
Language
Spanish
Major imports
manufactured goods, crude oil, chemicals, food
Major exports
bananas, petroleum products, shrimps, sugar
Currency
balboa (1 balboa = 100 centésimos)
Gross National Product
3,580 million US dollars (1981)
Status
republic

The land
Panama is a mountainous country with three dominant highland blocks. A central ridge, extending westwards from the canal, contains several volcanic cones near the Costa Rican border, including Chiriquí (3,477 m). In the southwest are the Azuero highlands, while east of the canal a range runs parallel to the coast into Colombia. Lowland areas comprise narrow coastal plains and fertile basins between the ranges. The lowlands are hot (27°C) and humid; mountain areas are cooler (17°C). Rainfall (May to November) is heaviest by the Caribbean (300 cm). Tropical forest predominates with savanna on the drier, Pacific coast.

Agriculture
Despite Panama s arable potential (rich soil and favourable climate) only 14% of the land is cultivated. Leading cash crops are bananas (grown round the Gulf of Panama and along the northeast), sugar (from the Perita Gulf lowlands), coffee (from the western uplands) and some cocoa, hemp and coconuts. Rice, maize and cassava are produced for food; cattle are raised on the Pacific savannas.

Forestry & fishing
Forests cover 60% of the country but are largely unexploited except for some production of mahogany. There is a well developed shrimp-fishing industry centred on Bocas del Toro, Chiriquí and the Gulf of Panama. Shrimps are a major export.

Mining & industry
There is little mining. Some limestone and salt are worked, but deposits of manganese, iron, copper and bauxite are so far undeveloped. Industries include oil-refining, food-processing, cement and clothing. In addition to farming, fishing and industry, receipts from the canal and services to the Canal Zone are vital sources of income.

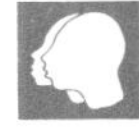

People
About 35% of the people (of European, Indian and Negro descent) live in Panama City and Colón (117,000) both enclaves in the Canal Zone. The rural population is mostly based on the Pacific coast, west of the canal.

Transport
The 7,000 km road network includes a section of the Pan-American Highway which runs the length of the country. The principal railway connects Cristóbal port (near Colón) with Panama City; most cargo destined for the capital is unloaded at Cristóbal and brought overland by rail. The Panamanian merchant fleet is one of the world's largest; ships are mainly foreign owned but registered in Panama because of low fees and lenient regulations. All maritime traffic for Colón and Panama is handled by the canal ports of Cristóbal and Balboa.

The Panama Canal Zone
The US-controlled Canal Zone is a narrow strip of land flanking the Canal. Extending 8 km on each side of the waterway, the Zone has a total area of 1,673 km² and about 50,000 inhabitants (mostly employed by the Panama Canal Company or the Canal Zone Government). The canal itself, opened in 1914, is 82 km long and cuts northwest to southeast across the isthmus from Cristóbal on the Caribbean to Balboa on the Pacific. By eliminating the long haul round Cape Horn, the canal has transformed trade between, on the one hand, the east coast of the Americas, Europe and the West Indies and, on the other, the west coast of the Americas, Australia and Asia. Coal, oil, grain, ores and metals are the principal cargoes carried by the 15,000 vessels that pass through the canal each year. The average transit time is 15 hours, including a 7-hour wait.

Caribbean Islands 1

Bahamas

Cuba

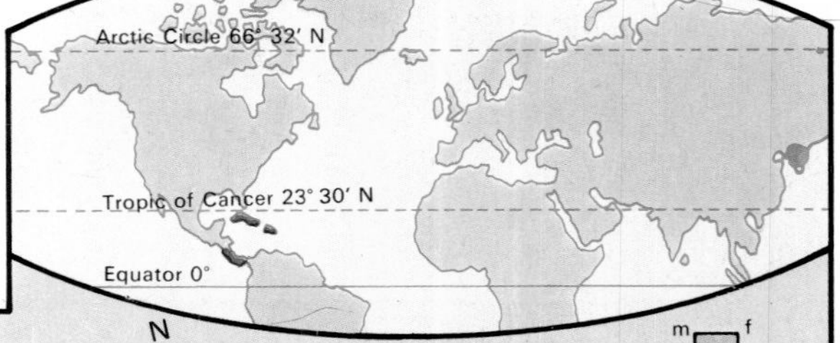

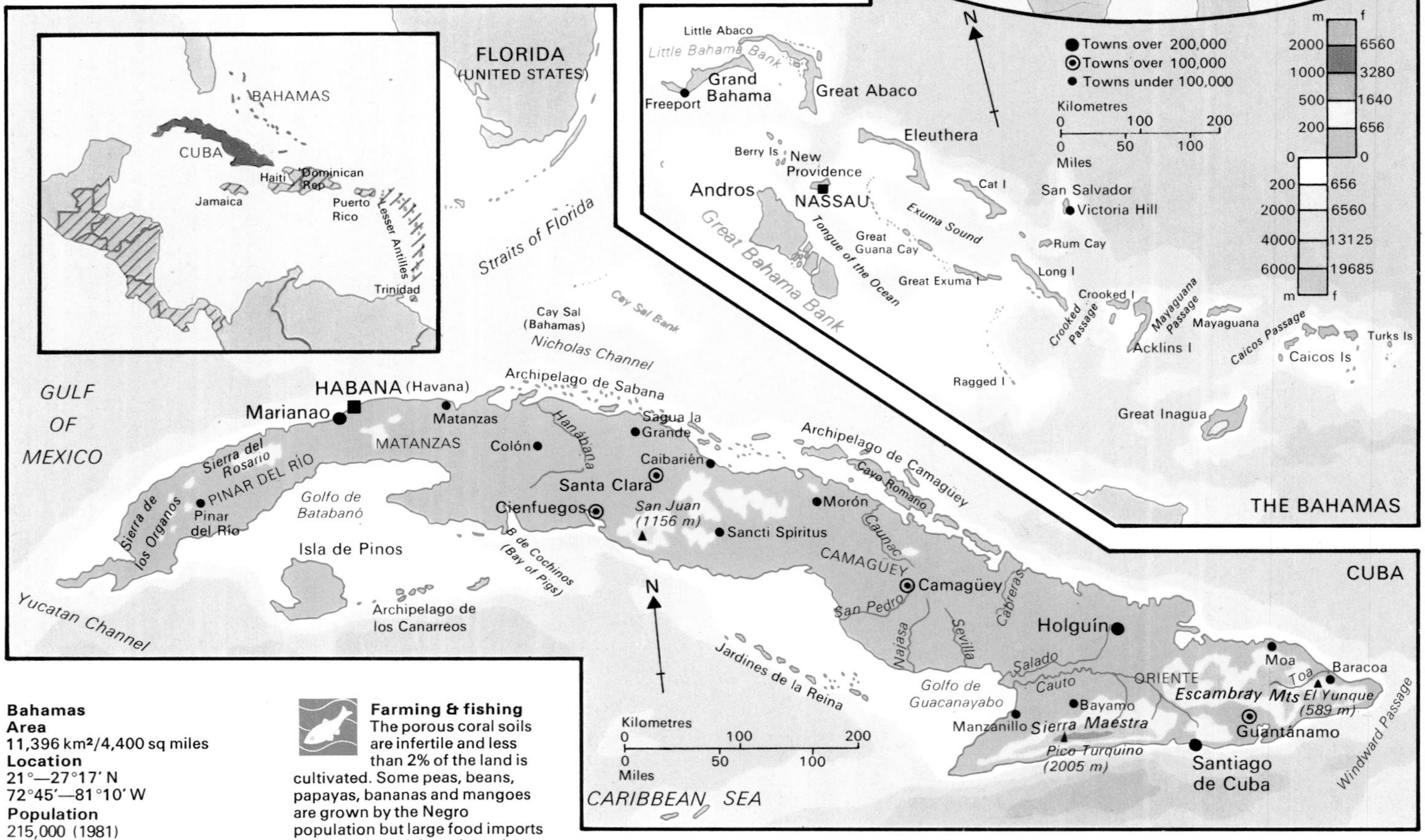

Bahamas
Area
11,396 km²/4,400 sq miles
Location
21°—27°17′ N
72°45′—81°10′ W
Population
215,000 (1981)
Population density
19 per km²/49 per sq mile
Capital and largest city
Nassau: 140,000 (1980)
Language
English
Major imports
crude oil, foods, machinery, vehicles
Major exports
petroleum, petrochemicals, cement, rum
Currency
dollar (1 dollar = 100 cents)
Gross National Product
880 million US dollars (1981)
Status
parliamentary state

Physical features
The Bahamas, extending 1,200 km southeastwards from Florida, consist of some 700 islands and over 2,000 cays and rocks; only 30 islands are inhabited. The archipelago, formed of coralline limestone, represents the highest parts of two submarine banks: the Little Bahama Bank and the Great Bahama Bank. All the islands are flat with sandy beaches, saltmarsh and mangrove along the coast. Inland, bare rock and cacti characterize the dry, eastern islands, while forests of pine and mahogany occur in the wetter west. Andros is the largest island, but New Providence is the most important and most populous, with 60% of the total population.

Climate
The climate is sub-tropical: winters are modified by the Gulf Stream and are mild (21°C) but summers are hot (29°C). Rain ranges from 75 cm in the east to 120 cm in the west.

Farming & fishing
The porous coral soils are infertile and less than 2% of the land is cultivated. Some peas, beans, papayas, bananas and mangoes are grown by the Negro population but large food imports are necessary. A few plantations produce tomatoes, cucumbers, onions, pineapples and citrus for export. Fishing is more profitable: the catch is mostly consumed locally, but some crayfish is frozen and sent to Florida.

Industry
The huge oil-tanker terminal at Freeport with its refinery and petrochemical complex is the main source of income. Tourism is next in importance: the sunny beaches and warm seas make the Bahamas a luxury resort. There is little other industry except for some rum-distilling, cement manufacture, saw-milling, fruit-canning and fish-freezing. Salt, produced by evaporation, is exported.

Transport
The growth of tourism has resulted in good sea and air links with the outside world, especially North America. There are numerous inter-island boat and plane services. Roads on New Providence and Grand Bahama are hard-surfaced and fairly extensive, but are less developed on the other islands.

Turks & Caicos
The Turks and Caicos Islands, at the southeast end of the Bahamas, are a British Colony. The group, consisting of six inhabited islands and about 30 cays, has a total area of 430 km². The 6,000 islanders live by fishing: crayfish provide 90% of all exports. Salt and conch shells are also exported. Tourism is being developed.

Cuba
Area
110,922 km²/42,827 sq miles
Location
19°52′—23°5′ N
74°10′—85° W
Population
9,688,000 (1981)
Population density
83 per km²/215 per sq mile
Capital and largest city
Habana: 1,925,000 (1981)
Language
Spanish
Major imports
food, machinery, transport equipment, fuels, chemicals
Major exports
sugar, nickel, tobacco, fish, citrus
Currency
peso (1 peso = 100 centavos)
Gross National Product
not available
Status
republic

Physical features
Cuba, the largest and most westerly of the Caribbean islands, is 1,200 km long but only 32-145 km wide. The coast is swampy, especially in the south, and is fringed with reefs, sandbanks and about 1,600 islands, including the large, forested Isla de Pinos (3,060 km²). Broad plains and low hills cover most of Cuba. The main highlands are the Sierra de los Organos and the Sierra del Rosario in the west, the Escambray Mountains in the centre and, in the east, the Sierra Maestra with Pico Turquino (2,005 m), Cuba's highest point. The rivers are mostly short, swift-flowing and seasonal.

Climate
The moderating effect of constant trade winds gives Cuba a mild climate; Habana averages 22°C in winter, 28°C in summer. During the wet season (May-November), 130 cm of rain falls on the lowlands rising to 250 cm in the mountains.

Agriculture
Sugar, accounting for 80% of exports, is the basis of the economy; it is grown throughout the island and Cuba ranks as the world's second largest sugar producer. Tobacco, cultivated in the west, is next in importance with coffee, from the eastern highland slopes, citrus and pineapples also exported. Rice is the staple food. Other major crops are pangola (for fodder), maize, potatoes, henequen and kenaf fibres (both used for sacking) and cotton. Dairy and beef cattle are kept on the central and eastern plains. Cuban agriculture is state controlled and 60% of farmland is state-owned.

Forestry & fishing
Less than 15% of the land is forested. Tropical hardwoods cover high slopes in the west while pine grows in the eastern mountains and on Isla de Pinos. To increase timber output and aid soil conservation, new forests are being planted—mostly of eucalyptus, pine and some cedar (for cigar cases). Fishing is organized into co-operatives and is expanding; Manzanillo and Habana are major centres.

Mining
Cuba has considerable mineral wealth. There are extensive nickel deposits in the eastern mountains and production is centred on Moa where there is a nickel and cobalt smelter. Manganese and copper occur in large quantities in the Sierra Maestra and in the western province of Pinar del Río and chromite is mined near Holguín and Camagüey. Iron reserves in the mountains of Baracoa are among the world's richest. Energy minerals, however, are lacking: Cuba has no coal and only a little oil. All mineral resources are nationalized.

Industry
Following the 1959 revolution, when Fidel Castro came to power, there has been steady industrial development. Aid from the Eastern Bloc, in the form of technical training and factory building, has played a major part in Cuba's industrialization programme. Processing agricultural products is the main industry and includes sugar-refining, textile manufacture, leather-working, fruit-canning and cigar production. The metallurgical and construction sectors are also important.

Transport
The main road is the 1,240 km-long Central Highway which runs from Pinar del Río via Habana to Santiago. About 60% of the railways serve the sugar estates. Habana is the main seaport with an international airport.

Caribbean Islands 2

Above: Dominican Republic
Top left: Jamaica
Left: Haiti

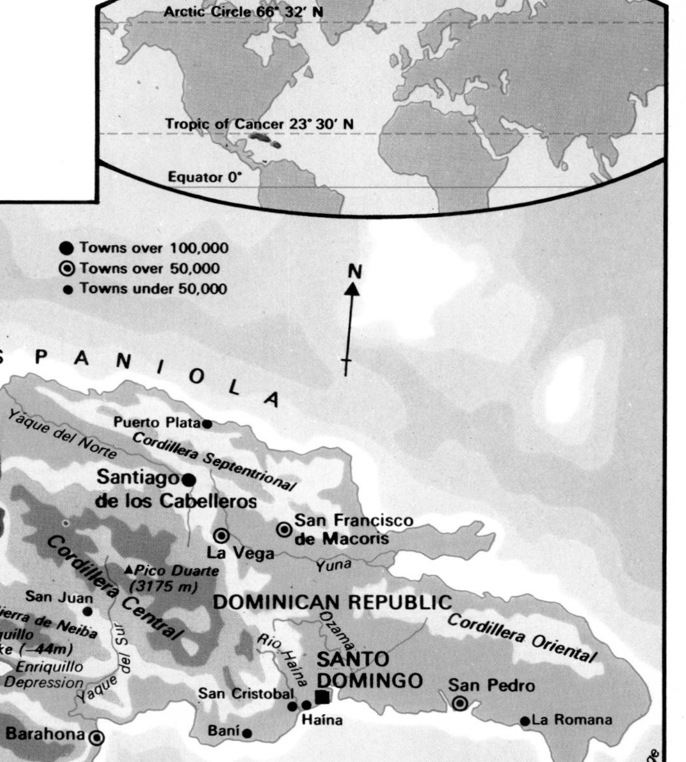

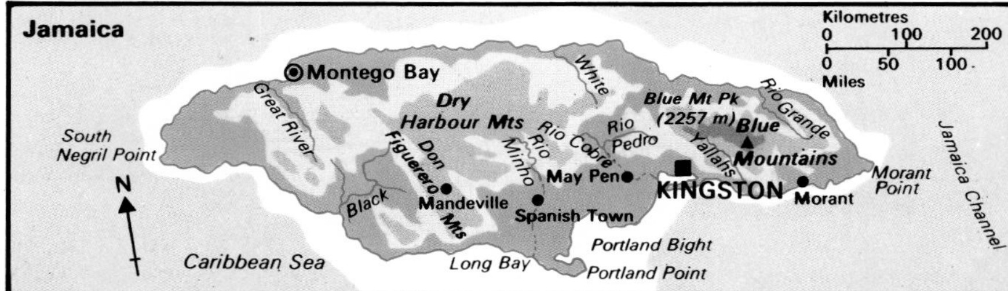

Jamaica
Area
11,424 km²/4,411 sq miles
Location
17°40′—18°30′ N
76°10′—78°20′ W
Population
2,194,000 (1981)
Population density
192 per km²/497 per sq mile
Capital and largest city
Kingston: 670,000 (1980)
Language
English
Major imports
consumer goods, foods, machinery vehicles, fuels, chemicals
Major exports
bauxite and alumina, bananas, sugar, rum
Currency
dollar (1 dollar = 100 cents)
Gross National Product
2,600 million US dollars (1981)
Status
parliamentary state

Physical features
Jamaica, the third largest Caribbean island, lies 150 km south of Cuba. In places the forested highland interior is almost impenetrable; it comprises rugged limestone plateaux in the centre and west and, in the east, the Blue Mountains reaching 2,257 m. The surrounding coastal plain is narrow in the north, but wider in the south and west. Rivers are swift flowing with steep, rocky courses.

Climate
Coastal areas are warm; tempeatures average 26°C but the upland interior is cooler. Rain, falling between August and November, ranges from 500 cm in the Blue Mountains to approximately 100 cm in the southwest.

Agriculture
A third of the land is farmed, producing a wide range of cash crops: sugarcane and citrus on the alluvial plains in the south and west; bananas along the wetter north coast; coffee in the Blue Mountains; pimento, ginger and cocoa in the interior; coconuts and tobacco. Sugar and bananas are most important. Rice, maize, vegetables and rootcrops are grown for food. Jamaica is increasing its dairy and beef cattle stocks.

Mining & industry
Jamaica has rich bauxite deposits in the Mandeville area and ranks as the world's second producer of bauxite and alumina. In recent years, a variety of industries have been established; products include textiles, shoes, cement and paints as well as traditional goods such as rum, molasses and cigars. After sugar, tourism is the chief source of income with Montego Bay as the leading resort.

Cayman Islands
The low lying, coral Cayman Islands, a self-governing British colony, are situated 300 km northwest of Jamaica and consist of Grand Cayman, Little Cayman and Cayman Brac with a total area of 260 km². Most of the 15,000 islanders live by fishing. Turtle products, shark hides and crayfish are the main exports. About 90% of the population is concentrated on Grand Cayman which has the capital, George Town.

Dominican Republic
Area
48,442 km²/18,703 sq miles
Location
17°40′—19° N
68°15′—71°55′ W
Population
5,592,000 (1981)
Population density
115 per km²/299 per sq mile
Capital and largest city
Santo Domingo: 1,551,000 (1981)
Language
Spanish
Major imports
machinery, chemicals, foods, vehicles, fuels
Major exports
sugar, ferro-nickel, cocoa, coffee, tobacco, bauxite
Currency
peso (1 peso = 100 centavos)
Gross National Product
7,070 million US dollars (1981)
Status
republic

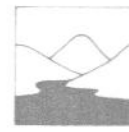

The land
The Dominican Republic extends over the eastern two-thirds of Hispaniola, the Caribbean's second largest island. Mountains cover the west and centre; the principal range is the Cordillera Central which rises to 3,175 m in Pico Duarte—the highest peak in the Caribbean. The central ranges are separated from coastal chains by the Yaque del Norte and Yuna rivers in the north and by the Enriquillo depression in the south; the Enriquillo salt lake (44 m below sea level) is the lowest point in the West Indies. The east is largely lowland. Temperatures average 26°C but are lower in the mountains; rainfall is heaviest in the north. Hispaniola lies in a hurricane belt.

Agriculture
Agriculture is the chief economic activity. Sugar, grown on plantations in the southeast, is the main cash crop and accounts for 50% of all exports. Other leading cash crops are coffee (from the coastal uplands), cocoa and tobacco (both cultivated on the northern plain) and bananas. Rice, maize and groundnuts are produced for domestic consumption. Stock-raising is concentrated in the north and east and dairying in the south.

Mining & industry
Mining makes a significant contribution to the economy: bauxite is exploited at Cabo Rojo, nickel at Bonao in the Cordillera Central, and rock salt in the Enriquillo lowland. Silver, copper and gypsum are also worked. Industrialization is progressing steadily: the principal sectors are food processing, cotton textiles, cement and fertilizer. Santo Domingo and the new port of Rio Haína are important manufacturing centres.

Haiti
Area
27,750 km²/10,714 sq miles
Location
18°—20° N
71°40′—74°30′ W
Population
5,104,000 (1981)
Population density
184 per km²/476 per sq mile
Capital and largest city
Port-au-Prince: 746,000 (1978)
Language
French
Major imports
foods, textiles, machinery, fuels
Major exports
coffee, bauxite, sugar, sisal, essential oils, handicrafts
Currency
gourde (1 gourde = 100 centimes)
Gross National Product
1,510 million US dollars (1981)
Status
republic

The land
Haiti, occupying the western third of Hispaniola, is a mountainous country. The main ranges thrust westwards into two peninsulas enclosing the Gulf of Gonâve. The principal lowlands are the Artibonite valley and the plain between Port-au-Prince and the Saumâtre salt lake. The climate is tropical but modified inland by altitude; rainfall decreases from 300 cm in the north to 50 cm in the south.

The economy
Haiti is one of the poorest Caribbean states. Its weak economy is based on peasant agriculture which employs 85% of the work-force and provides 80% of exports. Coffee is the main cash crop followed by sisal and sugar. Maize, millet, yams and rice are grown for food. Various minerals occur, but only bauxite from the south peninsula is mined. Apart from food-processing and handicrafts, there is little industry. Tourism is important.

Caribbean Islands 3

top left: **Trinidad and Tobago**
above: **Grenada**
left: **Barbados**

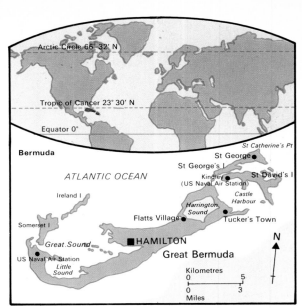

Arctic Circle 66° 32′ N
Tropic of Cancer 23° 30′ N
Equator 0°

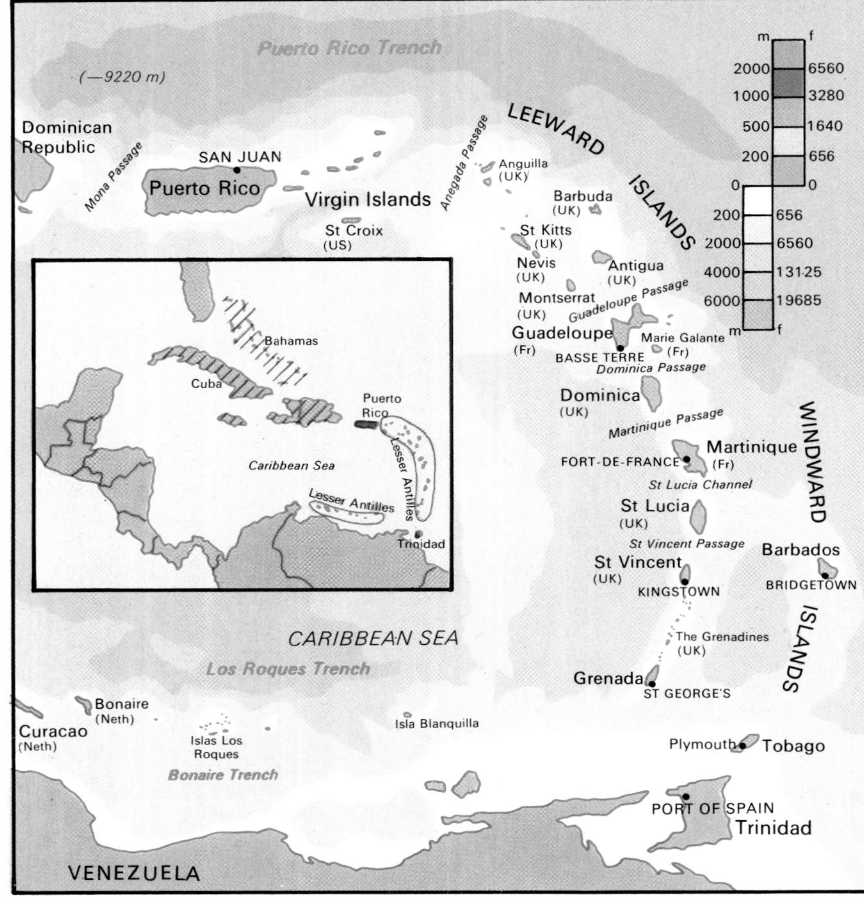

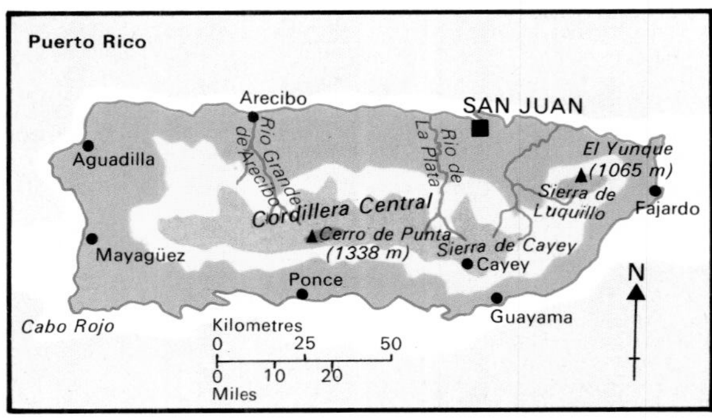

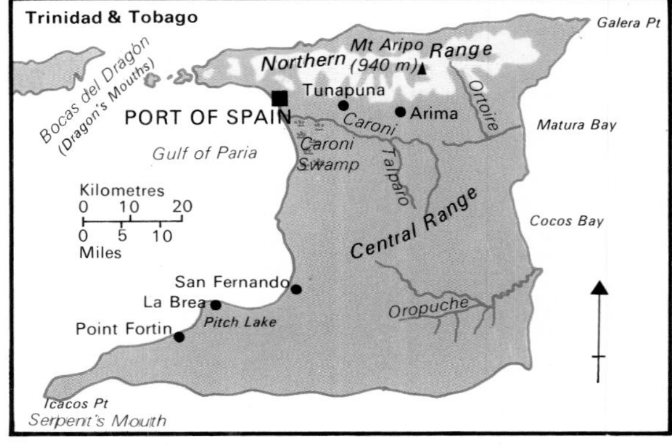

Trinidad & Tobago
Galera Pt
Bocas del Dragón (Dragon's Mouths)
Northern Range
Mt Aripo (940 m)
Tunapuna
PORT OF SPAIN
Caroni
Arima
Oropuche
Matura Bay
Gulf of Paria
Caroni Swamp
Tarapo
Kilometres
0 10 20
0 5 10
Miles
Central Range
Cocos Bay
San Fernando
La Brea
Pitch Lake
Point Fortin
Oropuche
Icacos Pt
Serpent's Mouth

Bermuda
Area
53.3 km²/20.6 sq miles
Population
61,000 (1981)
Population density
1,144 per km²/2,961 per sq mile
Capital and largest city
Hamilton: 1,617 (1980)
Language
English
Major imports
foods, textiles, vehicles
Major exports
essences, perfume, flowers

The British colony of Bermuda consists of some 300 small coral islands situated in the western Atlantic 1,120 km southeast of New York. The largest island, Great Bermuda, is 20 km long and, like the rest of the group, it is low-lying (no point exceeds 75m) and fringed with reefs. The climate, modified by the warm Gulf Stream, is mild with temperatures ranging from 16°C in winter to 30°C in summer. Rain occurs throughout the year and averages 150 cm. As only 20 islands are inhabited, Bermuda has one of the world's densest populations. Many islanders are involved in tourism—the colony's major source of income. Agriculture is limited to 5% of the land: the main crops are vegetables, flowers, bananas and citrus. Small-scale industry includes pharmaceuticals, beauty preparations and essential oils. The larger islands have a good road network and are connected by bridges and causeways; inter-island ferry services are good.

Puerto Rico
Area
8,891 km²/3,435 sq miles
Population
3,675,000 (1981)
Population density
413 per km²/1,070 per sq mile
Capital and largest city
San Juan: 519,000 (1980)
Languages
Spanish, English
Major imports
raw materials, foods, machinery
Major exports
sugar, tobacco, rum, petroleum and petroleum products

The Puerto Rican Commonwealth, politically linked with the US, lies about 2,400 km southeast of Florida and groups Puerto Rico (8,648 km²) with several smaller islands. The main island has a mountainous interior rising to 1,338 m surrounded by a narrow, alluvial coastal plain. The northeast trade winds keep average temperatures between 24°C and 27°C and bring heavy rains (500 cm) to north-facing slopes, but under 75cm to southern parts. In spite of industrialization, centred on the ports of San Juan, Ponce and Mayagüez, agriculture is still significant. About 50% of arable land is used for sugar; tobacco, coffee and pineapples are also major export crops. Sugarcane processing is the leading industry; other industries, such as textiles, electronics and petrochemicals, mostly use imported materials. The islands are popular with American tourists; 90% of all trade is with the US.

Trinidad & Tobago
Area
5,128 km²/1,980 sq miles
Population
1,185,000 (1981)
Population density
231 per km²/598 per sq mile
Capital and largest city
Port of Spain: 250,000 (1981)
Language
English
Major imports
crude oil, machinery, food
Major exports
petroleum and petroleum products, chemicals, sugar, asphalt

The tropical islands of Trinidad and Tobago form an independent state. Trinidad (4,828 km²) lies 11 km off Venezuela and consists of three east-west highland zones covered with rain forest and separated by broad alluvial plains. Tobago (300 km²), situated 32 km northeast of Trinidad, has a mountainous north and a low-lying coral limestone plateau in the south. Temperatures are generally high (28°C) with rainfall decreasing from 250 cm in the northeast to 120 cm in the west. Only 3% of the population lives on Tobago. Trinidad has two major resources: oil and pitch. There are oil fields in the south and in the Gulf of Paria; the pitch lake near La Brea is the world's largest asphalt deposit. Oil refining (including Venezuelan oil) and petrochemicals are the main industries, providing 80% of exports. About half the land is farmed and the chief cash crops are sugar, cocoa, coconuts and citrus.

Leeward Islands
The Leeward Islands, forming an arc on the Caribbean's northeast edge, comprise an inner chain of volcanic islands and an outer chain of coral reefs: Principal (and mountainous) islands are Guadeloupe (1,779 km²), the Virgin Islands (100 islands: total area of 497 km²), St Kitts (176 km²), Nevis (93 km²) and Montserrat (97 km²). The main low-lying outer islands are Anguilla (91 km²), Barbuda (161 km²) and Antigua (280 km²). The climate is humid and tropical, averaging 27°C with 130 cm of rain. Except in the Virgin Islands, agriculture is the basic economic activity. The main crops are sugar (St Kitts, Antigua), cotton (St Kitts, Nevis, Antigua, Barbuda), coconuts (Nevis, Montserrat), fruit and vegetables (Montserrat). Tourism is the chief source of income in the Virgin Islands and is also important in Antigua, St Kitts and Montserrat. Stock-rearing and fishing are significant in the Virgin Islands and Anguilla; Anguilla also produces salt. Off South America, Aruba (193 km²) and Curaçao (444 km²) depend on refining Venezuelan oil; nearby Bonaire (288 km²) is a major world supplier of aloes (from which is derived a laxative.)

Windward Islands
The Windward Islands, extending south from the Leewards to Trinidad, form the Caribbean's eastern perimeter. These islands are mountainous (of volcanic origin) and partly covered with dense rain forest. The chief islands in the group are Martinique (1,116 km²), Dominica (790 km²), St Lucia (616 km²), Grenada (344 km²) and, to the east, Barbados (430 km²). The climate is hot with average temperatures of 24°C in winter and 29°C in summer and heavy summer rainfall ranging from 120 cm to 300 cm; hurricanes sometimes occur. On all the islands, agriculture is the basis of the economy with sugar and bananas as the main crops. Other cash crops are cocoa, coconuts, citrus and cotton. Yams, cassava and groundnuts are grown for food. Dominica is noted for limes, Grenada for nutmeg and other spices and Barbados for shrimps. St Vincent (389 km²) ranks as the world's leading producer of arrowroot. Industry, based on agriculture, is small-scale: the principal products are refined sugar, molasses, rum, fruit juice and essential oils. Throughout the Windward Islands tourism is increasing in importance.

Colombia

Area
1,138,911 km²/439,734 sq miles
Location
12°30′N—4°15′ S
66°50′—79° W
Population
26,425,000 (1981)
Population density
23 per km²/60 per sq mile
Capital and largest city
Bogotá: 4,500,000 (1981)
Language
Spanish
Major imports
chemicals, machinery, metals, vehicles, paper, rubber
Major exports
coffee, textiles, fuel oil, rice, cotton, bananas, beef, flowers, sugar, emeralds
Currency
peso (1 peso=100 centavos)
Gross National Product
36,390 million US dollars (1981)
Status
republic

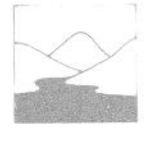

Physical features
Colombia, named after Christopher Columbus, is the only South American state with coastlines on both the Caribbean and the Pacific. The western part of the country is dominated by three parallel north-south ranges of the great Andes Mountains with altitudes of between 3,000 and 5,000 m; the Cordillera Occidental, the Cordillera Central and the main range, the Cordillera Oriental. These ranges are separated by the deep valleys of Colombia's two main rivers: the Cauca and the Magdalena. A lowland belt, up to 100 km wide, lies between the western mountains and the Pacific. In the north, the isolated Sierra Nevada de Santa Marta rises from the marshy Carribean plain to 5,684 m in Pico Cristóbal Colón, the country's highest point. Beyond the Andean ranges, the eastern two-thirds of the territory consists of vast savanna plains (the *llanos*) drained by Orinoco and Amazon tributaries.

Climate
Colombia's contrasting climate zones reflect the country's varied relief. Lowland areas, comprising the river valleys, coastal plains and llanos, are hot with mean annual temperatures of 24° to 30°C. At altitudes between 900 and 1,800 m, conditions are healthier and range from 16° to 22°C. A cooler zone from 1,800 to 3,000 m averages below 15°C. Bogotá at 2,650 m averages 14°C. The high mountain regions have freezing temperatures and snow-storms. Rainfall varies greatly, but is heaviest west of the Cordillera Occidental; some parts receive over 1,000 cm a year.

People
The Colombian people are the product of three ethnic types: native Indian, Spanish conqueror and Negro slave. Over the centuries, these groups have intermarried and today, *mestizos* (mixed Indian and white) constitute 60% of the population and *mulattoes* (Negro and white) a further 14%. Most Colombians live in the mountainous west; steady migration from rural areas is causing overcrowding in cities and shanty towns are a major social problem.

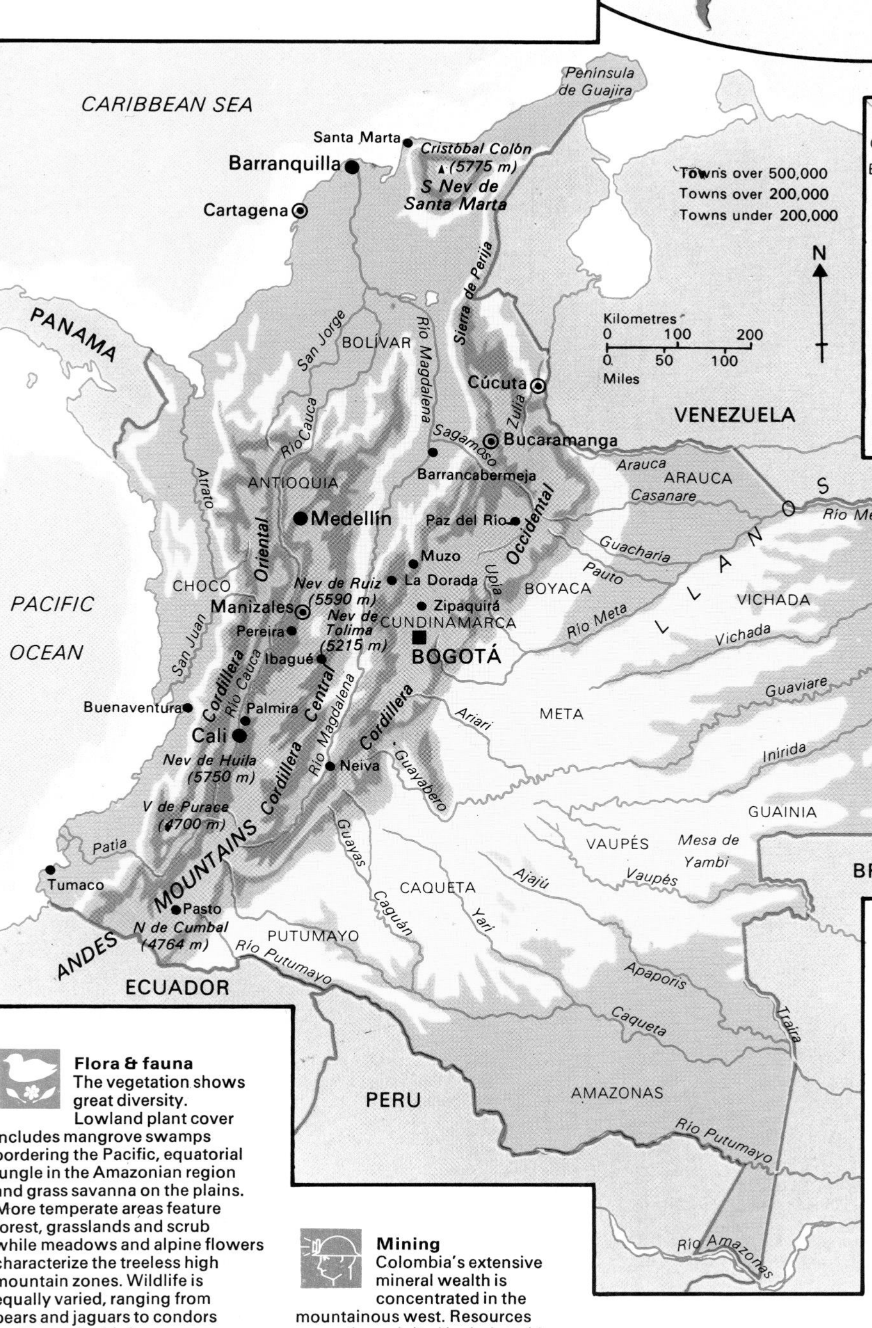

Flora & fauna
The vegetation shows great diversity. Lowland plant cover includes mangrove swamps bordering the Pacific, equatorial jungle in the Amazonian region and grass savanna on the plains. More temperate areas feature forest, grasslands and scrub while meadows and alpine flowers characterize the treeless high mountain zones. Wildlife is equally varied, ranging from bears and jaguars to condors and hummingbirds.

Agriculture
Although less than 5% of the country is cultivated, agriculture employs almost half the work-force and plays a major part in the economy. The range of relief and climate permits cultivation of many different crops: rice, bananas, sugar, cotton and cocoa in the tropical lowlands; coffee, maize, tobacco and beans in the temperate zone; potatoes, wheat, barley, deciduous fruits and fodder at higher, cooler altitudes. Coffee, providing 50% of all exports, is the dominant cash crop: Colombia ranks as the world's second largest coffee producer after Brazil. Stock-rearing is important on the vast llanos and the Caribbean lowlands; dairying occurs near major towns. Forest products include rubber and fibres but are not developed.

Mining
Colombia's extensive mineral wealth is concentrated in the mountainous west. Resources currently exploited include gold and silver in Antioquia department, platinum near the headwaters of the Atrato and the world's largest deposit of emeralds at Muzo. Salt is extracted from the great Zipaquirá mine and from pans along the Caribbean coast. Coal comes from Cundinamarca and Boyaca, the Guajira peninsula and the southern Cauca valley; iron ore also from the departments of Cundinamarca and Boyaca. Petroleum is found near Cúcuta, Barrancabermeja and in the Putumayo region. Copper, lead mercury and manganese also occur and further exploration is taking place. Principal mineral exports are emeralds and gold; the large volumes of crude oil formerly shipped abroad have largely been replaced by refined petroleum and petroleum products. Colombia is South America's largest producer of gold and coal.

Industry
Industry's contribution to the Colombian economy is becoming increasingly significant. Food-processing is the leading sector and includes rice-milling, sugar-refining, cheese and butter production, coffee-processing, fruit and vegetable canning, oil extraction and chocolate manufacture. The textile industry is next in importance. Other major manufactures are steel, refined petroleum and associated products, paper, cement, chemicals, pharmaceuticals, metal goods and wood products. Over 60% of the country's electricity is generated by hydro-power and further installations are planned: the role of natural gas is expanding. Except for the iron and steel complex at Paz del Río, manufacturing is centred on Bogotá, Medellín and Cali.

Transport
The country's rugged mountains and extensive forests form major obstacles to communications and many areas remain isolated. Consequently, air transport is important. In 1919, Colombia made aviation history by establishing the world's first commercial airline; today, domestic flights link over 400 centres. The 48,000 km road network includes the Caribbean Trunk Highway connecting the ports of Cartagena, Barranquilla and Santa Marta with the Venezuelan system and a section of the Simón Bolívar highway running from Venezuela to Ecuador. The railways are being modernized. On the Magdalena, the main waterway, steamers reach La Dorada, 960 km upstream. Barranquilla and Buenaventura are the chief ports.

Cities
Colombia's four main cities are widely dispersed. Bogotá, the capital, is located in the Cordillera Oriental. To the northwest, Medellín (2,000,000) lies in the Cordillera Central in a region noted for its coffee and orchids; it is the country's industrial capital and South America's largest textile producer. The third largest city, Cali (1,250,000), is situated in the fertile Cauca valley and is a commercial and agricultural centre; sugar and paper production are important. Near the mouth of the Magdalena lies Barranquilla (830,000)—the country's chief port.

Venezuela

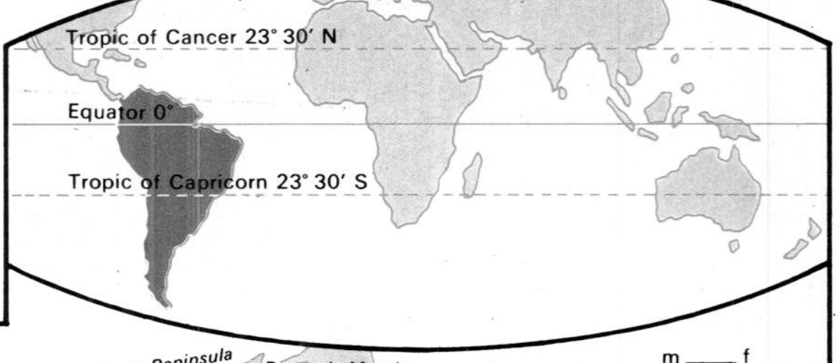

Tropic of Cancer 23° 30′ N
Equator 0°
Tropic of Capricorn 23° 30′ S

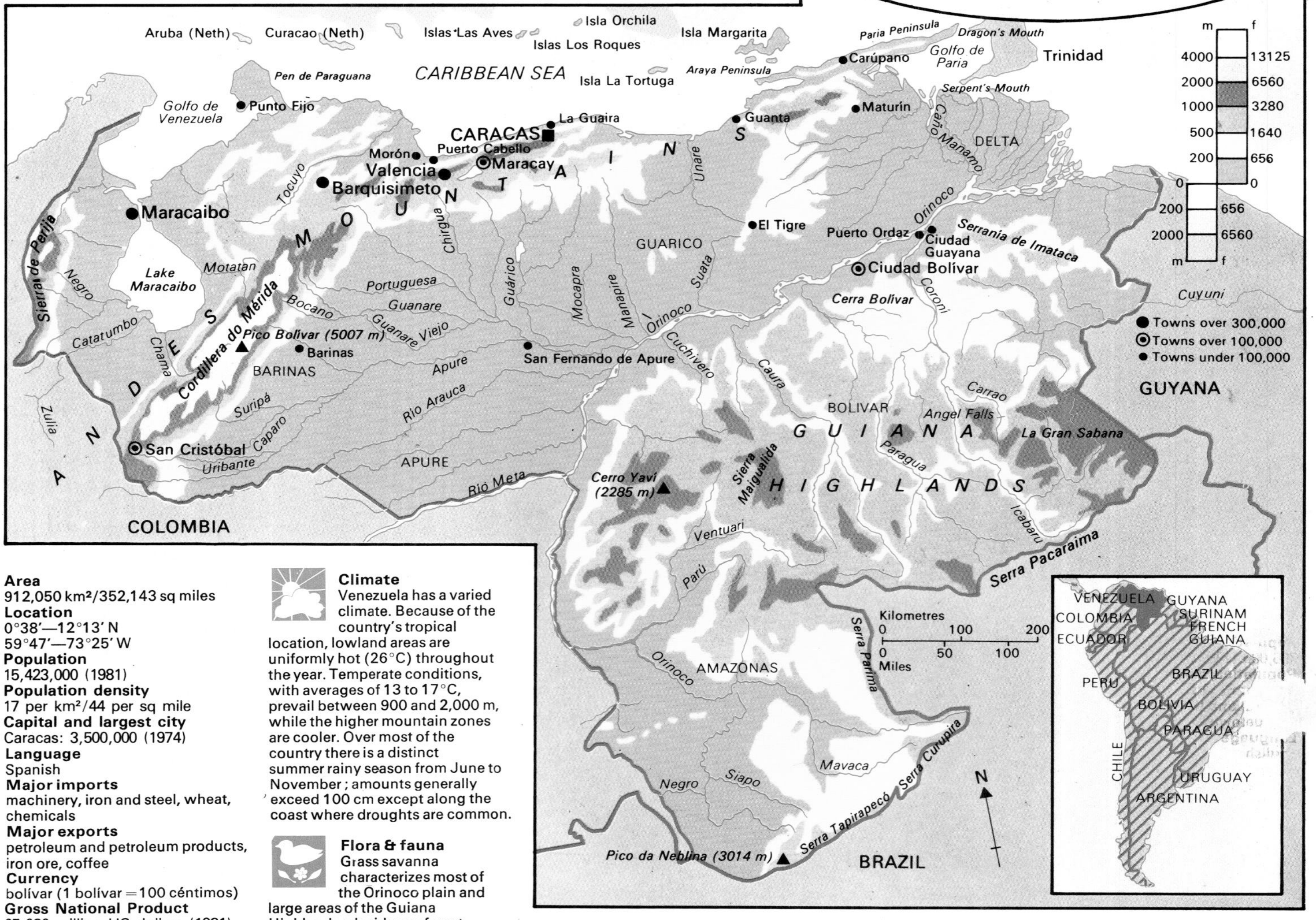

Aruba (Neth) Curacao (Neth) Islas Las Aves Isla Orchila Islas Los Roques Isla Margarita Isla La Tortuga CARIBBEAN SEA Pen de Paraguana Araya Peninsula Paria Peninsula Dragon's Mouth Golfo de Paria Serpent's Mouth Trinidad Golfo de Venezuela Punto Fijo La Guaira CARACAS Morón Puerto Cabello Valencia Maracay Barquisimeto Maracaibo Lake Maracaibo Carúpano Maturín Guanta El Tigre Puerto Ordaz Ciudad Guayana Ciudad Bolívar Cerra Bolívar DELTA Caño Manamo Orinoco Serrania de Imataca Cuyuni GUARICO BARINAS Barinas APURE San Fernando de Apure BOLIVAR San Cristóbal Pico Bolívar (5007 m) Cordillera do Mérida Sierra de Perija A N D E S M O U N T A I N S G U I A N A H I G H L A N D S Angel Falls La Gran Sabana Cerro Yavi (2285 m) Sierra Maigualida AMAZONAS Pico da Neblina (3014 m) Serra Tapirapecó Serra Curupira Serra Parima Serra Pacaraima COLOMBIA BRAZIL GUYANA

m f
4000 13125
2000 6560
1000 3280
500 1640
200 656
0 0
200 656
2000 6560

● Towns over 300,000
◉ Towns over 100,000
• Towns under 100,000

Kilometres 0 100 200
0 50 100 Miles

VENEZUELA GUYANA SURINAM FRENCH GUIANA COLOMBIA ECUADOR PERU BRAZIL BOLIVIA PARAGUAY CHILE URUGUAY ARGENTINA

Area
912,050 km²/352,143 sq miles
Location
0°38′—12°13′ N
59°47′—73°25′ W
Population
15,423,000 (1981)
Population density
17 per km²/44 per sq mile
Capital and largest city
Caracas: 3,500,000 (1974)
Language
Spanish
Major imports
machinery, iron and steel, wheat, chemicals
Major exports
petroleum and petroleum products, iron ore, coffee
Currency
bolívar (1 bolívar = 100 céntimos)
Gross National Product
65,080 million US dollars (1981)
Status
federal republic

Physical features
Venezuela divides into four regions: the Andes, the Maracaibo basin, the Orinoco lowland and the Guiana Highlands. The Andes enter the country from the west and divide into two ranges which enclose Lake Maracaibo (12,950 km²): to the west, the Sierra de Perija and to the east the magnificent Cordillera do Mérida with snowy peaks over 4,500 m; Pico Bolívar reaches 5,007 m. This latter range extends along the coast to the Paria peninsula near Trinidad. In the 16th century, Lake Maracaibo's swampy shore, fringed with huts on stilts, gave Venezuela its name: Little Venice. The Orinoco basin (300,000 km²) is a vast alluvial plain subject to flooding. The Orinoco, 3,000 km long, rises in the Guiana Highlands and hugs the edge of the massif before entering the sea via a huge delta. The Highlands are an ancient plateau with summits of over 2,000 m. They occupy half the country and are largely unexplored. The Highlands contain precipitous cliffs with many spectacular waterfalls; Angel Falls, the world's highest, has a drop of 980 m.

Climate
Venezuela has a varied climate. Because of the country's tropical location, lowland areas are uniformly hot (26°C) throughout the year. Temperate conditions, with averages of 13 to 17°C, prevail between 900 and 2,000 m, while the higher mountain zones are cooler. Over most of the country there is a distinct summer rainy season from June to November; amounts generally exceed 100 cm except along the coast where droughts are common.

Flora & fauna
Grass savanna characterizes most of the Orinoco plain and large areas of the Guiana Highlands; deciduous forest covers other parts of the plateau. Vegetation in the Andes ranges from thorn scrub in the drier regions to dense tropical jungle on the wet slopes. A variety of wildlife inhabits the humid Andean rain forest including mountain lions, anacondas and humming birds. Alligators, turtles and iguanas frequent the Orinoco and its tributaries.

Agriculture
About 30% of the workforce is engaged in agriculture although only 3% of the land is cultivated (mostly in the north, one of the main agricultural areas being the intermontane basin centred on Valencia). Subsistence farming predominates but some coffee, cocoa and sugar are exported. High quality coffee is mostly grown on the slopes of the Andes between 1,000 and 2,000 m; cocoa, sugar-cane, cotton and bananas are also produced in the Andean zone, but at lower altitudes where conditions are warmer and wetter; coconuts grow along the coast. Rice is the chief lowland food crop, while wheat, maize, barley, beans and potatoes are cultivated in the cooler uplands. Dairying is important in the Valencia and Caracas basins. South of the Andes, the Orinoco plain specializes in beef-cattle.

Forestry & fishing
Venezuela's forests, covering half the country, contain over 600 species of timber trees; exploitation is, however, limited because of inaccessibility. Fishing, both inland and coastal is also underdeveloped, but some sardines and tuna are canned for export.

Petroleum
Venezuela's important oil resources have made it one of South America's richest states. Since production began in 1917, the growth of the petroleum industry, now nationalized, has been phenomenal. With a current output of over 2 million barrels a day, Venezuela ranks as the world's third largest oil producer and its leading exporter. About 75% of production comes from the shore and shallow waters of Lake Maracaibo; there are also oil-fields in the Maturin basin and the Barinas region. Almost half the oil is refined in Venezuela. Natural gas is piped to Caracas and other centres where it is used as fuel and as a raw material in the petrochemical industry. The channel linking Lake Maracaibo to the Gulf of Venezuela has been deepened for tankers to enter Maracaibo port.

Mining
In addition to its valuable oil resources, Venezuela has vast iron-ore deposits and ranks as the world's tenth largest producer; production is centred on the Caroní valley in the Guiana Highlands. The Highlands are also rich in other minerals: gold, diamonds and manganese are exploited, but reserves of nickel, bauxite and chromium are underdeveloped because of poor communications. North of the Orinoco, mining activity includes asbestos near Puerto Cabello, coal and lignite in the Andean foothills, salt on the Araya peninsula and limestone. Copper phosphate, sulphur, vanadium, zinc and lead also occur.

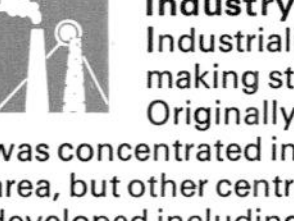

Industry
Industrialization is making steady progress. Originally, manufacturing was concentrated in the Caracas area, but other centres have developed including Ciudad Guayana (steel), Ciudad Bolívar (metallurgy), Morón (petro-chemicals) and Maracaibo (paper, food-processing, engineering). So far, natural gas is the main energy source but a giant hydro-scheme on the Caroní is being built to supply electricity to Venezuela and neighbouring states.

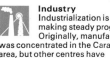

Transport
The 50,000 km road network is densest in the north and northwest and includes a section of the Pan American Highway from Caracas to Colombia. Except in the Highlands, where lines link iron ore mines to Ciudad Guayana, railways are unimportant and cover less than 500 km. Inland shipping is significant: sea-going vessels dock at ports on Lake Maracaibo and sail up the Orinoco as far as Ciudad Guayana. The main seaports are La Guaira, Puerto Cabello, Puerto Ordaz, Guanta and Maracaibo. Internal air services are important, especially in remote areas.

Cities
The population, concentrated in the Andean zone and northern coastal belt, is mainly urban: 75% of Venezuelans now live in towns and cities and by 1980 the figure is expected to exceed 80%. Caracas, situated in a steep-sided rift valley, is a modern city based on oil wealth; it is served by the port of La Guaira. Next in importance is the port and oil city of Maracaibo (655,000). Other major centres are Valencia (367,000), Barquisimeto (331,000), Maracay (255,000) and San Cristóbal.

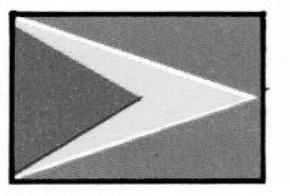

Guyana

Surinam

Guyana, Surinam and French Guiana

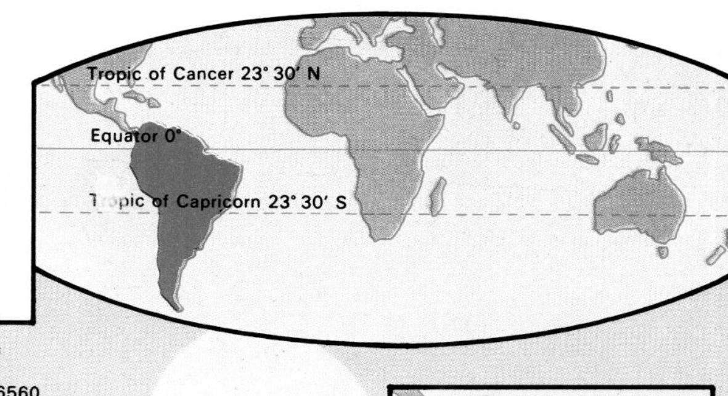

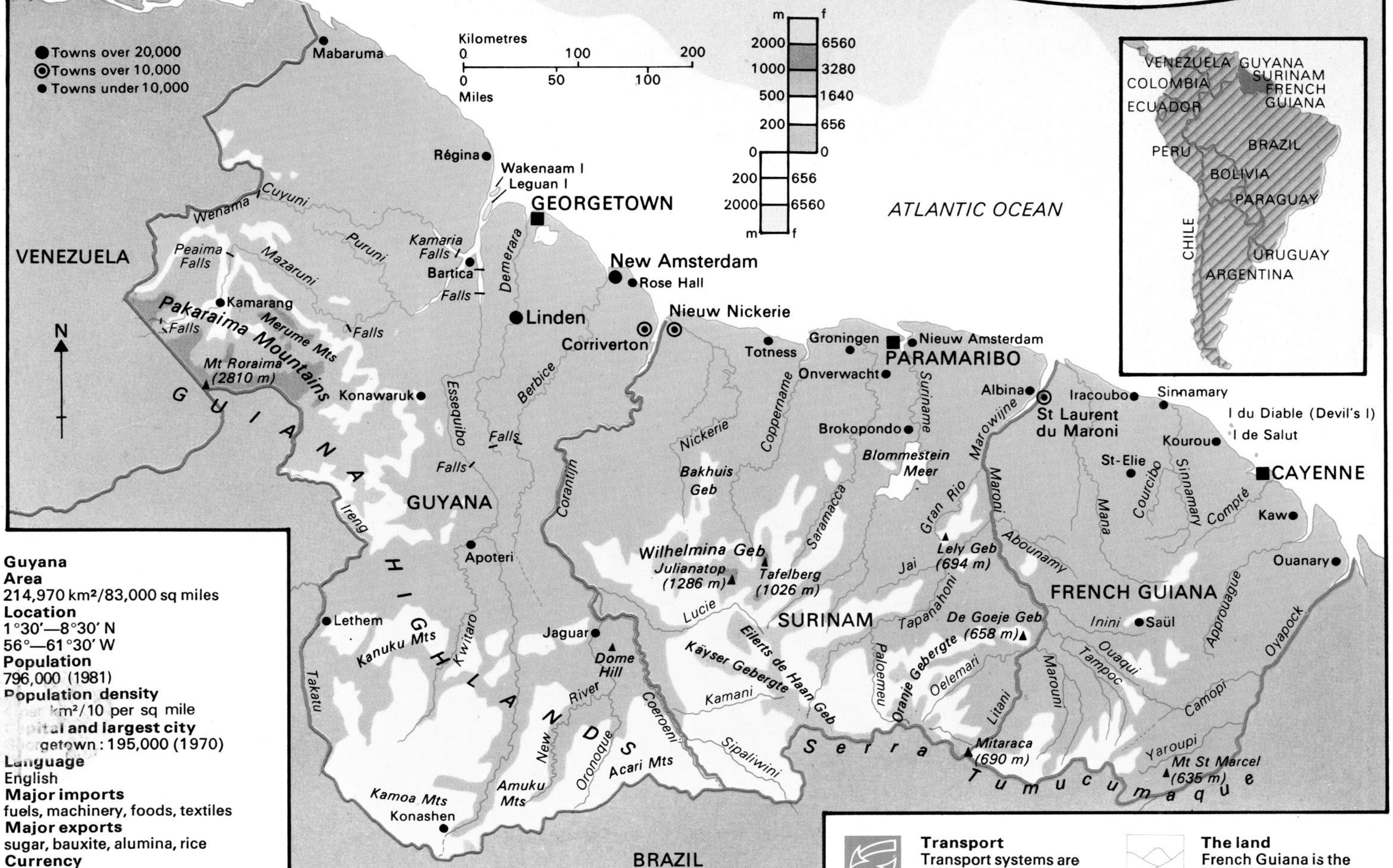

Towns over 20,000
Towns over 10,000
Towns under 10,000

Kilometres
0 100 200
0 50 100
Miles

m f
2000 6560
1000 3280
500 1640
200 656
0 0
200 656
2000 6560
m f

VENEZUELA
COLOMBIA
ECUADOR
PERU
GUYANA
SURINAM
FRENCH GUIANA
BRAZIL
BOLIVIA
PARAGUAY
CHILE
URUGUAY
ARGENTINA

ATLANTIC OCEAN
Mabaruma
Régina
Wakenaam I
Leguan I
GEORGETOWN
Cuyuni
Wenamu
Puruni
Kamaria Falls
Bartica
Demerara
Peaima Falls
Mazaruni
Falls
New Amsterdam
Rose Hall
Kamarang
Pakaraima Mountains
Merume Mts
Falls
Linden
Corriverton
Nieuw Nickerie
Mt Roraima (2810 m)
Konawaruk
Essequibo
Berbice
Falls
Falls
N
VENEZUELA
GUIANA HIGHLANDS
GUYANA
Ireng
Apoteri
Corantijn
Lethem
Kanuku Mts
Kwitaro
Jaguar
Dome Hill
Takatu
New River
Oronoque
Coeroeni
Kamoa Mts
Konashen
Amuku Mts
Acari Mts
BRAZIL
Totness
Groningen
Nieuw Amsterdam
PARAMARIBO
Onverwacht
Suriname
Coppername
Nickerie
Brokopondo
Blommestein Meer
Bakhuis Geb
Saramacca
Gran Rio
Wilhelmina Geb
Julianatop (1286 m)
Tafelberg (1026 m)
Lely Geb (694 m)
Jai
Lucie
SURINAM
Tapanahoni
Eilerts de Haan Geb
Kayser Gebergte
Kamani
Sipaliwini
Paloemeu
Oranje Gebergte
Oelemari
Litani
De Goeje Geb (658 m)
Serra Tumucumaque
Mitaraca (690 m)
Albina
Marowijne
St Laurent du Maroni
Maroni
Iracoubo
Sinnamary
I du Diable (Devil's I)
I de Salut
Kourou
St-Elie
Mana
Courcibo
Sinnamary
Comté
CAYENNE
Kaw
Abounamy
Ouanary
FRENCH GUIANA
Inini
Saül
Approuague
Oyapock
Ouaqui
Tampoc
Maroni
Camopi
Yaroupi
Mt St Marcel (635 m)

Guyana
Area
214,970 km²/83,000 sq miles
Location
1°30'—8°30' N
56°—61°30' W
Population
796,000 (1981)
Population density
[illegible] km²/10 per sq mile
[illegible]ital and largest city
[illegible]getown : 195,000 (1970)
Language
English
Major imports
fuels, machinery, foods, textiles
Major exports
sugar, bauxite, alumina, rice
Currency
dollar (1 dollar = 100 cents)
Gross National Product
580 million US dollars (1981)
Status
co-operative republic

The land
The coast, fringed with mangrove, sandbars and lagoons, is backed by a narrow plain lying below sea level. Some 20 km inland, the land rises to an area of dense tropical rain forest which gives way to mountains in the south-west and to a savanna-covered plateau in the south. The coast is hot and wet: Georgetown averages 28°C and has 230 cm of rain; in the interior, temperatures rainfall and humidity decrease with altitude.

The economy
Farming is the basic activity. Cultivated land is located in the coastal belt where sugarcane and rice are the main crops followed by citrus and coconuts. Output of groundnuts, palm oil, cotton and vegetables is increasing. Fishing and forestry are being expanded, but at present forests, covering 87% of the country, are underexploited. Guyana has considerable mineral resources: bauxite is a major export and significant amounts of gold, diamonds and manganese are also produced. Industrial development plans include a hydro-electric plant and an aluminium smelter in the Upper Mazaruni district of the Pakaraima Mountains.

Transport
Along the coast (the most populous and developed region) the road network is fairly dense and 75% paved. In the interior, however, where dense forest hampers communications. tracks are unsurfaced and less extensive, and access is primarily by river. The main waterways are the Berbice, Demerara, Essequibo, Cuyuni and Mazaruni. Georgetown and New Amsterdam are the chief seaports. Near the capital there is an international airport.

Surinam
Area
163,265 km²/63,037 sq miles
Location
1°50'—6° N
54°—58°10' W
Population
353,000 (1981)
Population density
2 per km²/6 per sq mile
Capital and largest city
Paramaribo : 151,500 (1971)
Language
Dutch
Major imports
manufactures, fuels, foodstuffs
Major exports
alumina, bauxite, aluminium, rice, forest products
Currency
gulden (1 gulden = 100 cents)
Gross National Product
1,070 million US dollars (1981)
Status
republic

The land
Coastal Surinam features mangrove swamps and sandy stretches of savanna. The thickly-forested interior climbs to a plateau over 1,000 m high. The country's main rivers, the Corantijn, Coppername, Saramacca, Suriname and Marowijne, drain northwards from the highlands. Inland, the hot, wet tropical climate is modified by altitude.

The economy
Bauxite is the mainstay of the economy and, together with alumina and aluminium, accounts for 90% of all exports. Alluvial gold is extracted from the rivers Marowijne and Tapanahoni, but other mineral resources are unexploited. Surinam's next most valuable assets are its forests which cover 85% of the country: products include lumber, plywood and balata (a type of latex). Although 75% of the workforce is in agriculture, output is inadequate and food imports are necessary. About 80% of farmland, concentrated in the coastal zone, is used for rice, the staple food. The area under rice is being doubled by reclamation and irrigation schemes. The other main crops are sugar, citrus, bananas and coconuts. Shrimp fishing is being developed. Other industries process timber, farm produce and fish.

Transport
Transport systems are poor: the road network is minimal and there is only one short railway. Inland, passengers and freight travel mostly by water using some 1,500 km of navigable rivers and canals; remote districts are also linked by air. Paramaribo is the chief seaport.

French Guiana
Area
91,000 km²/35,135 sq miles
Location
2°—5°45' N
52°—54°30' W
Population
63,000 (1981)
Population density
0.7 per km²/1.8 per sq mile
Capital and largest city
Cayenne : 30,000 (1975)
Language
French
Major imports
food, manufactures, petroleum products, cement, iron and steel
Major exports
timber, shrimps
Currency
franc (1 franc = 100 centimes)
Gross National Product
220 million US dollars (1981)
Status
French overseas department

Transport
Roads, totalling 500 km link the main centres which are all on the coast. Small craft, travelling along the coast and up the rivers, provide the chief means of transport. There are no railways. Cayenne is the major seaport.

The land
French Guiana is the smallest country in South America. The land is highest in the south and descends gradually to the swampy seaboard. Many streams, draining northwards through deep valleys, dissect the country; the two main rivers (the Maroni and Oyapock) flow along its borders. Except for mangrove and savanna in the coastal zone, dense rain forest blankets the territory. Its near-equitorial location gives French Guiana a hot, wet climate (27°C; 300 cm).

The economy
French Guiana is economically backward and relies heavily on French assistance. The forests, covering 90% of the total area and containing many valuable hardwoods, are the country's greatest resource, but apart from a very limited output of timber they are virtually unexploited. Mineral reserves, notably of gold, bauxite and tantalite, are similarly underdeveloped. Cultivation is confined to about 33 km² but the area could be greatly increased by draining the swampy coastlands. Subsistence farming predominates with cassava, bananas, maize, rice and sweet potatoes as the chief food crops. Sugarcane is the only significant cash crop. Some cattle, pigs and sheep are kept. Although the coastal waters are rich in fish there is little fishing except for shrimps and this is controlled by American companies for the US market.

Brazil

● Towns over 1 million
⊙ Towns over 500,000
• Towns under 500,000

Area
8,511,965 km²/3,286,473 sq miles
Location
5°15′N—33°45′S
34°50′—74°W
Population
120,507,000 (1981)
Population density
14 per km²/37 per sq mile
Capital
Brásílía: 1,177,000 (1980)
Largest city
São Paulo: 8,491,000 (1980)
Language
Portuguese
Major imports
crude oil, metal products, chemicals, machinery, transport equipment, wheat
Major exports
soya, sugar, coffee, iron ore, electrical apparatus, cocoa, cotton
Currency
cruzeiro (1 cruzeiro = 100 cents)
Gross National Product
267,730 million US dollars (1981)
Status
federated republic

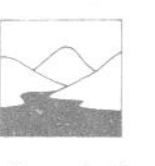

Physical features
Brazil, the world's fifth largest country, occupies almost half South America and has frontiers with ten states. It is a country of low-altitude plateaux and only 40% of the territory exceeds 200 m. The two upland regions are the vast central plateau and, north of the Amazon, the Guiana Highlands which contain the country's highest peak, Pico de Neblina (3,014 m). Both regions have similar features: rounded hills, low mountains, extensive tablelands and, in the south, great lava sheets. The two upland areas are separated by the Amazon basin (3,984,500 km²) covering almost half of Brazil. The Amazon, flowing 6,500 km to the Atlantic, is the world's second longest river after the Nile and the greatest by volume. This tremendous waterway is wide (320 km at its mouth) and deep: ocean-going vessels can sail 3,700 km upstream. As, from the foot of the Andes eastwards, the river falls only one centimetre per kilometre, widespread floods occur. Brazil's other lowland zones are the narrow coastal strip running from the northeast to Rio de Janeiro and, in the south and southwest, the Paraguay, Paraná and Uruguay river basins. The country's other main river is the São Francisco (2,900 km long) which rises in the Brazilian Highlands.

Climate
Around 93% of Brazil lies between the Equator and the Tropic of Capricorn and mean temperatures range from 18°C in the sub-tropical south to 27°C in the equatorial north. Rainfall, mostly between January and June, varies widely from region to region. The northeast is the driest area with long droughts and an annual total of under 70 cm; Amazonia, with over 200 cm of rain, is the wettest zone.

Flora & fauna
Brazil has several distinct vegetation zones. The Amazonian forest is the world's largest tropical rain forest with more species of flora than any other equatorial forest. South of the Amazon, the interior is covered with woodland savanna while the dry northeast features thorn scrub and cacti. Semideciduous forest occurs along the coast below Salvador and in the Paraná region. Pine forest and prairie characterize the extreme south. Apart from jaguars and tapirs, Brazil lacks large mammals but is rich in fish, reptiles, birds and insects.

Forestry & fishing
The Amazonian forest accounts for 75% of Brazil's timber resources but exploitation is limited by inaccessibility. Hardwood production (largely for export) is centred along the coast. Softwoods, from the southern forests, are mostly for domestic use. The fishing industry, spread along the 7,400 km coastline, is expanding: balsa rafts are used in the north, but in the south there are motorized fleets. Shrimp and lobster are exported.

Energy
The São Francisco and Paraná rivers form Brazil's chief energy resource. There are 30 hydro-plants under construction, including the world's largest power station at Itaipu.

Agriculture
Despite industrial expansion, agriculture remains vital to the economy: it provides 95% of domestic food needs, 60% of exports and employs almost half the workforce. The staple foods are rice, manioc, maize and beans: maize and beans are particularly important in the south and south-east; irrigated rice is grown in the extreme south but upland dry rice is grown elsewhere; manioc predominates in the northeast. Soya, cultivated in the south, is the main cash crop followed by sugar mostly grown in the southeast. Coffee is next in importance and Brazil ranks as the world's leading producer: 75% of output comes from the states of São Paulo and Paraná. Other major export crops are cocoa and bananas (from the hot wet coast between Salvador and Vitória), cotton (from Paraná, São Paulo and the northeast) and citrus and tobacco. Stock-raising is widespread and Brazil has the world's fourth largest beef herd; cattle are bred in the interior and brought to the seaboard for fattening. Dairying is developing.

Mining
Brazil's immense mineral wealth is underexploited. Mining activity is based on the state of Minas Gerais which has one of the world's largest reserves of iron ore as well as major deposits of nickel, bauxite, mica, beryl, quartz crystal, dolomite, gold, zirconium, niobium ore and diamonds. Elsewhere, lead, zinc, manganese, copper, tungsten, barite, chrome and asbestos are produced and many other minerals occur. Domestic output of coal and oil has to be supplemented by large imports. Mineral exports (13% of all exports) consist of iron ore, manganese, diamonds and niobium ore.

Industry
Brazil is Latin America's most industrialized state. The main industries, concentrated in the São Paulo region, are food-processing, textiles, iron and steel, vehicle manufacture, shipbuilding, chemicals, cement and electrical goods. Tourism is expanding: attractions include Rio de Janeiro and its beaches, Brásília and Amazonia.

Transport
Communications are handicapped by Brazil's enormous size and physical geography. Roads, totalling 1,400,000 km, carry 70% of all traffic. The network is expanding and recent projects include roads linking Brásília to all regions and the Trans-Amazonian Highway from the Atlantic to Peru. Railways, mostly in the southeast, play a minor role but are being modernized. As the forest is sparsely populated, there is relatively little traffic on the Amazon—the world's greatest inland waterway; Manaus is the main river port. Rio de Janeiro and Santos are the chief seaports followed by Paranagua, Recife, Salvador, Vitória and Rio Grande. Internal air services are being developed; Rio and São Paulo have the main international airports.

Cities
One South American in two lives in Brazil, giving it the world's seventh largest population. Most Brazilians inhabit the coastal zone, especially the southeast, and the interior is sparsely settled with an average of under one person per km². The population, growing by 3 million a year, is 60% urban. The largest city and chief industrial centre is São Paulo: Rio de Janeiro (5 million), the former capital, remains the cultural centre. Brásília, 900 km from the coast, was inaugurated in 1960 and is famous for its daring architecture. Other major cities are Belo Horizonte (1,800,000) Recife (1,200,000) and Salvador (1,018,000).

Ecuador

Area
455,452 km²/175,850 sq miles
Location
1°20′ N—5° S
75°15′—81° W
Population
8,605,000 (1981)
Population density
19 per km²/49 per sq mile
Capital
Quito: 800,000 (1981)
Largest city
Guayaquil: 1,000,000 (1981)
Language
Spanish
Major imports
raw materials, vehicles, building equipment
Major exports
petroleum, bananas, cocoa, sugar, fish, balsa, straw hats
Currency
sucre (1 sucre = 100 centavos)
Gross National Product
10,120 million US dollars (1981)
Status
republic

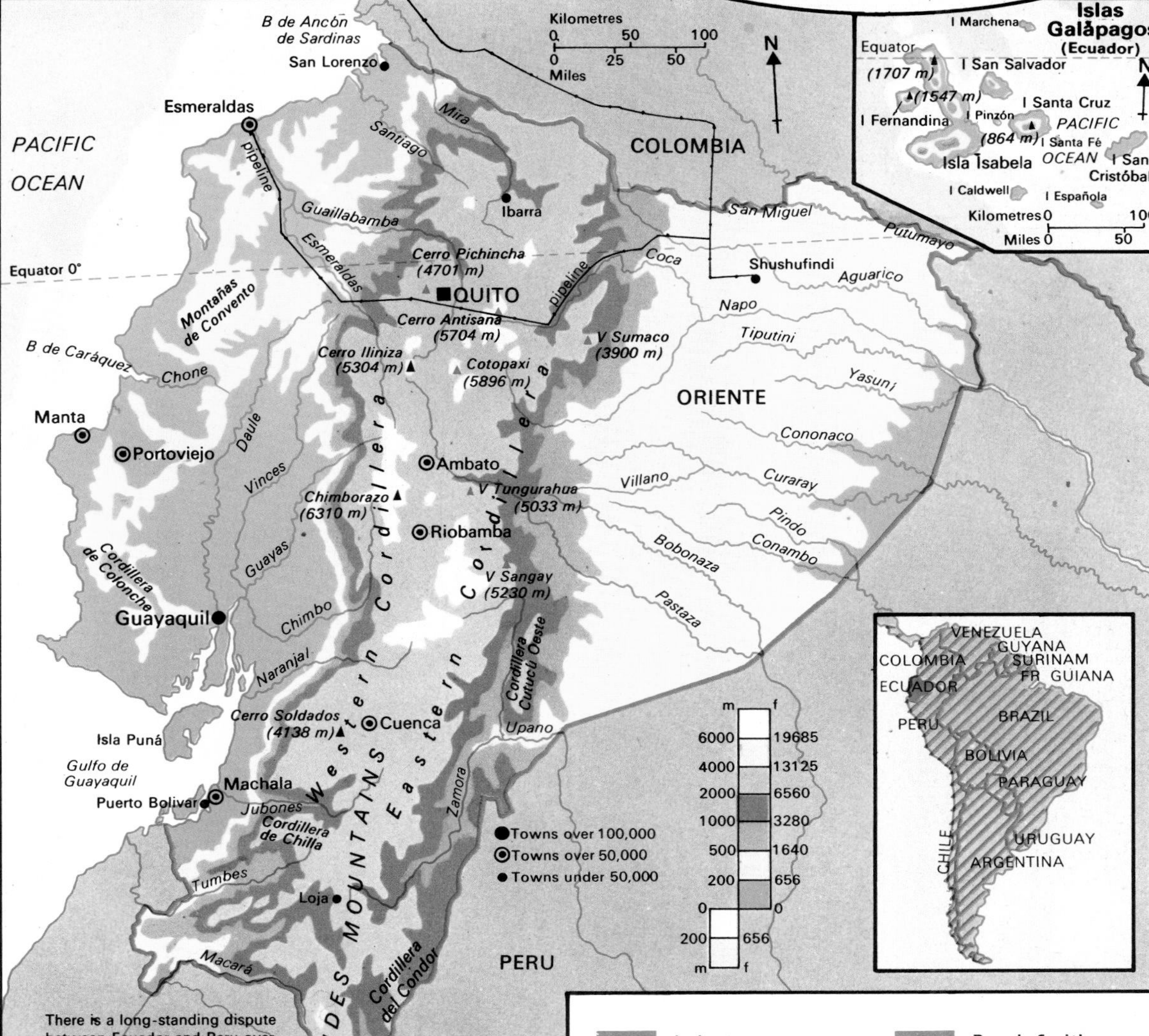

Physical features

The name Ecuador (Spanish for 'equator') is derived from the country's position astride the equator; just 25 km north of Quito stands the Equatorial Monument with its inscription 0°00′00″. The territory divides into three major regions: the Pacific plain, the central mountains and the eastern lowlands. The Pacific coastline, a hilly area broken by swampy river valleys, is most extensive in the south where the Guayas river flows across a wide plain and enters the Gulf of Guayaquil via a great delta. Central Ecuador is dominated by the Andes with two parallel north-south ranges containing over 30 volcanoes, among them Chimborazo (6,310 m) and the still active Cotopaxi (5,896 m). These two ranges are separated by a structurally complex trough which includes a series of inter-mountain basins. East of the mountains, the land falls away into the lowlands of the Amazonian basin. This eastern region, the *Oriente*, occupies a third of the country and remains largely unexplored.

Climate

Ecuador has a varied climate. The coastal zone, averaging 24°C, is humid in the north with two rainy seasons but arid in the extreme south. Temperatures decrease with altitude in the Andes and drop below freezing above the perpetual snowline. Quito, almost on the equator but situated at 2,860 m, averages 13°C and is known as the 'city of eternal spring'. In the mountains there is only one wet season (November-May) with about 145 cm of rain. Conditions in the Oriente are very warm and wet with temperatures of 27°C, 300 cm of rain and 90% humidity.

Vegetation

On the Pacific coast, the rain forests and mangrove swamps of the north give way southwards to thorn scrub, short-grass savanna and, near the Peruvian border, cacti and drought-resistant plants. In the mountain zone, forest predominates up to 3,500 m and is then replaced by grasses and shrubs up to the snowline. Dense tropical rain forest smothers the Oriente.

Agriculture

There are two agricultural zones: the tropical Pacific plain and the temperate Andean highlands. The three staple export crops (bananas, cocoa, coffee) dominate land use in the coastal region; bananas and cocoa are cultivated on lowland plantations while coffee comes from the coastal uplands and Andean foothills. Ecuador ranks as the world's leading banana exporter and second largest producer (after Brazil). Other crops grown in this fertile zone are sugarcane, cotton, pineapples, citrus and rice. In the mountains, the cooler climate favours stock-raising and the production of barley, wheat, maize, potatoes and vegetables; on the higher slopes (up to 3,600 m), Indians grow subsistence crops of potatoes.

Fishing

The Pacific waters are rich in fish and Ecuador's fishing industry, centred on Guayaquil and Manta, is expanding. The main species caught are tuna, sardine and shrimp.

Forestry

Ecuador's vast forests, covering 75% of the country, are under-exploited; this is especially true of the valuable, but inaccessible, hardwood resources of the Oriente. The coastal forests are important for Carludovica palm fibre (used in the manufacture of Panama hats) and lightweight balsawood; Ecuador is the world's chief producer of balsa. Castor-oil seeds, kapok, palm nuts (for making buttons) and quinine (from the cinchona tree) are among other forest products.

Mining

Oil is transforming the Ecuadorian economy. The newly-developed fields are located in the Oriente and production is piped across the Andes to the tanker port of Esmeraldas. Four refineries, with a total daily capacity of 100,000 barrels, are in operation and a gas liquefaction plant has been built on the Shushufindi field. Small-scale mining activities include copper and gold, both in the Andes.

Industry

The increasing role of oil in the economy has stimulated industrial development and manufacturing is expanding rapidly; the most important sectors are cement and steel, pharmaceuticals and petrochemicals. Long-established industries include textiles, food-processing, ceramics and the weaving of Panama hats. The main manufacturing centres are Quito, Guayaquil and Cuenca. Vast hydro-power potential in the Andes is mostly unexploited. Tourism, based on the country's scenic beauty and cultural heritage, is being developed.

Transport

Transport systems are greatly handicapped by forest and mountain. The road network basically comprises the Pan American Highway (running through the inter-Andean trough) with branch roads to the coast. River transport is important and the lower reaches of the Guayas, Mira and Esmeraldas are navigable for 200 km. The main seaport, Guayaquil, handles 75% of foreign trade (excluding petroleum); other leading ports are Manta, Esmeraldas, San Lorenzo and Puerto Bolívar. All major towns are linked by air; Guayaquil and Quito have international airports.

People & cities

Amerindians, some direct descendants of the Incas, form nearly 60% of the population and mestizos (mixed Indian/white) about 35%; whites, Negroes and mulattoes make up the remainder. The population is most sparse (less than 2%) in the Oriente and densest in the Andean basins. Quito, the world's second highest capital and a former Inca city, retains much of its Spanish colonial atmosphere. The largest city and chief port, Guayaquil, at the head of the Guayas delta, is the country's industrial and commercial capital.

Galápagos Islands

These islands, 1,000 km west of Ecuador, consist of 15 large and numerous small islands totalling 7,964 km². Volcanic in origin, many of the islands are arid lava cones, but the higher ones attract rain and are densely forested. Only five are inhabited and the 4,000 islanders live by farming and fishing (lobster and tuna). The archipelago is named after its giant tortoises; these and other animals (including various species of finches) helped Darwin develop his theory of evolution when he visited the islands in 1835. The Galápagos Islands are now a wildlife reserve.

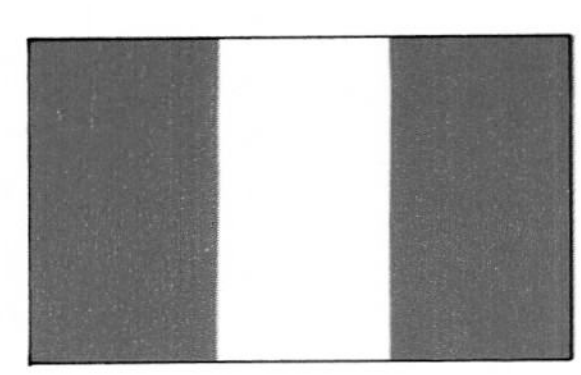

Peru

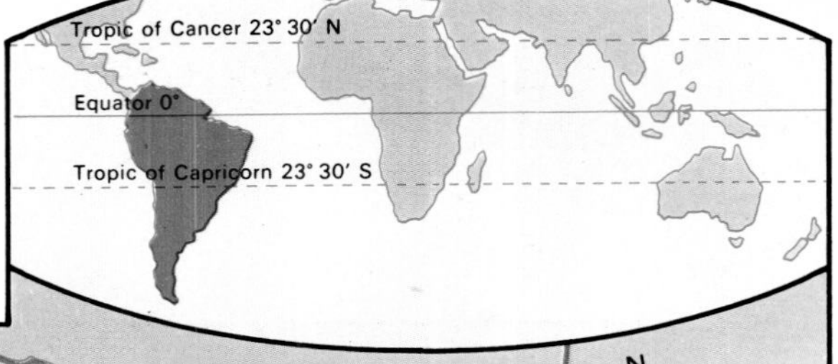

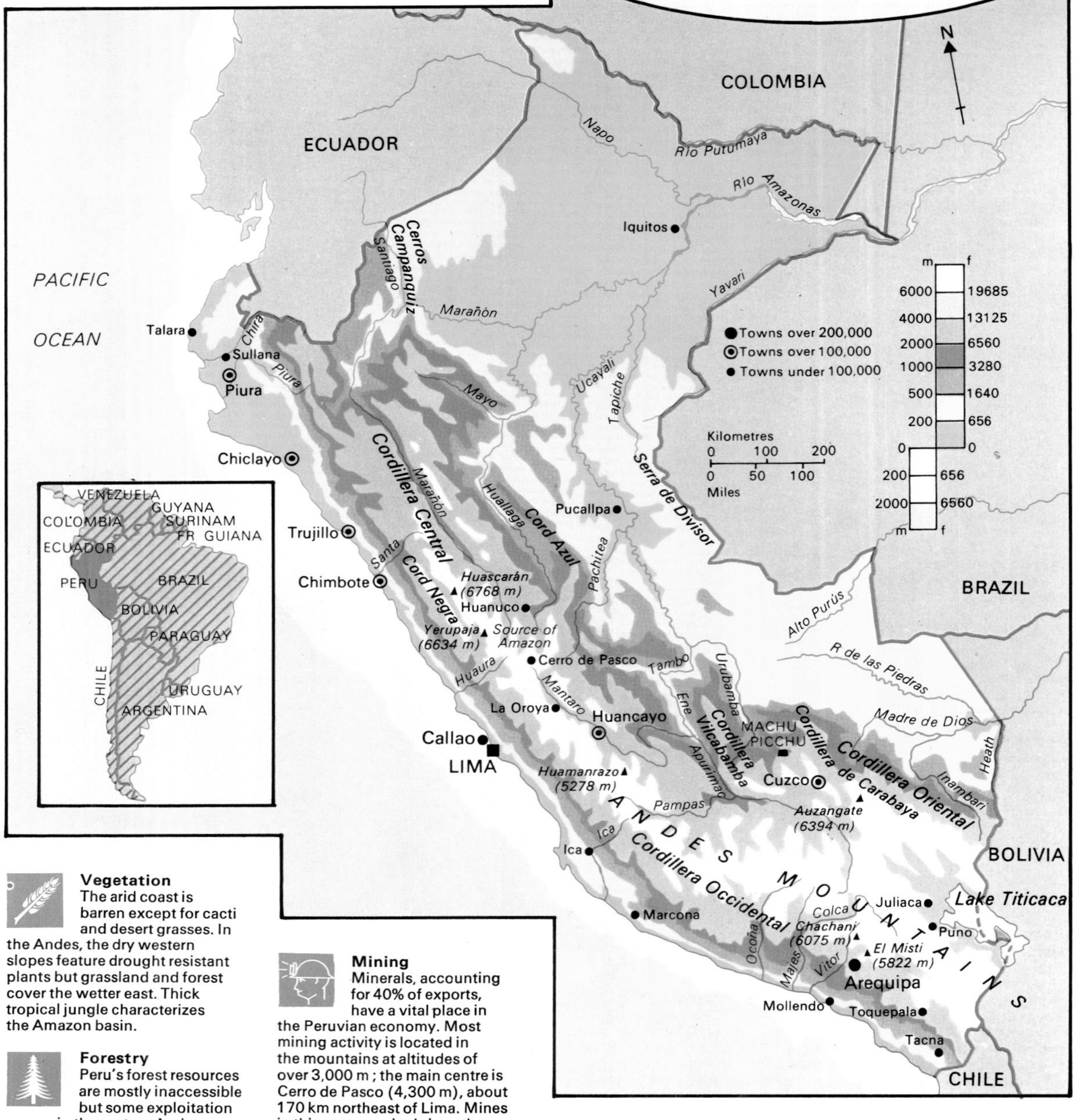

Area
1,285,220 km²/496,224 sq miles
Location
0°05′—18°20′ S
68°40′—81°20′ W
Population
17,031,000 (1981)
Population density
13 per km²/34 per sq mile
Capital and largest city
Lima: 3,100,000 (1979)
Language
Spanish, Quechua, Aymará
Major imports
machinery, foodstuffs, metal goods, transport equipment, chemicals
Major exports
copper, fish and fish products, silver, sugar, cotton, lead, iron, coffee
Currency
sol (1 sol = 100 centavos)
Gross National Product
19,980 million US dollars (1981)
Status
republic

Physical features

Peru, South America's third largest state contains three major relief regions: the coastal zone, Andes and Amazonian lowlands. A narrow strip of desert, broken by the valleys of short, fast flowing rivers, faces the Pacific. This coastal belt is widest in the north where it forms a dune-covered plain but almost non-existent further south where the mountains drop steeply to the sea in a series of plateaus and ledges. Inland, the massive bulk of the snow-capped Andes climbs to over 5,500 m; the country's highest peak, Huascarán, reaches 6,768 m. Many of the southern peaks are volcanic cones, including the beautifully symmetrical El Misti (5,822 m). Also in the south, on the Bolivian border, the Andean ranges enclose a high plateau containing Lake Titicaca, South America's largest lake (6,900 km²). Beyond the Andes, the land descends into the Amazon basin. Deep gorges, carved by some of the Amazon's main headwaters, dissect the eastern Andean slopes.

Climate

Coastal Peru is cool, cloudy and arid. Onshore winds are cooled by the cold Humboldt current and low, rainless cloud is then formed by condensation: Lima averages 18°C in temperature with 5 cm of rainfall. Andean temperatures vary with altitude: the annual mean at Arequipa is 14°C, 11°C at Cuzco and 5°C at Cerro de Pasco. Most rain falls between October and May and is heaviest in the eastern range. The Amazon basin is warm (26°C) and wet (up to 250 cm).

Fishing

Peru has developed the vast fish resources of the Pacific Ocean to become the world's foremost fishing nation. The catch, accounting for 15% of the world total, includes anchovy, tuna, bonito, mackerel, hake, shrimp and sardines. Anchovies are mostly processed into fishmeal (a protein-rish animal feed) and exported; Peru now supplies 45% of the world's fishmeal. Canned and frozen tuna and bonito are also major exports. In addition, guano is collected from the coastal rocks and is used as fertilizer.

Vegetation

The arid coast is barren except for cacti and desert grasses. In the Andes, the dry western slopes feature drought resistant plants but grassland and forest cover the wetter east. Thick tropical jungle characterizes the Amazon basin.

Forestry

Peru's forest resources are mostly inaccessible but some exploitation occurs in the eastern Andes. Products include mahogany, cedar, rubber, balata, milk caspi (a chewing gum base), quinine and coca (source of cocaine). The main outlet for these products is by river from the Amazon port of Iquitos.

Agriculture

Although 50% of the population depend on agriculture, only 3% of the land is cultivated and Peru is a major food importer. The most productive region is the irrigated coastal belt which is used for sugarcane, cotton, rice, vines, olives, citrus, bananas and tobacco. In the Andes, potatoes, beans, cereals and fruit are grown at varying altitudes. The farming potential of the eastern sector is undeveloped apart from some coffee, cocoa and subsistence crops. Sheep, llamas and alpacas are grazed on highland pastures. Agricultural exports include sugar, cotton, wool and coffee.

Mining

Minerals, accounting for 40% of exports, have a vital place in the Peruvian economy. Most mining activity is located in the mountains at altitudes of over 3,000 m; the main centre is Cerro de Pasco (4,300 m), about 170 km northeast of Lima. Mines in this zone, worked since the seventeenth century, yield silver, copper, lead, zinc, bismuth and vanadium. One of the world's largest stores of copper is found near Toquepala in the south, and large amounts of iron ore are exploited at Marcona on the coast. Other valuable deposits include tungsten, platinum, manganese, mercury, phosphate and potash. Peru is a major world producer of silver.

Industry

The manufacturing sector is expanding steadily and now includes food-processing, cotton and woolen textiles, petro-chemicals, steel, cement, oil-refining, metallurgy and vehicle-assembly. Peru's fishmeal industry, with over a hundred plants, is the largest in the world. Except for smelters and refineries in mining zones, industrial development is mainly situated along the coast and the Lima-Callao region in particular.

Energy

Peru's considerable energy resources include coal at Cerro de Pasco, vast hydro-power potential in the Andes and oil on the northwest coast near Talara, in the Ucayali valley and near Lake Titicaca.

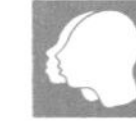

People & towns

About 41% of Peruvians are Amerindians, 39% are mestizos and a further 19% are whites. Two-thirds of the population, including many scattered Indian groups, live in the mountains; the chief Andean city is Arequipa (561,000) in its magnificent setting below El Misti. The coastal zone, although containing only a quarter of the population, dominates the country economically; in addition to Lima, industrial centres include Callao (420,000), Trujillo (242,000), Chiclayo (190,000) and Chimbote (159,000).

Transport

Surface systems are poor because of the difficult terrain and so air services from Lima to all parts of the country are important. There are two main railways: the spectacular Central Railway runs from Callao up into the Andes, climbing 4,800 m in 170 km while the other connects the southern port of Mollendo with the world's highest steamship service across Lake Titicaca to Bolivia. The main features of the road network are the 3,400 km section of the Pan American Highway which follows the coast and the 800 km Trans-Andean Highway from Lima to Pucallpa. Llama trains are used in the high Andes where no roads exist. In the remote eastern lowlands the Amazon is the main artery, but distances are formidable: the chief river port, Iquitos, is 3,700 km from the Atlantic. Callao, near Lima, is the country's leading seaport.

Bolivia

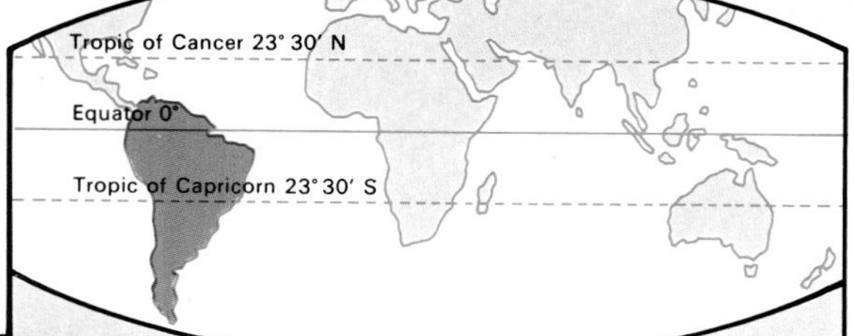

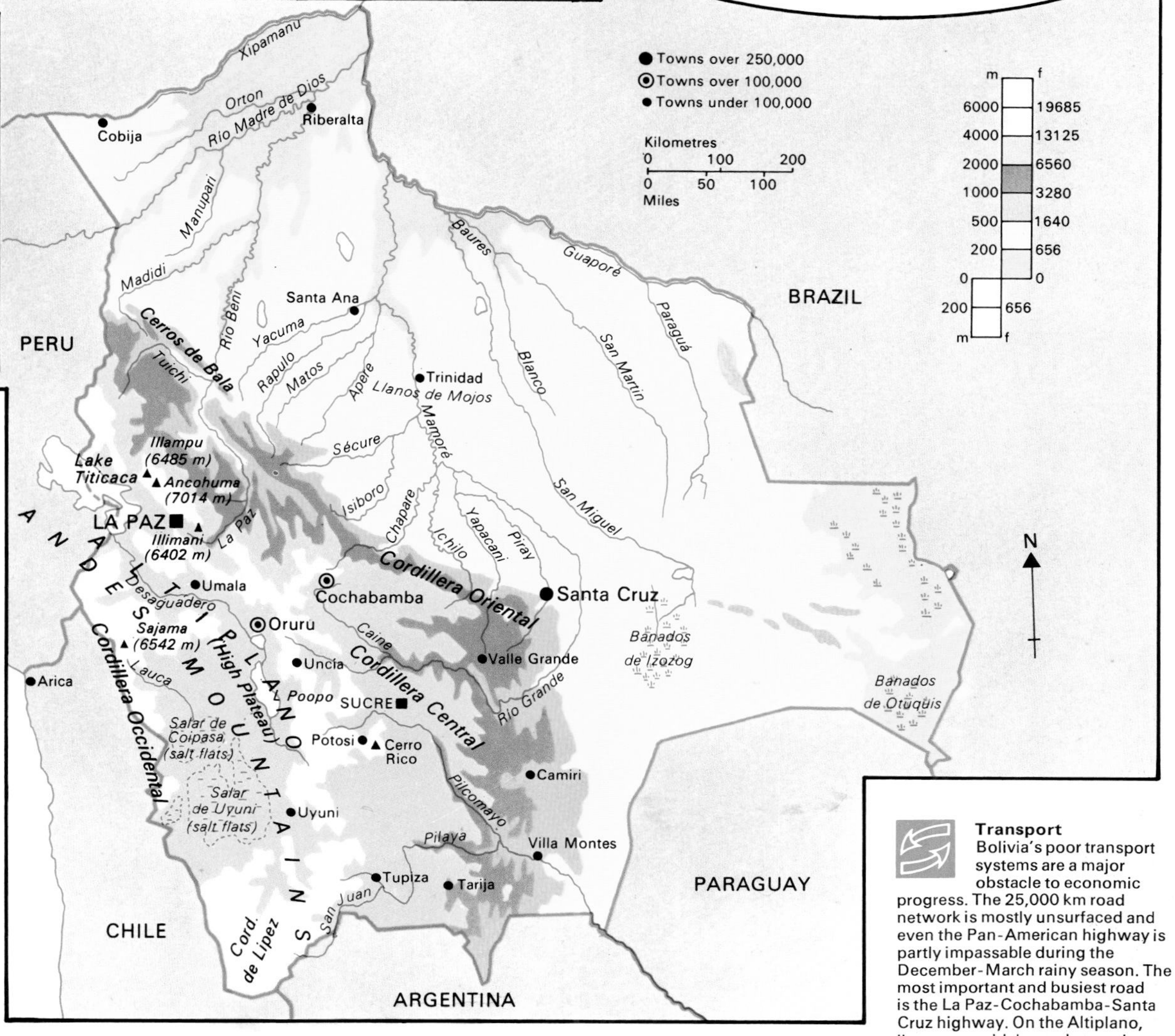

Area
1,098,587 km²/424,165 sq miles
Location
9°40′—22°40′ S
57°30′—69°40′ W
Population
5,721,000 (1981)
Population density
5 per km²/13 per sq mile
Administrative capital
La Paz: 880,000 (1982)
Legal capital
Sucre: 63,000
Language
Spanish
Major imports
machinery, foodstuffs, vehicles, iron and steel goods
Major exports
tin, silver, crude petroleum, other minerals, wool, nuts, skins
Currency
peso (1 peso = 100 centavos)
Gross National Product
3,440 million US dollars (1981)
Status
republic

Physical features

Land-locked Bolivia has two sharply contrasting regions: the mighty Andean system in the west and the low eastern plains. The Andes are at their widest in Bolivia (640 km) and comprise two chains: the western branch, along the Chilean border, features volcanic peaks over 6,000 m; the snow-capped eastern ranges include the lofty summits of Ancohuma (7,014 m), Illampu (6,485 m) and Illimani (6,402 m). Between these two chains lies the Altiplano (high plateau) at 4,000 m. At the plateau's northern end is Lake Titicaca, the world's highest navigable lake, drained southwards by the Desaguadero into shallow Lake Poopó. From here, the water disperses into vast and barren salt flats in the south of the Altiplano. Beyond the eastern ranges, the land falls in a tangle of ridges and gorges to the great plains that cover 70% of the country.

Climate

Bolivia is one of South America's driest regions: apart from the north-east, which shares the high rainfall of the Amazon basin, annual rainfall ranges from 60cm near Lake Titicaca and in the eastern foothills to 10 cm on the desert-like southern Altiplano. Temperatures are high on the lowlands but decrease with altitude in the mountains: Cochabamba at 2,500 m averages 18°C while La Paz at 3,665 m averages 9°C.

Peoples

The country's sparse population is unevenly distributed with three out of four living on the Altiplano. About 50% of the people are Amerindians, 35% mestizos and the rest whites. The Indians belong to three ethnic groups: Quechua, Aymara and Guarani. The largest group, the Quechuas (1 million) are mostly found in the southeast of the plateau; the Aymaras (750,000) inhabit the northern Altiplano; the Guaranis live near the Paraguayan border.

Flora & fauna

On the treeless Altiplano, natural vegetation is sparse; coarse grass predominates giving way to cacti and other drought-resistant plants in the south. The banks of Lake Titicaca are thick with totora reeds, used by Indians for making boats and thatching. The eastern Andean valleys are forested in the north and scrub-covered further south. Dense tropical jungle flourishes on the northeast lowlands while savanna and swamp characterize the southeast. Wildlife includes vicunas and condors in the Andes and, at lower levels, jaguars, pumas and alligators.

Agriculture

Although 70% of the population is engaged in agriculture (mostly at subsistence level), Bolivia is not self-sufficient in food. Arable farming is centred on the valleys of the Andean foothills and the Santa Cruz area. Sugar, coffee and cotton are exported while rice, bananas, cassava and maize are the main food crops. Conditions on the Altiplano are unsuitable, but some potatoes, barley and native crops are grown, especially near Lake Titicaca. Livestock farming includes cattle in the Andean valleys and the Santa Cruz region and llamas, alpacas and sheep on the Altiplano. There is some export of wool and skins.

Forestry & fishing

Forests, covering 40% of the territory, occur mostly in the Andean foothills and the northeast lowlands. Although they contain valuable hardwoods such as walnut and mahogany, timber output is low because of transport difficulties. Rubber, from wild trees, and brazil nuts are the main forest exports. Commercial fishing is centred on Lake Titicaca and the Pilcomayo river in the south.

Mining

Mining has played a fundamental part in the economy since 1534 when the Spaniards discovered vast silver reserves at Cerro Rico, making Bolivia the world's leading silver producer. By the 1900s, silver output had declined and tin was the major export; Bolivia is now the world's second largest supplier of tin. Other minerals produced in significant amounts and exported are copper, antimony, tungsten, silver, zinc, lead, bismuth and gold. Further deposits are so far unworked because of inadequate transport. Most minerals occur in a belt about 800 km long and 100 km wide, running along the eastern Andean chain. Minerals make up 95% of exports, tin accounting for 60%. Oil and natural gas are exploited in the southeast and are exported, via pipeline, to Argentina and Chile.

Industry

There is little manufacturing and most consumer goods have to be imported, but the development of oil and gas resources is expected to stimulate industrialization. Factories are mostly located in La Paz, Cochabamba and Santa Cruz.

Transport

Bolivia's poor transport systems are a major obstacle to economic progress. The 25,000 km road network is mostly unsurfaced and even the Pan-American highway is partly impassable during the December-March rainy season. The most important and busiest road is the La Paz-Cochabamba-Santa Cruz highway. On the Altiplano, llamas are widely used as pack animals. The skeletal rail network, totalling only 3,500 km, links the main urban centres and connects with neighbouring systems. As Bolivia has no coastline, trade passes through the Pacific ports of Antofagasta and Arica in Chile and Matarani in Peru (via Lake Titicaca). In addition to Lake Titicaca, the Beni, Pilcomayo, Desaguadero and Mamoré river systems provide 19,000 km of navigable waterway. The national airline, Lloyd Aereo Boliviano, flies to Peru, Brazil, Argentina, Chile and operates internal services.

Cities

In 1898, attempts to move the capital from isolated Sucre to the more vigorous and accessible La Paz resulted in civil war; since then, Sucre, a commercial and agricultural centre, remains the legal capital while La Paz is the seat of government. La Paz, lying in a river valley of the same name at an altitude of 3,665m, ranks as the world's highest capital. Next in importance are the cities of Santa Cruz (300,000), Cochabamba (216,000) and Potosi (77,000). Santa Cruz and Cochabamba both have some industrial development, including oil refineries; Potosi is a major mining centre.

Paraguay

Uruguay

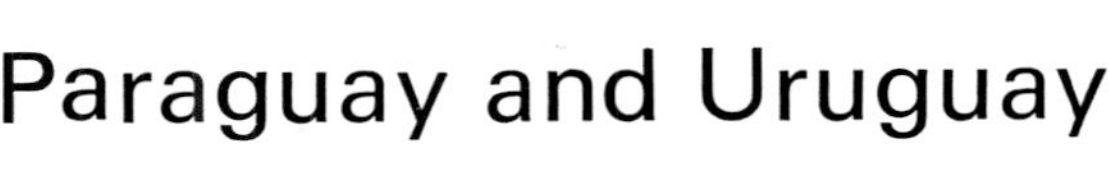

Paraguay and Uruguay

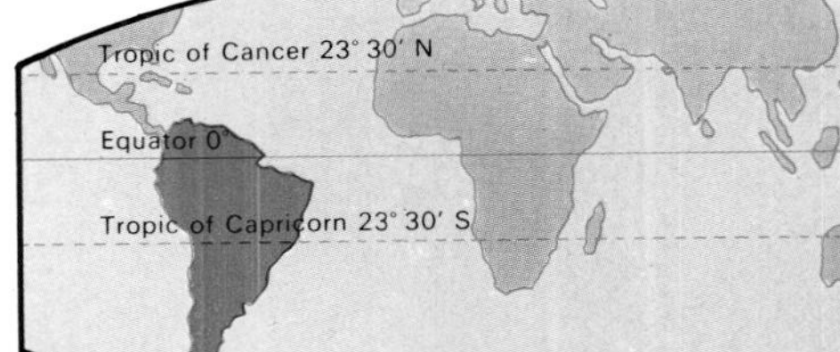

Paraguay
Area
406,752 km²/157,047 sq miles
Location
19°20'—27°40' S
54°15'—62°40' W
Population
3,057,000 (1981)
Population density
8 per km²/19 per sq mile
Capital and largest city
Asunción: 482,000 (1979)
Language
Spanish, Guarani
Major imports
fuels, machinery, vehicles, iron and steel, foodstuffs
Major exports
meat products, timber, tannin, cotton, tobacco
Currency
guarani (1 guarani = 100 centimos)
Gross National Product
4,970 million US dollars (1981)
Status
republic

Physical features
The river Paraguay, flowing from north to south, divides the country into two distinct regions. To the west stretches the Gran Chaco, a vast, monotonous lowland of alluvial silts, shifting streams and brackish swamps. East of the Paraguay lies an undulating upland zone, 300 to 600 m high. Apart from the Paraguay, the main rivers are the Paraná (which flows through a deep canyon) and the Picomayo. Vegetation includes deciduous and evergreen forests on the eastern plateau, marsh and palm savanna on the Paraguay plain and grass, and thorn scrub and quebracho thicket on the Chaco.

Climate
The climate is sub-tropical with relatively high temperatures throughout the year. Asunción averages 28°C in January and 17°C in July. Rainfall, heaviest in summer, decreases from 150 cm in the uplands to under 80 cm on the Chaco.

Transport
For landlocked Paraguay, river transport provides a vital trade outlet to the Atlantic ports of Buenos Aires and Montevideo. Large vessels can reach Concepción on the Paraguay and Puerto Stroessner on the Paraná; smaller boats navigate the tributaries. Asunción, 1,520 km from the sea, is the chief port. The road network is being improved; two major highways link Asunción with Paranagua port in Brazil via Puerto Stroessner and with Encarnación. The main railway also runs from the capital to Encarnación where it connects with the Argentinian system. Domestic air services are expanding.

People & towns
The population is 98% mestizo (mixed Spanish and Guarani Indian); minority groups include 40,000 Indians, 14,000 Mennonites (of German and Canadian origin) and 8,000 Japanese colonists. Most people live east of the Paraguay and, except for Mennonite and Indian settlements, the Chaco is virtually uninhabited. The country's only large town is Asunción; other important urban centres are Encarnación, Concepción and Villarrica.

Farming & forestry
Agriculture, concentrated in the east, is the basic economic activity and employs 50% of the population. Cattle-raising is the leading sector with livestock products accounting for 30% of all exports. Arable farming, mostly at subsistence level, covers only 2% of the land. Crops grown for local use are maize, cassava, rice, sugarcane, wheat, yerba maté (tea), coffee and a variety of fruits. Some tobacco, cotton and oilseeds are cultivated for export. Although forest resources are underexploited, they provide 25% of exports, mainly quebracho timber and tannin from the eastern Chaco.

Industry
Paraguay ranks as one of South America's poorest states. Industry is basically limited to processing farm and forest products and includes meat-canning, oilseed-crushing, cotton-ginning, sawmilling and tannin extraction. Nearly all manufacturing is located in Asunción. Small deposits of iron, copper and manganese exist but are so far unworked. Eastern Paraguay has vast hydro-power potential and there are plants on the Acaray and Monday rivers.

Uruguay
Area
186,925 km²/72,172 sq miles
Location
30°—35° S
53°—58°25' W
Population
2,929,000 (1981)
Population density
16 per km²/41 per sq mile
Capital and largest city
Montevideo: 1,300,000 (1979)
Language
Spanish
Major imports
crude oil, machinery, chemicals, vehicles
Major exports
wool, meat, hides
Currency
peso (1 peso = 100 centesimos)
Gross National Product
8,260 million US dollars (1981)
Status
republic

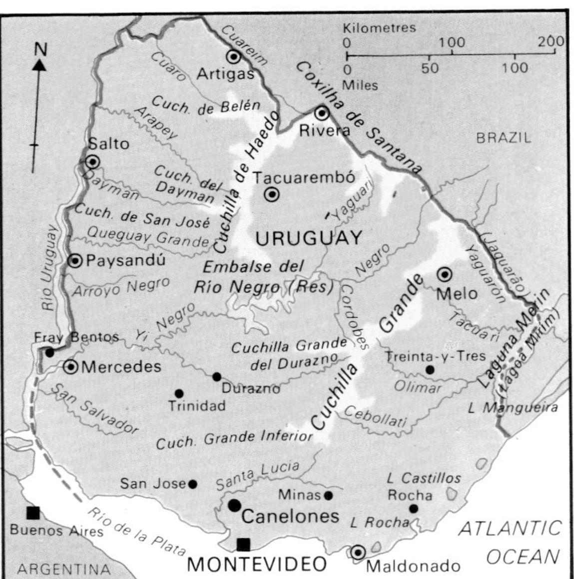

Physical features
Uruguay is the continent's third smallest state and the only one lying wholly outside the tropics. Gently rolling hill country, rising to 500 m in the north, covers most of the territory. Lowland areas comprise the flood plain bordering the Uruguay and Plata and the sandy coastal belt, fringed by lagoons. The Plata system, which includes the Uruguay and Negro, dominates the country's drainage.

People & towns
As most Uruguayans are of European descent, the mestizo element accounts for under 10% of the population. Four out of five people live in urban centres. Montevideo, with 45% of the entire population, is one of South America's largest cities. The country's other main towns—Salto, Paysandú, Mercedes and Fray Bentos—are all on or near the Uruguay; Canelones, Durazno and Rivera are important regional centres.

Climate
The climate, modified by the sea's proximity, is uniform throughout the country. Average temperatures range from 11°C in winter to 23°C in summer. Rainfall, about 120 cm, occurs mostly in autumn and winter but there is no marked dry season.

Agriculture
Uruguay is primarily a pastoral country with 80% of its land used for livestock. The 11 million cattle and 15 million sheep are mostly bred north of the Negro then fattened further south; animals and animal products make up about 50% of all exports. Arable farming is less important and is concentrated in the south on the Uruguay and Plata plains. Crops include wheat, maize, rice, potatoes, oilseeds, sugarcane and beet. Some fruit and vegetables are exported.

Mining & industry
Mining activity is limited to some quarrying of marble and granite. The lack of minerals and other raw materials hampers industrial growth, consequently, most manufacturing remains linked to agriculture: canned meat, sugar, woollen fabrics, vegetable oils and wine are some of the leading products. Other expanding sectors include light-engineering, chemicals, cement and paper. About 75% of industry is concentrated in Montevideo. Major hydro-power schemes are under construction on the Negro and Uruguay and are expected to stimulate industrial development.

Transport
The country's size and topography have resulted in good road and rail networks, both converging on Montevideo. The Uruguay is bridged at Fray Bentos and Paysandú and there are ferries across the Plata; both rivers are busy waterways. Montevideo is the chief port followed by Fray Bentos, Paysandú and Salto. The national airline operates local services and flies to other South American countries.

Chile

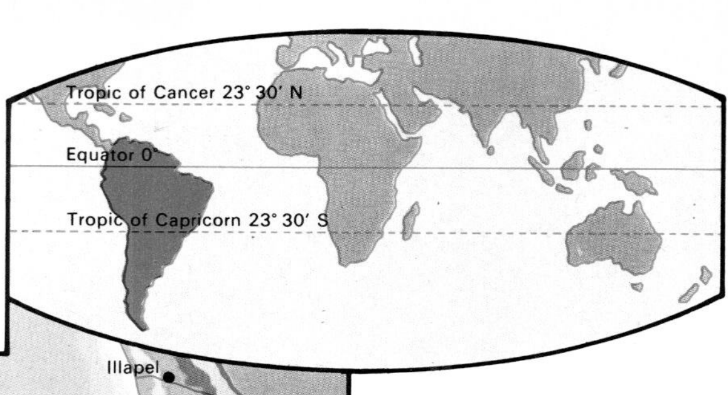

Area
756,946 km²/292,257 sq miles
Location
17°30′—56° S
67°—75°40′ W
Population
11,292,000 (1981)
Population density
15 per km²/39 per sq mile
Capital and largest city
Santiago: 4,000,000 (1980)
Language
Spanish
Major imports
foodstuffs, machinery, electrical goods, transport equipment
Major exports
copper, iron ore, chemical products, paper and pulp, fruit and vegetables
Currency
peso (1 peso = 100 centavos)
Gross National Product
28,890 million US dollars (1981)
Status
republic

Physical features

Chile, only 200 to 300 km wide, extends along the Pacific coast for almost 5,000 km. This long, narrow land is overshadowed by the Andes which run north-south along its entire length and occupy half the area. The mountains are highest in the north and centre where they rise to 6,880 m in Ojos del Salado, Chile's highest peak. In the south, the chain is lower and fragmented with lakes, deep valleys, glaciers, fjords and thousands of offshore islands. West of the Andes is Chile's main lowland area, the Central Trough, which features salt lakes and flats in the north but gives way further south to an alluvial zone; below Puerto Montt the trough has been drowned. A low coastal range separates the trough from the ocean; in the far south, the range is submerged and appears as a maze of islands. Rivers, short and fast-flowing, all drain into the Pacific. Chile lies in an unstable zone and is subject to earthquakes and tidal waves.

Climate

Because of its length, Chile spans various climatic zones. The north is very arid—years can pass without rain—but the Andes and the cold Humboldt current modify temperature. Between latitudes 31° and 37°, Mediterranean conditions prevail: temperatures average 10°C in July, 27°C in January and rainfall (occurring in winter) totals 75 cm. Southern Chile is cool and wet with summer temperatures of 20°C and all-year rain (120 cm). The extreme south, including the islands and western Tierra del Fuego, is stormy with high winds, lashing rain (500 cm) and heavy snow; temperatures range from —4°C to 15°C.

Flora & fauna

The desert north is barren except for small valley oases and stunted scrub on the Andean foothills. Grassland and deciduous forest characterize 'Mediterranean' Chile while the south is densely forested with Chile pine (monkey-puzzle), evergreen beech, larch, cypress and thick undergrowth. Wildlife includes pumas, mountain goats, guanacos, condors and parrots.

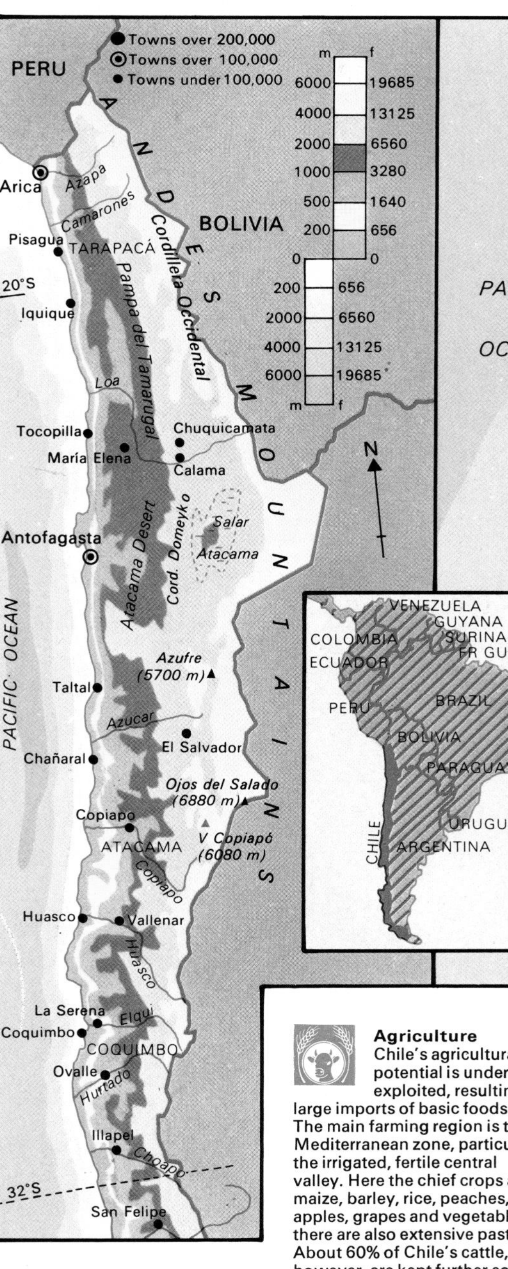

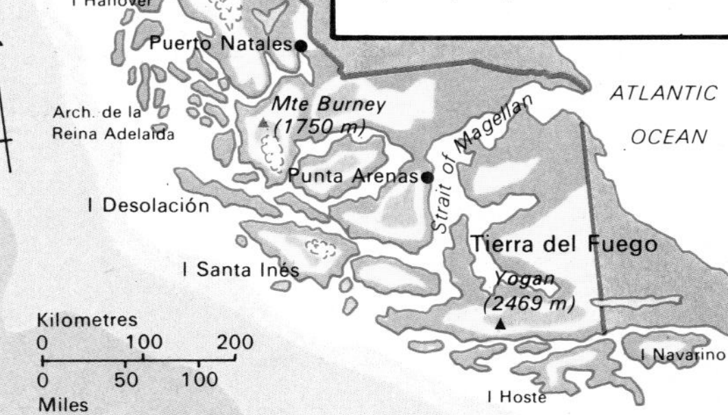

Mining

Chile's wealth lies in its minerals which are mostly located in the north. Copper, providing 80% of exports, dominates the economy. Reserves represent 40% of the world total and Chile ranks as the third largest copper producer and second exporter. The main mines are at Chuquicamata, El Teniente and El Salvador. High grade iron ore, occurring in Atacama and Coquimbo provinces, is next in importance followed by nitrates from the northern desert; iodine and potassium salts are major by-products. In addition to these leading minerals, many others exist; those worked include gold, silver, manganese, lead, zinc, sulphur and molybdenum. There is some coal-mining near Concepción and oil (from fields in Tierra del Fuego and the Strait of Magellan's north shore) provides 30% of domestic requirements.

Agriculture

Chile's agricultural potential is under-exploited, resulting in large imports of basic foods. The main farming region is the Mediterranean zone, particularly the irrigated, fertile central valley. Here the chief crops are maize, barley, rice, peaches, apples, grapes and vegetables; there are also extensive pastures. About 60% of Chile's cattle, however, are kept further south on small farms in the forest zone; these farms also grow most of the country's wheat, oats and potatoes. In the extreme south, on the Patagonian steppe and in Tierra del Fuego, large flocks of sheep are grazed. Agricultural exports (only 5% of all exports) include wine, fresh and dried fruit, wool and meat.

Forestry & fishing

Southern Chile, between Concepción and Puerto Montt, is extensively forested but, so far, commercial exploitation of timber is limited. The quick-growing pine is the basis of paper and cellulose manufacture, while oak, beech and elm are supplied to the construction industries. Traditionally, Chileans eat few fish, but efforts are being made to boost fish consumption and expand the fishing industry; some shellfish and fishmeal are exported.

Energy

As domestic supplies of oil, natural gas and coal are inadequate, Chile's vast hydro-power potential is being developed to meet the country's expanding energy needs. Most hydro plants are located in the Andes, but the resources of the coastal range are also being harnessed. At present, about half of Chile's electricity is water-generated.

Industry

In recent years, manufacturing has grown significantly and now employs a quarter of the total workforce. Many plants process domestic raw materials to produce steel, woollen textiles, cement, wine, dried fruit, paper, cellulose, furniture, leather goods, petrochemicals and so on, but other sectors have to rely on costly imported materials. Industry is concentrated in the three main urban centres: Santiago, Valparaíso and Concepción.

Transport

Chile's extraordinary shape has a major impact on transport systems. Coastal shipping has always been significant, especially in the south where there are no surface routes beyond Puerto Montt; the road to Punta Arenas, the world's southernmost city, passes through Argentina. The Santiago-Valparaíso road and the Pan-American Highway, from Arica to Puerto Montt, are the two most important roads. Railways consist of a main line between Pisagua and Puerto Montt with branches. Most imports pass through Valparaíso, the chief port; mineral exports are shipped from Antofagasta, San Antonio, Huasco and Chanaral. There are five international airports.

People and towns

Widespread intermarriage between the Spanish and Indian communities has resulted in a predominantly mestizo population. About 70% of Chileans live in the 'Mediterranean' zone which contains the country's three largest cities: Santiago, Valparaíso (248,000) and Concepción (210,000). Santiago, in its beautiful setting below the Andes, is the country's economic hub and houses over a third of the population. The second city and chief port is Valparaíso. Concepción, near the mouth of the Bío Bío, is a modern city which has been rebuilt many times after earthquakes; its port is Talcahuano.

Argentina

Area
2,791,810 km²/1,077,919 sq miles
Location
22° — 55° S
53°40′ — 73°30′ W
Population
28,174,000 (1981)
Population density
10 per km²/26 per sq mile
Capital and largest city
Buenos Aires: 2,908,000 (1980)
Language
Spanish
Major imports
machinery, metals, chemicals, vehicles, paper
Major exports
cereals, meat, linseed, wool, hides, textiles
Currency
peso (1 peso = 100 centavos)
Gross National Product
72,120 million US dollars (1981)
Status
federal republic

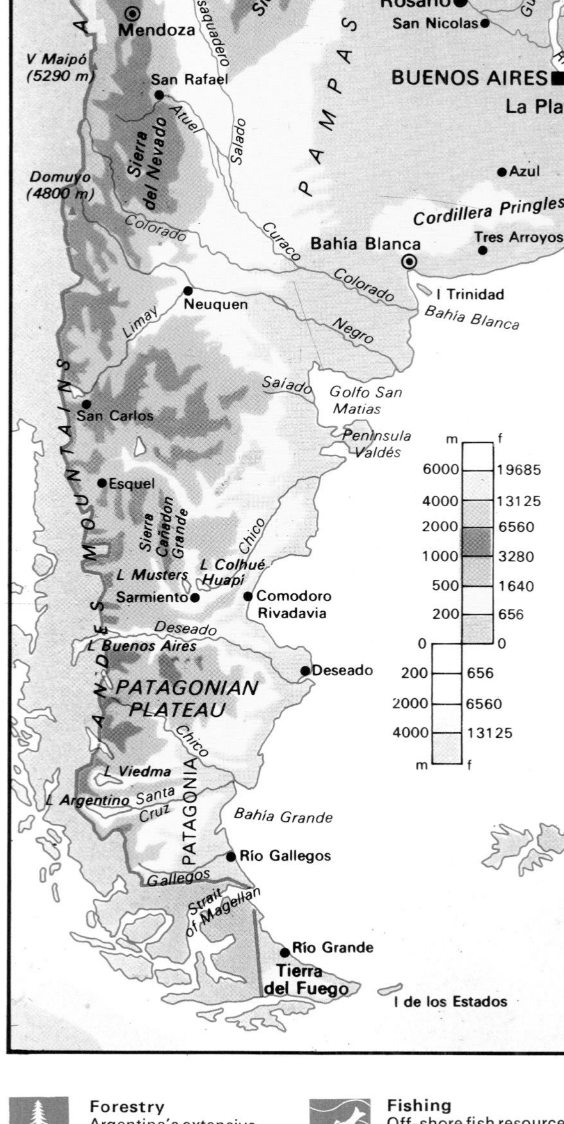

Physical features

Argentina, South America's second largest state, occupies most of the continent below the Tropic of Capricorn and east of the Andes. For nearly 4,000 km, the country's western boundary runs along the high Andean crestline. Towards the north, the mountain zone widens to include a bleak, desert plateau some 4,000 m high. South of this lies Cerro Aconcagua (7,163 m), highest peak in the Western Hemisphere. East of the northern highlands lies the Chaco, an extensive lowland made up of alluvia swept down from the Andes and crossed by the rivers Salado, Bermejo and Pilcomayo. Mesopotamia, the region between the Paraná and Uruguay rivers, is low lying except for a spur of the Brazilian plateau in the northeast. Fanning out from Buenos Aires is Argentina's heartland, the *Pampas*: vast and monotonous grasslands that cover 20% of the country. Southwards, towards the Colorado river, the land rises slowly; beyond the river extends the Patagonian plateau, a rugged, desolate lakeland.

Climate

Argentina's climate, spanning 33° of latitude, ranges from subtropical heat to sub-antarctic cold. The north has hot, wet summers (25°C) and long, dry, mild winters (13°C); rainfall increases from 50 cm in the west to 120 cm in the east. Buenos Aires averages 23°C in summer and 10°C in winter with both temperature and rainfall decreasing towards the southwest. Patagonia is arid and windy and although winters are not severe (2°C), summers are short and cool (16°C).

Population

The indigenous Indians, decimated by the Spaniards, now number under 30,000 and are concentrated in the northwest. As there has been little intermarriage, 97% of Argentinians are white and only 2% (found in the Andean zone) are mestizos. Two-thirds of the people live on the pampas which contain, in addition to the capital, such major cities as Rosario (800,000), Córdoba (800,000), La Plata (400,000) and Sante Fé (310,000). Greater Buenos Aires, with over 9.5 million inhabitants, is South America's largest urban centre.

Agriculture

Agriculture, centred on the pampas, forms the base of the economy: it supplies most of the country's food and provides 90% of all exports. Stockraising is the principal sector, making Argentina the world's largest raw-meat exporter and fourth largest producer of both beef and wool. Pasture covers almost half the territory: 50 million cattle are grazed on the pampas and 45 million sheep are kept, mostly in Patagonia. Arable farming, occupying 11% of the land, is also concentrated on the pampas. Wheat is the leading crop followed by maize, linseed, alfalfa (for fodder) and sunflower seed. Crops grown beyond the pampas include rice, tea and maté in Mesopotamia; cotton in the Chaco; sugar-cane and citrus in the northwest. Vines are cultivated in the Andean foothills, especially near Mendoza; Argentina ranks as the fourth largest wine producer in the world.

Mining

Apart from oil and natural gas, Argentina lacks mineral wealth and has to import supplies for industry. There are small, scattered deposits of iron ore, lead, zinc, tin, silver, gold, copper, sulphur, tungsten, mica, manganese, cobalt, vanadium and uranium, but only a few of these are worked. Some coal is mined in southern Patagonia but it is low-quality and located too far from urban areas to be important. Argentina is, however, self-sufficient in oil: the main fields are in Patagonia, centred on Comodoro Rivadavia and in the western provinces. Natural gas occurs in the same areas and a network of oil and gas pipelines crosses the country.

Industry

Not surprisingly, much of Argentinian industry is based on agriculture; products include wool and cotton textiles, canned meat, cigarettes, wine, vegetable oils, flour, sugar and leather goods. Other major sectors are steel, petro-chemicals, engineering, cement, electronics and motor cars. Buenos Aires is the main manufacturing centre, but San Nicolas (on the Paraná) has the country's leading steel plant and San Lorenzo (further upstream) is the site of a giant refining and petrochemical complex.

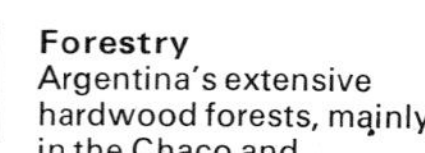

Forestry

Argentina's extensive hardwood forests, mainly in the Chaco and northern Mesopotamia, are under-exploited. A significant product is tannin dye, extracted from the quebracho tree. Softwoods have to be imported.

Fishing

Off-shore fish resources have recently been developed. The fishing industry, centred on Mar del Plata, supplies fish (principally hake and anchovy) for human consumption and for processing into animal feeds.

Transport

Argentina's transport services, among the best in South America, are mostly concentrated on the pampas. However, the 40,000 km rail network, spreading out from Buenos Aires, serves all areas except Patagonia; international routes include a spectacular trans-Andean line to Santiago (Chile). The road system, totalling 944,000 km, is being improved for although major highways are good, minor roads are generally unsurfaced and many become impassable in rain. There are steamer services on the Río Plata, Paraguay, Paraná and Uruguay. The main port, handling 75% of trade, is Buenos Aires followed by Bahía Blanca, Rosario and La Plata. Internal air services, vitally important in remote Patagonia, are well-developed; three international airports link Argentina to all parts of the world.

Flora & fauna

The cold Andean plateau is barren apart from scattered tussocky grasses and stunted drought-resistant shrubs; forests of beech and pine characterize the foothill zone except in the arid south. Deciduous woodland, spiny thorn scrub, savanna and swamp cover the Chaco; Mesopotamia has rolling grassy plains and dense forests. The wide, treeless grasslands of the pampas are richest in the wetter east. In Patagonia, vegetation is reduced to low bushes and coarse grasses. Wildlife includes jaguars, pumas, alligators and parrots in the forests; condors and vultures in the Andes; and the guanaco (wild llama) and rhea (ostrich-like bird) on the pampas.

Atlantic Ocean Islands

Falkland

St Helena

Azores
The Azores, politically part of mainland Portugal, have a total area of 2,335 km² and comprise nine main islands in three widely separated groups: São Miguel and Santa Maria in the east; Graciosa, Terceira, São Jorge, Pico and Faial in the centre; Flores and Corvo to the northwest. The archipelago, 1,300 km west of Portugal, is volcanic in origin. Mountain masses rise steeply from rocky coastal belts and reach 2,351 m on Pico. The climate is mild and damp: the temperature averages 16°C and rain, falling throughout the year, 100 cm. Most of the 292,000 islanders live along the coast and are engaged in farming and fishing. Cereals, fruits, sugar cane, vegetables and tobacco are grown while the fish catch mainly consists of tunny and mullet. Exports include oranges, pineapples, bananas, canned fish and sperm whale oil. The chief towns are the capital on Ponta Delgada, Angra and Horta—all major ports.

Madeira
Madeira, administered as part of Portugal, lies 700 km southeast of the Azores. The volcanic archipelago, 796 km² in area, comprises two inhabited islands, Madeira and Porto Santo, plus uninhabited islets and rocks. Madeira, the largest island, consists of central mountains rising to 1,861 m in Pico Ruivo, forested spurs and deep valleys; Porto Santo is hilly. The climate is warm and humid with average temperatures of 17 to 21°C and 50 cm of rain a year. Agriculture dominates the economy: coastal areas and terraced lower slopes are used for growing vines, sugar cane, cereals and a wide range of fruits and vegetables. Wine, bananas and sugar are the main exports. There is some fishing for tunny and swordfish. Tourism is important and traditional handicrafts, notably embroidery and wickerwork, are commercially significant. Funchal the capital, is the major port and leading tourist centre; Vila is the chief town on Porto Santo. The total population of the archipelago is about 266,000.

Canary Islands
The Canary Islands, part of Spain, have an area of 7,273 km² and a population of 1,170,000. Situated 100 km off the African coast, the archipelago consists of two groups: to the west, the mountainous islands of Tenerife, Gran Canaria, La Palma, Gomera and Hierro are all peaks rising directly from the ocean floor; Pico de Teide (3,718 m) on Tenerife is Spain's highest point. In the east, Lanzarote, Fuerteventura and adjacent islets are of volcanic origin. The climate is warm but uncertain rainfall often causes drought and irrigation is necessary. Agriculture is the main economic activity. Bananas, citrus, sugar cane, vegetables, coffee, dates, and tobacco are grown below 400 m and cereals, grapes and potatoes up to 700 m. Bananas, tomatoes and sugar are the chief exports. There is some local fishing for sardines and tunny. Tourism is important. The leading towns are Las Palmas and Santa Cruz de Tenerife and these are also the major ports.

Cape Verde Islands
The Republic of the Cape Verde Islands lies in the central Atlantic 480 km west of Africa. It comprises 10 islands and 5 islets. The Islands, with a total area of 4,033 km², are divided into two groups: are divided into two groups: Barlavento (windward) and Sotavento (leeward)—the prevailing winds being northeast. Of volcanic origin, the islands are mountainous and rugged and Fogo has an active volcano. The climate is hot (25°C) and humid but there is little rain and droughts are common. About 10% of the territory is used for agriculture with maize and beans as the main food crops while coffee, bananas and peanuts are grown for export. Other exports are canned tuna, salt (produced on Sal, Maio and Boa Vista), pozzolana (a volcanic rock) and corals. Industry includes food-processing and textiles. The capital is Praia on São Tiago but Mindelo on São Vincente is the chief commercial centre, main port and a major refuelling station for transatlantic shipping. Sal has an international airport. The islands have a total population of 306,000.

São Tome e Príncipe
The Republic of São Tome e Prícipe in the Gulf of Guinea is 270 km off the African coast and has a total area of 964 km². The two main islands, São Tome (854 km²) and Príncipe, are of volcanic origin and consist of rugged, jungle-covered highlands with Pico de Tome reaching 2 024 m. Situated just north of the equator, the islands have a hot and humid climate. A third of the land has been cleared for agriculture and the economy is based on cocoa (accounting for 60% of exports) and coffee—both grown on plantations. Other products exported include coconuts, palm oil, copra and cinchona. The main food crops are cassava, sweet potatoes and yams—there is also some fishing. Nearly all the 82,000 inhabitants live on São Tome and work on the plantations. Most of them are contract labourers from the Cape Verde islands.

Falkland Islands
The Falkland Islands are a British colony lying in the south Atlantic some 500 km off the Argentine coast. The group, with a total area of 12,200 km², comprises two main islands—East Falkland (6,495 km²) and West Falkland (5,880 km²)—plus 200 smaller islets. The desolate landscape consists of mountains and moorlands while the coast is broken by deep fjords. Strong winds and low temperatures characterize the climate. Almost the entire territory is used for sheep-farming. There are some 600,000 sheep with wool the main product but some hides are also exported. Postage stamps are another source of income. Small quantities of oats, potatoes and vegetables are grown, but nearly all the islands' food is imported. About 2,000 people live in the colony, half of them in Stanley—the only town. There is a monthly shipping service from Stanley to Montevideo and direct sailings to the United Kingdom several times a year. Inter-island transport is by seaplane.

St Helena
The British colony of St Helena, a volcanic island 1,900 km off west Africa, has an area of 122 km² and a population of 5,000. Edged with steep cliffs, it has a mountainous interior rising to 823 m in Diana's Peak. The climate, influenced by the southeast trade winds, is temperate. Farmland covers a quarter of the island: potatoes and other vegetables are the main crops and there are some cattle. Fish provides the main source of protein. Jamestown (population 1,600) is the capital and chief port.

Ascension Island
Situated 1,120 km northwest of St Helena, Ascension (88 km²) is of volcanic origin and is barren except on Green Mountain (875 m). The climate is tropical but dry. Only 4 ha are cultivated, producing vegetables and fruit. The 1,050 inhabitants are mostly employed in the telecommunications and satellite tracking stations situated there. Georgetown is the main settlement. The island, a dependency of St Helena, is famous for its wild life—particularly sea turtles (which lay their eggs on the beaches) and sooty terns.

Tristan da Cunha
The Tristan da Cunha group, halfway between the Cape and South America, is a dependency of St Helena. Tristan (98 km²) is the largest island and consists of a volcanic cone 2,000 m high. The 295 inhabitants live by farming (potatoes, sheep, cattle) and fishing. There is a crayfish-freezing plant. 50 km south are the small islands of Inaccessible and Nightingale. Rugged Gough Island (90 km²) lies 400 km to the southeast. All 3 islands are uninhabited and are noted for their rare plants and birds.

Mauritania, Morocco and Western Sahara

Morocco

Mauritania

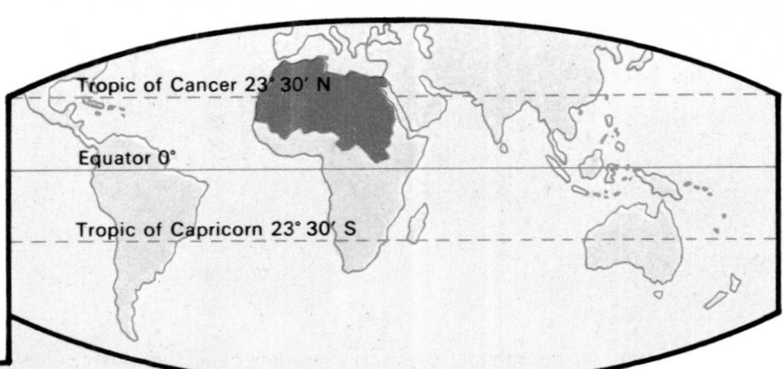

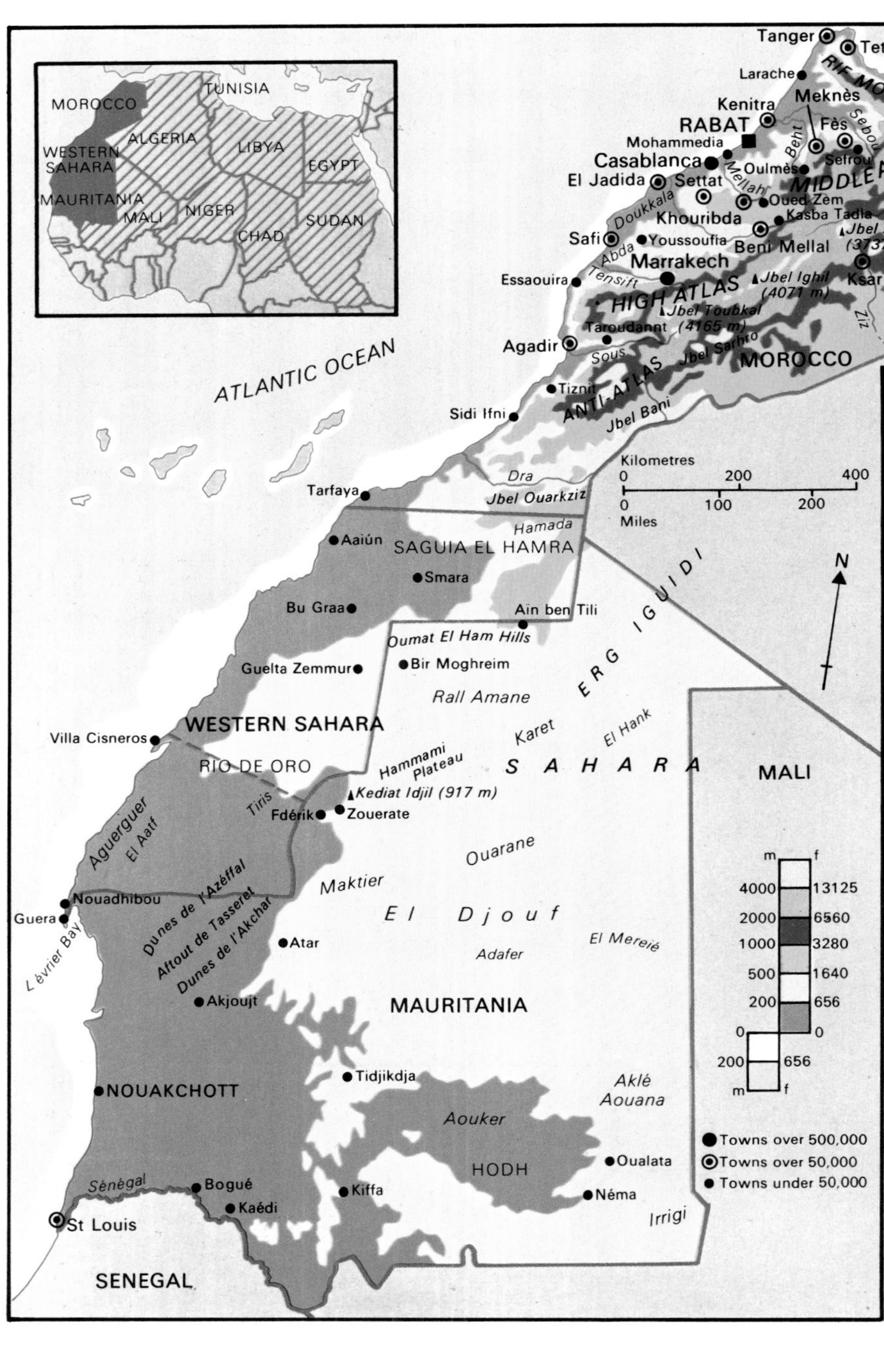

Morocco
Area
458,730 km²/177,117 sq miles
Location
27°40′–35°50′N ; 1°–13°10′W
Population
20,891,000 (1981)
Population density
46 per km²/118 per sq mile
Capital
Rabat: 865,000 (1980)
Largest city
Casablanca: 2,357,000 (1980)
Language
Arabic
Major imports
food, fuels, textiles, vehicles, machinery, iron and steel
Major exports
phosphates, citrus fruits, fish, tomatoes, lead ore, wine
Currency
dirham (1 dirham = 100 centimes)
Gross National Product
17,960 million US dollars (1981)
Status
constitutional monarchy

The land
Morocco is a rugged country dominated by the Atlas mountains. These mountains sweep across the centre from northeast to southwest and rising from 2,750 m in the Middle Atlas to over 4,000 m in the High Atlas ; Jbel Toubkal (4,165 m) is the highest peak. To the south the Anti-Atlas (the uplifted edge of the Saharan platform) reaches 2,000 m. The coastline is extensive : in the north, the Rif mountains rise steeply from the Mediterranean while the Atlantic seaboard is flanked by lowland areas such as the Sebou, Oumer Rbia, Tensift, Sous and Dra river basins. The longest river, the Moulouya, flows into the Mediterranean. Northern Morocco has a Mediterranean climate with hot, dry summers and warm, wet winters ; the Atlas zone is dryer and colder while the southeast, verging the Sahara, is very hot and arid.

Transport
The mountainous interior is largely uninhabited except for nomadic tribesmen and, consequently, the 25,000 km road network is mainly concentrated in the populated coastal areas. Railways (40% electrified) cover 1,770 km. Main lines link Casablanca to Tanger, Marrakech and Algeria (via Oujda) ; branch lines connect with the mining areas. Casablanca, handling 75% of Moroccan trade, and Safi are the chief freight ports ; Tanger is important for passengers. Other major ports are Mohammedia, Kenitra and Agadir. Royal Air Maroc is the national airline.

Agriculture
Farming and fishing employs 70% of Moroccans, supplies 85% of the country's food needs and provides 40% of total exports. Arable land is concentrated along the coast where the main crops are wheat, barley, sugarbeet, oilseed, cotton, olives, citrus, almonds and vegetables. Berber tribesmen graze sheep and goats in the mountain valleys and camels in the arid south ; some cattle are raised on the lowlands. Forests cover many highland areas and products include cork, cedar timber and tannin. The Atlantic coastal waters abound in tunny, sardines, mackerel and anchovies. Agadir, Safi, Casablanca and Essaouira are the chief fishing ports. The leading agricultural exports are citrus, tomatoes, processed fish and olive oil. Morocco ranks as the world's second largest citrus exporter.

Mining & industry
Morocco is a major world producer of phosphates, mined at Khouribga and Youssoufia and exported via Casablanca and Safi. Cobalt, lead, zinc and manganese are also worked in significant quantities. Supplies of energy minerals (coal, oil and gas) are inadequate and fuel is imported ; 80% of electricity used comes from hydro-electric power plants. Industry mainly consists of preparing goods for export (olive processing, fish-canning, fruit-packing, wine-making and phosphate-processing). Flour-milling and sugar-refining serve the domestic market. Textiles, leatherwear, vehicles, cement, paper and chemicals are also important. Casablanca is the leading industrial centre.

Cities
Casablanca, extending 20 km along the Atlantic coast, ranks as Morocco's largest and most important city and port. The country's second city, Marrakech (1,224,000), is the chief town in the south. Known as the 'red city' because of its red clay buildings, it is a trading centre for the Atlas and Sahara regions. Fès (745,000), the former northern capital, is a major religious centre. The present capital of Rabat is mainly administrative.

Western Sahara
Formerly Spanish Sahara, Western Sahara (266,000 km²) is part administered by Morocco. The other part was occupied by Morocco in 1980, when Mauritania gave up its administration. It is a desert country with a dune covered coastal plain rising inland to a plateau 300 m high; in the northeast, mountains reach 600 m. The 75,000 inhabitants are mostly nomads who live by herding sheep, goats and camels ; some barley and maize are grown. The fishing industry, based at Guera, is important. The territory's principal resource is the Bu Graa phosphate deposits. These are among the richest in the world but are not yet exploited. Fish, phosphates and skins are exported.

Mauritania
Area
1,030,700 km²/397,950 sq miles
Location
14°49′–27°23′N ; 4°50′–17°W
Population
1,560,000 (1981)
Population density
1.5 per km²/4 per sq mile
Capital and largest city
Nouakchott: 250,000 (1981)
Languages
Arabic and French
Major imports
machinery, transport equipment, foodstuffs, fuels
Major exports
iron ore, fish, cattle, copper
Currency
ougiya (1 ougiya = 5 khoums)
Gross National Product
710 million US dollars (1981)
Status
republic

The land
Mauritania consists of a vast plateau sloping down from 220 m in the northeast to 45 m in the southwest. The monotonous landscape is broken by a series of west-facing scarps, including the Adrar range (490 m), and by isolated peaks such as the Kediat Idjil (917 m). Half the plateau consists of gravel desert ; the remainder is dune-covered. Southwest Mauritania is drained by tributaries of the Sénégal ; elsewhere, the plateau is dissected by wadis (dry riverbeds) that are very occasionally filled with floodwater. A hot, arid climate with summer temperatures of 30°C and under 10 cm of rain annually prevails over most of the country. The coast is cooler, the south wetter.

The economy
Agriculture, mostly stock-raising, supports 85% of the population. Cattle are bred in the south, sheep and goats along the desert fringe and camels in the north. Arable farming is confined to the alluvial Sénégal region and the oases. Millet and dates are the main crops ; maize, beans, yams and cotton are also grown. The waters of Lévrier Bay are rich in fish and the fishing industry, based at Nouadhibou, is important. There are extensive deposits of iron ore at Zouerate and copper at Akjoujt. Iron ore, accounting for 80% of exports, is shipped from Nouadhibou ; copper from Nouakchott. There is little industry apart from food-processing and packaging.

Tunisia and Algeria

Tunisia

Algeria

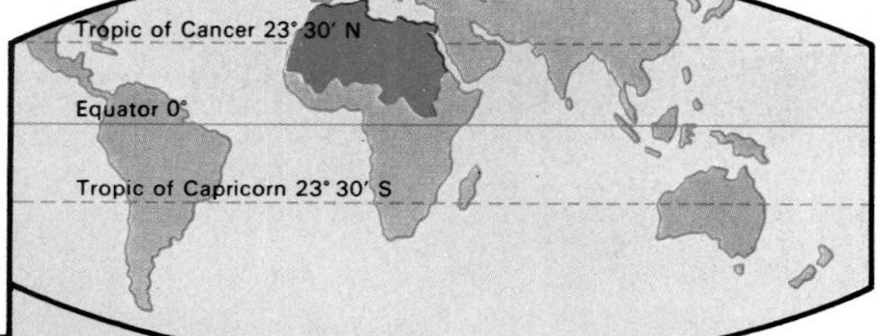

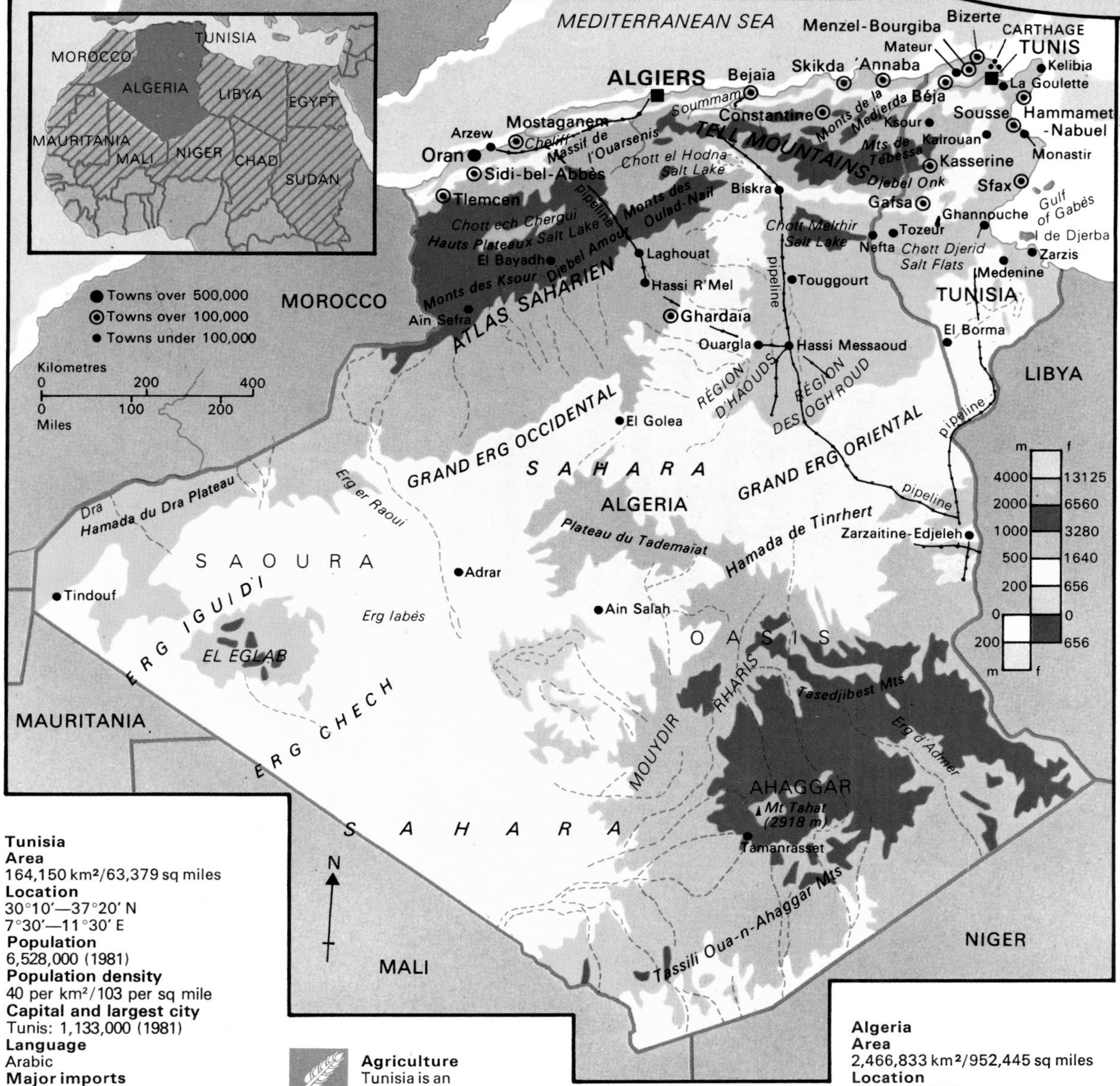

Tunisia
Area
164,150 km²/63,379 sq miles
Location
30°10′—37°20′ N
7°30′—11°30′ E
Population
6,528,000 (1981)
Population density
40 per km²/103 per sq mile
Capital and largest city
Tunis: 1,133,000 (1981)
Language
Arabic
Major imports
machinery, metal goods, transport equipment, foodstuffs
Major exports
oil, olive oil, phosphates, wine, citrus, iron and steel
Currency
dinar (1 dinar = 1,000 millimes)
Gross National Product
9,300 million US dollars (1981)
Status
republic

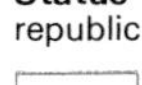

The land
Northern Tunisia consists of a plateau some 500 m high. This plateau, an extension of the Atlas mountains, is drained by the Medjerda—the only permanent river. Steppe lands and salt flats, such as the Chott Djerid, characterize central Tunisia which merges southwards with the Sahara. The coast has warm dry summers and mild winters: Tunis averages 12°C in January and 25°C in August. Inland conditions are more extreme: winter temperatures on the plateau drop to 0°C while the desert records over 50°C in summer. Rainfall is low, decreasing from 80 cm in the north to 10 cm in the south.

Agriculture
Tunisia is an agricultural country and 60% of the population lives off the land. The main cereals are wheat and barley grown in the Medjerda valley. Wine-grapes and citrus predominate in the northeast, olives along the coast between the Gulfs of Hammamet and Gabès, and dates in the desert oases. Other crops include sugarbeet, potatoes, tomatoes, figs, apricots and almonds. There is little irrigation and crop yields fluctuate because of the variable rainfall. Animals, mostly sheep, are grazed on the southern steppes. Other products include cork and esparto grass.

Mining
Tunisia is a leading world producer of phosphates. Production is centred on the Gafsa region and phosphates, phosphoric acid and fertilizers are major exports. Iron ore, lead and zinc are also mined and exported. Oil, supplying domestic needs and accounting for 40% of total exports, comes from El Borma and the Gulf of Gabès; natural gas from Ras el Tib and near Sfax.

Industry
Food processing is the main industry: products include olive oil, wine, sugar (at Béja), flour, canned fish and preserved fruit and vegetables. Paper is made from esparto grass at Kasserine, and wool and leather are also processed. Among newer projects are an oil refinery at Bizerte, a steel complex at Menzel-Bourgiba and a phosphoric acid plant at Ghannouche. Other industries include cement, vehicle assembly, fertilizers and electronics. Tourism is based on east coast resorts such as Hammamet-Nabeul and Djerba.

Tunisian transport
Except for the coastal highways to Libya, road and rail networks are concentrated in northern Tunisia. The main seaports are Tunis-La Goulette, Bizerte, Sousse and Sfax. Tunis-Air, the national airline, operates internal and overseas flights; international airports are situated at Tunis, Djerba and Monastir.

Algeria
Area
2,466,833 km²/952,445 sq miles
Location
19°—37°10′ N
8°30′W—12°E
Population
19,602,000 (1981)
Population density
8 per km²/21 per sq mile
Capital and largest city
Algiers: 3,250,000 (1980)
Language
Arabic
Major imports
machinery, iron, steel, transport equipment, foodstuffs, textiles
Major exports
oil, wine, gas, fruit and vegetables, iron ore
Currency
dinar (1 dinar = 100 centimes)
Gross National Product
42,010 million US dollars (1981)
Status
republic

Algerian transport
About 90% of surfaced roads (27,000 km) are in the north. The 4,000 km rail network connects with Morocco and Tunisia and serves the main ports; Algiers, Oran, 'Annaba, Bejaïa, Skikda and Arzew. Air Algérie is the national airline with airports at Algiers, Oran and 'Annaba.

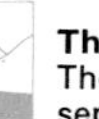

The land
The Tell mountains separate the rocky coast from a belt of high plateaux (1,200 m) and interior basins containing salt lakes such as the Chott el Hodna and the Chott ech Chergui. The southern rim of this semi-arid zone is formed by the Atlas Saharien. Beyond this mountain wall lies the Sahara, occupying 80% of the country and consisting of bare rock, gravel deserts and *ergs* (vast sand seas). In the southeast the desert rises to Algeria's highest peak, Mt Tahat (2,918 m). The coast has a Mediterranean climate—12°C in January, 27°C in August; the desert has frosts in winter but high summer temperatures. Rain varies from 100 cm in the eastern Tell to zero in the Sahara.

Agriculture
Agriculture, employing half the people, is confined to the coastal zone and adjacent valleys. Grapes are the main cash crop and wine accounts for 65% of agricultural exports. Other leading crops are wheat, barley, olives, citrus, vegetables and tobacco. The Tell and plateau are used for grazing, mostly sheep and goats; the plateau also yields esparto grass. Forests cover parts of the Tell and Atlas ranges; products include timber, cork and dye barks. The oases have date palms and Algeria is a major producer of dates. Sardine, anchovy and tunny fishing is important. Algeria is not self-sufficient in food and large imports are necessary.

Mining
Oil and gas make up 75% of Algerian exports. The two main oilfields, accounting for 60% of total output, are Hassi Messaoud and Zarzaitine-Edjeleh; there are refineries at Hassi Messaoud, Arzew, Skikda and Bejaïa. By 1980, gas is expected to be more important than oil. Production is centred on Hassi R'Mel. In the mid-1970s, gas was liquefied before export but direct pipelines to Spain and Italy were planned. Oil and gas are used to generate 75% of the country's electricity; hydro-electric power supplies the remainder. There are deposits of iron ore (Ouenza), lead-zinc (El Abed) and phosphates (Djebel Onk). Copper, mercury, antimony, marble and salt also exist.

Industry
Excluding oil, 40% of industrial output consists of foodstuffs such as wine, olive oil, dried fruit and flour. Other manufactures based on domestic agriculture are cigarettes, leather goods, textiles and paper. Large scale industrial development, with the emphasis on heavy industry, dates from independence in 1962. Modern concerns include oil refineries, gas liquefaction plants, an iron and steel complex at 'Annaba, fertilizer plants at Arzew and Annaba, a chemical factory, engineering works and cement plants. Algerian industry is 70% state-controlled.

Libya

Area
1,759,540 km²/679,358 sq miles
Location
19°—33°10′ N
9°10′—25° E
Population
3,085,000 (1981)
Population density
1.8 per km²/4.5 per sq mile
Capital and largest city
Tripoli: 860,000 (1981)
Language
Arabic
Major imports
machinery, foodstuffs, transport equipment, textiles, chemicals, building materials
Major exports
petroleum and petroleum products
Currency
dinar (1 dinar = 1,000 dirhams)
Gross National Product
26,080 million US dollars (1981)
Status
republic

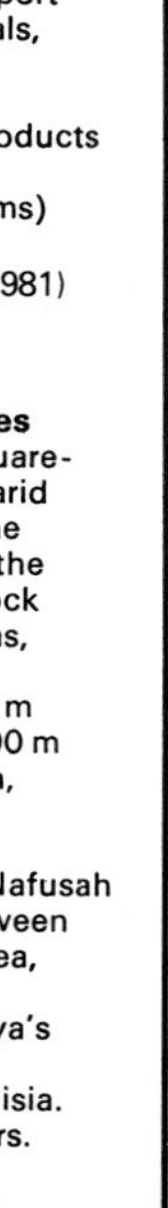

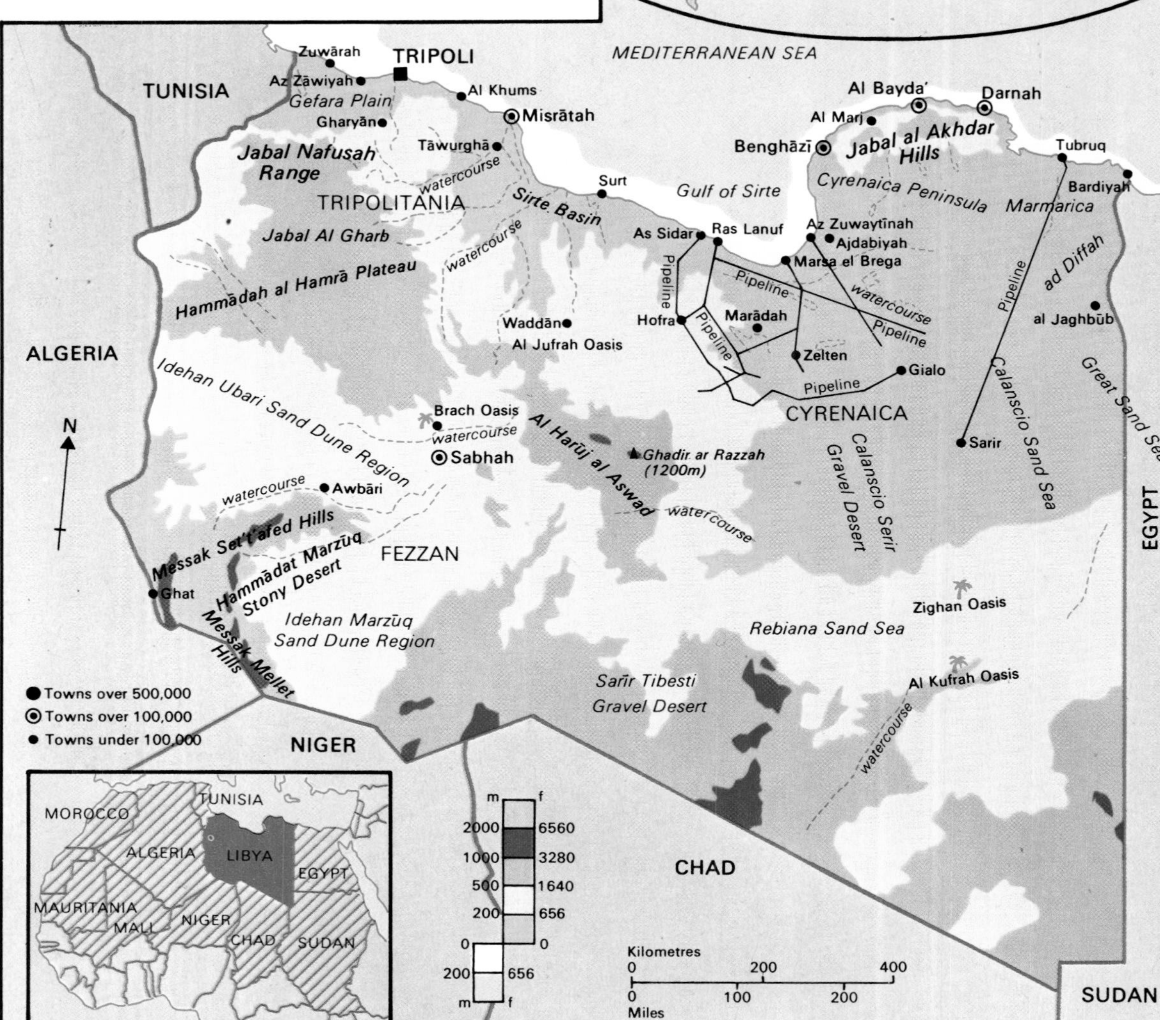

Physical features
Libya, roughly square-shaped, is a vast, arid land. Except for the Mediterranean coastal belt, the country consists of barren rock deserts, undulating sand seas, salt-marsh depressions and mountains that rise to 1,200 m in the southwest and to 1,800 m in the southeast. In the north, the coast is flanked by the Jabal al Akhdar hills in the northeast and by the Jabal Nafusah range in the northwest. Between the Jabal Nafusah and the sea, the coastal strip widens and forms the Gefara plain—Libya's most fertile zone—which extends westwards into Tunisia. There are no permanent rivers.

Climate
Climatically, Libya is influenced by both the Mediterranean and the Sahara. The coastal region has a Mediterranean climate: winters are mild with 25 to 40 cm of rain and summers hot and dry. Tripoli averages 13°C in January, 28°C in July. Conditions in the desert interior are extremely hot and arid: annual rainfall ranges from 0 to 12 cm and summer daytime temperatures rise to 45°C but fall at night to under 30°C. An unpleasant feature of the summer months (April to September) is the *ghibli*, a burning southerly wind that brings dust and sand storms and temperatures of over 50°C.

Crops
Arable land covers less than 2% of the total area and is confined to the Gefara plain, the lower slopes of the Jabal Nafusah and Jabal al Akhdar, the Cyrenaica peninsula coast (especially near Al Marj) and inland oases such as Al Kufrah, Brach and Al Jufrah. Farming is most intensive in the northwest: dates, olives, citrus, groundnuts, potatoes, melons and tomatoes are grown along the Gefara coast while further inland the plain supports wheat and barley (the main cereals), olives, vines, citrus and almonds. Olives, vines, figs, apricots, apples and tobacco thrive on the Jabal Nafusah. Vines, olives and dates are important in Cyrenaica and dates predominate in the oases. Libya is not self-sufficient in agriculture and food accounts for 30% of imports. Some olives, tomatoes, groundnuts and almonds are exported.

Irrigation
Since rainfall is negligible, irrigation is vital for Libyan agriculture. The Gefara plain is the most intensively irrigated area but there are other major irrigation and reclamation schemes in the Al Kufrah oasis, the Jabal al Akhdar, the Tāwurghā region, at Awbāri, Sarir and in the Brach/Sabhah district. There is also some irrigated land at oases in the south where wells penetrate underground water. Libya's groundwater resources are, however, limited and supplies for irrigation are reducing the water table.

Livestock
Before the discovery of oil, agriculture (in particular, livestock farming) was the basis of the economy: hides, skins and wool were leading exports. Animals are still important as three-quarters of Libya's productive land is suitable only for grazing. Nomads, accounting for 22% of the population, herd sheep and goats along the desert margins and products include meat, milk, wool and skins. Camels and donkeys are kept for draught purposes. Dairying is being developed on the northeast and northwest coastal belts.

Oil
Oil, discovered in 1957 has transformed Libya from a poor agricultural state into one of Africa's richest nations. Petroleum now dominates the Libyan economy and accounts for 97% of total exports. The most important fields are in the Sirte basin and include Zelten, Hofra, Gialo and Sarir. These are linked by pipeline to terminals at Tubruq, Ras Lanuf, As Sidar, Az Zuwaytīnah and Marsa el Brega. Libya is the leading oil producer in Africa and the fourth largest producer in the Middle East.

Mining
Libya's mineral resources are largely unsurveyed and unexploited. Marine salt is produced near Tripoli, natron (a sodium carbonate compound) is mined in the southwest and chalk, limestone and marble are quarried. Important iron ore reserves have been discovered in the southwest but other mineral deposits are less significant. These include potash and sulphur in the Sirte basin and potassium and magnesium salt in the Marādah region. Mining activity is hampered, however, by inadequate transport systems.

Fishing
Although Libya has a 1,900 km coastline, fishing is of limited importance. The industry is most developed in the northwest and is based at Misrātah, Zuwārah and Al Khums. The catch consists of tunny, mullet and sardine.

Industry
Ambitious programmes of industrialization financed by oil revenues are being checked by a lack of skilled labour, poor communications and a small domestic market. Traditionally, Libyan industry consists of processing local raw materials: manufactures include olive oil, cigarettes, matting, carpets, leather goods, flour, embroidered fabrics and paper (made from esparto grass which grows wild). Recently established industries produce cement, soft drinks, soap, detergents, textiles, petroleum and petrochemicals. Large-scale projects planned for the future cover foodstuffs (canned fruit and vegetables, date processing, dairy products), building materials (iron and steel, aluminium fittings, glass, bricks, cement), clothing, footwear and animal feedstuffs. Tripoli and Benghāzī are the chief industrial centres.

Transport
Libya's transport system is poor but is currently being developed. The 6,000 km road network includes two major highways: a coastal road links Tripoli and Benghāzī (and extends east to Alexandria and west to Tunis) and a route from Tripoli to Sabhah. Minor roads serve the Tripoli and Benghāzī regions and link the oil fields to the Gulf of Sirte ports. A highway to Al Kufrah is under construction and road links with Niger and Chad are planned. The railways have not been in operation since 1964. Tripoli is the main port followed by Benghāzī, Darnah and Tubruq. Libyan Arab Airlines operate international flights from Tripoli and Benghāzī.

Cities
Most Libyans live on the coastal plains in the northwest and northeast and 25% of the population is concentrated in the two main cities: Tripoli and Benghāzī. Tripoli, founded by the Phoenicians, is the administrative, commercial and industrial capital and a major tourist centre. Benghāzī (370,000) is also industrialized. The third largest town is Misrātah (194,000).

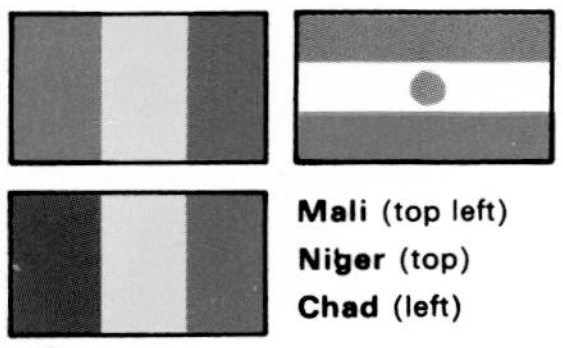

Mali, Niger and Chad

Mali (top left)
Niger (top)
Chad (left)

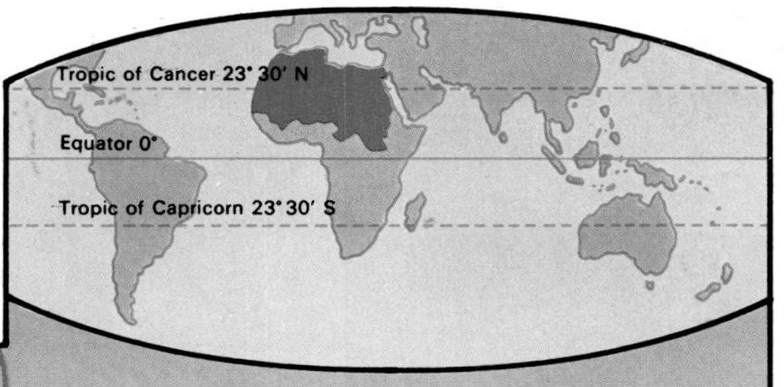

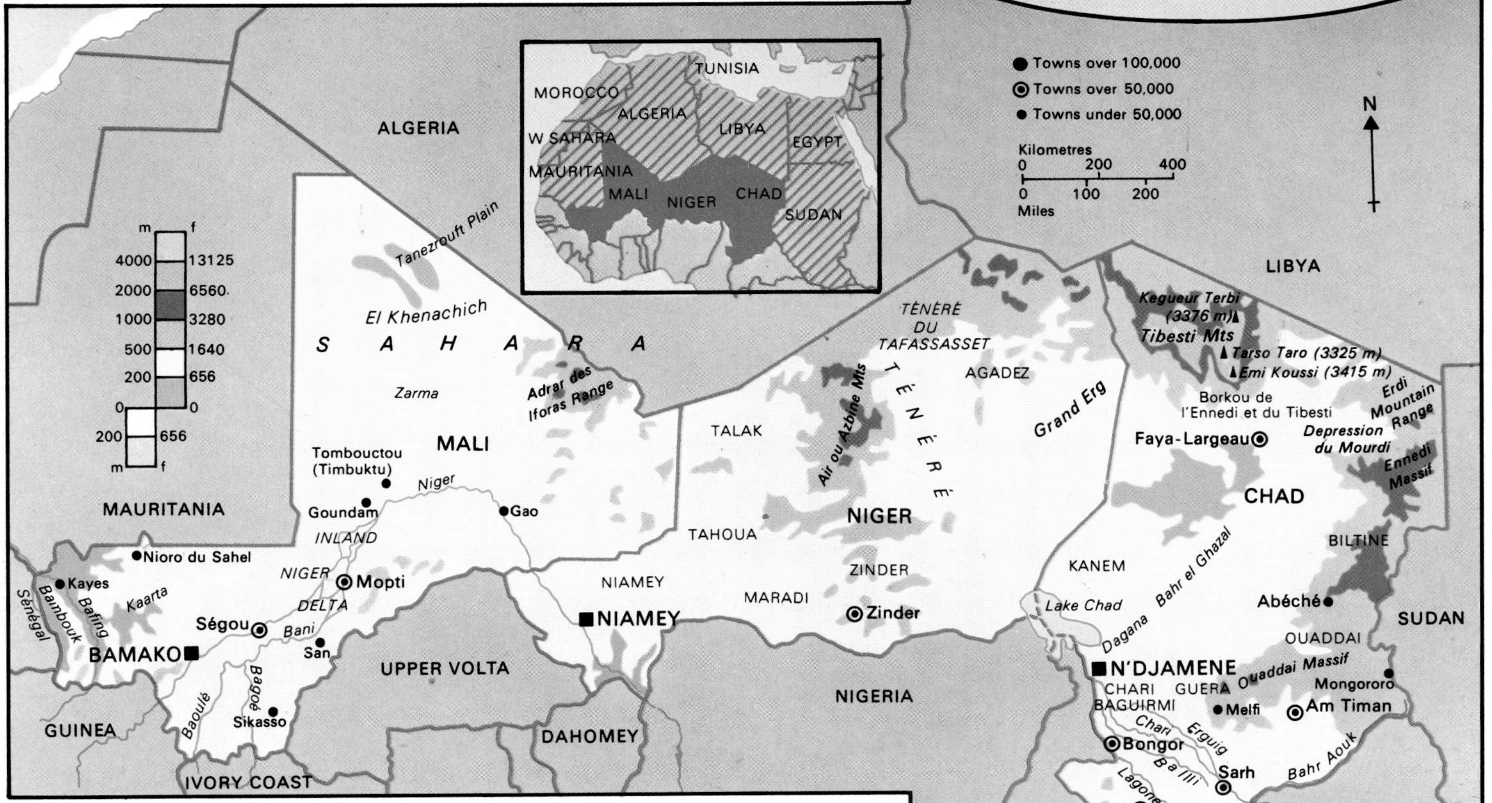

Mali
Area
1,240,000 km²/478,767 sq miles
Location
10°6′—25°N
12°10′W—4°15′E
Population
6,881,000 (1981)
Population density
6 per km²/14 per sq mile
Capital and largest city
Bamako: 620,000 (1981)
Language
French
Major imports
foodstuffs, machinery, vehicles, fuels, chemicals
Major exports
cotton, livestock, groundnuts, vegetable oils, dried fish
Currency
franc (1 franc = 100 centimes)
Gross National Product
1,340 million US dollars (1981)
Status
republic

Mali: the land
Mali is a vast land-locked state. The northern half of the country is part of the Sahara and consists of gravel-covered plateaux and great sand seas. The Adrar des Iforas range, rising to over 1,000 m, dominates the northeastern corner. Southern Mali is crossed by the Niger—in its middle section, between Ségou and Tombouctou, the river splits into numerous channels and flows through a swampy shallow basin, called the Inland Niger Delta, which floods annually. The mountainous southwest is drained by the Sénégal. Mali has a hot, arid climate. In the desert, temperatures reach 60°C and rainfall is negligible; the south is cooler and wetter with temperatures of 30°C and 75 cm of rain falling June to October.

The economy
Arable farming is mainly confined to irrigated areas in the Niger delta. The main food crops are millet, rice and sorghum; maize, yams and cassava are also grown. Cotton and groundnuts are the chief cash crops and sugar-cane and tobacco are being developed. Livestock (cattle, sheep and goats) is important, particularly in central Mali. There is extensive fishing on the Niger and 20% of the catch is exported. Limestone and marble are quarried but known deposits of other minerals, such as iron, bauxite, manganese, phosphates and gold, have yet to be exploited. Industry, based on local produce, is small-scale and includes rice-milling, sugar-refining, groundnut oil extraction, cotton-ginning and cement manufacture.

Niger
Area
1,267,000 km²/489,190 sq miles
Location
11°40′—23°28′N
0°20′—16°E
Population
5,704,000 (1981)
Population density
4.5 per km²/12 per sq mile
Capital and largest city
Niamey: 300,000 (1982)
Language
French
Major imports
vehicles, textiles, fuels, food, machinery, iron and steel
Major exports
uranium, live animals, groundnuts and groundnut oil, cotton
Currency
franc (1 franc = 100 centimes)
Gross National Product
1,890 million US dollars (1981)
Status
republic

Niger: the land
Landlocked Niger is two-thirds desert; in the north centre the monotony of the Saharan landscape is broken by the volcanic Air ou Azbine mountains rising to nearly 2,000 m. The country is lowest around Lake Chad in the southeast and along the river Niger valley in the southwest. Niger is hot (Niamey averages 35°C) and dry: annual rainfall decreases from 56 cm along the Nigerian border to 18 cm in the centre.

Agriculture
Arable land, covering only 3% of the country, is located in the south on the sandy soils of the Nigerian border and along the Niger valley (irrigated by seasonal flooding). Food crops include millet, sorghum and, to a lesser extent, maize, cassava, onions and rice. The main cash crops are groundnuts and cotton. Cattle are grazed on the pastures in the Niger valley with sheep and goats kept on the desert margins. Half the fish catch, from the Niger and Lake Chad, is exported.

Mining & industry
Uranium, mined at Arlit, is Niger's leading export. Some salt and tin are also produced in the Air ou Azbine. Other mineral resources, including iron ore from Say and gypsum and phosphates at Tahoua, are still unexploited. Rice mills, flour mills, cotton ginneries, slaughter houses, tanneries and groundnut oil extraction plants all rely on domestic agricultural produce. Newer projects include a textile factory, a cement works and some light industries.

Chad
Area
1,284,000 km²/495,750 sq miles
Location
7°25′—23°28′N
15°—24°E
Population
4,549,000 (1981)
Population density
3.5 per km²/9 per sq mile
Capital and largest city
N'Djamene: 303,000 (1979)
Language
French
Major imports
fuels, foodstuffs, vehicles, minerals, textiles, machinery
Major exports
cotton, meat, livestock, hides and skins
Currency
franc (1 franc = 100 centimes)
Gross National Product
490 million US dollars (1981)
Status
republic

Chad: the land
Chad is named after the lake on its western border. Lake Chad (16,000 km²) is marshy with an average depth of only 4 m. It is fed by the Chari and Logone—the only rivers to be used for irrigation and navigation. From the lake, at an altitude of 250 m, the country fans out forming a great basin rimmed by the Tibesti mountains (3,400 m) in the north and by the Ennedi and Ouaddai massifs in the northeast and east. Temperatures average 28°C; rainfall ranges from 120 cm in the extreme south to 2 cm at Faya.

Agriculture
Agriculture forms the basis of the Chad economy and most people live by farming and stock-raising. Arable land is limited to the southern part of the country. Sorghum, millet and rice are produced for food, while cotton and groundnuts are the leading cash crops. Wheat, maize, cassava, sugar-cane and tobacco are also grown; dates predominate in the northern oases. Cattle graze on the open grasslands of central Chad and sheep, goats and camels are herded in the more northerly, arid zone. The rivers Chari and Logone and Lake Chad are rich in fish which is dried and either sold locally or exported.

Mining & industry
Chad's mineral resources are mostly unsurveyed. Natron, produced in the Lake Chad region, is the only mineral of commercial significance. It is used as salt for human consumption, for preserving meat and skins and in soap production. There is little manufacturing. Cotton-ginning is the main industrial activity. Other concerns include a sugar refinery, textile mill, abattoirs, flour and rice mills, groundnut oil extraction plants and a bicycle-assembly works. In Chad, as in Mali and Niger, transport is a major problem—roads are few and railways non-existent. All three countries are land-locked and far from any port. This hinders foreign trade.

Egypt

Area
1,002,000 km²/386,873 sq miles
Location
22°—31°35′ N
25°—35°40′ E
Population
43,290,000 (1981)
Population density
43 per km²/112 per sq mile
Capital and largest city
Cairo: 11,000,000 (1981)
Language
Arabic
Major imports
foodstuffs, machinery, chemicals, transport equipment
Major exports
cotton, rice, cement, phosphates, petroleum and products, onions
Currency
pound (1 pound = 100 piastres)
Gross National Product
28,160 million US dollars (1981)
Status
republic

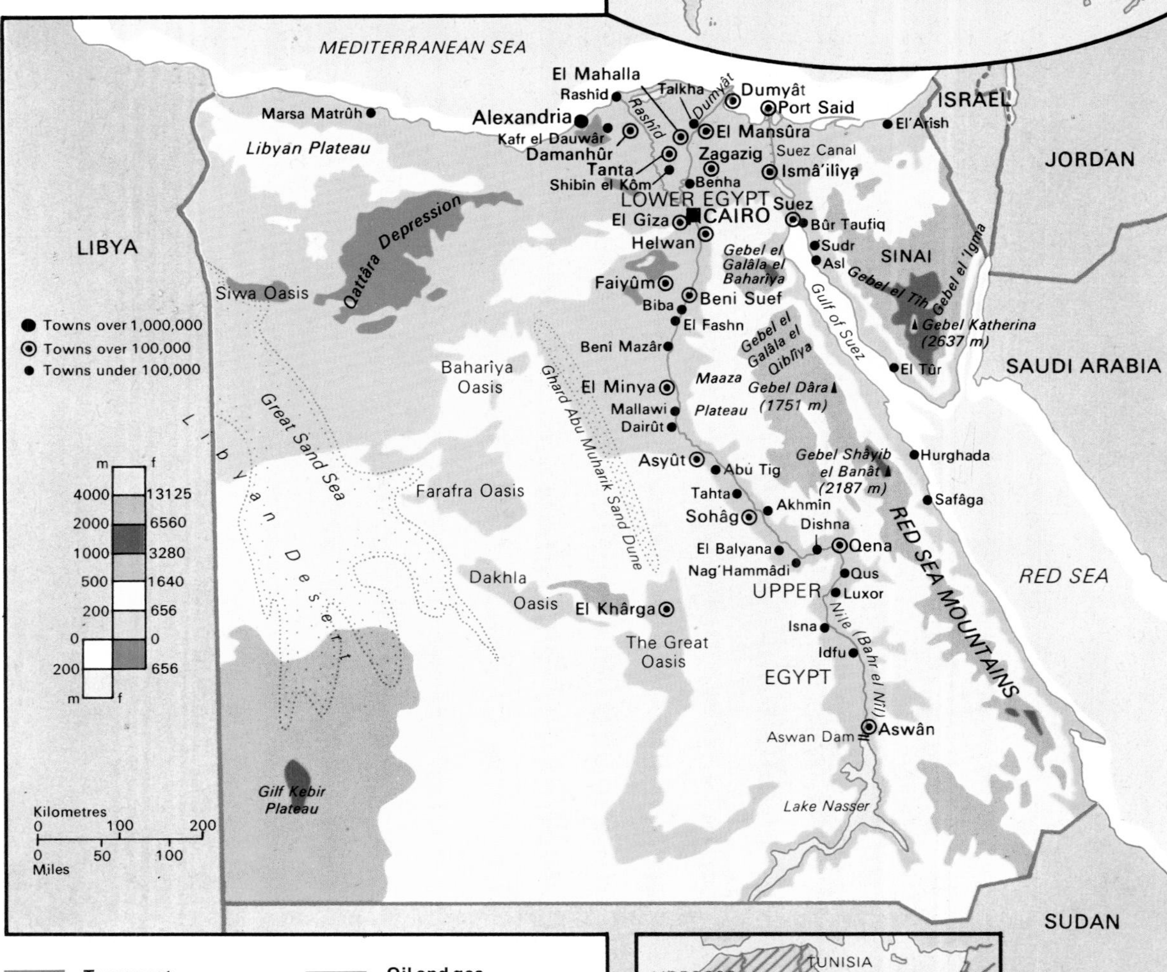

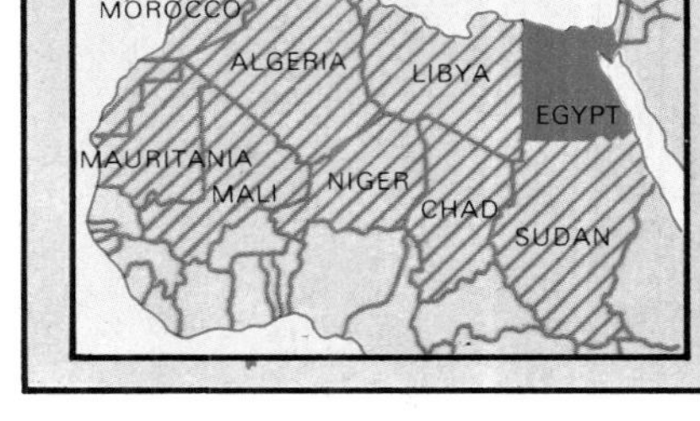

Physical features

About 96% of Egypt is desert. The area west of the Nile is an arid plateau some 200 m high, crossed by belts of sand dunes in the centre and west. There are also several depressions with accessible underground water which are cultivated and settled such as the Qattâra Depression and the oases of Baharîya, Siwa, Farafra, Dakhla and Khârga. The desert extends east of the Nile to the Red Sea mountains, a coastal range 1,500 to 2,000 m high. To the northwest, these highlands give way to a barren limestone plateau which stretches east into Sinai; southern Sinai is mountainous, rising to 2,637 m in Gebel Katherîna. The Nile is Egypt's most important feature. For 300 km from the Sudanese border, the narrow valley is flooded by Lake Nasser formed by the giant Aswan dam. Below Aswân, the valley widens—this is a densely populated region. The Nile divides 25 km north of Cairo into the Rashîd and Dumyât—the two main channels of the 22,000 km² delta. The alluvial deltaic plain is fringed with lagoons and swamps along the coast.

Climate

Egypt is very hot and dry. In summer (May to October) temperatures rise to 37°C in Cairo and 43°C in the desert during the day, but at night can drop by as much as 20°C. Winter is slightly cooler with midday averages of 21°C in the north and 27°C in the south. Rainfall is minimal: Cairo receives only 6 cm annually, while the desert often has no rain at all. The prevailing wind is northerly, but in March and April hot winds from the Sahara bring scorching sandstorms. The Mediterranean coast is milder and wetter with 25 cm of rain a year.

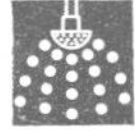

Irrigation

Irrigation is vital to Egyptian agriculture. The Nile is the basic source of water and, with the aid of dams and barrages, supplies an extensive network of distributary canals. The most important scheme is the Aswan dam which holds back valuable flood water. In desert oases, wells reach the underlying water table.

Transport

Transport systems, centred on Cairo, are well developed in the Nile delta and valley. The 25,000 km road network includes major highways from the capital to Alexandria, Port Said, Ismâ'ilîya, Suez and Aswan. Railways, totalling 4,300 km, serve the delta and run south to Aswân; there is also a line linking the Baharîya iron ore mines to Helwan. There is considerable inland shipping on the delta waterways and the Nile. The Suez canal, closed from 1967 to 1975, is being deepened and widened. About 80% of Egypt's imports and exports pass through Alexandria, the chief seaport. Port Said is the other main Mediterranean port, while Suez handles trade with the Far East. The national airline, Egyptair, operates domestic and overseas services; there are international airports at Cairo, Alexandria, Luxor, Aswân and Marsa Matrûn.

Mining

Phosphates, iron ore, manganese, salt and asbestos are the chief minerals exploited in Egypt. The main phosphate reserves are in the eastern desert and on the Red Sea coast, particularly near Isna and Safâga. Iron ore is mined east of Aswân and in the Baharîya oasis area. There are manganese deposits east of Luxor and in southwestern Sinai. Other minerals worked in small quantities include gypsum, talc, lead-zinc and tungsten; there are adequate supplies of building stones.

Oil and gas

Petroleum makes a significant contribution to the economy: Egypt is now self-sufficient in oil and has moved into the export market. The total annual output is 18 million tonnes: 60% of this comes from off-shore fields in the Gulf of Suez; the bulk of the remainder is produced along the western shore of the Gulf of Suez. There are also oilfields in Sinai. Refineries are situated in Suez, Mostorod, Tanta and Alexandria and a pipeline is under construction from Suez to Alexandria. Natural gas, from fields in the delta and the western desert, is used to power industries in Helwan and Talkha. Oil, however, is the country's principal source of energy followed by hydro-electric power.

Cities

Cairo, the 'city of victory', was built in 968 at the head of the Nile delta. The largest city in Africa and the Middle East, it contains some of Islam's finest architecture and also has a priceless collection of Pharaonic treasures in the Egyptian Museum. There is some manufacturing in the city, but heavy industry is concentrated at Helwan. Alexandria (2,520,000), at the western edge of the delta, was founded by Alexander the Great in 332 BC. The ruins of its famous lighthouse (one of the Seven Wonders of the World) can still be seen. It is Egypt's main industrial centre and leading port with a canal link to the Nile.

Agriculture

Agriculture is the main sector of the economy: it employs over half the workforce and provides 50% of exports. Although farmland, confined to the Nile valley, delta and oases, covers only 5% of the total area, most of it yields two or three crops a year. The main crop is cotton, grown on 14% of the cultivated area; Egypt leads the world in the production of long-staple cotton. Egypt also ranks as the world's third largest rice exporter. Ricefields, accounting for 10% of farmland, are mainly in the delta region. The leading food crops are wheat and maize and the country is self-sufficient in cereals. Other crops include sugarcane, millet, barley, beans, onions, potatoes, citrus and dates. Livestock farming is being developed in order to supply domestic meat and milk requirements. Cattle and buffaloes are also kept as draught animals and nomads herd sheep and goats in the desert. There is local fishing along the Nile and coast.

Industry

Manufacturing is steadily developing and now accounts for 14% of employment and 35% of exports. Industry is largely located in the delta region—the main centres being Helwan, Shubrâ el Kheima (a Cairo suburb), Mahalla el Kubra, Kafr el Dauwâr and Alexandria. There is also some development in the Suez canal zone. Textile manufacture, using cotton, wool, silk and artificial fibres, is the leading sector and supplies 30% of the total industrial output. It is based on Mahalla el Kubra, Kafr el Dauwâr and Shubrâ el Kheima. Food-processing is next in importance: this includes flour-milling, sugar-refining and fruit and vegetable-canning. Other major industrial products include cement (Cairo, Alexandria), iron and steel (Helwan), petro-chemicals (Suez), engineering (Helwan), fertilizers (Talkha) and aluminium (Nag'Hammâdi). Tourism is growing and new resorts are planned for Marsa Matrûh and the Pyramids (Gîza).

Sudan

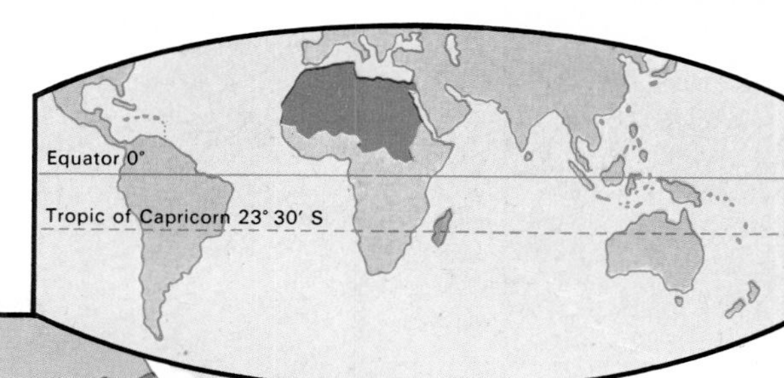

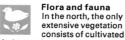

Flora and fauna

In the north, the only extensive vegetation consists of cultivated fruit trees (mostly date palms) along the Nile and in oases. The desert gives way to a broad belt of savanna which in turn gives way to stretches of equatorial rain forest and vast expanses of elephant grass. Papyrus, in the Sudd swamp, grows up to 5 m high. Except for antelope, addax and ostrich, there is little life in the desert, but the savanna and southern forests are the home of many animals including elephants, giraffes, buffaloes, hippopotami, crocodiles, leopards, lions, hyenas and white and black rhinoceros.

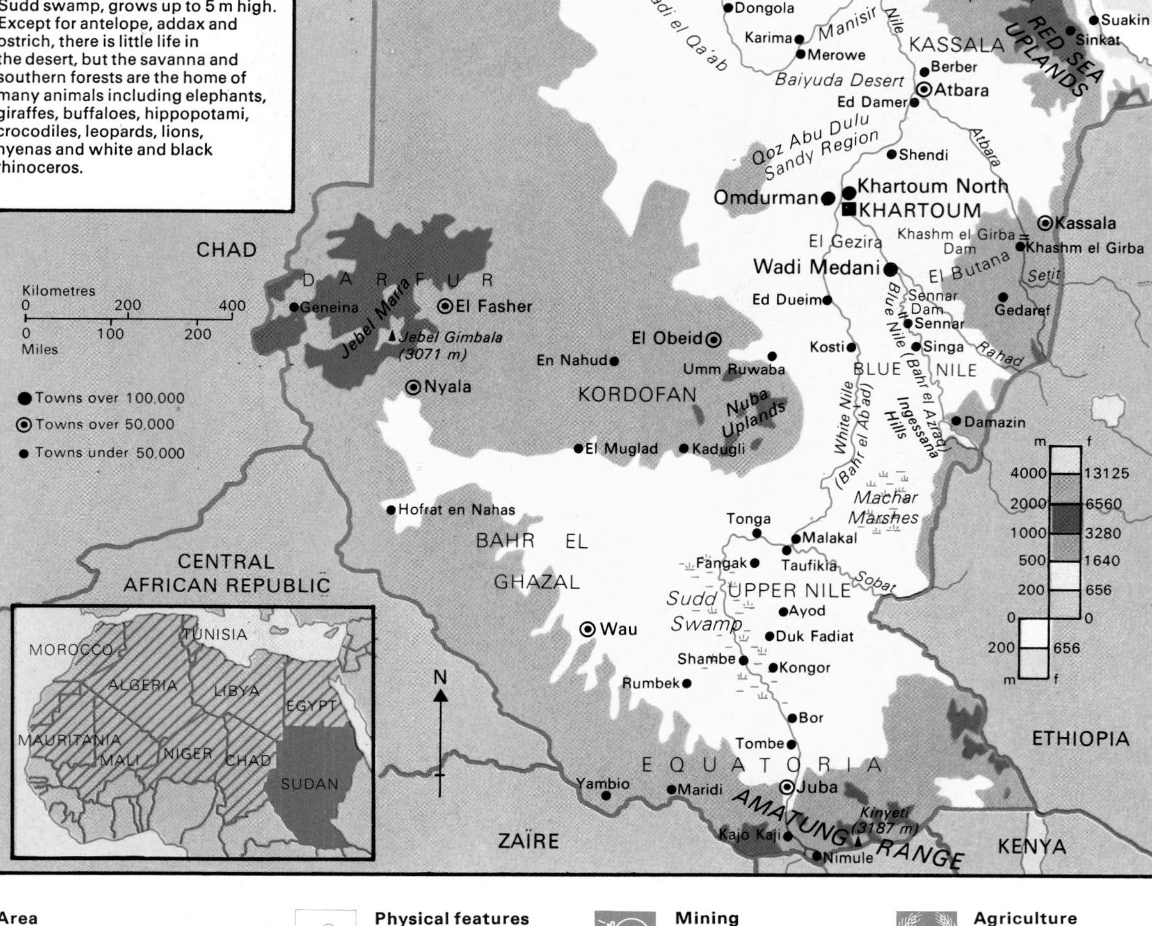

Area
2,505,824 km²/967,500 sq miles
Location
3°40′—22°N
21°50′—38°30′ E
Population
19,242,000 (1981)
Population density
8 per km²/20 per sq mile
Capital
Khartoum: 334,000
Language
Arabic
Major imports
machinery, vehicles, textiles, metals, chemicals, petroleum
Major exports
cotton, gum arabic, sesame, groundnuts, animal feeds, hides and skins
Currency
pound (1 pound = 100 piastres)
Gross National Product
7,390 million US dollars (1973)
republic

Tourism

A growing number of tourists visit Sudan each year. Attractions include big game hunting and photo safaris, archeological remains in the Nile valley (some dating from 4,000 BC), fishing and skin-diving in the Red Sea.

Physical features

Sudan, the largest state in Africa, has only 640 km of coast-line and that is situated along the Red Sea. Most of the country consists of a vast plateau which is crossed by the Nile and edged by mountains on the east, south and west. The foothills of the Ethiopian plateau extend along the eastern border and the Red Sea coast; the southern Amatung range contains the country's highest peak, Kinyeti (3,187 m), and in the extreme west the Jebel Marra massif rises to 3,071 m. The Nubian desert is an extension of the Sahara which occupies a third of the territory in the north. A huge papyrus swamp, the Sudd, created by the seasonal flooding of the White Nile and its tributaries covers southern Sudan. The Sudd, one of the largest swamps in the world, acts as a reservoir and the flow of the White Nile is consequently relatively even throughout the year. In contrast, rivers draining the Ethiopian highlands (the Sobat, Blue Nile and Atbara) are torrential during the rainy season but otherwise almost dry. The White and Blue Niles meet at Khartoum to form the Nile.

Mining

The mineral resources of Sudan are largely unexploited. There is limited production of iron ore in the Red Sea uplands, chromite in the Ingessana hills, copper at Hofrat en Nahas and gold near Wadi Halfa and in Kassala province. Deposits of mica, manganese and quartz are also worked and marble is quarried in the Red Sea hills. Output from the salt pans at Port Sudan meets domestic requirements and provides a surplus for export. Other minerals known to exist include lead, asbestos, barites, zinc, graphite, sulphur, talc, gypsum and oil (discovered in the Red Sea). Minerals account for less than 1% of total exports: salt is most important, but some copper, iron, mica, manganese and chromite are also exported.

Forestry

The central savanna is largely composed of acacia trees which provide Sudan with its second most important export: gum arabic. Sudan supplies over 90% of the world's gum arabic, used in the manufacture of perfume, confectionery and adhesives.

Agriculture

Agriculture dominates the Sudanese economy. Although less than 5% of the land is farmed, the country is self-sufficient in basic foods and Sudan's chief exports are agricultural products. About 15% of arable land is irrigated. The main irrigation scheme, using water from the Sennar Dam on the Blue Nile, is in El Gezira while another major project based on the new Khashm el Girba dam on the Atbara, serves the El Butana region which now specializes in sugarcane. Cotton is the principal cash crop: long-staple varieties are grown under irrigation, especially in El Gezira; short-staple cotton, cultivated in the extreme south and the Nuba uplands, is rainfed. Other crops include wheat, maize, sesame, groundnuts, millet, oilseeds, sorghum, dates, citrus and mangoes. Tea, coffee, rice and tobacco are being developed in the south. Livestock is important: nomads rear camels, sheep and goats in the north, cattle in the south. Cotton accounts for 60% of total exports; groundnuts, sesame, hides and skins are also exported. There is fishing along the Red Sea coast.

Climate

As Sudan lies wholly in the Tropics and is almost completely land-locked, it has a tropical, continental climate. Maritime influences from the Red Sea are confined to the coastal plain and the eastern slopes of the Red Sea hills. Temperatures are always high: in Khartoum they range from 32°C in winter (November—March) to 41°C in summer (April—June). Rainfall increases from under 5 cm in the north to 150 cm in the south. The rainy season corresponds to July—October in the centre, but lengthens to March—October in the south. In the Nubian desert, dry northerly winds prevail and sandstorms are common.

Industry

Sudan is primarily an agricultural country and manufacturing is underdeveloped. Sudanese industry is mainly concerned with processing agricultural raw materials for the domestic market. There are flour-mills, canning plants, textile mills, tanneries and soap factories. The principal industries centred on the overseas market are cotton-ginning, groundnut-shelling and date-processing. By 1980, Sudan aims to export sugar and textiles: the most important sugar factory is at Khashm el Girba, while new textile plants are being built with foreign aid. Industrial growth is hampered by inadequate power supplies although some industries (cotton-ginning, sugar and oil processing) generate their own electricity from by-products. Although all major towns are supplied, many parts of Sudan are without electricity.

Transport

Sudan has an inadequate transport system. Most of the roads are cleared tracks which become impassable after rain. There are only 330 km of surfaced roads and 60% of these are in the Khartoum area. The 4,750 km rail network connects the major centres and is used for nearly all freight movements. There is all-year shipping on the Nile between Kosti and Juba and between Dongola and Karima; other routes are seasonal. Port Sudan, the only seaport, is to be developed following the re-opening of the Suez canal. Sudan Airways operates international and domestic services. A petroleum pipeline links Khartoum to Port Sudan.

Cities

The population is unevenly distributed: half the country is uninhabited and most Sudanese live in the Nile valley, Khartoum and the provincial capitals. Khartoum is three cities in one. The old town, Khartoum (meaning 'elephant trunk' after the shape of its site), was a centre of the slave and ivory trade in the last century. On its northeast side is Omdurman (300,000), a commercial centre famous for its livestock market. Across the river to the north of the old city is the industrial town of Khartoum North (150,000).

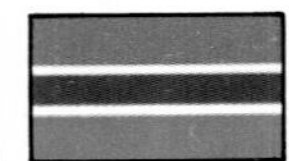
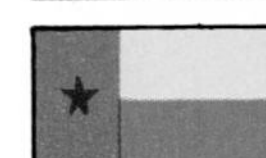

Senegal (top left)
Gambia (top)
Guinea Bissau (left)

Senegal, Gambia and Guinea Bissau

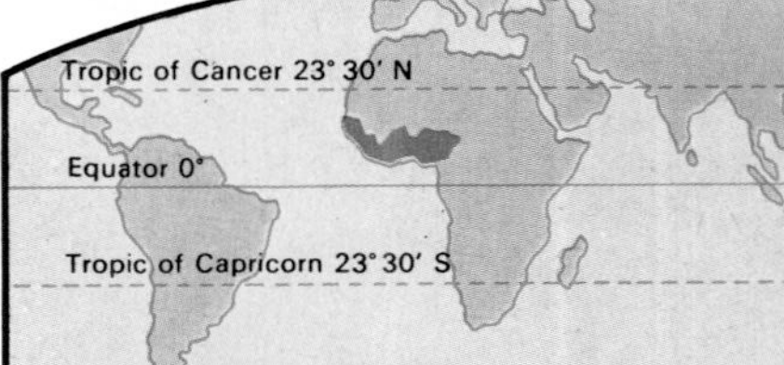

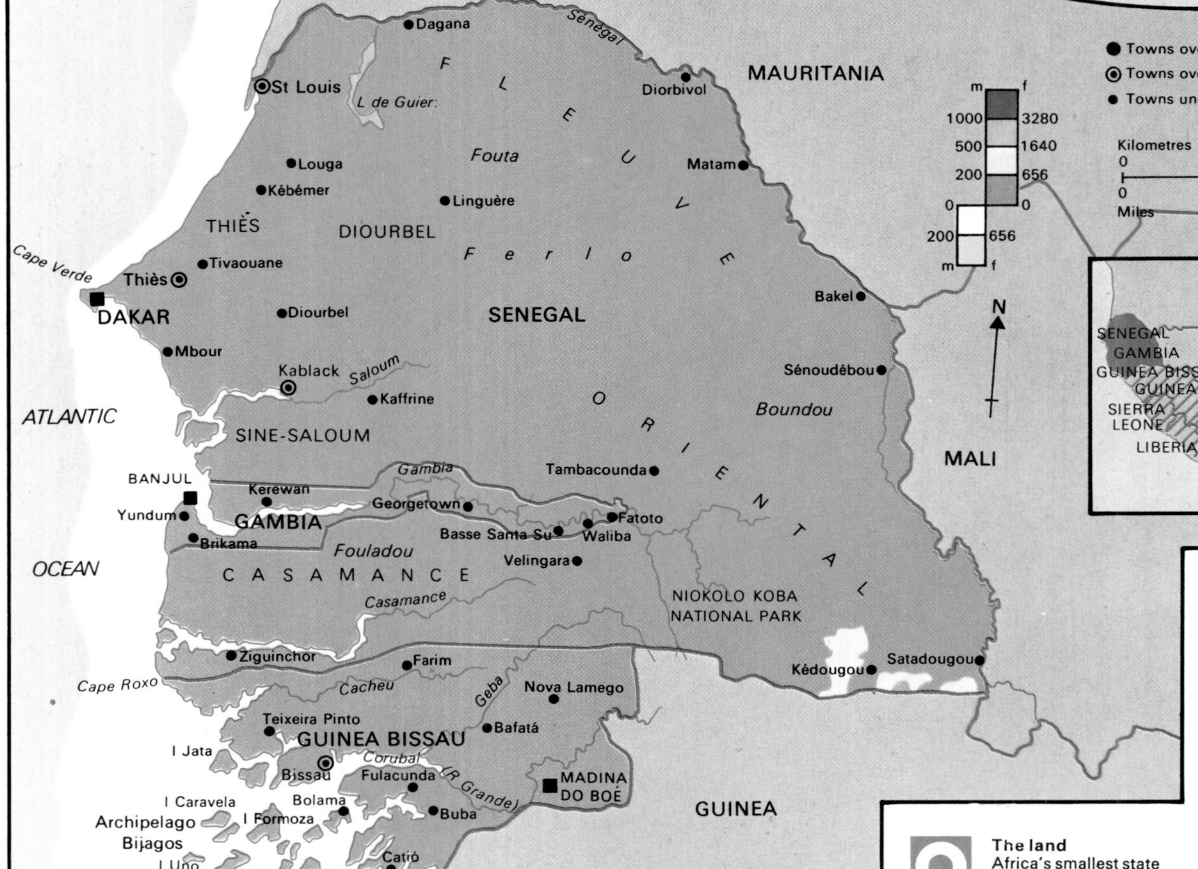

Senegal
Area
196,192 km²/75,750 sq miles
Location
12°20′—16°30′ N
11°20′—17°33′ W
Population
5,862,000 (1981)
Population density
30 per km²/77 per sq mile
Capital and largest city
Dakar: 980,000 (1980)
Language
French
Major imports
foodstuffs, machinery, petroleum products, vehicles
Major exports
groundnut oil, oilseed cake, phosphates, fish, cotton textiles
Currency
franc (1 franc = 100 centimes)
Gross National Product
2,530 million US dollars (1981)
Status
republic

The land
Except for uplands along the east and south-east borders, Senegal consists of monotonous, low-lying plains crossed by the wide valleys of the Casamance, Gambia, Saloum and Sénégal rivers. Sand dunes and swamps fringe the Atlantic while Cape Verde (Africa's most westerly point) is of volcanic origin. Inland, Senegal is hot (29°C) and, in the south, has up to 160 cm of rain (wet season: June to October). The coast is much cooler (22°C) and drier (average annual rainfall is 50 cm).

Industry & mining
Rich deposits of lime and aluminium phosphates near Thiès provide Senegal with a valuable export. Small quantities of ilmenite, zircon, rutile and sea salt are also produced and some limestone is quarried. Processing domestic raw materials accounts for 90% of manufacturing. Groundnut oil extraction, employing 25% of the industrial workforce, is the main industry but others produce flour, sugar, canned fish, cement, cotton textiles and shoes. Chemical, metallurgical and engineering industries are being developed. Dakar is the chief industrial area.

Transport
Senegal's 13,300 km road network includes major routes to neighbouring countries and the trans-Gambian highway from Ziguinchor to Kaolack. There are five main railway lines totalling 1,200 km. River traffic is important on the Sénégal, Saloum and Casamance. Dakar is the main seaport and has an international airport; Air Afrique (jointly owned by eleven African countries) flies overseas while Air Senegal operates internally.

Agriculture
Groundnuts dominate the economy: they are grown on 50% of the cultivated area and provide 75% of export earnings. Cotton is being developed as a second cash crop. The main food crops are millet, sorghum and rice with cassava, maize, sugar-cane, fruit and vegetables also grown. Cattle, sheep and goats are raised in the drier northern region. Fish, from rivers and sea, supplement the national diet and are also processed for export. Some gum arabic is produced.

Gambia
Area
11,371 km²/4,265 sq miles
Location
13°10′—13°50′ N
13°50′—16°50′ W
Population
587,000 (1981)
Population density
52 per km²/138 per sq mile
Capital and largest city
Banjul: 40,000 (1982)
Language
English
Major imports
foodstuffs, textiles, machinery, transport equipment, fuels
Major exports
groundnuts, groundnut oil, oilseed cake, palm kernels, fish
Currency
dalasi (1 dalasi = 100 butut)
Gross National Product
220 million US dollars
Status
republic

The land
Africa's smallest state is a narrow strip bordering the navigable section of the Gambia river. The country extends east for 320 km and has an average width of 35 km, broadening at the estuary to 48 km. The river banks are edged with mangrove swamps, backed by seasonally flooded grasslands called *banto faros*; behind these lie low sandy plateaux. The coast, with its palm-fringed beaches, is the centre of an expanding tourist industry. The climate is hot and dry with a short, intense wet season in summer. Banjul averages 25°C and has 125 cm of rain. Inland temperatures reach 28°C.

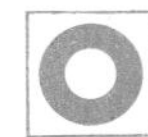

The economy
Gambia is economically dependent on groundnuts. This one cash crop, grown on the sandy uplands, accounts for 70% of the cultivated area and provides 95% of total exports. Food crop production (sorghum, millet and maize) is also centred on the higher, flood-free zone and rice cultivation is being developed in the banto faros. There is some fishing for shad, shrimp and prawns. Apart from groundnut shelling and oil extraction, other concerns (mostly in Banjul) are small-scale—these include fish processing and cotton-spinning and weaving. The river, navigable to Fatoto, is the main highway; ocean-going vessels reach Georgetown. Transport is otherwise poor: there are no railways or internal air services and few all-weather roads. Banjul is the main seaport and the country's international airport is at Yundum.

Guinea-Bissau
Area
36,125 km²/13,948 sq miles
Location
11°—12°40′ N
13°40′—16°45′ W
Population
790,000 (1981)
Population density
22 per km²/57 per sq mile
Capital
Madina do Boé
Largest city
Bissau: 110,000 (1979)
Language
Portuguese
Major imports
rice, textiles, fuels
Major exports
palm kernels, groundnuts, timber
Currency
escudo (1 escudo = 100 centavos)
Gross National Product
150 million US dollars (1981)
Status
republic

The land
The coast with its shallow, drowned estuaries, mangrove swamps and palm trees, is backed by a plain rising to a low, savanna-covered plateau. Near the Guinea border, uplands reach 300 m. Islands, including the Bijagos archipelago, lie offshore. The main rivers (Cacheu, Geba and Corubal) are also major routeways. Guinea-Bissau is hot and wet: temperatures average 26°C and rainfall, occuring May to October, is over 200 cm.

The economy
Guinea-Bissau is an agricultural country. The staple crop is rice, grown in the coastal swamps and along flooded river valleys. Other food crops are maize, beans, cassava and coconuts. The main agricultural exports are groundnuts (grown in the interior) and oil-palm products (from the coast and islands). Livestock is kept on the plateau. Oil and bauxite have been discovered but remain unexploited. Except for some food processing, there is little industry. Waterway transport is important as there are no railways and few roads. Bissau is the main port and has an international airport.

Guinea & Sierra Leone

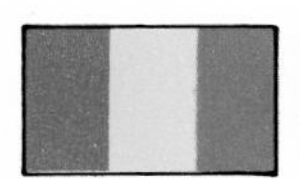
Guinea

Sierra Leone

Sierra Leone
Area
72,325 km²/27,925 sq miles
Location
6°55′—10° N
10°15′—13°20′ W
Population
3,574,000 (1981)
Population density
49 per km²/128 per sq mile
Capital and largest city
Freetown: 500,000 (1980)
Language
English
Major imports
textiles, machinery, foodstuffs, vehicles, chemicals, fuels
Major exports
diamonds, iron ore, coffee, cocoa beans, palm kernels, bauxite
Currency
leone (1 leone = 100 cents)
Gross National Product
1,140 million US dollars (1981)
Status
republic

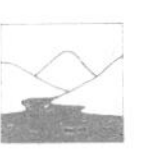

Physical features
Sierra Leone's 340-km-long coast is low lying except where the rocky Freetown peninsula rises to 900 m. The coastal plain, crossed by the rivers Moa, Sewa, Jong, Rokel, Great and Little Scarcies, is characterized by mangrove swamps, grasslands and rain forests; the plain stretches inland for 100 km then climbs to a plateau 450 m high with savanna and woodlands. Near the eastern border, mountains reach heights of over 1,750 m.

Climate
The climate is tropical with an average temperature of 26°C and marked wet and dry seasons. During the wet season (May to October) over 300 cm is recorded. From December to February (in the middle of the dry season) the northeasterly *harmattan wind* lowers temperatures and brings a haze of very fine dust across from the Sahara.

Mining
Minerals (diamonds, iron ore, bauxite and rutile) account for 85% of total exports. Diamonds are found mostly in river gravels in the southeast and east. Iron ore, mined near Marampa, is exported via Pepel. Sierra Leone's reserves of bauxite and rutile are among the largest in the world; exports are shipped from Bonthe. Chromium, gold, platinum and molybdenum have also been discovered.

Industry
There is little industry. Freetown has a few factories producing goods such as cigarettes, soap, textiles, shoes, biscuits, sweets, beverages, plastics and paper for the domestic market. In the rest of the country, industry is concerned with processing agricultural and forest products including palm oil extraction, rice milling, fish canning and furniture construction. Among traditional village activities are fish curing and smoking, hand weaving and leatherwork.

Transport
Rivers are a vital element in Sierra Leone's transport system and are used extensively for carrying freight. The 8,000 km road network is only 10% hard-surfaced. Railways have been closed with the exception of a line from the Marampa mine to Pepel port. Freetown is the leading port, handling all imports and agricultural exports. Sierra Leone Airways flies internally and overseas from Freetown international airport.

Agriculture
Agriculture employs 75% of Sierra Leoneans. Rice is the chief food crop, followed by sorghum, millet, groundnuts, cassava and maize. Export crops are coffee, cocoa beans, palm kernels, kola nuts, ginger and piassava (a fibre obtained from the leaf stalks of certain palms). Cattle raising is important in the north, while poultry, eggs and pork are produced on the Freetown peninsula. The forests yield lumber—mainly mahogany. Canoe-based fishing for bonga and sardines is significant.

Guinea
Area
245,857 km²/95,000 sq miles
Location
7°20′—12°40′ N
7°40′—15° W
Population
5,571,000 (1981)
Population density
23 per km²/59 per sq mile
Capital and largest city
Conakry: 575,000 (1980)
Language
French
Major imports
textiles, fuels, rice, machinery and metals
Major exports
alumina (Al_2O_3), pineapples, palm kernels, coffee, bananas
Currency
syli
Gross National Product
1,660 million US dollars (1981)
Status
republic

Guinea: the land
The coast, with its swamps and shallow estuaries, is backed by a plain some 60 km wide. Beyond the plain, the Fouta Djallon rises to over 1,000 m comprising a level plateau dissected by deep valleys. This great sandstone block gives birth to West Africa's three main rivers: the Niger, Gambia and Sénégal. Smaller rivers, such as the Fatala and Konkoure, flow west into the Atlantic Ocean. Grasslands, drained by the Niger, lie to the east; in the extreme southeast, the isolated Guinea Highlands reach 1,768 m at Mt Nimba. The climate is hot and wet. Conakry averages 27°C and has 430 cm of rain between April and October. The Fouta Djallon is drier (180 cm) and slightly cooler (25°C), but on the Niger plain temperatures rise to 40°C.

Agriculture
Agriculture is mainly concentrated along the coast and in the fertile valleys of the Fouta Djallon. The leading cash crops are pineapples, coffee, palm kernels, bananas and citrus. Rice, grown in the coastal swamps and in the flooded valleys of the Niger plain, is the staple crop; millet, maize, cassava and groundnuts are also produced for domestic consumption. The Fouta Djallon is the chief livestock region and cattle, sheep and goats are grazed on its pastures. There is some production of hardwoods from the rain forests on the coastal plain. Fishing is of local significance only.

Mining
Mining plays a dominant role in the economy. Guinea has the world's third largest bauxite deposits and ranks as the sixth bauxite producer; the chief mines are at Fria, Boké and Dabola. The bauxite is converted to pure alumina (aluminium oxide) on site; alumina accounts for 60 % of exports. Iron ore is worked in the Nimba region. Diamonds are found near Macenta; limestone and gold are mined to a lesser extent.

Industry
Manufacturing is mainly based on local raw materials and includes rice milling, groundnut oil extraction, fruit and meat canning, orange juice pressing and cement production. There is a textile mill and a vehicle assembly plant. A plant under construction in 1976 will convert alumina to aluminium using hydro-electricity.

Transport
Communications in Guinea are poor. The principle road runs from Conakry to Kankan (the chief city in the interior) with secondary roads branching off to provincial towns and neighbouring countries. Less than 5% of the road network is hard-surfaced. The only main railway also connects Conakry to Kankan but local lines run from the Fria and Boké bauxite mines to the coast. A new line is being built to serve the Mt Nimba iron ore deposits. Conakry, the leading port, has an international airport.

Liberia and Ivory Coast

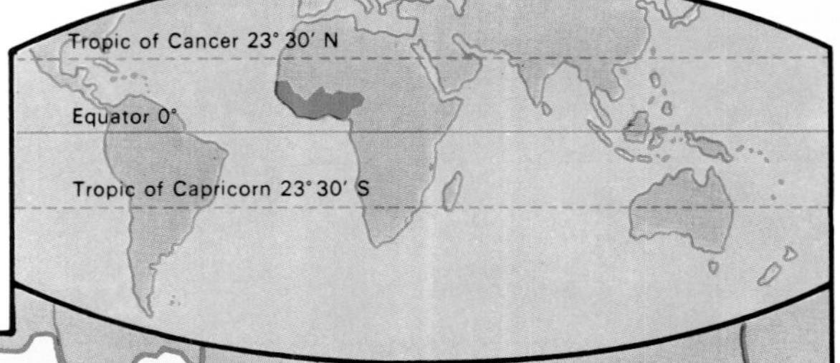

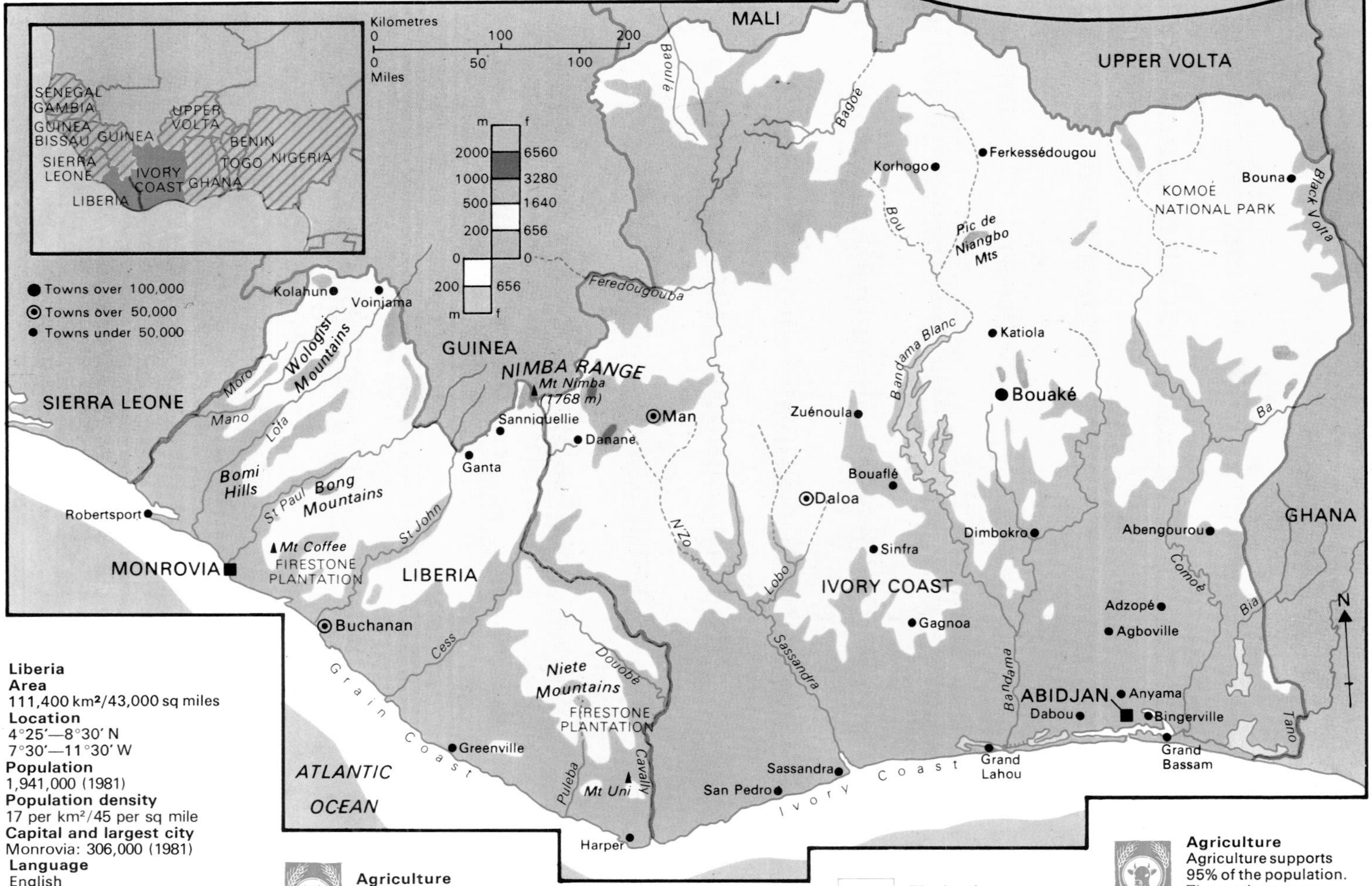

Liberia

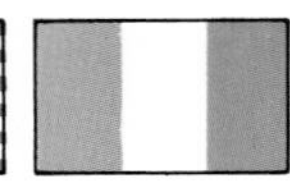

Ivory Coast

Liberia
Area
111,400 km²/43,000 sq miles
Location
4°25′—8°30′ N
7°30′—11°30′ W
Population
1,941,000 (1981)
Population density
17 per km²/45 per sq mile
Capital and largest city
Monrovia: 306,000 (1981)
Language
English
Major imports
machinery, transport equipment, manufactured goods, food, fuels, chemicals
Major exports
iron ore, rubber, diamonds, palm kernels, timber, cocoa, coffee
Currency
dollar (1 dollar = 100 cents)
Gross National Product
1,010 million US dollars (1981)
Status
republic

The land
Liberia, founded by freed American slaves in 1847, is Africa's oldest republic. Behind the swampy shoreline and low coastal plain, the land rises to a forested, undulating plateau some 500 m high. There are several small mountain ranges up to 1,800 m in height. The main rivers flow along parallel northwest-southeast courses. The climate is equatorial with high temperatures (27°C), high humidity (80%) and high rainfall: between May and October, 375 cm of rain falls along the coast and 250 cm in inland areas.

Industry
Manufacturing, centred on Monrovia, is limited. Products include canned fish, tyres, cement, beer, explosives and chemicals. Monrovia consumes 95% of the country's electricity (75% of which comes from the Mt Coffee hydro-electric plant). The iron and rubber industries have their own supply.

Agriculture
Three Liberians out of four live off the land. Rice is the staple crop, grown on 33% of farmland, but low yields make imports necessary. The other basic food is cassava. Rubber is Liberia's second main export and chief cash crop accounting for 24% of the area under cultivation. Over half the output comes from plantations held by the Firestone Tyre Co. who ship the rubber, as latex concentrate and crepe, to the US. Coffee and cocoa are also major commercial crops. Tropical forests cover 25% of the country and products include timber and palm kernels. A few cattle and goats are raised in the interior.

Mining
Liberia's fortunes largely depend on minerals, particularly on iron ore which accounts for 70% of total exports. Mines are located in the Bomi Hills, the Nimba range, the Bong mountains and at Mano river; further reserves have been discovered. There are rail links from the Bomi, Bong and Mano river mines to Monrovia and from Nimba to Buchanan. Iron ore accounts for 90% of cargo handled by Monrovia port. Liberia ranks as Africa's leading producer and the world's fourth largest exporter of iron ore. Diamond production, from the Lofa river area, is significant and gold deposits are worked on a small scale. Bauxite, manganese, kyanite, lead-zinc, copper and rutile also occur.

Transport
The main road runs from Monrovia via Ganta into Guinea with branches serving east and west Liberia. There are no railways apart from the lines carrying iron ore to the coast. Monrovia, with its free zone, is the chief port followed by Buchanan, Greenville and Harper. The registration of foreign ships under a Liberian flag of convenience contributes to the national income and gives Liberia the world's largest merchant navy. East of Monrovia there is an international airport.

Ivory Coast
Area
322,463 km²/124,504 sq miles
Location
4°25′—10°30′ N
2°30′—8°30′ W
Population
8,505,000 (1981)
Population density
26 per km²/68 per sq mile
Capital and largest city
Abidjan: 1,690,000 (1981)
Language
French
Major imports
machinery, vehicles, metals, petroleum
Major exports
coffee, timber, cocoa, palm oil
Currency
CFA franc (1 franc = 100 centimes)
Gross National Product
10,190 million US dollars (1981)
Status
republic

The land
Inland, the Ivory Coast consists of a savanna-covered plateau about 300 m in altitude but rising to over 1,000 m in the northwest. A fertile, forested plain separates the plateau from the coast which is fringed by lagoons and sand-bars. The climate is equatorial: in the south, temperatures are high (27°C) and rainfall is heavy (200 cm); the north is slightly cooler and drier.

Transport
The country's transport system is centred on Abidjan. The road network radiates from the capital and includes highways to all five neighbouring states. The only railway runs north from the capital to Upper Volta. Abidjan is also the main port; situated on a lagoon, the city has access to the sea via the Vridi canal. Other ports are Sassandra, Tabou and San Pedro. Air Ivoire operates internally and Air Afrique internationally from Abidjan.

Forestry
Dense forests cover 40% of the country, mainly in the south, and contain over 30 commercially valuable species including teak, mahogany, ebony and cedar. Timber accounts for 25% of total exports and the Ivory Coast ranks as Africa's leading exporter of tropical woods. There are many sawmills and plywood plants. Kola nuts are also important.

Agriculture
Agriculture supports 95% of the population. The staple crops are maize and millet in the northern savanna, rice in the southwest, and yams, plantains and cassava in the southeast. The leading cash crop is coffee, grown in cleared zones in the south and accounting for 35% of total exports. The other major tree crop is cocoa, cultivated mainly in the southeast and providing 25% of total exports. Bananas and pineapples are also important. The Ivory Coast is the world's third largest producer of coffee and cocoa, fourth producer of pineapples and sixth of bananas. Other commercial crops include oil palms (4th largest supplier), rubber in the southwest, copra along the coast and cotton and sugarcane in the centre and north.

Mining & industry
Mining activity is limited to alluvial diamonds in the river Bou and manganese near Grand Lahou. Iron ore is known to exist in the northwest. Since the 1960s there has been considerable industrial development. Food-processing is the most important sector and products range from powdered coffee, cocoa butter and beer, to flour (using imported wheat), canned pineapples and frozen fish. New concerns include a vehicle assembly plant, textile mill, cigarette factory, plastics works and paper factory. Most power stations are oil-fired, but hydro-electric plants are in operation on the rivers Bia, Bandama and Kossou.

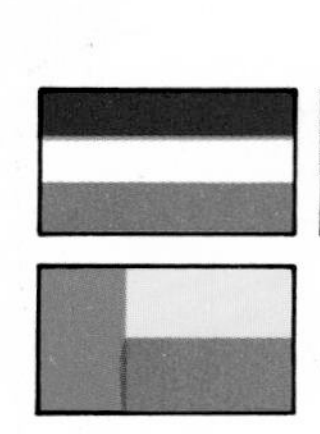

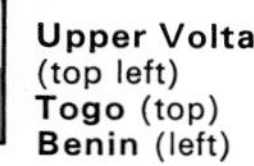

Upper Volta, Togo and Benin

Upper Volta (top left)
Togo (top)
Benin (left)

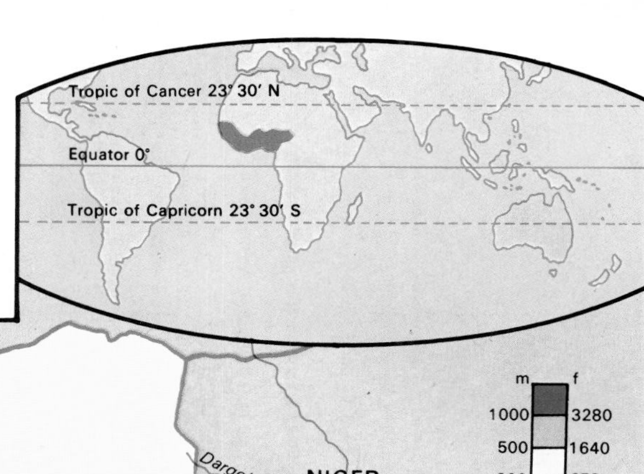

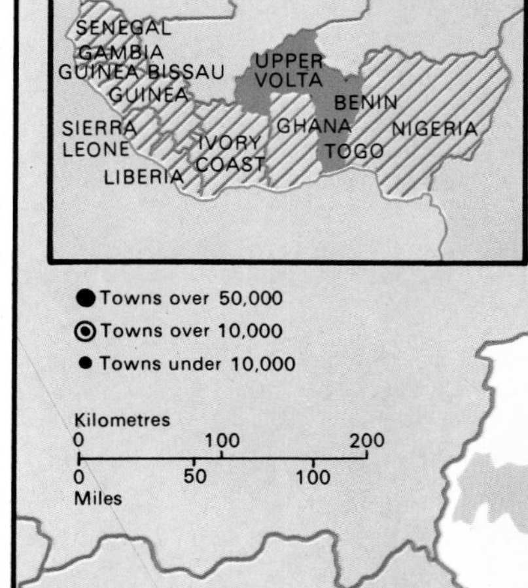

Upper Volta
Area
274,121 km²/105,838 sq miles
Location
9°30′—15°05′ N
5°30′ W—2°25′ E
Population
6,325,000 (1981)
Population density
23 per km²/60 per sq mile
Capital and largest city
Ouagadougou: 200,000 (1981)
Language
French
Major imports
iron and steel, foodstuffs, fuels, textiles, machinery
Major exports
animals, cotton, groundnuts, hides, skins, sesame, karité nuts
Currency
franc (1 franc = 100 centimes)
Gross National Product
1,490 million US dollars (1981)
Status
republic

The land
Upper Volta is landlocked and consists of a plateau some 300 m high and tilted slightly southwards. This granite block, covered with poor, infertile soils and savanna-type vegetation, is crossed by the deep valleys of the Black Volta, Red Volta and White Volta which meet in Ghana to form the Volta. The climate is hot and dry with temperatures of up to 40°C and 90 cm of rain a year which falls between June and September.

The economy
Agriculture is the basis of the economy and employs 95% of the population. Subsistence farming predominates and exports (of sesame, groundnuts, karité nuts and cotton) largely consist of surplus production. The main food crops are sorghum in the south and millet in the north; others are maize, rice and yams. Cocoa and sugar have been introduced. Cattle, sheep and goats are raised in the north and east; live animals, meat, hides and skins account for 40% of total exports. Large manganese deposits at Tamboa are being developed but other mineral assets are, so far, unexploited. Industrial development is limited.

Transport
A railway line runs from Ouagadougou to Abidjan port in Ivory Coast and there are plans to extend the line to Niger with branch lines to the mines at Tamboa. The capital is the hub of the 9,000 km road network and also has an international airport. Air Volta links 50 towns internally while Air Afrique goes overseas.

Benin
Area
112,613 km²/43,480 sq miles
Location
6°20′—12°25′ N
0°55′—3°50′ E
Population
3,595,000 (1981)
Population density
32 per km²/83 per sq mile
Capital
Port Novo: 123,000 (1980)
Largest city
Cotonou: 215,000 (1980)
Language
French
Major imports
textiles, food, chemicals, machinery, vehicles
Major exports
palm kernels, nuts and oil, cotton, coffee, tobacco, groundnuts
Currency
franc (1 franc = 100 centimes)
Gross National Product
1,140 million US dollars (1981)
Status
republic

The land
Benin is about 96 km wide and extends 656 km north from the Gulf of Guinea to the Niger. The coast, with sand-bars and lagoons, is backed by a belt of fertile clay. Beyond this lies a seasonally-flooded swamp. The rest of the country consists of forested and savanna-covered plateaux 150 m high. In the northwest, the Atakora mountains reach 650 m, but in the northeast the land slopes down to the Niger. The average temperature is 27°C with 130 cm of rain (less inland).

The economy
About 90% of the people live off the land and Benin is self-sufficient in basic foods. Maize and cassava are grown in the south, millet in the north. Cattle, sheep and goats are kept in the north, pigs in the south. Oil palm plantations cover half the cultivated area and oil palm products account for 40 % of exports. Other cash crops are groundnuts, cotton, coffee, tobacco and cocoa. The only mineral worked is limestone. Industries are few and mainly consist of processing farm products for export.

Transport
Cotonou, which has an international airport and a new harbour, is the hub of Benin's transport system. Railways link this major city to Lomé (Togo), Parakou and Pobé. The two main highways are also centred on Cotonou: one runs east-west to Nigeria and Togo, the other goes north to Niger. The lagoons and the Ouémé, Mono and Couffo rivers are navigable.

Togo
Area
56,000 km²/21,621 sq miles
Location
6°10′—11°10′ N
0°10′ W—1°51′ E
Population
2,664,000 (1981)
Population density
48 per km²/123 per sq mile
Capital and largest city
Lomé: 283,000 (1980)
Language
French
Major imports
machinery, vehicles, chemicals, oil, food, cement, iron, steel
Major exports
phosphates, cocoa, coffee, palm kernels, cotton, tapioca
Currency
franc (1 franc = 100 centimes)
Gross National Product
1,010 million US dollars (1981)
Status
republic

Transport
Togo's transport systems are centred on Lomé. Three railway lines connect Lomé with Anécho, Palimé and Blitta. The 7,000 km road network is 10% hard-surfaced; the two main routes are from Lomé to Upper Volta and along the coast between Ghana and Benin. Lomé has a deepwater port and an international airport; Air Togo operates domestic flights while Air Afrique (6% owned by Togo) flies overseas.

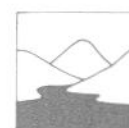

The land
Togo is Africa's second smallest state. Behind the sandy, lagoon-fringed coast, a low plateau, composed of fertile red clay soils, stretches inland for 30 km. The land then rises to a 450 m high tableland drained by the Mono. This central upland is bordered in the north and north-west by the forested Togo-Atakora chain which has peaks up to 900 m. Beyond this lies the savanna-covered Oti plateau. The climate is hot and humid; temperatures average 27°C and about 75 cm of rain falls on the coast increasing to 180 cm inland.

Agriculture
Agriculture supports 90% of the population and provides over 50% of exports. Cash crops include cocoa, coffee and palm kernels, grown in the south, and coffee and groundnuts in the north. Food production includes yams, cassava, millet, sorghum and maize. Rice, sugarcane, fruit and vegetables are grown under irrigation. Livestock (kept in the north) and fish supplement the national diet.

Mining & Industry
Phosphates, mined northeast of Lomé, account for almost half of total exports. There is also some production of limestone and marble, but iron ore, bauxite, uranium and chromite deposits are not yet exploited. Electricity comes from a thermal station at Lomé and a hydro-electric power station at Palimé, with some imported from Ghana. Industry, based on agricultural produce, is small-scale and includes coffee roasting, cassava flour-milling, cotton-ginning and palm-oil extraction. A few consumer goods are manufactured.

Ghana

Tropic of Cancer 23° 30' N
Equator 0°
Tropic of Capricorn 23° 30' S

Area
238,540 km²/92 100 sq miles
Location
4°45'—11°10' N
3°15' W—1°20' E
Population
11,830,000 (1981)
Population density
50 per km²/128 per sq mile
Capital and largest city
Accra: 1,000,000 (1981)
Language
English
Major imports
food, machinery, manufactured goods, chemicals, fuels
Major exports
cocoa beans and products, timber, gold, diamonds, manganese, bauxite
Currency
cedi (1 cedi = 100 pesewa)
Gross National Product
4,770 million US dollars (1981)
Status
republic

Physical features
Two-thirds of the country consists of the low-lying basin of the Volta river and its tributaries, the Black Volta, White Volta and Oti. To the north, west and south-west, this savanna-covered plain is rimmed by great sandstone escarpments. These scarps overlook a 300 m high plateau in the northwest and the dissected Ashanti plateau in the southwest. In the east, an upland range rises to 600m along the Togo border. Near the end of its course, 70 km from the sea, the Volta flows through a narrow gorge; at this point the Akosombo dam holds back the river to form Lake Volta, one of the world's largest man-made lakes.

Climate
Southern Ghana, exposed to the monsoonal south-west wind, has two wet seasons (May-June and October-November) with an average annual rainfall of 180 cm; the south-east corner, however, is sheltered and relatively dry with Accra having under 80 cm of rain a year. In the north there is only one wet season (June to October) with annual totals of between 100 and 130 cm of rain. During the rest of the year, the arid dusty harmattan wind from the Sahara blows across the interior. Temperatures are high with annual averages ranging from 26°C on the coast to 30°C inland.

Agriculture
Agriculture is the most important sector of the economy. It employs about 60% of the population but accounts for less than 25% of Ghana's surface area. Around 30% of farmland is used for the main cash crop, cocoa, which provides 65% of all exports. Ghana ranks as the world's leading cocoa producer the annual output from the Ashanti plateau area being about 400,000 tonnes. Other cash crops, also grown in the southern half of the country, are coffee, copra, bananas, kola nuts, oil palms, tobacco and rubber. The chief food crops are plantain, maize, cassava, yams and cocoyams in the south and guinea corn, millet, groundnuts and sheanuts in the drier north. Cattle-raising is limited to the tsetse-free northern savanna and the Accra plain by the coast.

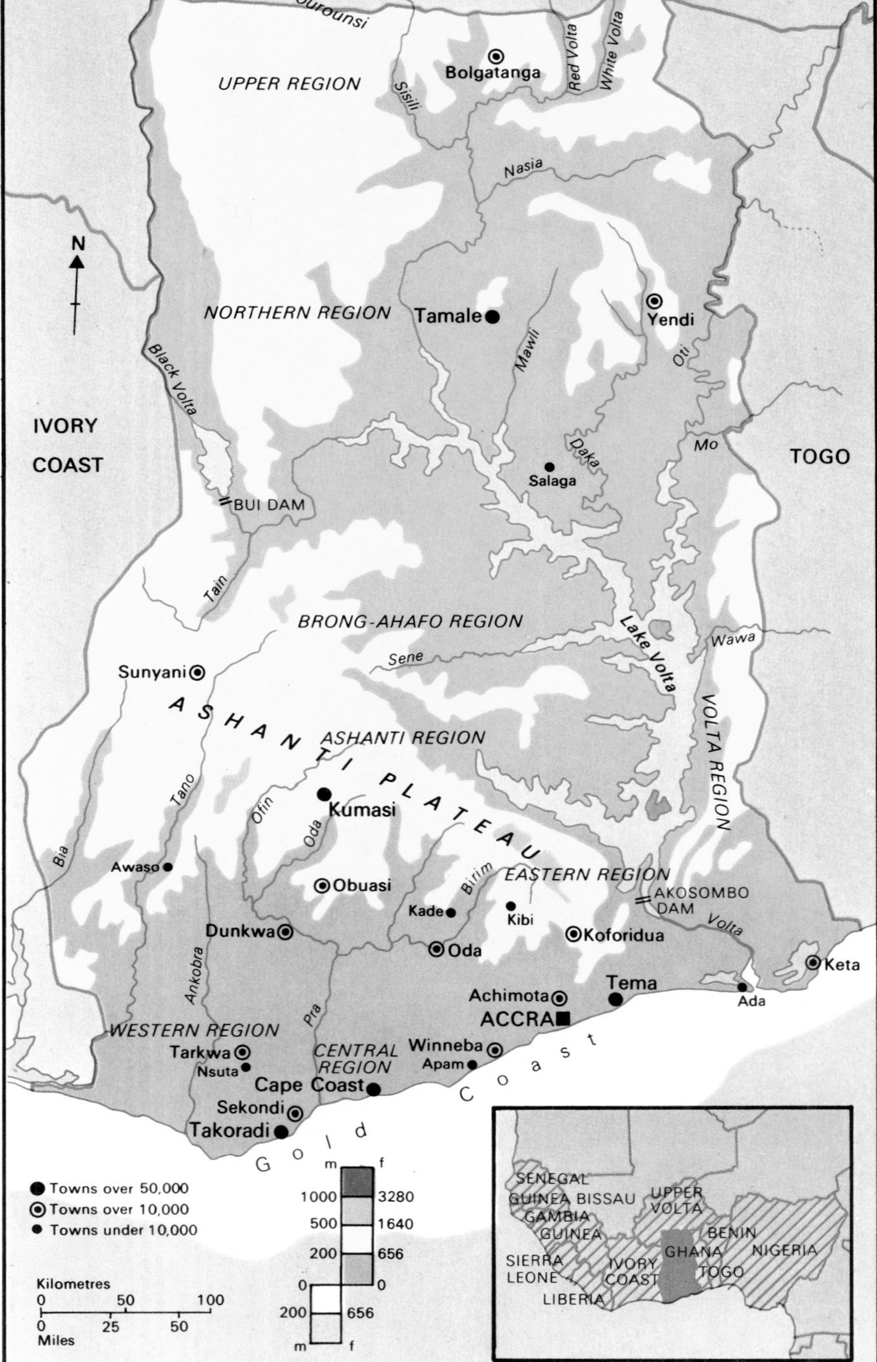

Forestry
Tropical rain forests cover much of the Ashanti plateau and commercially valuable species include wawa (African whitewood) sapele and African mahogany. The industry is centred in the south-west and logs are floated down such rivers as the Ankobra and Ofin to the coast for processing or export. Timber accounts for 15% of total exports; half is shipped as logs, the remainder as sawn timber, plywood and veneer. The timber processing industry is being expanded.

Fishing
The fishing industry is well developed and supplies about 90% of domestic requirements. Just over a third of the catch comes from Lake Volta. Traditional canoes, often equipped with outboard motors, predominate and these operate from open beaches along the coast; there are also some motorized vessels working from harbours. The principal fishing centres are Takoradi, Winneba and Apam; Tema, with its modern facilities, is the base of the deep-sea fishing fleet.

Cities
Accra, which is a corruption of *nkran* (the name of the black ants found locally), grew up round three villages and now extends 25 km along the coast. Also on the coast is Sekondo-Takoradi (160,900); in 1963 the old town of Sekondi merged with the modern port of Takoradi to form a single city. Sekondi harbour is now used by fishing boats and pleasure craft. Kumasi (345,100), at the heart of the cocoa region, is a major industrial town and route centre.

Mining
Mining, centred on the Ashanti plateau, is a leading source of income and provides almost 20% of total exports. Gold, as the country's previous name of *Gold Coast* suggests, is important and accounts for 50% of mineral exports. Some gold is extracted from river deposits, the rest is mined; Obuasi has one of the world's largest gold mines. Diamonds are next in importance and provide a further 30% of mineral exports, with production based on Oda and Kade in the Birim valley northwest of Accra. The other minerals exploited are manganese at Nsuta and bauxite at Awaso; bauxite deposits at Kibi are to be developed. Salt is obtained from the sea and lagoons. Oil exists offshore.

Lake Volta
Completed in 1965, the Akosombo dam on the Volta has created a giant lake. Lake Volta is 320 km long and covers 8,482 km² or 3.5% of Ghana's total surface area. The lake has several functions. Primarily, it is a source of hydro-electricity: the Volta dam supplies over 90% of the country's electricity and provides power for export to Togo and Benin. As a reservoir, the lake stores water for domestic and industrial consumption and for irrigation; sugar and rice are to be grown under irrigation along the 7,200 km shoreline. Freshwater fisheries have been established and provide the surrounding area with a valuable source of protein. Lake Volta is navigable and serves as a major route from the north to the coast.

Industry
About 70% of the hydro-electricity generated is consumed by the country's largest concern, the aluminium smelter at Tema. The two other main industries process timber and cocoa; about 12% of cocoa exports are in the form of cocoa butter and paste. Small-scale manufacturing, aimed at the local market, includes flour-milling, sugar-refining, brewing, meat-processing, vehicle assembly, textiles, chemicals and some oil refining. Industrial development is centred on Accra-Tema, Sekondi-Takoradi and Kumasi.

Transport
Road and rail networks are most dense in southern Ghana. Roads total 32,000 km but many are impassable during the wet season; main routes radiate from Accra and Kumasi. The rail network serves the mining and cocoa regions and forms a triangle linking Takoradi, Kumasi and Accra with several branch lines. Exports of manganese, bauxite, logs and cocoa account for 80% of freight carried. The two main ports, Takoradi and Tema (replacing Accra port) are both artificial; a third deep-water port was under construction in 1976. Ghana Airways operates domestic and international services from Accra airport, the largest in the country.

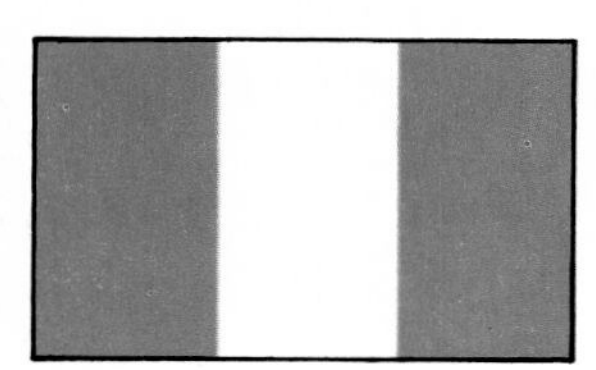

Nigeria

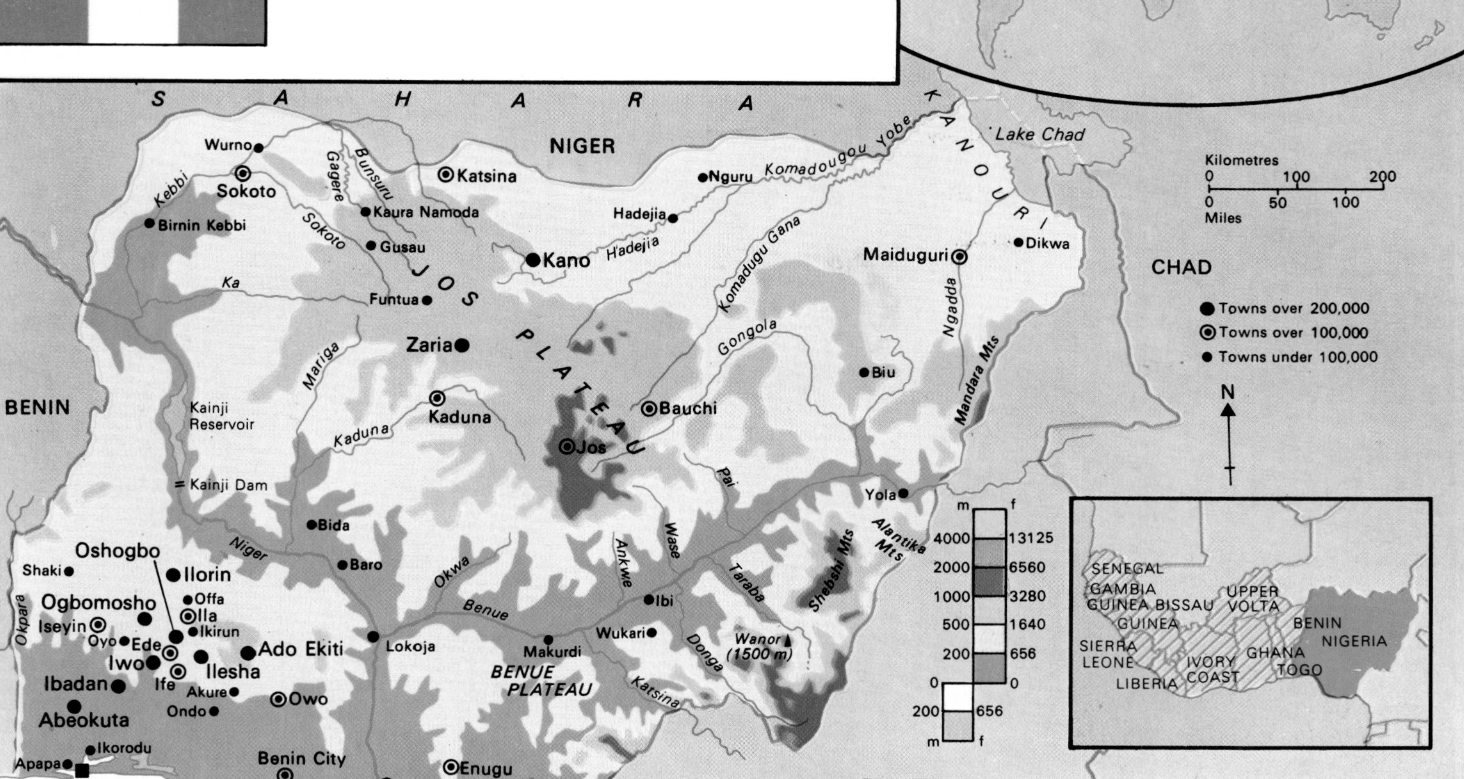

Area
923,773 km²/356,669 sq miles
Location
4°20′—13°15′ N
3°—14°40′ E
Population
87,603,000 (1981)
Population density
95 per km²/246 per sq mile
Capital and largest city
Lagos: 1,400,000 (1982)
Language
English
Major imports
machinery, iron and steel, textiles, vehicles, food
Major exports
petroleum, cocoa, groundnuts, rubber, palm kernels, tin, timber, hides and skins, cotton
Currency
Naira (1 Naira = 100 kobo)
Gross National Product
76,170 million US dollars (1981)
Status
federal republic

Flora and fauna

Mangrove swamps line the coast; behind lies a belt of tropical rain forest containing hardwood trees and oil palm. Savanna predominates on the plateau with tall grasses and some trees such as baobab and tamarind. Short grass and thorny trees characterize the far north. Nigeria's wildlife is plentiful. Camels, lions, cheetahs, hyenas and a few giraffes roam the savanna; elephants and chimpanzees are found in the forests; crocodiles and hippopotamuses live in the rivers. Leopards are plentiful but gorillas almost extinct.

Physical features

Nigeria's main feature is the Niger—the third longest river in Africa. It flows south-eastwards across west Nigeria to Lokoja where it is joined by its main tributary, the Benue. The river then continues due south and enters the Gulf of Guinea through a broad delta. Behind the lagoons and swamps of the coastal belt lies a thickly-forested hilly region which gives way to the wide Niger and Benue valleys. The northern half of the country consists of the undulating Jos plateau which rises to over 1,500 m in the centre. This tableland is a major watershed with streams flowing both north and south. In the extreme north, the land drops to a sandy plain some 600 m high which merges into the Sahara. Another range runs along the Cameroun border.

Climate

Nigeria's climate is influenced by two winds: the dessicating Harmattan from the Sahara and the moisture-laden south-west wind. The Harmattan, with its dust haze, blows during the dry season (November-April) and causes daily variations of temperature, particularly in the north: at Kano, temperatures range from 8°C to 43°C. The wet south-west wind prevails from May to October bringing rain which decreases inland. Over 400 cm falls on the coast, but only 50 cm near Lake Chad. Coastal humidity is high.

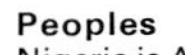

Peoples

Nigeria is Africa's most populous state. The population comprises over 250 ethnic groups each with its own language or dialect. The four largest groups are the Yoruba (13 million) in the southwest, the Ibo (8 million) in the southeast, the Hausa (7 million) and the Fulani (5 million) in the north. Other prominent groups are the Edo in the Benin area, the Tiv, Nupe and Kanuri on the plateau and the Ibidio in the southeast. Although English is the offical language, 35% of the population (mainly in the north) speak Hausa; the Yoruba language predominates in the west and Ibo in the east. The south, in particular the southeast, is the most densely populated region with densities of up to 400 per km². The north-centre and northwest, with cities such as Sokoto and Kano, are also well populated, but the middle zone and the Lake Chad area are largely uninhabited.

Agriculture

Two-thirds of the population work in agriculture, which provides 60% of total exports. The various cash crops are grown in distinct zones: cocoa in the west, rubber in the mid-west, oil-palm in the east, groundnuts and cotton in the north, soybeans in the Benue basin and tobacco in the north and west. Nigeria ranks as the world's second largest cocoa exporter. The country is almost self-sufficient in basic foods: yams and cassava are grown in the south; millet, maize and rice in the north. Cattle are grazed on the northern savanna.

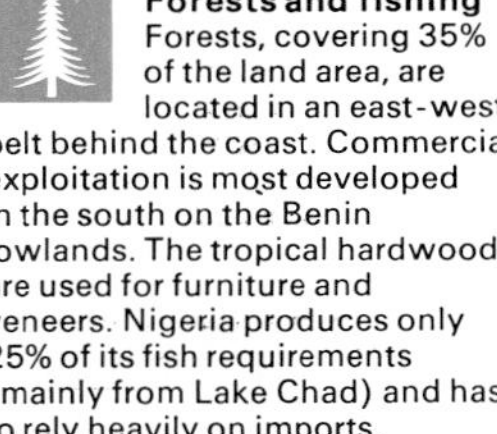

Forests and fishing

Forests, covering 35% of the land area, are located in an east-west belt behind the coast. Commercial exploitation is most developed in the south on the Benin lowlands. The tropical hardwoods are used for furniture and veneers. Nigeria produces only 25% of its fish requirements (mainly from Lake Chad) and has to rely heavily on imports.

Mining

Mining makes a significant contribution to Nigeria's economy. Petroleum, occurring in the southern part of the country, accounts for a third of all exports; production is centred on the Niger delta. Columbite and tin, both mined on the Jos plateau, are next in importance; Nigeria holds first place for world production of columbite. Coal is worked near Enugu. Marble, limestone, lignite and gold are mined in small quantities.

Industry

Nigeria's industry is expanding rapidly. The principal sector is food-processing and products include palm oil, groundnut oil, beer, sugar, margarine, fruit juices and canned foods. The textile and leather industry, located mainly in the north, supplies two-thirds of the country's needs. Cement manufacture is important with plants at Lagos, Sokoto and Enugu. New industries include vehicle-assembly and chemicals and there is an oil refinery at Port Harcourt. Two more refineries, an iron and steel complex, gas liquefaction plants and more cement works were being planned in 1976. Main industrial centres are Lagos and Ibadan in the west, Port Harcourt, Enugu, Aba and Calabar in the east and Kano, Zaria, Kaduna and Jos in the north.

Energy

With its reserves of coal, lignite, oil and natural gas, Nigeria has considerable energy resources. Traditionally, oil and coal-fired thermal stations are the major source of electricity, but the new dams at Kainji on the Niger supply cheap hydro-electric power for the country's developing industries.

Transport

The rail network, totalling 3,500 km, comprises two main lines: Port Harcourt to Maiduguri and Lagos to Kano, with branches to Kaura Namoda, Nguru and Baro. There are 38,000 km of roads, 17% hard-surfaced. The principal highways run north-south with east-west branches. On the 6,500 km of inland waterways, shipping is mostly seasonal: the Niger, Benue and Cross are the most important rivers with the Benue used for Cameroun transit freight. Boats also ply the coastal lagoons between Lagos and the Cross estuary. Lagos and Port Harcourt are the chief ports, followed by Warri, Calabar, Koko and Sapele. Nigerian Airways operate domestic and overseas services from Kano and Lagos.

Cities

Lagos stands on a series of lagoon islands. As well as being the administrative capital, it is also the country's commercial and industrial centre accounting for 30% of total manufactures. Apapa, the port of Lagos, handles 50% of Nigeria's foreign trade. The other main towns—Ibadan (1 m), Ogbomosho (432,000), Oshogbo (282,000) and Ilorin (282,000)—are all in the south. The one exception is Kano (400,000) which is in the north. Built of mud and enclosed by a 17 km long wall, Kano originated as a trans-Sahara trading centre.

Somalia and Djibouti

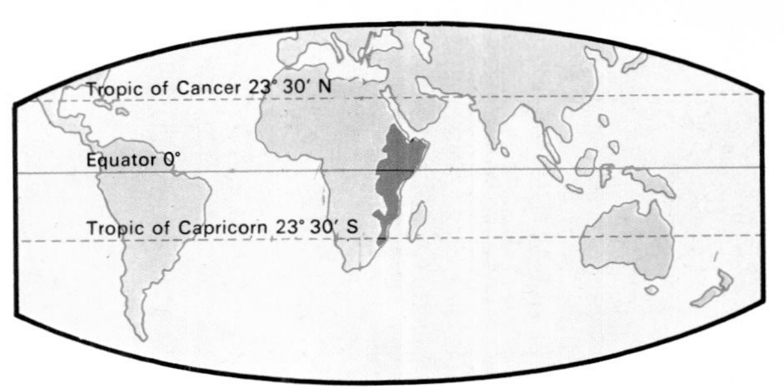

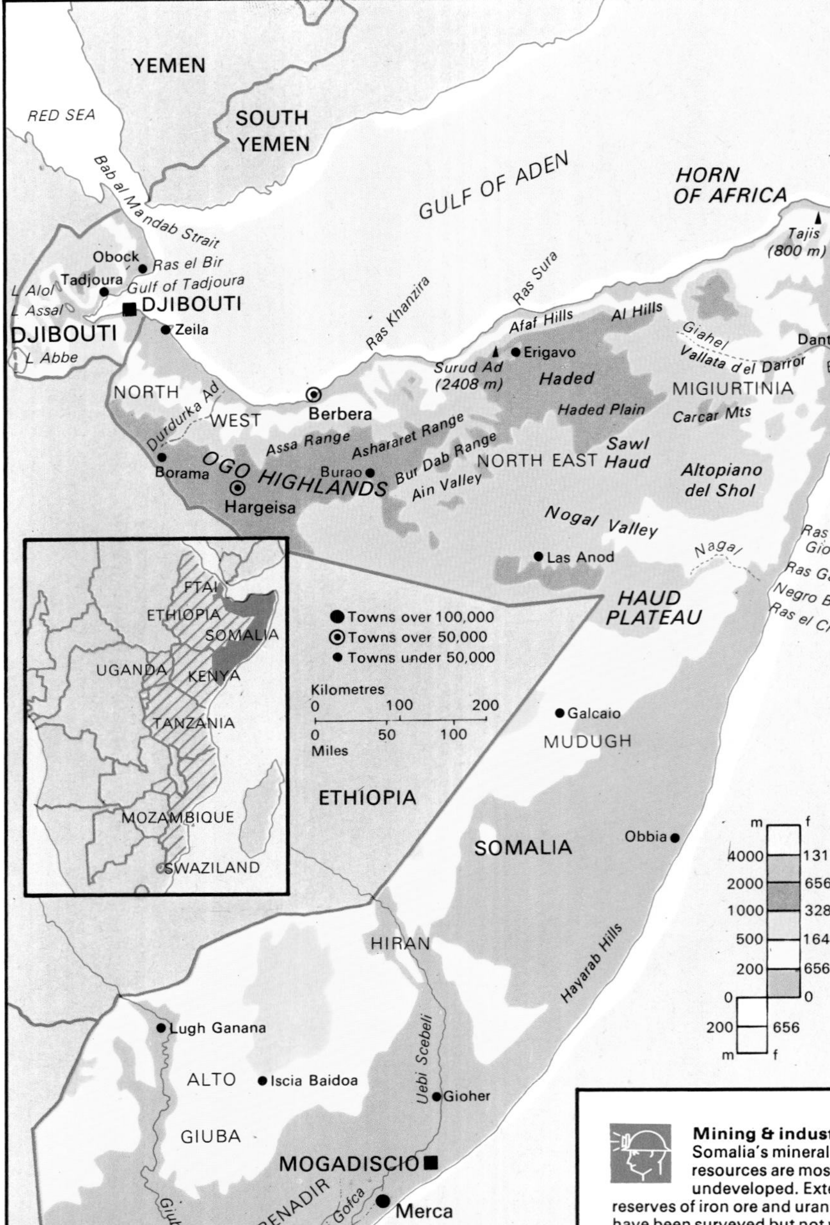

Transport
Somalia's transport system is inadequate: there are no railways, the road network is poor and the two rivers are navigable for small craft only. Somali Airlines operates an internal service between Mogadiscio, Berbera, Chisimaio and Hargeisa: Mogadiscio and Hargeisa have international airports. The two chief ports are Mogadiscio and Berbera, but Merca and Chisimaio handle the banana trade. The merchant fleet, which is jointly owned with Libya, is being expanded.

Mining & industry
Somalia's mineral resources are mostly undeveloped. Extensive reserves of iron ore and uranium have been surveyed but not yet exploited. Manganese, feldspar and columbite also occur. Some meerschaum (a clay-like substance used for smoking-pipes) is produced and gypsum (from deposits near Berbera) is supplied to the cement industry. Salt is mined near Zeila in the northwest. In the last decade, the industrial sector has expanded and now includes sugar refining, flour milling, meat packing, fish canning, tanning, textiles, cigarettes and matches. Two recent projects are an iron foundry at Mogadiscio and a cement plant at Berbera. An oil refinery is under construction.

People & towns
The Somalis, a well defined ethnic group, are basically nomadic and only 10% live in towns. Four of the five main centres are ports: Mogadiscio, Merca (100,000), Berbera (50,000) and Chisimaio (30,000); Hargeisa (60,000) has a pleasant site in the uplands.

Somalia
Area
637,661 km²/246,201 sq miles
Location
12°N—1°45′ S
41°—51°20′ E
Population
4,392,000 (1981)
Population density
7 per km²/18 per sq mile
Capital and largest city
Mogadiscio: 400,000 (1981)
Languages
Somali, Arabic
Major imports
machinery, transport equipment, cereals, chemicals, fuels
Major exports
live animals, bananas, hides and skins, meat
Currency
shilling (1 shilling = 100 cents)
Gross National Product
1,240 million US dollars (1981)
Status
republic

Physical features
The Somali Republic lies along the coast of the African Horn, the continent's northeastern corner. Most of the country consists of a low plateau under 500 m which extends to the coast in the north and east. The tip of the Horn, Cape Guardafui, is a sheer 300 m high precipice. Ras Hafun promontory, Africa's most easterly point, is 160 km south of the cape. Parallel to the Gulf of Aden coast, a mountain belt rises above the plateau to altitudes of 2,000 m. The south-eastern coast, bordering the Indian Ocean, is flanked by a wide, sandy plain. This arid lowland is crossed by the country's only two rivers: the Giuba (which enters the sea near Chisimaio) and the Uebi Scebeli which usually disappears into marshes near the coast.

Climate
Inland Somalia is hot and dry; coastal areas are hot and humid. The Gulf of Aden shore is one of the world's hottest regions: average temperatures at Berbera are 24°C in January (the coldest month) and 54°C in July (the hottest); the annual average for Mogadiscio is 27°C. Precipitation is light: the winter monsoon brings 5 cm of rain to the north coast; the summer monsoon brings 50 cm to the central plateau.

Agriculture
Somalia is a pastoral country: 80% of the population, mostly nomads, depend on livestock-raising and about 20 million animals (sheep, goats, cattle and camels) are grazed on the interior plateau. Arable farming is confined to irrigated zones bordering the Giuba and Uebi Scebeli rivers where maize, sorghum, sugarcane and bananas are the main crops; production of cotton, rice, groundnuts, sesame and citrus fruit is increasing. Live animals, hides and skins, meat and meat products provide over 60% of total exports and bananas account for a further 30%. Some frankincense and myrrh, from aromatic shrubs on the plateau, are also exported. Fishing is being developed.

Djibouti
Area
21,783 km²/8,410 sq miles
Location
10°55′—12°45′ N
41°40′—43°25′ E
Population
381,000 (1981)
Population density
17 per km²/45 per sq mile
Capital and largest city
Djibouti: 200,000 (1980)
Language
French
Major imports
excluding transit trade: textiles, machinery, food
Major exports
excluding transit trade: skins, leather, shoes
Currency
franc (1 franc = 100 centimes)
Gross National Product
180 million US dollars (1981)
Status
republic

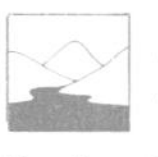

Physical features
The republic of Djibouti, formerly French Somaliland and later the French Territory of the Afars and Issas, is arid and barren. It consists of stony desert with extensive lava sheets and volcanic hills, some rising to over 1,500 m. A depression, parallel to the Red Sea, contains the salt lakes Alol and Assal; there are no permanent rivers. The Gulf of Tadjoura thrusts inland for some 50 km. Apart from mangroves along the coast, palms in the dry watercourses and sparse stretches of forest in upland areas, vegetation consists of stunted acacia and scrub.

Climate
FTAI has a hot, humid climate. Along the coast, temperatures average 28°C but rise to 45°C in July, the hottest month. Inland, conditions are slightly cooler. Rainfall, occurring in winter (October to February) is very low: under 10 cm a year.

People
The territory's name incorporates its two main ethnic groups: the Afars (82,000) and the Issas (62,000). Both groups are Moslem nomadic pastoralists. The Afars live mostly in the north and the Issas, a Somali tribe, in the south. The only important centre is Djibouti, the capital and port.

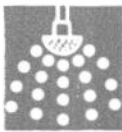

The economy
The shortage of water severely restricts arable farming but dates and vegetables are grown on a small scale under irrigation at oases. The rural population is largely nomadic and lives by herding camels, sheep, goats and a few cattle; there is some fishing in the Gulf of Aden. Mineral production is limited to salt, obtained by evaporation from the sea and Lake Assal, but deposits of gypsum, sulphur, mica and amethyst are thought to exist. Most of the FTAI's income, however, is derived from transit trade. Djibouti, as an important port and the coastal terminus of the Addis Ababa railway, handles a major share of Ethiopian exports—in particular, coffee, hides and skin, and oil seeds.

Ethiopia

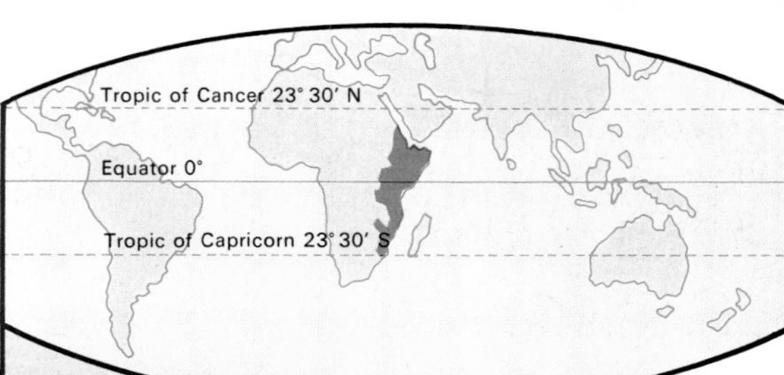

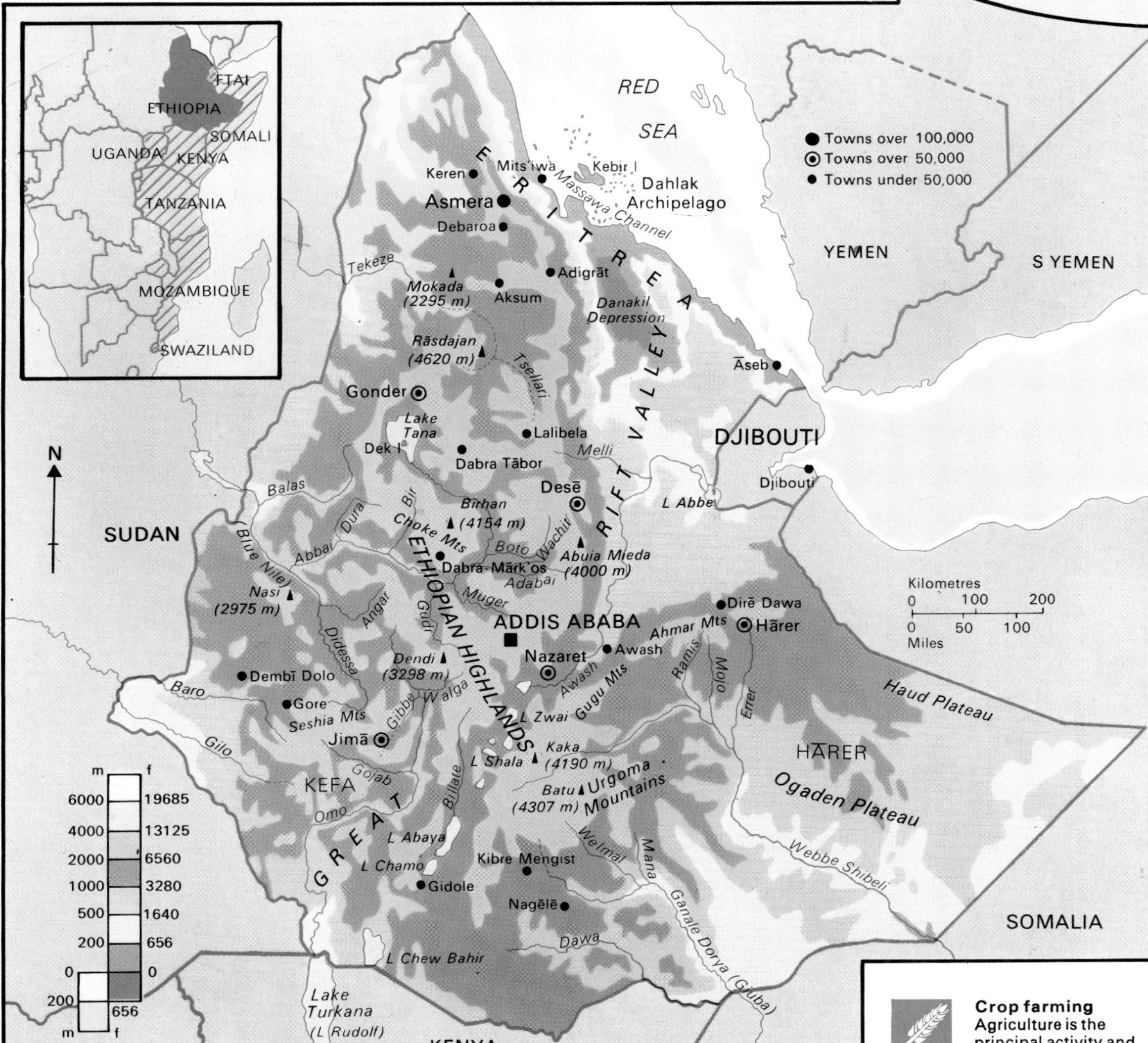

Area
1,221,905 km²/471,778 sq miles
Location
3°30′—18° N
33°—48° E
Population
31,800,000 (1981)
Population density
26 per km²/67 per sq mile
Capital and largest city
Addis Ababa: 1,200,000 (1981)
Languages
Amharic, English
Major imports
machinery, vehicles, textiles, food, fuels, chemicals
Major exports
coffee, fruit, vegetables and pulses, hides and skins, sesame seeds, meat
Currency
dollar (1 dollar = 100 cents)
Gross National Product
4,530 million US dollars (1981)
Status
republic

Flora & fauna
Arid grasslands predominate below 1,800 m while the plateau forests have mostly been cleared for firewood and agriculture. Wildlife includes elephants, lions, rhinoceros, hyenas, ostriches, flamingos and eagles.

Physical features
Ethiopia's main feature is a high plateau (mean altitude 2,400 m) of volcanic origin. This plateau is split by the Great Rift Valley along a northeast-southwest line between the town of Awash and Lake Turkana. The Rift Valley, a long, narrow trench dotted with lakes, broadens in the north to form the parched Danakil depression which is mostly below sea level. North and west of the valley, the Ethiopian Highlands rise above the plateau to over 4,000 m and include Africa's third highest peak, Rāsdajan (4,620 m). This mountain zone is broken by steep gorges, some 1,500 m deep, cut by rivers such as the Abbai (Blue Nile) and Omo. The Abbai rises in the country's largest lake, Tana, and carves its way towards the Sudan in an enormous arc. The Urgoma mountains, to the east of the Rift Valley, are less rugged. In the northeast, the plateau drops sharply to a narrow plain fringing the Red Sea; the 800 km coastline lies wholly within Eritrea, a former Italian colony that now forms part of Ethiopia. In the southwest lies the arid Ogaden plateau.

Climate
Climate is influenced by altitude. On the plateau conditions are pleasant: Addis Ababa (2,400 m) averages 14°C in July, the coolest month, and 18°C in March, the hottest. In contrast, areas below 1,800 m (the coastlands and southern plains) are very hot; the Danakil depression is one of the world's hottest places with day temperatures of over 55°C. Humidity is high by the Red Sea. Rainfall ranges from 10 cm in the northeast to over 200 cm in the southwest: 80% of the annual total falls between June and September with smaller amounts between February and April.

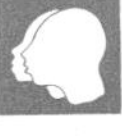

People
Ethiopia contains about 40 ethnic groups with 70 languages and 200 dialects. The main peoples are the Christian Amhara and the predominantly Muslim Galla. The Amharas, from the central plateau, are the traditional ruling class although outnumbered by the pastoral Galla who account for 50% of the population and live in the south and east. In the far south and west, there are Negro and Nilotic tribes.

Crop farming
Agriculture is the principal activity and supports 95% of the population. Cultivated land, covering only 10% of the country, is concentrated on the plateau. The leading food crops are teff (a type of millet), wheat, barley and oats. Sugar and cotton are grown under irrigation in the Awash valley. Coffee, taking its name from the southwest province of Kefa where it originated and still grows wild, is the chief cash crop and accounts for over 50% of exports. The main plantations are in the southwest and on the eastern plateau in Hārer province. Other commercial crops are pulses (peas, beans, lentils), oilseeds (in particular, sesame), vegetables, and fruits such as citrus, apricots, figs and grapes. Gum arabic, beeswax, frankincense and myrrh are collected from the bush but have little economic value.

Livestock & fishing
Cattle, sheep and goats are reared on the plateau and the lower, arid grasslands. Livestock products, such as meat, milk and ghee (butter), are important and supply local requirements while hides and skins are a major export. Fishing is being developed at Mits'iwa and Āseb and pearl fishing takes place off the Dahlak archipelago.

Mining
Mineral production is limited. Some gold is mined at Kibre Mengist in the south and near Asmera and small amounts are exported. Potash and salt are obtained from the Danakil depression, copper is exploited at Debaroa in Eritrea and limestone is quarried on a small scale. Natural gas has been located in the Ogaden plateau and zinc, manganese and platinum also occur. The Red Sea coast is being prospected for oil.

Industry
Industrial development is in its early stages and the manufacturing sector employs less than 5% of the total workforce. Food processing is the most important branch and includes sugar refining, vegetable oil extraction, coffee cleaning, fruit, meat and vegetable canning and the manufacture of dairy produce. Other industrial products are textiles, cement, cigarettes, leather goods, pharmaceuticals and furniture. Addis Ababa and Asmera are the principal manufacturing centres. Ethiopia lacks adequate power supplies but output has been increased by recent hydro-electric power installations on the Awash.

Transport
Ethiopia's rugged mountains, escarpments and gorges make communications difficult. Animals are still widely used: horses and mules on the plateau and camels on the plains. A network of main roads radiate from Addis Ababa to Asmera, Dirē Dawa, Hārer and Jimā with two new highways connecting the capital to the Red Sea port of Āseb and with Nairobi (Kenya). Altogether, roads (mostly unsurfaced) cover 8,000 km. The main railway (780 km) links Addis Ababa to Djibouti and carries a major share of imports and exports. External trade also passes through the Eritrean ports of Mits'iwa and Āseb and via the Giuba river in the south to the Somali port of Chisimaio. Ethiopian Airlines provide a domestic service to over 40 towns and fly overseas from the international airports at Addis Ababa, Asmera and Dirē Dawa.

Towns
Addis Ababa has a pleasant site in the Ethiopian highlands. Its modern, cosmopolitan centre with tall buildings and wide, tree-lined avenues contrasts sharply with the sprawling mass of tin-roofed, mud huts that house most of the capital's million people. The second largest city is the Eritrean capital, Asmera (240,000) which is linked to Mits'iwa port.

Tourism
The spectacular scenery and long, rich history of Ethiopia give it considerable tourist potential. Attractions include the Blue Nile Falls (Bahir Dar), Awash Game Park, 800-year-old rock-hewn churches at Lalibela, island monasteries on Lake Tana and medieval castles at Gonder.

Uganda

Area
236,860 km²/91,451 sq miles
Location
4°16′ N—1°30′ S
29°36′—35° E
Population
13,047,000 (1981)
Population density
55 per km²/143 per sq mile
Capital and largest city
Kampala: 480,000 (1980)
Language
English
Major imports
machinery, transport equipment, chemicals, food, fuels
Major exports
coffee, cotton, tea, copper, hides and skins, oilseeds
Currency
shilling (1 shilling = 100 cents)
Gross National Product
2,890 million US dollars (1981)
Status
republic

● Towns over 50,000
◉ Towns over 20,000
• Towns under 20,000

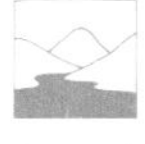

Physical features

Uganda is situated on a plateau more than 900 m above sea level which forms the floor of the Great Rift Valley. There are highlands to the east and west. In the east lies Mt Elgon (4,321 m), an extinct volcano, while in the west, between Lakes Edward and Albert, is the Ruwenzori range which rises to 5,110 m in snow-capped Mt Stanley. This range falls sharply to the Semliki river valley which broadens into the Nile Rift Valley. The plateau is characterized by undulating plains, low hills and swampy tracts. Over 15% of Uganda is covered by lakes, including parts of Victoria, Edward and Albert; Lake George and, in the central swampy area, Lakes Kyoga, Kwania and Bisina. The main rivers are the Semliki, Albert Nile and the fast-flowing Victoria Nile with its rapids and waterfalls and the spectacular Kabalega Falls.

Agriculture

In the north, where there is a marked dry season, food crops include maize, millet and pulses; in the wetter south, plantains, sweet potatoes, cassava and bananas are the staples. Coffee is the main cash crop; two main types are grown: *robusta* and *arabica*. Robusta predominates, partly because of its suitability for instant coffee, and is grown around Lake Victoria; arabica is grown on higher ground, particularly on the slopes of Mt Elgon. Cotton is next in importance and is produced in central parts of the plateau. Coffee and cotton make up 85% of all exports. Other commercial crops are tea (from the Ruwenzori region and the southwest), tobacco (from the northwest), sugarcane (grown on estates near Lake Victoria) and groundnuts. In areas with less then 75 cm of rain a year, in the east especially, cattle, sheep and goats are kept.

Energy

Uganda lacks energy minerals and the country's power comes from the hydro-electric plant at the Owen Falls dam near Jinja. Construction began in 1948 and the last turbine, the tenth, was installed twenty years later. The Owen Falls scheme supplies electricity to all Uganda and sends some to Kenya via a direct power line to Nairobi.

Climate

Although Uganda lies on the Equator, its climate is modified by altitude. Temperatures are fairly uniform throughout the year averaging 23°C on the plateau and 27°C in the Nile Rift Valley. In the equatorial south, rain occurs every month—often as violent thunderstorms—with two wetter periods (March-May, October-November). In the north, there is a dry season from December to February. Amounts vary from under 75 cm in the northeast to over 150 cm on the shores of Lake Victoria and up to 400 cm in the Ruwenzori mountains. Most parts of the plateau receive about 100 cm of rain a year.

Flora & fauna

Tall elephant grass occurs in the wetter areas, merging into rain forest in the south and southwest. Bush savanna covers drier regions, changing to semi-desert vegetation in the north-east. Uganda's wildlife, which is partly protected in three national parks, includes antelopes, elephants, lions, leopards, giraffes, gorillas and the rare white rhinoceros.

Forestry & fishing

Forests, covering only 7% of Uganda, are mostly found in the southwest. Hardwoods predominate: cedar is used for building and camphor and podocarp (yellow-wood) for furniture. Softwood plantations are being developed. With over 35,000 km² of lakes and rivers, Uganda has one of the world's largest fresh-water fisheries. Production averages 11 kilos per inhabitant and comes mainly from lakes Victoria, Kyoga, Edward and George. Carp and tilapia are the main species caught; some frozen fish is exported.

Industry

Most industries are based on the country's agriculture and include cotton ginning, textile weaving, coffee processing, tea packing, cigarette manufacture, sugar refining, flour milling, vegetable oil extraction and leather curing. Other industries process minerals and wood and include copper smelting, cement manufacture, fertilizers, plywood and paper production. Some consumer goods are produced. Kampala, Jinja-Bugembe and Tororo are the chief industrial centres.

Mining

Copper, accounting for 6% of total exports, is Uganda's chief mineral resource. It is mined at Kilembe in the Ruwenzoris and railed to Jinja for smelting. All copper exports are sent to Japan. Limestone (used for cement) and phosphate (for fertilizer) are mined near Tororo and there is some production of tin, tungsten and beryl in the southwest. Other minerals existing include gold, nickel, cobalt (in the Kilembe copper ore), bismuth and mica.

People & towns

Uganda is one of Africa's most densely populated countries. The Nile roughly divides the country ethnically: to the north and east are the Nilotics and Nilo-Hamitics (related to Sudanese peoples); to the south and west are the Bantu or Africans who account for 70% of the population. Three main towns are situated by Lake Victoria: Kampala (the capital) and the industrial hub formed by Jinja (100,000) and Bugembe (50,000). The fourth largest town is Mbale (25,000) at the foot of Mt Elgon. Less than 10% of the population live in towns.

Tourism

Uganda has great tourist potential. Its scenery ranges from verdant lake shores to snowy mountain peaks and its abundant wildlife includes a wide variety of birds by the lakes and swamps. There are three national parks (Kidepo, Ruwenzori and Kabalega) and 14 game reserves.

Transport

Because of Uganda's inland position, good external communications are vital to trade. There is a direct rail link, via Tororo, to the Kenyan port of Mombasa which handles the bulk of Ugandan imports and exports. Substantial amounts of coffee, cotton and sugar are also shipped across Lake Victoria from Bukakata, Port Bell (Kampala) and Entebbe to Kisumu (Kenya) and then sent by rail to Mombasa. Internally, the railway serves only a small part of the country (Tororo-Arua, Tororo-Kasese) and road transport is growing in importance. The 46,000 km road network (25% all-weather) includes a major highway into Kenya. Uganda's international airport is at Entebbe, 40 km from Kampala.

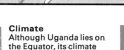

Kenya

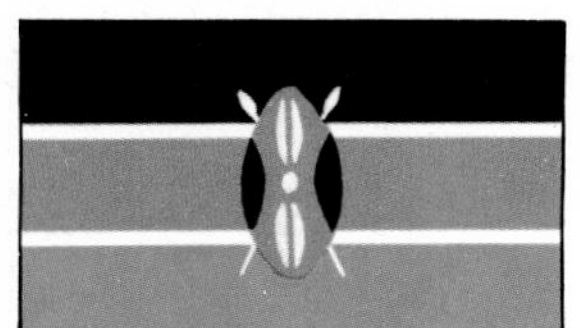

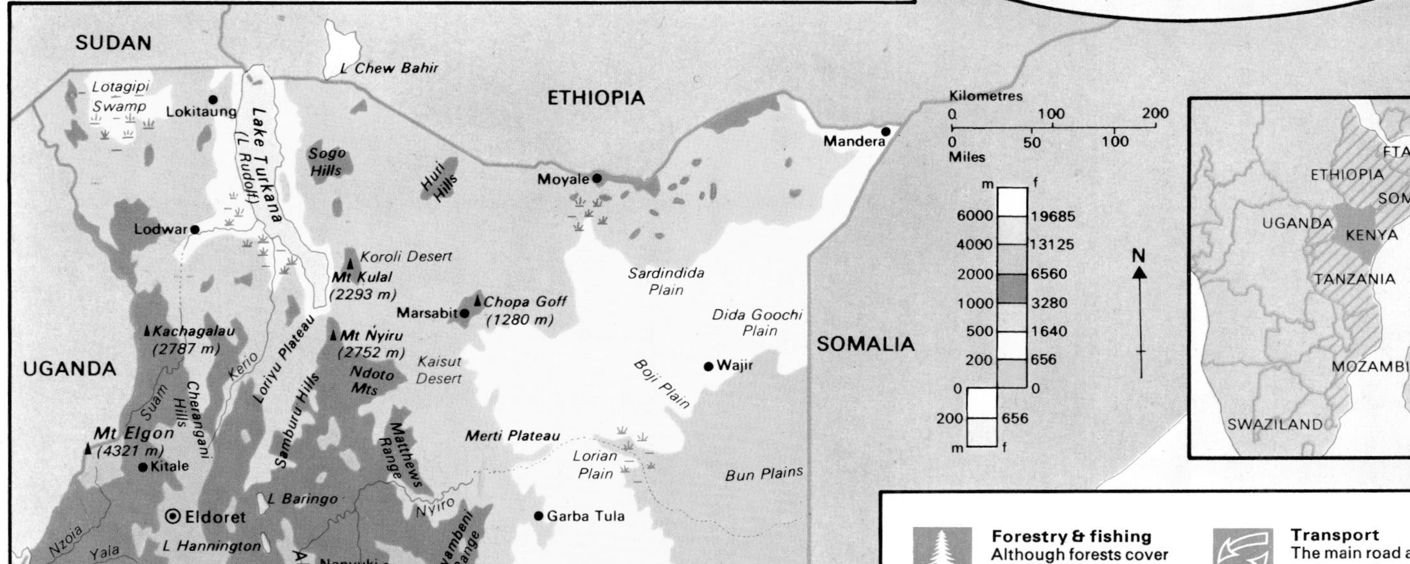

Area
582,647 km²/224,960 sq miles
Location
4°35′ N — 4°40′ S
33°58′ — 41°45′ E
Population
17,363,000 (1981)
Population density
30 per km²/77 per sq mile
Capital and largest city
Nairobi: 1,000,000 (1980)
Languages
Swahili, English
Major imports
machinery, oil, vehicles, fertilizers, food
Major exports
coffee, petroleum products, tea, sisal, fruit and vegetables, meat, pyrethrum
Currency
shilling (1 shilling = 100 cents)
Gross National Product
7,280 million US dollars (1981)
Status
republic

Climate

As Kenya straddles the equator, there are no marked seasonal changes. Temperatures are high on the humid coast but modified inland by altitude: Mombasa averages 26°C, Nairobi 20°C and Eldoret 17°C. Although no month is really dry, there are two wetter seasons: the long rains (March to June) and the short rains (November to December). Amounts vary from over 100 cm in the highlands, the Lake Victoria region and along the coast to under 50 cm on the Nyika and only 10 cm in the northeast where semi-desert conditions prevail.

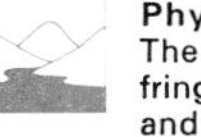

Physical features

The narrow coastal belt, fringed with rain forest and mangrove swamps, is backed by a vast, arid, scrub-covered plain, the Nyika, which makes up 60% of the territory. The rest of the country, mostly at altitudes of between 1,500 m and 2,500 m, consists of rugged plateaux with grass savanna and forested mountains and includes the 150 km long Aberdare Range (3,994 m) and two mighty peaks: Mt Elgon (4,321 m) on the Ugandan border and Mt Kenya (5,200 m), Africa's second highest summit. This highland zone is cut by the Great Rift Valley which forms a north-south trench, 600 to 900 m deep and contains several lakes including Lake Turkana (Rudolf), 2,473 km². From the western rim of the Rift Valley, the plateau slopes down to the shores of Lake Victoria. The main river, the Tana, drains off Mt Kenya and the Aberdare range and enters the Indian Ocean at Kipini. Many small rivers flow into Lakes Turkana and Victoria.

Agriculture

Agriculture dominates the economy, employing 75% of the population and supplying 80% of all exports. Cultivated land, only 15% of the total area, is concentrated along the coast, in the Tana valley and in the highlands. Maize, found on almost every farm, is the staple food followed by yams, nuts, cassava, wheat and rice. Commercial farming is centred on the highlands. Coffee, grown south of Mt Kenya, is the chief cash crop and provides 30% of total exports. Tea, from the Kericho and Limuru districts, is next in importance and Kenya ranks as Africa's largest tea producer. Other major cash crops are sisal (grown in the coastal belt and along the Nairobi railway), pyrethrum (Kenya produces 80% of the world's supply of this non-toxic insecticide obtained from a white daisy), fruit and vegetables. Copra and coir are produced along the coast. The plateau grasslands support an expanding livestock industry.

Forestry & fishing

Although forests cover only 3% of the country they are commercially important. The coastal mangrove swamps yield tanning bark and poles for building (highly suitable as the wood is resistant to rot and white ants). Above 1,700 m, the highland forests include cedar (for construction and making pencils), camphor and podocarp (for furniture) and bamboo and eucalyptus (for pulp and paper). There are several plywood mills and a fibre-board factory. The Eldoret and Kitale districts have extensive wattle plantations; wattle bark, used in tanning, is a major export. Fishing is primarily based on the lakes.

Mining & energy

Kenya is steadily developing its mineral resources. The most important product is sodium carbonate dredged from Lake Magadi and railed, via a special branch line, to Mombasa. Fluorspar output, from the Kerio valley, is increasing rapidly and is mostly exported. Other minerals exploited are lead-silver-zinc at Kinangoni, limestone at Koru and Kajiado, rubies, green garnets and magnetite. Electricity is generated partly by thermal stations using imported fuels and partly by hydro-electric schemes in the highlands; some power is imported from the Owen Falls hydro station in Uganda.

Industry

Over half of the manufacturing sector is based on processing primary agricultural products and includes coffee milling, meat packing, fruit canning, flour milling, sugar refining, fish freezing, cotton ginning, tanning, rope and sacking manufacture, coir matting and pyrethrum extraction. Other industries produce textiles, clothing, wood, furniture, paper, chemicals, cement and light engineering goods. Vehicle assembly plants have been built in the 1970s. Nairobi is the chief manufacturing centre followed by Mombasa which has a wide range of industries including a ship repair yard and an oil refinery (a major export earner). Other industrial centres are Nakuru, Kisumu, Eldoret, Thika.

Transport

The main road and rail route runs from Mombasa through Nairobi and across the highlands into Uganda. There are branch lines off this railway to Tanzania (via Voi), Nanyuki and Kisumu (the chief port on Lake Victoria). Only 10% of the 47,500 km road network is paved. Mombasa is the main port which also serves Uganda, parts of northern Tanzania and eastern Zaire. There is an international airport at Nairobi and internal air services link the capital with Mombasa, Malindi and Kisumu.

Towns & people

About 95% of the population is African and includes around 40 different tribes. The Kikuyu (nearly 2 million—the largest ethnic group) are from the highlands south of Mt Kenya, followed by the Luo (1,200,000) and the Luhya and Kamba (one million each). Most of the people are cultivators or pastoralists and less than 10% live in towns. Nairobi, in the highlands (1,700 m) mid-way between the Indian Ocean and Lake Victoria, is East Africa's leading industrial and commercial centre. Kenya's second city is the busy port and tourist resort of Mombasa (400,000). Kisumu is a lake port and the commercial centre of a major grain-producing area.

Tourism

Kenya is the land of the safari and tourism has overtaken coffee as the leading foreign exchange earner. The country's three main attractions are its coasts, its scenery and its wildlife. The coast has some of the world's finest beaches where the blue ocean contrasts with white sand and green palms. The interior is visually magnificent, ranging from desert to snow-covered Mt Kenya, from vast savannas to the dramatic Rift Valley. Large areas have been set aside as national parks for the conservation of wildlife and contain lions, elephants, giraffes, antelopes, zebras, jackals, baboons, hyenas, buffaloes and many other animals. Lake Nakuru is famous for its flamingos. Almost half a million tourists visit Kenya annually.

Tanzania

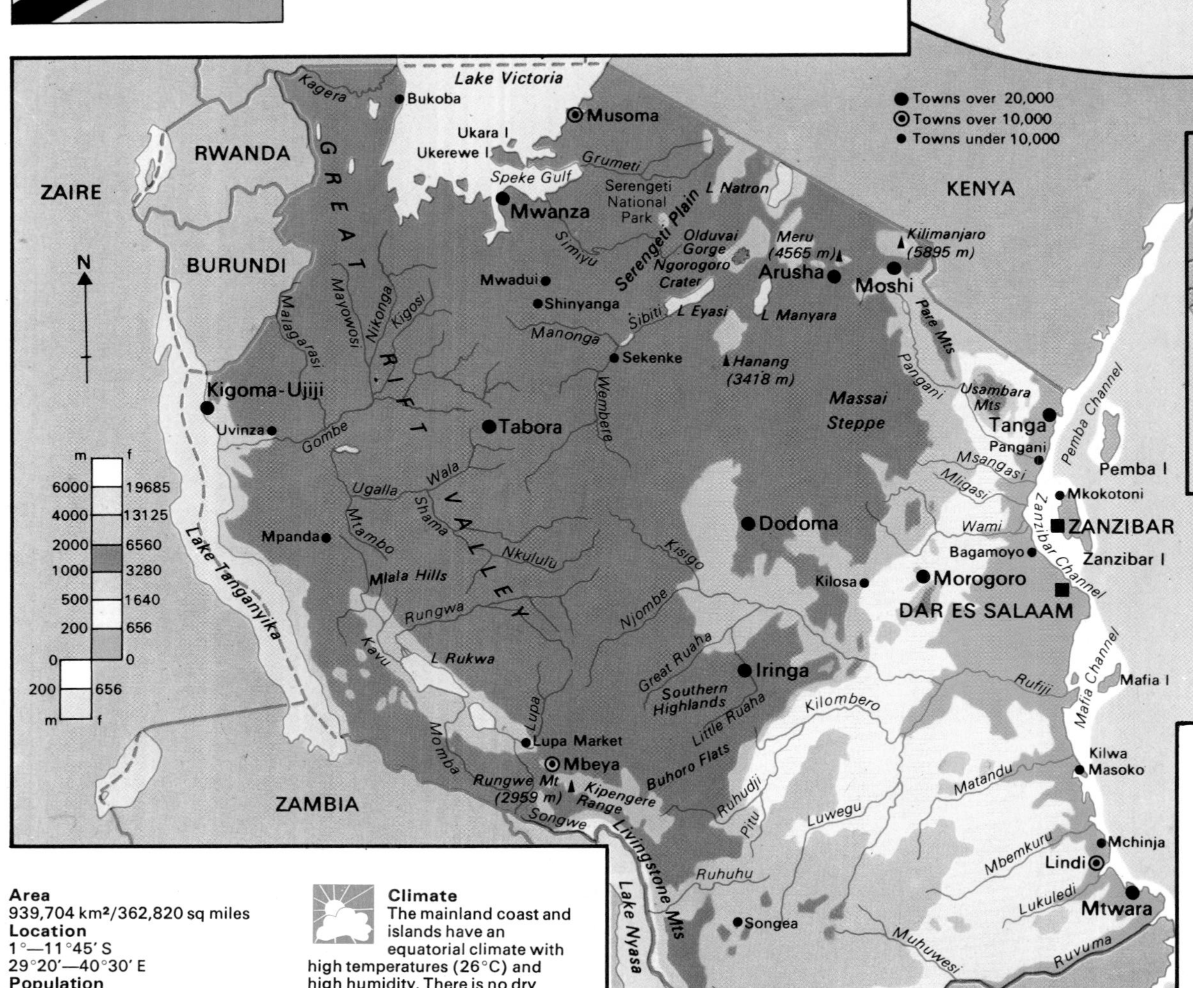

Area
939,704 km²/362,820 sq miles
Location
1°—11°45′ S
29°20′—40°30′ E
Population
19,137,000 (1981)
Population density
20 per km²/53 per sq mile
Capital and largest city
Dar es Salaam: 700,000 (1981)
Language
Swahili
Major imports
machinery, vehicles, fuels, food, textiles, iron and steel
Major exports
coffee, cotton, cloves, sisal, diamonds, cashew nuts
Currency
shilling (1 shilling = 100 cents)
Gross National Product
5,260 million US dollars (1981)
Status
republic

Physical features

Tanzania, East Africa's largest state, was formed in 1964 by the union of Tanganyika and Zanzibar. Tanganyika, the mainland, consists of a great plateau, 1,000 m high, with flat, grassy plains, woodlands and isolated hills. The plateau is broken by mountains in the southwest and northeast, including Africa's highest peak, Kilimanjaro (5,895 m). The territory contains 53,500 km² of water including part of Lake Victoria in the north and sections of Lakes Tanganyika and Nyasa on the western border of the Great Rift Valley. The coastal plain, flanking sandy beaches and mangrove swamps, is narrow except along the lower course of the Rufiji, the country's longest river. Zanzibar (1,658 km²) and Pemba (984 km²) are low-lying coral islands fringed with reefs.

Climate

The mainland coast and islands have an equatorial climate with high temperatures (26°C) and high humidity. There is no dry season and rainfall varies from 180 cm on Zanzibar to 120 cm at Dar es Salaam. The plateau is hot and dry: temperatures, with extreme daily variations (up to 20°C), average 22°C while rain (falling between November and April) seldom exceeds 70 cm.

Mainland agriculture

The severe handicaps imposed by the tsetse fly and low rainfall mean that less than 10% of the country is cultivated. Crop-growing is confined to the coastal plain, the northeastern highlands and to the areas bordering Lakes Victoria and Nyasa where rainfall is slightly higher. Subsistence farming predominates. Maize and millet are the basic foods, followed by groundnuts, rice, cassava and bananas. Coffee, cotton, sisal and cashew nuts make up 50% of total exports; Tanzania is the world's leading sisal producer. Coffee is grown on the slopes of Kilimanjaro and in the Bukoba district; cotton comes from the Mwanza region; sisal is produced in the Dar es Salaam and Tanga regions; cashew nuts are cultivated along the coast between the Rufiji and the Mozambique border. Other cash crops include tea, coconuts (copra and oil), pyrethrum and tobacco. Irrigation has been developed for the Kilimanjaro coffee plantations and for sugar plantations near Arusha and in the Kilombero valley. Cattle-raising is important but is limited to tsetse-free zones.

Island agriculture

In contrast to the mainland, Zanzibar and Pemba are largely self-sufficient in food. As their east coasts have dry, infertile soil, arable farming is based on the central and western zones. Rice, maize, millet, cassava and bananas are the staple foods. The main cash crop, cloves, accounts for 90% of the islands' exports. Two-thirds of output comes from Pemba and together the islands supply 80% of the world's cloves. Coconut palms are widespread and coconut products (copra, oil, rope and matting) are the other leading exports. In an attempt to diversify commercial farming, cocoa, citrus fruits and tobacco are being developed.

Forestry & fishing

Tanzania's few forests have been substantially reduced by shifting cultivation, but re-afforestation programmes are now making good this loss. Highland areas yield hardwoods such as camphor and mahogany, while the mangrove swamps along the coast provide building timber and tanning bark. In Zanzibar, fish are a major source of protein; sardines and tuna are also exported. On the mainland, almost 90% of the catch comes from inland waters, notably Lake Victoria.

Mining

Mining is centred on the country's diamond deposits at Mwadui in the north and diamonds provide 7% of total exports. Some gold is produced in the Musoma, Sekenke and Lupa districts and salt is obtained from seawater along the coast. The new Tanzam railway, linking Tanzania and Zambia, opens up the mineral potential of the southwest and extensive reserves of coal and iron ore are being surveyed near the Livingstone mountains

Industry

Industrial development is in its early stages and is mostly based on agricultural produce. It includes cotton ginning, coconut-oil extraction, textile manufacture, coffee processing, rice milling and cement manufacture (from coral limestone). There are also factories producing soap, paint, plastics, shoes, beer and light engineering goods. An oil refinery has been built at Dar es Salaam and a fertilizer plant at Tanga. Dar es Salaam, Tanga and Mwanza are the main industrial centres. Tanga benefits from the country's principal hydro-electric installation which is on the Pangani river. There is considerable hydro-power potential in the southwest.

Transport

Although the 3,000 km rail network is inadequate, it does connect the major producing areas to the coast. The central line (1,246 km) runs inland from Dar es Salaam via Dodoma and Tabora to Kigoma on Lake Tanganyika; branch lines go to Mwanza and Mpanda. In the north, a line links Tanga to Arusha while the southwest is now served by the new Tanzam line from Dar es Salaam to Zambia. The main ports are Dar es Salaam, Tanga and Mtwara on the coast and Mwanza on Lake Victoria. East African Airways (Tanzanian Region) operates internally and there are international airports at Dar es Salaam, Arusha, Lindi and Tabora.

Tourism

Tanzania has the finest game parks in Africa: the most famous, the Serengeti National Park, covers 13,000 km² and contains a million animals including elephants, lions, antelopes, giraffes, leopards, zebras, buffaloes, rhinoceros and hippopotami. Tanzania also offers tourists scenic landscapes and some of the continent's principal historic sites; the oldest human fossil on record (1.5 million years) was found at Olduvai Gorge in the north.

Towns

About 94% of Tanzanians, who are mostly African, live in rural areas and there are few large towns. Dar es Salaam, the 'haven of peace', is the main industrial centre and chief port, but the title of capital is to be transferred to Dodoma (46,000), an old, centrally-located trading settlement. Tanzania's second largest town, the port of Zanzibar, dates back to the 8th century when the Arabs colonized the island. The other main centres, Tanga (103,000), Mwanza (111,000) and Arusha (55,000), are being developed.

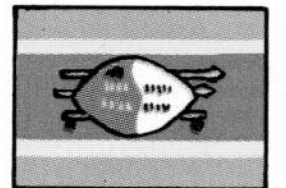

Swaziland **Mozambique**

Swaziland and Mozambique

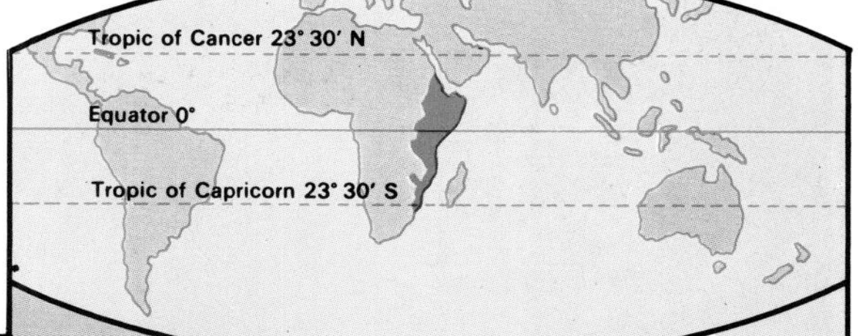

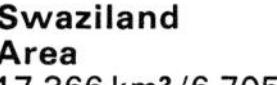

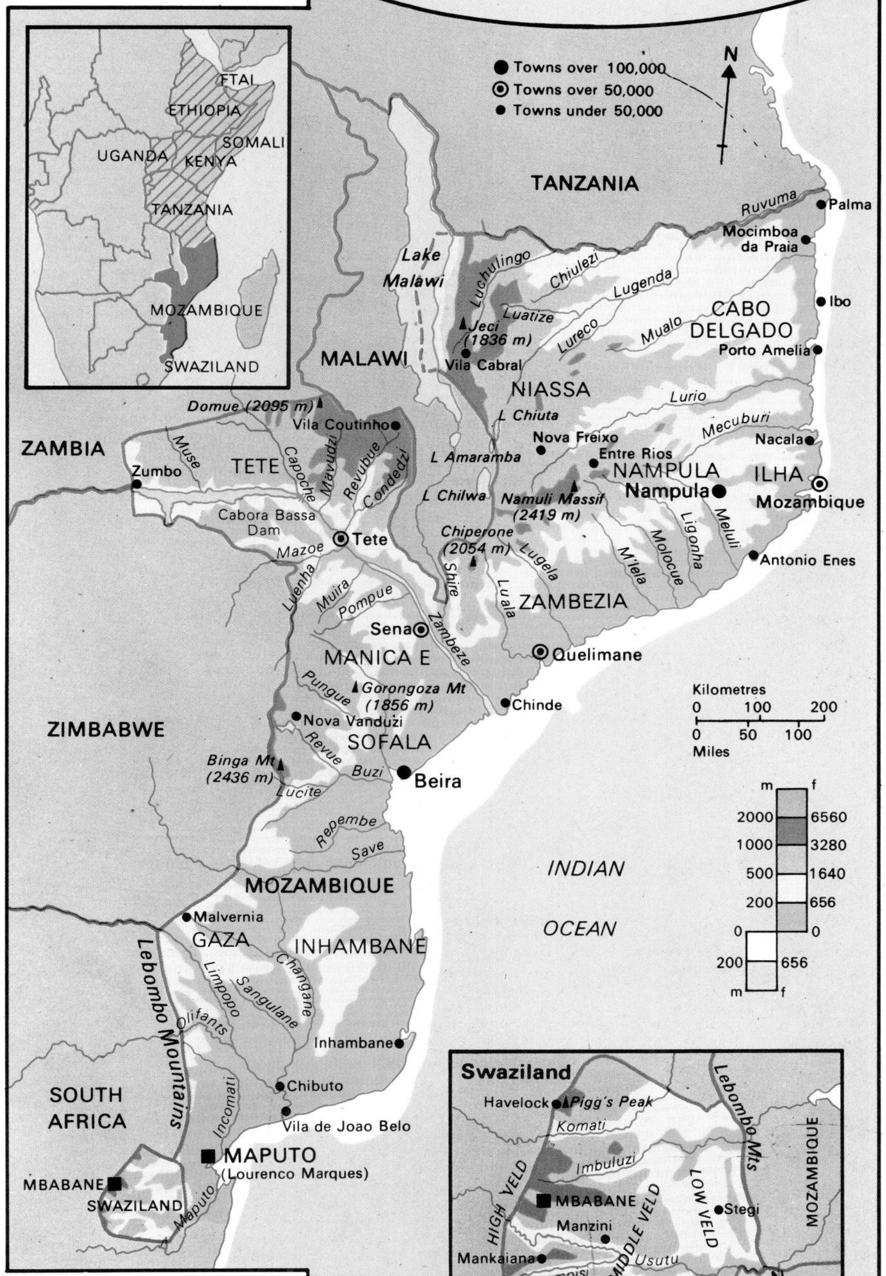

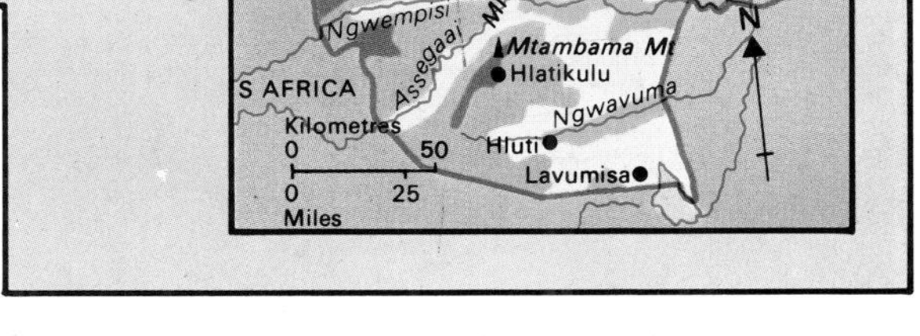

Swaziland
Area
17,366 km²/6,705 sq miles
Location
25°30'—27°20' S
31°—32°20' E
Population
641,000 (1981)
Population density
37 per km²/96 per sq mile
Capital and largest city
Mbabane: 33,000 (1982)
Languages
Siswati, English
Major imports
machinery, vehicles, manufactured goods, fuels, chemicals
Major exports
sugar, woodpulp, iron ore, asbestos, citrus, canned fruit, meat and meat products
Currency
lilangeni (1 lilangeni = 100 cents)
Gross National Product
480 million US dollars (1981)
Status
absolute monarchy

Physical features
Swaziland, smaller than Wales, is wedged between Mozambique and South Africa. There are three main regions: the rugged High Veld (averaging 1,200 m) in the west, the undulating Middle Veld (600 m) in the centre and, in the east, the malarial Low Veld (300 m). The low Lebombo mountains run along the Mozambique border. The main rivers, such as the Imbuluzi, Usutu and Ngwavuma, flow east from the High Veld across the country and cut through the Lebombo in deep gorges while the Komati swings north into South Africa finally to join the Sabie.

Climate
The climate varies with altitude. The High Veld is cool and wet with annual averages of 16°C in temperature and 120 cm of rain, while the Low Veld is hot and dry (21°C temperature and 65 cm of rain). Rain occurs mainly as heavy summer storms and causes extensive soil erosion.

Agriculture
Farming, mostly at subsistence level, supports 70% of Swazis; maize is the staple food. Commercial agriculture, under non-Swazi control, includes sugar (accounting for 25% of total exports), citrus, cotton, rice, pineapples and tobacco. Apart from cotton, these export crops are grown under irrigation. About 15% of the country is cultivated. Cattle are widespread and over-grazing contributes to soil erosion; live animals and meat are exported. Forests have been planted to conserve the soil and now provide 20% of exports. Woodpulp is the chief product.

Mining & industry
Iron ore and asbestos make up a third of total exports. Iron ore, mined northwest of Mbabane, is taken by rail directly to Maputo (Mozambique) and shipped to Japan. Asbestos comes from the Havelock mine near Pigg's Peak. Coal is produced in the southeast and 50% of output is exported. Industrial development, centred around a hydro-electric power scheme on the Usutu, mainly consists of sugar refineries, pulp mills and fruit-canning plants.

Transport
The 2,400 km road network is 70% surfaced and includes, in the east, a major highway from South Africa to Mozambique. The 220 km railway, built for carrying iron ore, links with the Mozambique system. Manzini (10,000), the country's commercial centre, has the principal airport and there are connecting flights by Swazi Air to Johannesburg and Maputo.

Mozambique
Area
784,961 km²/303,073 sq miles
Location
10°30'—26°50' S
30°15'—40°45' E
Population
12,485,000 (1981)
Population density
16 per km²/41 per sq mile
Capital and largest city
Maputo: 755,000 (1980)
Language
Portuguese
Major imports
machinery, transport equipment, base metals, oil, wheat
Major exports
cashew nuts, cotton and textiles, sugar, wood, tea, sisal
Currency
escudo (1 escudo = 100 centavos)
Gross National Product
not available
Status
republic

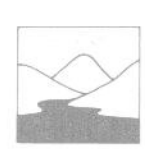

Physical features
Mozambique is a straggling country extending 2,700 km from north to south and varying in width from 80 km in the south to 800 km in the centre along the Zambeze. A broad coastal lowland, including the Zambeze and Limpopo deltas, occupies about 40% of the territory. Infertile, sandy soils predominate except for alluvial zones bordering rivers such as the Limpopo, Save, Buzi, Pungue and Zambeze. In the south, the coastal plain stretches inland almost to the western border, but in the centre and north the interior is undulating, rising to 900 m on the north-western plateau; the plateau surface is broken by the Namuli massif (2,419 m).

Climate
The coastal belt is hot, humid and unhealthy with temperatures averaging 22°C in winter and 29°C in summer. The interior uplands are only slightly cooler. Rain, falling during the summer months between November and May, is heaviest along the coast (150 cm at Beira) with inland areas, excluding the plateau, drier.

Agriculture
About 90% of the workforce is engaged in agriculture. Subsistence farming predominates: maize, yams, cassava, groundnuts and bananas are the basic crops. Commercial farming, supplying 80% of total exports, is mostly located near the major ports. The main cash crops are cashew nuts (Mozambique is the world's chief producer), cotton, sisal and coconuts (for copra) with tea grown on the plateau and sugar from irrigated areas in the Zambeze and Limpopo valleys. Some cattle are kept in the south. Rain forests along the rivers provide hardwoods for export.

Mining & energy
When developed, Mozambique's mineral resources could transform the economy. They include coal, iron ore, copper, fluorite, gold, bauxite, diamonds and the world's largest deposits of tantalite and second largest of beryl. There are also big reserves of natural gas. So far, only the coal at Tete is exploited in significant quantities. Electricity is generated by coal-fired thermal stations and hydro-electric power plants on the Revue and Zambeze (the Cabora Bassa project).

Industry
The country's few industries, based on local produce, include sugar refineries, cotton mills, tea factories and copra and cashew processing plants.

Transport
Over 75% of trade passing through the main ports (Maputo, Beira, Mozambique, Nacala) is handled on behalf of other states: Zaire, Zambia, Malawi, S Africa and, before 1976, Rhodesia. The rail network reflects this transit trade—there are east-west lines linking the interior to the coast, but no north-south routes. There are also good road connections to neighbouring states. Maputo and Beira have international airports.

Towns
The chief towns are on the coast. Maputo, formerly Lourenço Marques, is not well situated for a capital city as it is remote from most of the country, but it is the leading port and manufacturing centre and has become a tourist centre. Beira, the second largest city, is one of Africa's busiest ports. The two main towns in the north are the new ports of Nacala and Mozambique. Quelimane and Inhambane are regional centres.

Cameroun

Central African Empire

Cameroun and Central African Empire

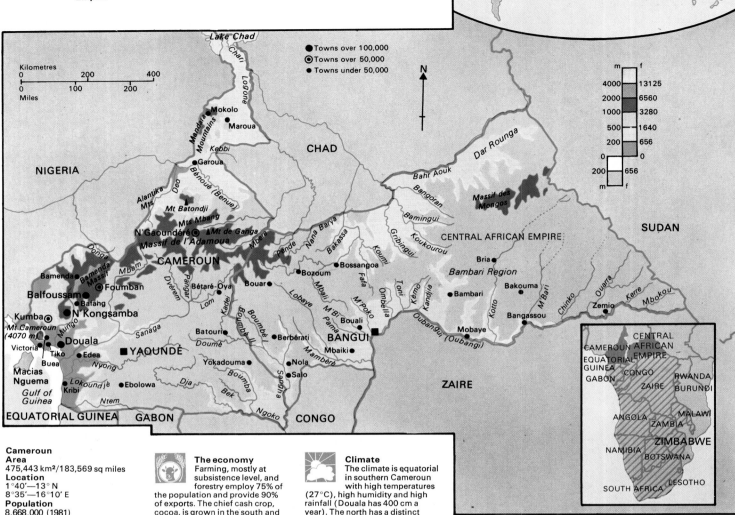

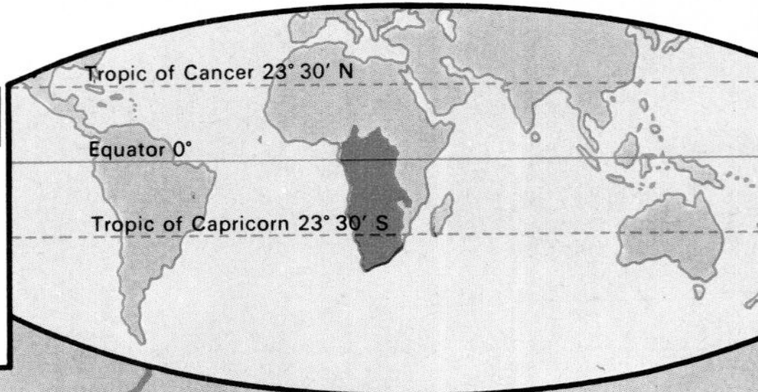

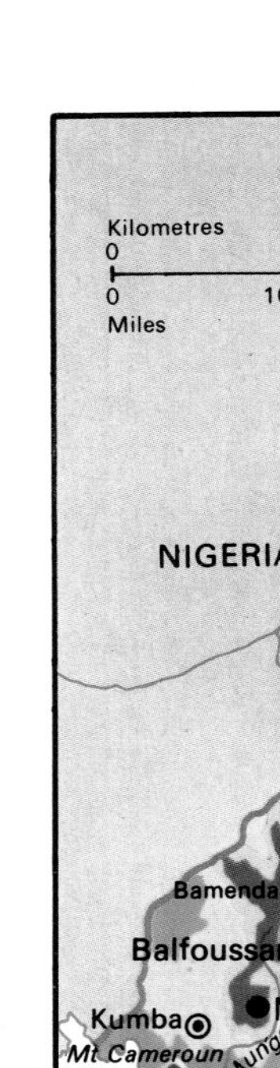

Cameroun
Area
475,443 km²/183,569 sq miles
Location
1°40'—13° N
8°35'—16°10' E
Population
8,668,000 (1981)
Population density
18 per km²/47 per sq mile
Capital
Yaoundé: 400,000 (1979)
Largest city
Douala: 500,000 (1979)
Languages
English, French
Major imports
manufactured goods, transport equipment, machinery, food, fuels
Major exports
cocoa, coffee, timber, aluminium, cotton, bananas
Currency
franc (1 franc = 100 centimes)
Gross National Product
7,630 million US dollars (1981)
Status
republic

Physical features
Behind the narrow swampy coastal plain lies an upland belt covered with dense rain forest. This zone merges northwards into the central plateau where high grasslands rise to over 1,000 m. In the northern part of the country, savanna slopes down to the shores of Lake Chad. Mountains extend along the western border reaching their highest point in volcanic Mt Cameroun (4070 m) which dominates the coastline. The central plateau acts as a watershed: to the north, streams flow either into the Benue (and then into the Niger) or into Lake Chad via the Logone; southwards, streams drain into the Sanaga and Sangha (a tributary of the Congo).

The economy
Farming, mostly at subsistence level, and forestry employ 75% of the population and provide 90% of exports. The chief cash crop, cocoa, is grown in the south and accounts for 32% of total exports; coffee, produced in the south-west highlands, represents a further 25%. Other export crops are cotton and groundnuts from the north, timber, bananas, palm kernels, rubber and tobacco from the south. Yams and rice are grown for food in the south, millet and sorghum in the north. Livestock is raised on the central grasslands and northern savanna. About 60% of the country's fish is taken from inland waters, notably the lower Lagone and Lake Chad. Because of poor communications, bauxite deposits in the central plateau are not fully exploited and the Edea aluminium smelter, the main industry, uses imported ore. Other industries, concentrated in the Douala-Yaoundé region, are small-scale and consist of processing local produce. The hydro-electric power station at Edea on the Sanaga provides 95% of the country's electricity.

Transport
Inadequate transport is retarding industrial development. The main railway runs from Douala to N'Gaoundéré and will, eventually, extend to Chad. At the moment, goods from the north go to Garoua and are exported through Nigeria via the Benue. Douala handles 90% of sea trade and is the main port followed by Tiko, Kribi and Victoria. The 40,000 km road network is being improved. Douala and Yaoundé have airports.

Climate
The climate is equatorial in southern Cameroun with high temperatures (27°C), high humidity and high rainfall (Douala has 400 cm a year). The north has a distinct dry season (from November to February) and rainfall is less with only 60 cm near Lake Chad.

Central African Empire
Area
622,985 km²/240,535 sq miles
Location
2°10'—11° N
14°25'—27°20' E
Population
2,379,000 (1981)
Population density
3.8 per km²/10 per sq mile
Capital and largest city
Bangui: 367,000 (1981)
Language
French, Sangho
Major imports
machinery, vehicles, textiles
Major exports
diamonds, coffee, cotton, timber, tobacco
Currency
franc (1 franc = 100 centimes)
Gross National Product
770 million US dollars (1981)
Status
empire

Physical features
The Central African Empire lies land-locked in the heart of Africa and consists of a savanna-covered plateau some 760 m high. This upland block acts as a watershed: to the north, streams drain into the Chari, Logone and their tributaries; southwards, most streams flow into the Oubangui and so into the Congo. Dense rain forest covers the southwest.

Climate
In the south, there is a short dry season from December to January and a long wet season from June to October; annual rainfall averages 200 cm. The north has a longer dry season, from November to April, with less rain—about 80 cm a year. Temperatures are high and average 27°C.

Transport
The empire's transport systems are poorly developed. Only a third of the roads in the 21,000 km network are all-weather and there are no railways. Inland waterways play a significant role in carrying freight and there is considerable seasonal traffic on the Oubangui and Sangha. The Oubangui is navigable below Bangui and barges ply between the capital and Brazzaville (Congo). From Brazzaville goods are taken by rail to the coast. Salo is the chief port on the Sangha but, upstream, Nola is being developed as a timber port. The empire's products are also exported via Cameroun: a main road connects Bangui to Douala and there are plans to link the two countries by rail. Such a railway would cross the south-western region and help develop the area's agricultural, forest and mineral resources. Bangui is the centre for domestic and international air services.

Agriculture
In the Central African Empire, 90% of the population live off the land, yet only 2% of the land area is under cultivation. Subsistence farming predominates and the principal food crops are millet, maize, sorghum, beans, cassava, groundnuts and rice. The leading cash crops, mainly from the southwest, are cotton and coffee which together account for over 40% of total exports. Tobacco, rubber, sisal and palm kernels are also exported. Timber production from the southwestern forests is hampered by poor transport facilities; at present, logs are floated down the Oubangui and Congo rivers for export. Stock-rearing is hindered by the tsetse fly and is largely confined to herds kept by nomads in the west and in the Bambari region.

Mining & industry
Alluvial diamonds, from the west of the country, make up half the empire's exports. Important reserves of uranium, located near Bakouma, are so far unexploited. Industry is limited to a few concerns processing primary materials, especially cotton: there are several cotton ginneries and a spinning, weaving and dyeing complex. The hydro-electric power station at Bouali is the chief source of electricity.

Equatorial Guinea and Gabon

Equatorial Guinea   Gabon

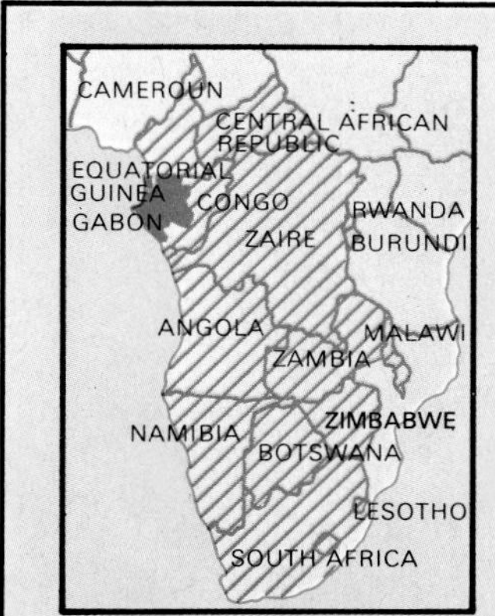

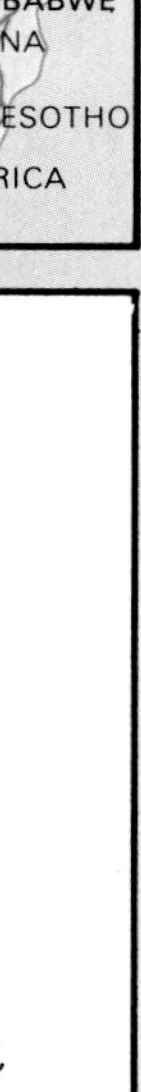

Equatorial Guinea
Area
28,051 km²/10,831 sq miles
Location
3°45'N—1°25'S
5°35'—11°20'E
Population
346,000 (1981)
Population density
12 per km²/32 per sq mile
Capital and largest city
Malabo: 60,000
Language
Spanish
Major imports
vehicles, fuels, tobacco, cement, machinery
Major exports
cocoa, coffee, timber, palm oil, copra, bananas
Currency
peseta (1 peseta = 100 centimos)
Gross National Product
62 million US dollars (1981)
Status
republic

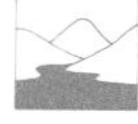

The land
Equatorial Guinea consists of the mainland territory of Río Muni (26,017 km²) and five islands: Macías Nguema, formerly Fernando Poo (2,034 km²), Pigalu (17km²), Corisco (15 km²) and Elobey Grande and Elobey Chico (together covering 2.5 km²). Río Muni comprises a plateau which rises in a series of steep steps from the densely forested coastal plain; mountains, reaching 1,200 m, rim the plateau. The principal river, the Benito, divides the country in two. Macías Nguema, the main island, is formed from several extinct volcanoes; thick forests cover the coastal lowlands while savanna and grasslands characterize the interior mountains. Santa Isabel, the highest peak, reaches 3,007 m. An unhealthy equatorial climate prevails with high temperatures, humidity and rainfall. Malabo averages 26°C and has 200 cm of rain a year; Rio Muni is slightly drier than the islands.

Towns
The capital, Malabo, is on the north coast of Macías Nguema and stands on cliffs overlooking a natural harbour formed from a submerged volcano crater. Bata (27,000) is the mainland's chief town and leading port with Niefang, Mikomeseng, Ebebiyin and Evinayong serving as market centres in the interior. Pigalu island is over-populated and many people leave to work in Río Muni or Macías Nguema.

The economy
Equatorial Guinea's economy, based on agriculture and forestry, is undeveloped. Cocoa is the main cash crop, accounting for over half of total exports; 90% of output comes from the fertile Macías Nguema where it is mostly grown on plantations. Coffee, providing 25% of exports, comes from the Cameroun border region of Río Muni. Other commercial crops are palm oil from the mainland, bananas from Macías Nguema and copra from Pigalu. Cassava and sweet potatoes are the staple foods and there is some livestock on the uplands of Macías Nguema. Fishing is well established off the islands. Timber accounts for 16% of exports and production is centred on the forests of Río Muni; okoumé, a softwood used in making plywood, and mahogany are the principal species exploited. Industry is very limited and is confined to small-scale processing of primary products such as cocoa, coffee and timber. Macias Nguema is more developed than Rio Muni.

Transport
There are no railways and only 1,200 km of roads, mostly unsurfaced. The main tarred routes run from Bata to Rio Benito and Ebebiyin and from Malabo to Luba and Ri-Aba. Malabo, handling general cargo and cocoa, is the chief port followed by Luba (bananas), Bata (general cargo), Rio Benito (wood) and Puerto Iradier (wood). Malabo and Bata have international airports.

Gabon
Area
267,000 km²/103,088 sq miles
Location
2°15'N—3°55'S
8°45'—14°30'E
Population
669,000 (1981)
Population density
2.5 per km²/6.5 per sq mile
Capital and largest city
Libreville: 225,000 (1978)
Language
French
Major imports
machinery, metals, transport equipment, chemicals, textiles, foodstuffs
Major exports
crude oil, timber and wood products, manganese, uranium
Currency
franc (1 franc = 100 centimes)
Gross National Product
2,550 million US dollars (1981)
Status
republic

Climate
Gabon's hot, wet climate is typically equatorial. High humidity and high temperatures (26 to 28°C) prevail throughout the year and there is no dry seaon except in the south. Rainfall, averaging 250 cm, is heaviest in the northwest: Cocobeach, near Equatorial Guinea has up to 400 cm of rain a year.

Physical features
Gabon, situated astride the equator, is dominated by the Ogooué river system. Except for the extreme northwest and southwest, the Ogooué and its tributaries drain the entire territory and have cut their way through the broad forested plateau, some 600 m high, occupying the interior. Mountains, up to 1,800 m in altitude, edge the plateau. The sandy coastal plain, fringed with mangrove swamps, is narrow in the north and south but widens in the Ogooué region.

Mining & industry
Minerals dominate the economy and account for over 60% of exports. Petroleum, from fields at Gamba and off Port Gentil, is the most important followed by manganese from Moanda in the southeast (this ore is exported by rail via the Congo). Gabon ranks as the world's leading exporter of manganese. Uranium is mined at Mounana, also in the southeast. Large reserves of iron ore at Mekambo, in the northeast, are to be exploited; zinc, gold and phosphate also occur. The industrial sector, based on local raw materials, is poorly developed; it includes plywood and veneer factories, an oil-refinery at Port Gentil, coffee and oil-palm processing plants and flour mills.

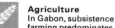

Agriculture
In Gabon, subsistence farming predominates. The staple crops grown are cassava, maize, yams, rice and bananas but output is not sufficient and food imports are necessary. Cash crop production is very limited with coffee, cocoa, palm oil and kernels accounting for less than 1% of total exports. Coffee and cocoa are grown in the fertile north-west, oil palms and coffee in the Lambaréné region. Few animals are kept because of the tsetse fly. After minerals, timber is Gabon's principal resource providing 35% of exports. Forests cover 75% of the country and include valuable hardwoods as well as okoumé. The okoumé tree grows only in Gabon, Río Muni and Congo; Gabon is the world's largest producer of okoumé wood, used for plywood and veneers. Other timbers exported are mahogany, ebony and walnut.

Transport
Economic development is hampered by inadequate communications. Roads are poor and often impassable during rain. The only railway links the Moanda mine with the Congo network, but a trans-Gabon line is planned and work has begun on the first stage, Owèndo to Booué. The Ogoové is navigable up to Ndjolé. There is a new deep-water port at Owendo. As well as an international airport at Libreville, there are over 80 airfields, many of them owned by timber and mining concerns.

Congo and Zaire

Congo,

Zaire

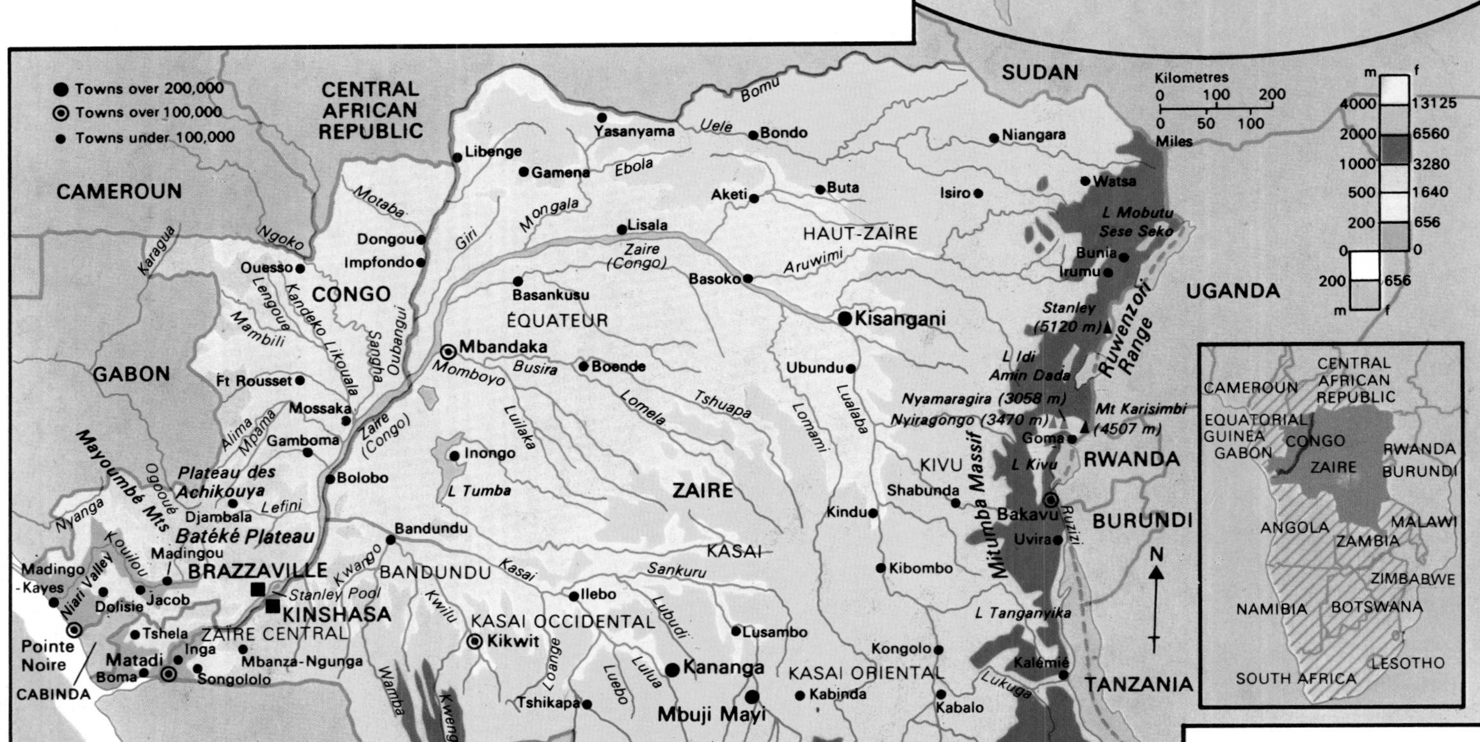

Congo
Area
342,000 km²/132,000 sq miles
Location
3°40′ N—5° S
11°—18°40′ E
Population
1,658,000 (1981)
Population density
5 per km²/13 per sq mile
Capital and largest city
Brazzaville: 200,000 (1980)
Language
French
Major imports
machinery, iron and steel, vehicles, chemicals
Major exports
timber, veneers, plywood, sugar, potash
Currency
franc (1 franc = 100 centimes)
Gross National Product
1,840 million US dollars (1981)
Status
republic

The land
The Congo's short coastline, backed by lagoons, is sandy in the north but more swampy in the south. From the narrow coastal plain, the Mayoumbé mountains rise steeply to almost 800 m. Beyond this forested ridge lies the broad Niari valley, edged to the north by the Chaillu massif which acts as a divide between drainage into the Kouilou and the Zaïre. Further inland, the country consists of the savanna-covered Batéké plateau which is dissected by the forested valleys of tributaries of the Zaïre. For 1,000 km, the eastern border is formed by the Zaïre and a major tributary, the Oubangui. The climate is typically equatorial with high temperatures ranging from 21 to 27°C and a high annual rainfall of between 200 and 260 cm. There is no dry season except during winter in the extreme north (between December and January) and south (between June and July).

Forestry & farming
Forests, covering half the country, provide the Congo with its leading export: timber. Production is centred on the Mayoumbé and Chaillu highlands, especially along the Congo-Océan railway and the Sangha in the north. Okoumé and mahogany are the main commercial species. Agriculture employs 70% of the population. The chief export crops—sugar, tobacco and groundnuts—are grown in the Niari valley; this fertile depression is also used for food crops such as cassava, maize, bananas and rice and dairy farming. Other cash crops are coffee and cocoa from the forested zones and palm oil from northern river valleys.

Mining & industry
The country's chief mineral resource is potash, mined near Pointe Noire. Petroleum (offshore), lead, zinc, tin, coppper, gold and diamonds are also produced. Iron ore, phosphate and bauxite have been discovered. Industries, located in Brazzaville, Pointe Noire and the Niari valley, process local raw materials. They include sawmills, plywood plants, flour mills, sugar refineries and cigarette factories.

Transport
The 515 km Congo-Océan railway, from Pointe Noire to Brazzaville, plus navigable stretches of the rivers Zaïre, Oubangui and Sangha form the country's principal highways. A main road links Pointe Noire, the chief seaport, with Brazzaville and Ouesso and with Gabon. There are international airports at Brazzaville and Pointe Noire.

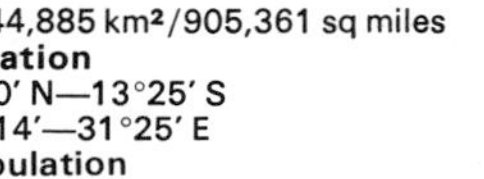

Zaire
Area
2,344,885 km²/905,361 sq miles
Location
5°30′ N—13°25′ S
12°14′—31°25′ E
Population
29,777,000 (1981)
Population density
13 per km²/33 per sq mile
Capital and largest city
Kinshasa: 3,000,000 (1981)
Language
French
Major imports
machinery, vehicles, petroleum products, cereals, textiles, chemicals, iron and steel
Major exports
copper, cobalt, diamonds, coffee, palm oil and kernels, zinc, rubber, tin
Currency
zaire (1 zaire = 100 makuta)
Gross National Product
6,280 million US dollars (1981)
Status
republic

Cities
Kinshasa, the capital, stands on the shore of Stanley Pool at the lower limit of inland navigation on the Zaïre. Kananga (600,000), in the heart of the country, is the chief town of the Kasai province. Zaire's third largest city, Lubumbashi (400,000), is the capital of Shaba in the extreme northeast.

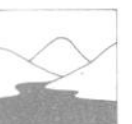

Physical features
After the Sudan, Zaire is the largest state in Africa. Its major feature is the world's sixth longest river, the Congo or Zaïre (4,800 km). The Zaïre rises in the Shaba plateau and curves across the country from the southeast to the southwest; below Kinshasa it breaks through mountains in a series of falls before widening into a 150 km long estuary. The Zaïre basin, forming the major part of the republic, is a vast shallow depression 300 to 600 m above sea level. It contains swamps and lakes, such as Tumba and Mai Ndombe, and an intricate network of tributaries, among them the Lomami, Kasai and Kwango. The basin is almost entirely surrounded by uplands. To the east, the edge of the Great Rift Valley features lakes Mobutu, Idi Amin, Kivu, and Tanganyika and high ranges including the Mitumba and Ruwenzori massifs.

Climate
Zaire has an equatorial climate averaging 27°C and 160 cm of rain. Rain occurs throughout the year near the equator but is more seasonal towards the tropics.

Agriculture
Subsistence farming is widespread. Basic foods are cassava, maize, yams, rice, groundnuts and bananas. Cash crops play a minor role in th economy; the main products are coffee, palm oil and kernels, cotton, rubber and sugar. Livestock is limited and provides only 6% of meat requirements. Forestry is underdeveloped.

Mining & industry
Minerals dominate Zaire's economy and account for 70% of exports. Large deposits of copper, cobalt, manganese, zinc, tin and uranium occur in Shaba making it the republic's most productive area. Zaire holds first place for world production of cobalt and sixth for copper. Half the world's supply of industrial diamonds comes from alluvial deposits in the Kasai river. Gold is mined northwest of Lake Mobutu. There are few industries.

Energy
Zaire has ample energy resources: coal at Luena, petroleum offshore, uranium in Shaba and, above all, rivers which provide half of Africa's water-power potential. The country's main hydro-electric power station is on the lower Zaïre at Inga; with a total capacity of 30,000 MW, it is one of the world's largest.

Transport
The country's size plus the fact that its major producing areas lie far inland make transport a vital issue. The main network, which is 16,400 km long, is formed by the Zaïre and its tributaries; Kinshasa is the chief river port. The leading sea ports are Matadi, linked by rail to Kinshasa, and Boma on the northern bank of the Zaïre estuary. Kinshasa, Lubumbashi and Kamina have international airports.

Rwanda and Burundi

Rwanda

Burundi

Rwanda
Area
26,338 km2/10,169 sq miles
Location
1°—2°50′ S
28°50′—30°55′ E
Population
5,346,000 (1981)
Population density
203 per km²/526 per sq mile
Capital and largest city
Kigali: 157,000 (1981)
Languages
Kinyarwanda, French
Major imports
vehicles, petroleum products, chemicals, cereals, machinery, textiles
Major exports
coffee, tin, tea, tungsten, pyrethrum
Currency
franc (1 franc = 100 centimes)
Gross National Product
1,340 million US dollars (1981)
Status
republic

Physical features
Landlocked Rwanda is one of Africa's smallest and most densely populated states. The western part of the country, containing Lake Kivu, occupies a section of the Great Rift Valley. In the northwest, the volcanic Virunga range includes the country's highest peak, Mt Karisimbi (4,507 m). The land slopes down from these mountains to a hilly central plateau 2,000 m high then, further east, gives way to a region of swamps and lakes which border the upper Kagera river.

Climate
The climate is warm with relatively low rainfall occurring in two wet seasons (January-May, October-December); Kigali averages 19°C and 100 cm of rain a year. Altitude modifies temperature: mountain areas are cooler, while the Great Rift Valley is slightly hotter (23°C).

Agriculture
Subsistence farming is the main economic activity. The chief food crops are maize, sorghum, sweet potatoes, cassava, beans, peas and rice; bananas are grown for food and for beer-making. Cash crops are developing slowly and account for less than 10% of total agricultural production. Coffee provides 69% of exports; others are tea, cotton and pyrethrum (from which an insecticide is made). Livestock is being increased. Rwanda's forests have largely been destroyed for fuel; conservation measures include reafforestation and limits on charcoal-burning.

Industry
Industry is poorly developed and is concerned with processing farm products such as coffee, tea, sugar and bananas (beer). There are also some small-scale textile, chemical and engineering plants.

Energy
Rwanda's relief is ideal for power production. In addition to a big hydro-electric plant on the Ruzizi, there are three other stations. Further projects are planned, especially in the Kagera basin.

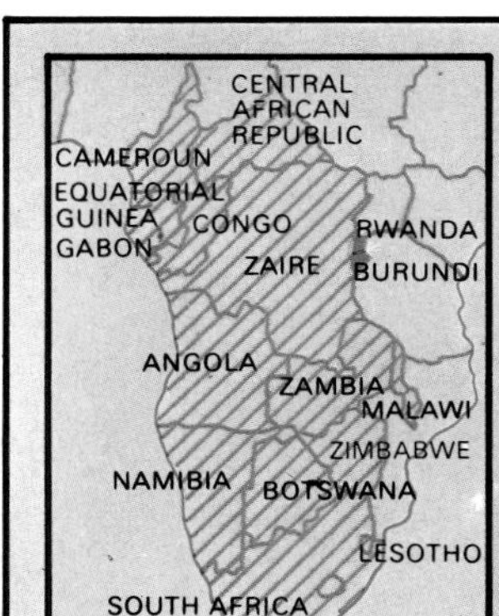

Mining
Tin and some tungsten are mined east of Lake Kivu and together account for 16% of exports. Methane gas, from under the lake, is exploited with the assistance of Zaire.

Transport
Foreign trade is hindered by Rwanda's landlocked position. Normally, 80% of imports come via Kenya (Mombassa) and Uganda but blockades of and by Uganda in the 1970s paralyzed Rwanda's economy. Some trade is handled by the ports of Dar es Salaam (Tanzania) and Matadi (Zaire). Roads are poor except for main routes to neighbouring states; there are no railways. There is a steamer service on Lake Kivu from Kibuye to Zaire. Kigali has an international airport.

Burundi
Area
27,834 km2/10,747 sq miles
Location
2°20′—4°30′ S
29°—30°50′ E
Population
4,229,000 (1981)
Population density
152 per km²/394 per sq mile
Capital and largest city
Bujumbura: 200,000 (1980)
Languages
Kirundi, French
Major imports
textiles, chemicals, petroleum products, metals, machinery
Major exports
coffee, hides and skins, cotton, tea, minerals
Currency
franc (1 franc = 100 centimes)
Gross National Product
990 million US dollars (1981)
Status
republic

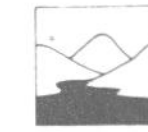

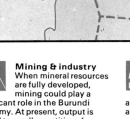

The land
To the west, Burundi is bordered by the Ruzizi river and Lake Tanganyika, both lying on the floor of the Great Rift Valley. The steep eastern edge of this valley consists of a narrow mountain range averaging 1,800 m in altitude. The remainder of the country comprises broken plateaux (between 1,300 and 1,700 m) sloping down to the Malagarasi river in the southeast. The Rift Valley is dry for its latitude and hot: Bujumbura averages 23°C and 75 cm of rain (falling between February and May). The plateau is cooler (averaging 20°C) and wetter (125 cm).

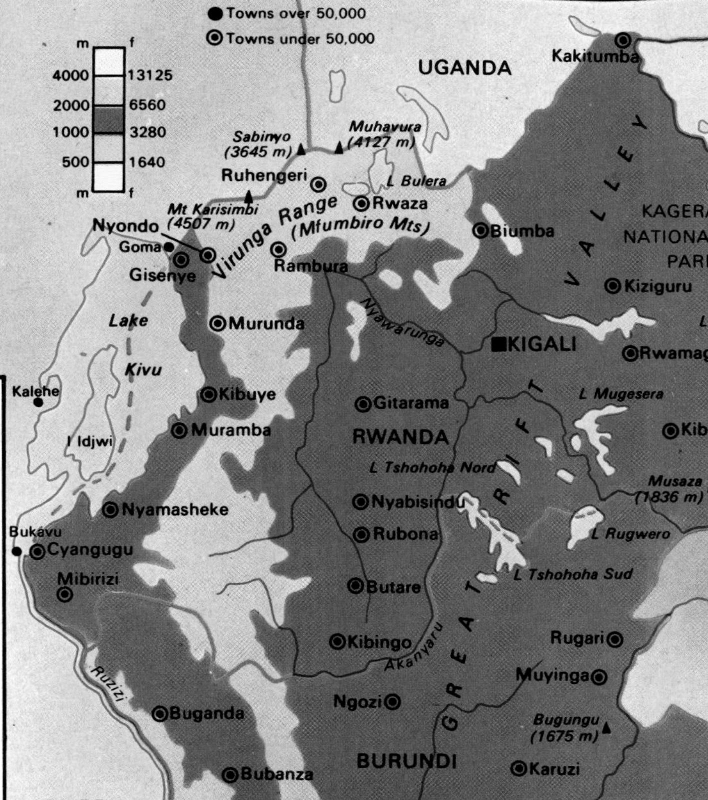

Mining & industry
When mineral resources are fully developed, mining could play a significant role in the Burundi economy. At present, output is limited to small quantities of cassiterite (tin), bastnasite, gold and kaolin. Oil has been located in the Ruzizi valley and large reserves of nickel have also been discovered. Deposits of phosphates, potash and feldspar also occur on the Ruzizi plain. Apart from a few small concerns in Bujumbura processing local produce (coffee, cotton, tea, fish and so on) there is little industry. There is a hydro-electric power installation on the Ruzizi.

Transport
The road network is extensive but in very poor condition: out of a total of 6,000 km, only 130 km are hard-surfaced. The two main routes connect Bujumbura to Zaire and Rwanda. There are no railways. Lake Tanganyika plays a vital role in Burundi's overseas trade. The two main routes to the exterior are by steamer from Bujumbura either to Kalémié in Zaire and so, via river and rail, to Matadi (2,000 km), or to Kigoma in Tanzania and then by train to Dar es Salaam (1,400 km). Bujumbura has an international airport with the national airline, STAB, operating services to Rwanda and Zaire.

Agriculture
Burundi is one of the world's poorest states. About 90% of the population are engaged in agriculture, mostly at subsistence level. As the Rift Valley is hot and arid, arable farming is concentrated on the adjoining mountain slopes. Food crops include beans, cassava, maize, sweet potatoes, yams and bananas; millet, wheat and barley are grown in the higher zones. There is some rice production in the Ruzizi valley. The main cash crop, providing 80% of total exports, is coffee; other commercial crops are cotton and tea. Cattle, grazed on the plateau, are important for their hides. There is a small fishing industry on Lake Tanganyika.

People
Burundi's economic development has been hindered by friction between the two main ethnic groups: the aristocratic and former ruling group, the Tutsi (15% of the population), and the Hutu farmers (84%).

Angola and Namibia

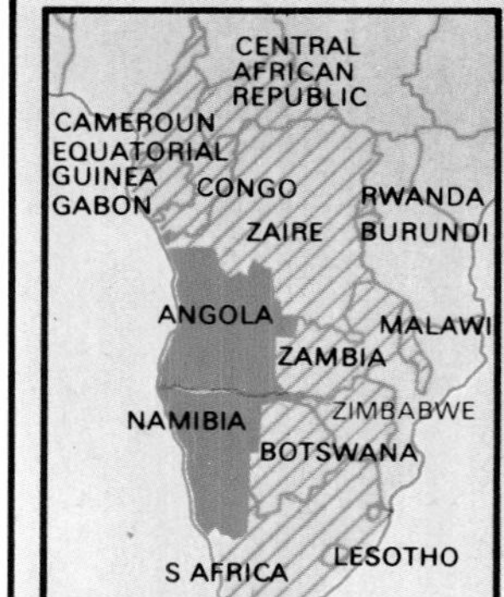

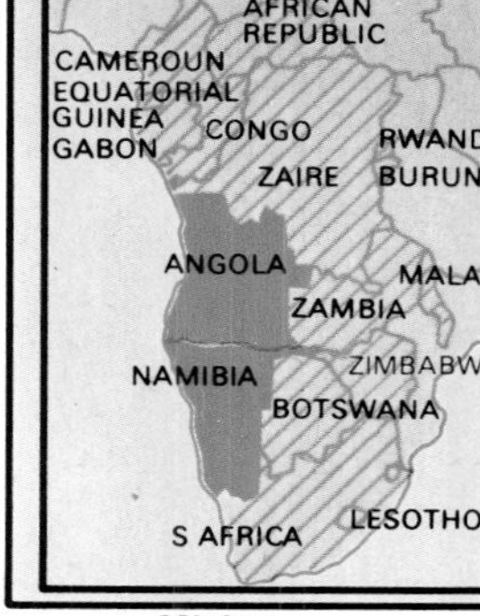

Angola
Area
1,246,700 km²/481,351 sq miles
Location
4°20'—18° S
11°50'—24°10' E
Population
7,784,000 (1981)
Population density
6 per km²/16 per sq mile
Capital and largest city
Luanda: 480,000 (1980)
Language
Portuguese
Major imports
vehicles, iron and steel, machinery, pharmaceuticals, textiles, cereals
Major exports
crude petroleum, coffee, iron ore, diamonds, fishmeal, sisal, cotton
Currency
escudo (1 escudo = 100 centavos)
Gross National Product
not available
Status
republic

Physical features

Angola, which includes Cabinda (a coastal enclave separated from the main territory by Zaire) is an immense country. The 1,600 km Atlantic coast is bordered by a narrow plain that rises in giant steps to the central plateau. This great tableland, ranging in altitude from 1,000 to 2,000 m, covers 60% of the country. Its northeast slopes are drained by the Kwango and Kasai (both tributaries of the Zaïre) while the headwaters of the Zambezi rise in the east. The Cuanza, flowing west, is Angola's longest river (960 km) and is navigable up to Dondo. Other rivers which run into the Atlantic, such as the Dande, Catumbela and Cunene, have steep courses suitable for hydro-electric schemes.

Climate

Angola has a tropical climate, but temperatures are modified inland by altitude and along the coast by the cool Benguela current: Luanda averages 23°C. The wet season, from October to March, brings about 130 cm of rain in Cabinda, decreasing to under 30 cm of rain in the south.

Industry

Industry is developing steadily. The leading sector is food-processing, followed by textiles using local cotton. The main industrial centres are the city-ports of Luanda, Lobito, Benguela and Moçâmedes, but new factories are being built inland. Power is mostly of hydro-electric origin: there are important dams on the Cuanza and Catumbela and on the Cunene where a second major plant is planned.

Transport

In recent years, communications have greatly improved and Angola now has an extensive network of all-weather roads. Railways extend inland from the main ports but do not interconnect. The main line runs from Lobito via Benguela into Zaire and carries a considerable volume of transit trade. The leading ports are Moçâmedes, Luanda, Lobito, Cabinda and Benguela. Luanda has an international airport and the Angolan airline, TAAG, also operates internally.

Mining

Angola is rich in minerals. Oil is the principal resource and provides 50% of total exports; the main field lies off Cabinda but vast reserves have been discovered off Santo Antonio do Zaire. Diamonds from the northeast are another 10% of exports. Significant quantities of iron ore, copper and manganese are also produced. Other minerals occurring include bauxite, gypsum, phosphate, uranium, iron and gold.

Agriculture

The basic food crops are cassava, yams and maize in the north and millet in the south. Coffee, the main cash crop, is chiefly grown on plantations north of the Cuanza river—it accounts for 25% of total exports, making Angola Africa's second most important coffee producer. The other major export crops are sisal (grown along the coast), cotton (from the plateau) and bananas (produced in the northwest). Some oil palm products, coconuts and tobacco are also exported. Livestock is limited, largely because of the tsetse fly and inadequate pasture. Fishing, based on Porto Alexandre, Moçâmedes and Benguela, is important and there are several processing and canning plants; fresh fish, fishmeal and oil are exported. Forests in Cabinda yield valuable hardwoods and there are softwood plantations, used for pulp and paper, near Benguela.

Namibia
Area
823,172 km²/317,827 sq miles
Location
17°—29° S
11°45'—25°05' E
Population
1,015,000 (1981)
Population density
1.2 per km²/3.2 per sq mile
Capital and largest city
Windhoek: 1,000,000 (1981)
Languages
English, Afrikaans
Major imports
machinery and transport equipment, foodstuffs
Major exports
diamonds, copper, lead, zinc, fish products, livestock, karakul pelts
Currency
rand (1 rand = 100 cents)
Gross National Product
1,990 million US dollars (1981)
Status
international territory.
(South Africa continues to administer Namibia in spite of a ruling by the International Court of Justice in 1971 that its administration is illegal.)

The land

Namibia is a vast, arid territory. A narrow, dune-covered desert belt, the Namib, runs 1,600 km along the entire Atlantic seaboard. The rest of the country consists of a plateau with an average height of 1,100 m but which rises to over 2,000 m in the centre. Semi-desert scrub gives way northeastwards to grasslands and tree savanna. There are no permanent rivers apart from those flowing along the borders, such as the Cunene, Okovango, Orange and Zambezi. The main climatic feature is low rainfall, especially along the coast where less than 2 cm falls annually; on the plateau, amounts range from 5 cm in the south to 60 cm in the north. Temperatures are modified in the Namib by the cool Benguela current: Walvis Bay averages 17°C, Windhoek (at 1,700 m) averages 19°C.

Mining

Namibia's wealth lies underground. Diamonds, accounting for 60% of minerals exported, are produced between Oranjemund (which has the world's richest gem diamond mine) and Lüderitz. Copper, worked at Otavi, is next in importance; the ore also contains large amounts of lead and zinc. Uranium is obtained from a huge opencast mine at Rossing. Smaller quantities of tin, vanadium, manganese and rock salt are extracted elsewhere. A new hydro-electric plant at Ruacana will greatly increase power supplies.

Agriculture

After mining, the main economic activities are fishing and subsistence farming. Fishing, for pilchards and snoek, is important and there are canning and processing plants at Walvis Bay and Lüderitz. The population is concentrated on the plateau, particularly in the better-watered north where some maize, potatoes, beans and groundnuts are grown, partly under irrigation. However, Namibia is primarily a pastoral country and livestock accounts for 90% of farming activity. Cattle are raised on most parts of the plateau and karakul sheep are kept in the centre and south; the tightly-curled pelts of the new-born lambs are a valuable export.

Botswana

Lesotho

Botswana and Lesotho

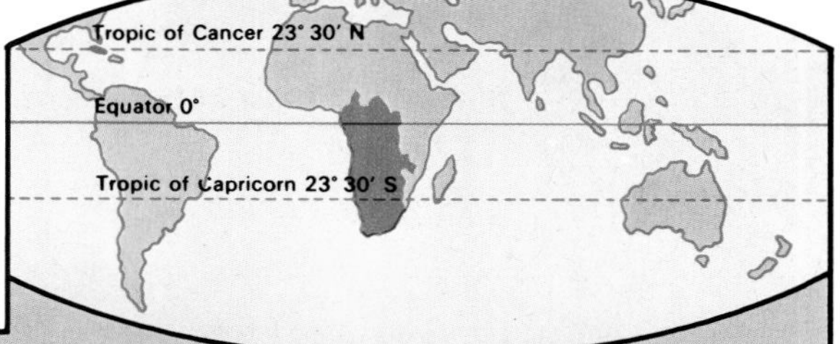

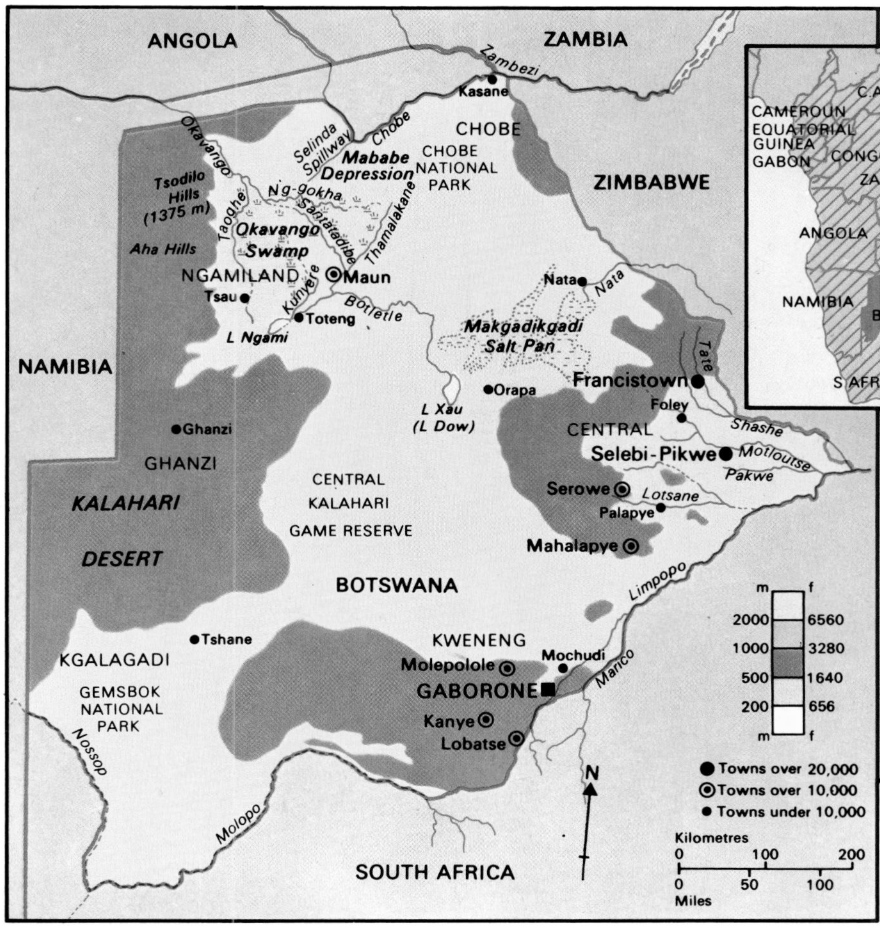

Botswana
Area
575,000 km²/222,000 sq miles
Location
17°50′—26°50′ S
20°—29°20′ E
Population
930,000 (1981)
Population density
1.6 per km²/4 per sq mile
Capital and largest city
Gabrone: 59,000 (1981)
Second largest city
Selebi-Pikwe: 23,000 (1975)
Languages
Tswana, English
Major imports
machinery, manufactured goods, vehicles, foodstuffs, petroleum products, chemicals
Major exports
meat and meat products, diamonds, copper, nickel, hides
Currency
pula (1 pula = 100 thebe)
Gross National Product
940 million US dollars (1981)
Status
republic

People
About 80% of Batswana (people of Botswana) live in the eastern part of the country which contains the capital and other major towns: Selebi-Pikwe, Serowe (16,000), Kanye (11,000) and Molepolole (10,000). The population, almost totally African, comprises eight main tribes; the largest is the Bamangwato. Botswana is also the home of one of Africa's oldest races, the Kalahari Bushmen.

The land
Botswana is a dry, bush-covered plateau some 900 m high. Around 85% of the territory consists of the Kalahari—a semi-desert country with scrub, grasslands, sand dunes and sandstone ridges. Apart from border rivers (Chobe, Zambezi, Limpopo and Molopo) drainage is internal and the only permanent watercourse is the Okavango. This river loses itself in a vast inland delta (10,000 km²), the Okavango swamp, from which there is a seasonal flow through Lake Ngami and the Botletle river to the extensive Makgadikgadi Salt Pan. The climate is hot and dry: temperatures average 21°C and rainfall decreases from 60 cm in the north and east to a scant 10 cm in the south and west.

Transport & tourism
Communications are poor and many areas in the west and south are not easily accessible. All-weather roads connect the main centres in the east; most of these towns are also linked by the Rhodesia-South Africa railway which crosses the country. Air Botswana flies to neighbouring states and also operates internally between Gaborone, Francistown, Selebi-Pikwe and Maun. Tourism is being developed with wildlife as the chief attraction; several national parks and game reserves have been created with facilities for visitors such as lodges and safari camps.

Agriculture
Although mining is becoming more important, Botswana is primarily a pastoral country. An extensive programme of sinking boreholes and damming small rivers has increased the area available for agriculture and almost 70% of the territory is now used for grazing. There are an estimated two million cattle, one million goats and half a million sheep; animal products form a major share of exports. Arable farming, limited to the wetter, eastern area, is at subsistence level. Half the area under cultivation is used for sorghum; other foods grown are maize, millet and beans. Cash crops are being introduced and include cotton, groundnuts and sunflower seeds. The Okavango Swamp, with its irrigation potential, may be developed for agriculture.

Mining & industry
Botswana's underground wealth is transforming the economy. The diamond mine at Orapa, fully operational since 1972, is the world's second largest and another mine is being developed nearby. In the northeast, there are vast deposits of copper and nickel and the Selebi-Pikwe mining complex began production in 1974. Some coal is exploited at Mahalapye, while manganese and asbestos, also occurring in the eastern sector, are produced in smaller amounts. Meat processing is the main industry.

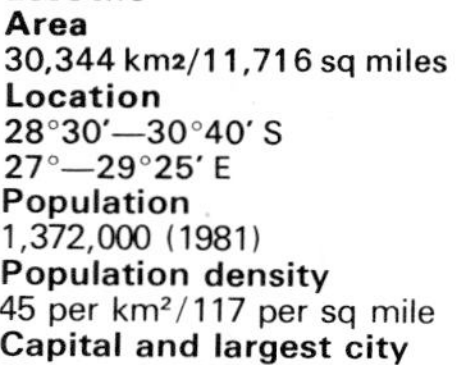
Lesotho
Area
30,344 km²/11,716 sq miles
Location
28°30′—30°40′ S
27°—29°25′ E
Population
1,372,000 (1981)
Population density
45 per km²/117 per sq mile
Capital and largest city
Maseru: 75,000 (1981)
Languages
Sesotho, English
Major imports
foodstuffs, machinery, transport equipment, manufactured goods, petroleum products
Major exports
wool and mohair, live animals, diamonds, labour
Currency
rand (1 rand = 100 cents)
Gross National Product
740 million US dollars (1981)
Status
constitutional monarchy

The land
Lesotho, entirely surrounded by South Africa, is a rugged highland state. In the north and east, the Maloti range and Drakensberg (Dragon mountains) lie above 2,300 m, rising to 3,482 m in the country's highest peak, Thabana Ntlenyana. This mountain zone, southern Africa's main watershed, is drained by the Orange and its tributary, the Caledon. Rugged foothills (over 2,000 m) cover the rest of the territory except in the west where the land drops to an undulating plain 1,500 m above sea level. Because of altitude, Lesotho has a mild, moist climate. Although summer temperatures reach 33°C, the annual average at Maseru is 15°C. Rainfall ranges from 70 cm in the west to 100 cm in the Drakensberg.

People
Lesotho is a purely African territory. Its people, the Basotho, live mostly on the western lowlands but some have settled in mountain valleys. Over-population plus lack of resources and industry have caused many people to seek work in South Africa: 40% of the adult male workforce is continually absent.

The economy
In spite of poor soils, steeply sloping land and serious soil erosion, subsistence agriculture supports 80% of Basotho. Arable farming predominates in the west with maize, sorghum and wheat as the main crops, but production falls short of demand and cereal imports are high. The more fertile basalt uplands in the east are used for grazing cattle, sheep and goats; livestock products, in particular wool and mohair, form the chief exports. Alluvial diamonds are also exported. Manufacturing, except for some handicrafts, is almost nonexistent, but tourism is emerging as a growth industry. Attractions include spectacular mountain scenery, prehistoric caves and rock paintings.

Transport
Transport systems are inadequate. There are 900 km of gravel roads and a further 3,000 km of dirt roads and tracks; on the lowlands, many of these are impassable during the summer rains. Apart from the 1.6 km line connecting Maseru to the South African network, there are no railways. Lesotho National Airways flies from Maseru to Johannesburg; there are also over 30 airstrips for local flights.

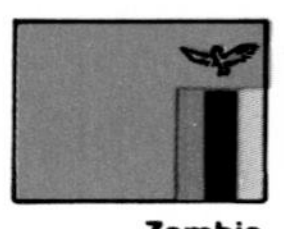

Zambia

Malawi

Zambia and Malawi

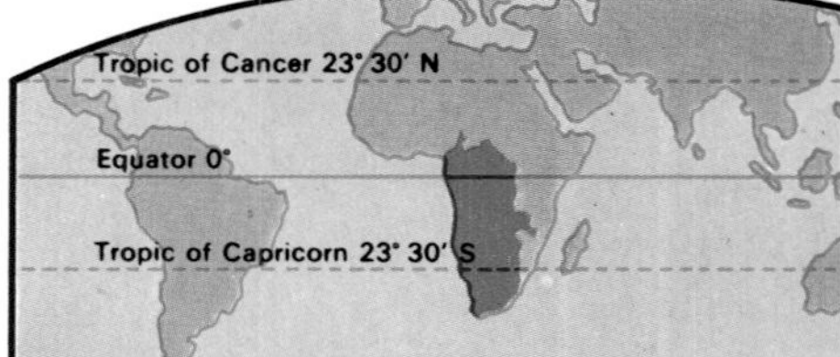

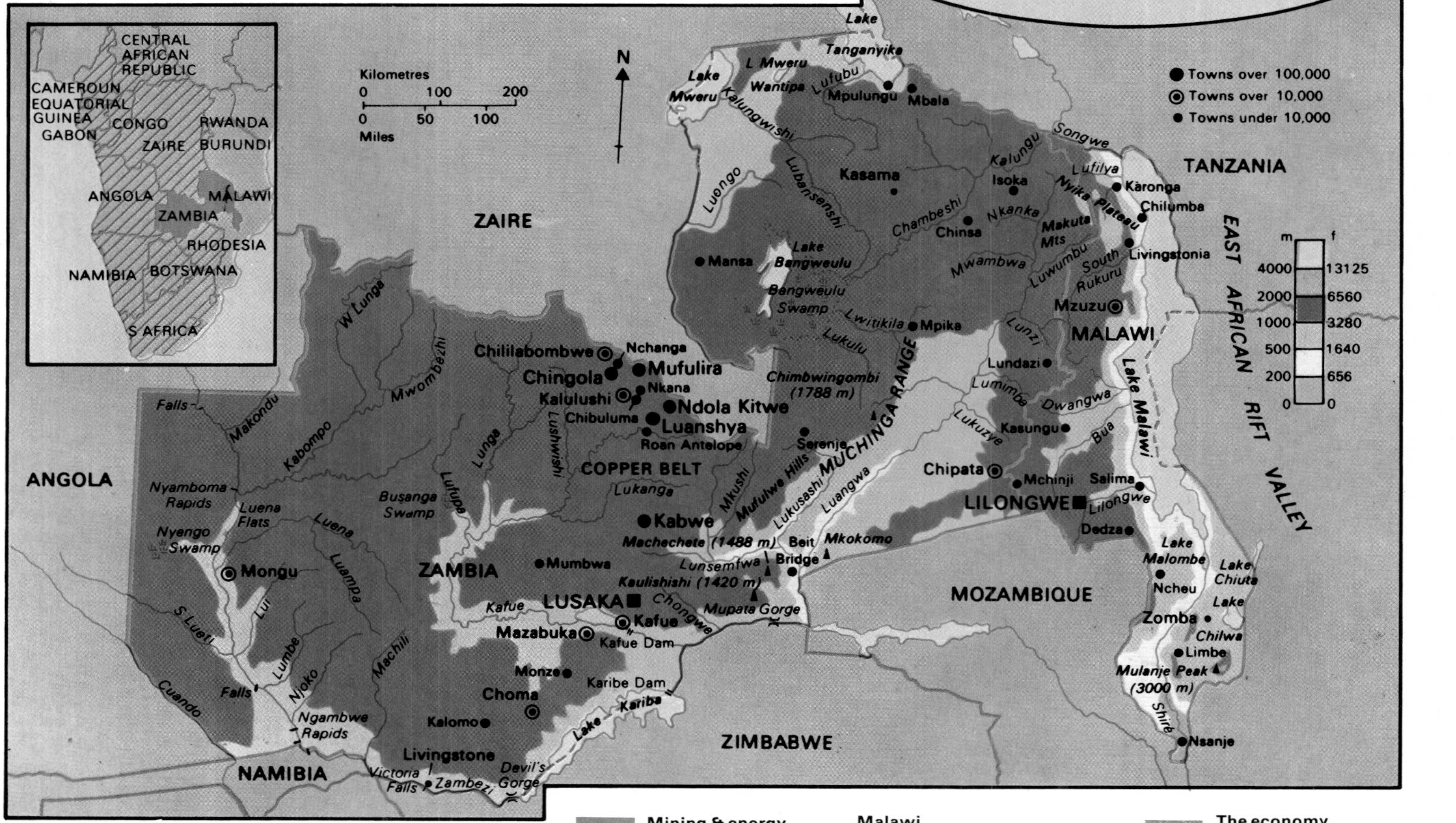

Zambia
Area
752,618 km²/290,586 sq miles
Location
8°15′—18°10′ S
22°—33°40′ E
Population
5,842,000 (1981)
Population density
8 per km²/20 per sq mile
Capital and largest city
Lusaka: 538,000 (1982)
Language
English
Major imports
machinery and transport equipment, oil, chemicals, food
Major exports
copper, other metals
Currency
Kwacha (1 Kwacha = 100 ngwee)
Gross National Product
3,490 million US dollars (1981)
Status
republic

Physical features

Landlocked Zambia lies on a plateau 1,000 m high, rising to 1,500 m in the central Muchinga range and to over 2,000 m along the mountainous northeastern border. The upland is dissected by rivers flowing through broad, deep valleys: in the west, the Zambezi and Kafue, in the centre, the Luangwa. The Zambezi's course includes the spectacular Victoria Falls and Lake Kariba (5,180 km²) one of the biggest man-made lakes in Africa. The plateau is so flat that drainage is poor and there are extensive waterlogged areas such as the Nyengo swamp, Luena flats, Busanga swamp, Bangweulu swamp and the Chambeshi valley in the north.

Climate

Zambia's tropical climate is modified by altitude. On the plateau conditions are pleasant but in the valleys it is torrid and unhealthy: Lusaka (1,277 m) averages 17°C in the cool season (May-August) and 24°C in the hot season (September-October); the corresponding figures for Beit Bridge (400 m) on the Luangwa river are 21°C and 31°C. Rain, falling from November to April, ranges from 150 cm in the north to 75 cm in the south. Humidity is high in the valleys.

Agriculture

In most parts, subsistence agriculture predominates; the basic foods are millet, groundnuts, beans and cassava. Large-scale farming has developed along the Livingstone-Lusaka-Copper Belt railway line: beef and dairy cattle are raised between Livingstone and Lusaka, while the area north of the Kafue river is used for maize, cotton, tobacco, sugar and potatoes. Tobacco is also cultivated near Chipata and there are coffee plantations in the Mbala district in the extreme north. Some tobacco, cotton and coffee are exported.

Industry

The industrial sector is under-developed. Food, textiles and cement are the main products. Newer projects include a vehicle-assembly plant at Livingstone and a chemical plant at Kafue.

Mining & energy

Copper, providing 90% of total exports, dominates the Zambian economy. Production is concentrated in the Copper Belt where the chief mines are at Nchanga, Mufulira, Roan Antelope Chililabombwe and Chibuluma; further deposits have been discovered in the northwest. Zambia ranks as the world's third-largest copper producer. Other minerals exported are cobalt, from the Nkana and Chibuluma mines, and lead and zinc from Kabwe. Zambia is rapidly increasing its power supplies: coal is mined 200 km northeast of Livingstone and a major hydro-electric power (HEP) station has been built at the Kariba dam. There is a new HEP scheme on the lower Kafue and oil is piped from Dar es Salaam (Tanzania) to a refinery at Ndola.

Transport

Zambia is handicapped by its landlocked position. Political events of the mid-1970s have stopped goods, mainly copper, from being exported via Rhodesia and Angola. Copper is now sent by road or the new Tanzam railway to Dar es Salaam, and by road to the Mozambique ports of Beira and Nacala via Malawi. There are plans for a direct road link with Mozambique. Some trade is handled by Mpulungu port on Lake Tanganyika. Zambia has an adequate network of roads but many are impassable during rain. The rivers, punctuated by falls and rapids, are unsuitable for navigation but small craft ply Lake Bangweulu. The national airline is Air Zambia.

Malawi
Area
118,485 km²/45,747 sq miles
Location
9°30′—17°10′ S
32°45′—35°50′ E
Population
6,241,000 (1981)
Population density
53 per km²/136 per sq mile
Capital
Lilongwe: 103,000 (1980)
Largest city
Blantyre: 222,000 (1980)
Languages
ChiChewa, English
Major imports
vehicles, petroleum products, chemicals, machinery
Major exports
tobacco, tea, groundnuts, cotton, maize
Currency
Kwacha (1 Kwacha = 100 tambala)
Gross National Product
1,250 million US dollars (1981)
Status
republic

The land

Malawi is a long, narrow mountainous country bordering the southern-most part of the East African Rift Valley. The lakes occupying the valley—Malawi (570 km long), Chilwa and Chiuta—make up 20% of the total surface area. The rest of the country consists of highlands, 1,000 to 1,500 m in altitude, but rising to 2,400 m on the Nyika plateau and to 3,000 m in Mulanje Peak. In the south, the uplands are cut by the deep Shiré valley. Temperatures vary with altitude but are generally high: Zomba averages 20°C, Nsanje, 24°C. During the November-March wet season, most parts receive between 75 and 100 cm of rain.

The economy

Malawi is an agricultural country and farm products account for 75% of exports. Tobacco, grown on the Shiré highlands and in the Lilongwe area, is the chief cash crop. Other commercial crops are tea (from plantations on the slopes of Mulanje Mountain), groundnuts (from the central highlands) and cotton (from the lake shore and Shiré valley lowlands). About 75% of all cultivated land is used for maize, the staple food; any surplus is exported. Other food crops are cassava and millet. Livestock is limited by the tsetse fly. About 25% of Malawi is forested and production of woods such as mahogany, cedar and eucalyptus is increasing. There is some fishing in Lake Malawi. Industry, based on farm produce, includes tea and tobacco processing; fish, fruit and vegetable canning; cigarette and cotton textile manufacture. Hydro-electric power stations are being developed.

Towns & transport

Lilongwe, in the central highlands, replaced Zomba (24,000) as the capital in 1975. The chief industrial and commercial centre, however, is Blantyre in the south. The railway, from Nsanje to Salima, is linked directly to the Mozambique ports of Beira and Nacala; a spur is to be built from Salima to Lilongwe. The road network (10,670 km long) is centred on Blantyre and Lilongwe and is 50% all-weather. There are cargo and passenger services on Lake Malawi. Air Malawi flies overseas, from Blantyre airport, and internally.

Zimbabwe

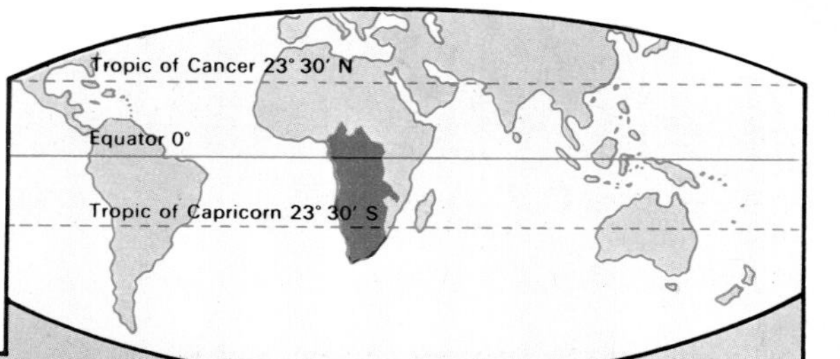

Area
390,623 km²/150,820 sq miles
Location
15°40′—22°25′ S
25°20′—33° E
Population
7,190,000 (1981)
Population density
18 per km²/48 per sq mile
Capital and largest city
Harare (Salisbury): 657,000 (1980)
Language
English
Major imports
machinery, transport equipment, petroleum products
Major exports
asbestos, chrome, tobacco, maize, copper, meat, sugar
Currency
dollar (1 dollar = 100 cents)
Gross National Product
6,260 million US dollars (1981)
Status
Republic; formerly the self-governing British colony of Rhodesia.

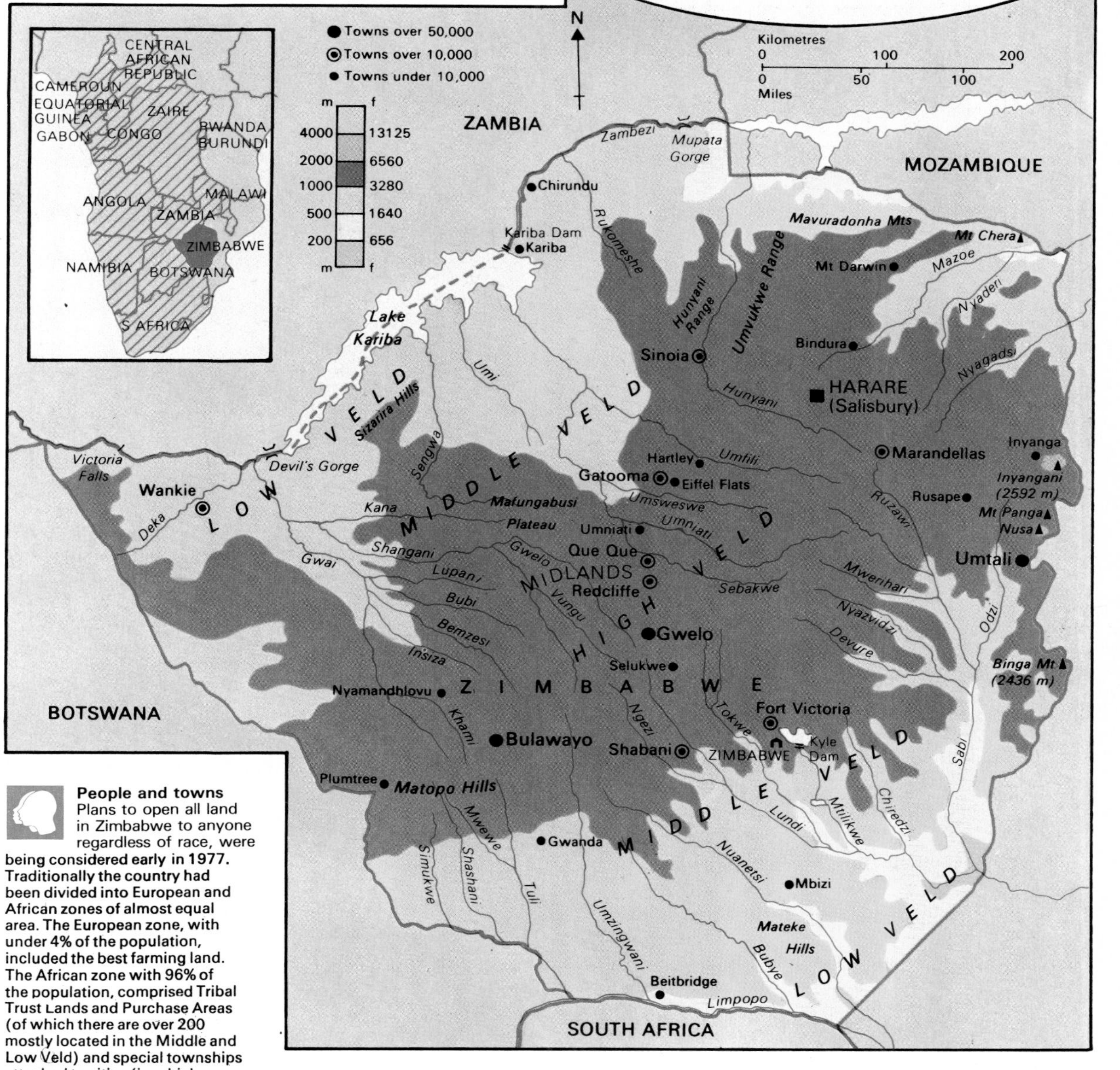

Physical features

Landlocked Rhodesia is a rugged plateau country lying between two great rivers: the Zambezi in the north and the Limpopo in the south. The central region consists of the High Veld, a wide upland belt over 1,200 m high which runs from the northeast (where it is most extensive) to the southwest. This is flanked by the Middle Veld, 900—1,200 m, which gives way to the Low Veld, land under 900 m comprising the Zambezi, Limpopo and Sabi basins. Tree savanna, densest in the north, covers highland areas while hardwood forests fringe the river valleys.

Climate

Although Zimbabwe lies wholly within the tropics, its climate, because of altitude, is more temperate than tropical. On the High Veld and Middle Veld, summers are warm and winters cool, often with night frosts. Harare averages 21°C in November (the hottest month) and 13°C in July (the coolest month). In contrast, the deep river valleys are hot and humid with temperatures of up to 50°C in November. Rain, usually with thunderstorms, occurs in summer (November to March) and decreases from 250 cm in the northeast to 50 cm per year in the southwest.

UDI

At official talks in 1964-5, Britain refused to grant Rhodesia independence until its white leaders accepted (black) majority rule. In order to preserve white supremacy, the Rhodesian government unilaterally declared independence (1965) and, five years later, set up a republic. Britain proclaimed both these moves illegal and, since UDI, officially ceased trading with the colony. The UN also imposed economic sanctions. In 1976, as a result of growing economic and political pressures, including guerilla attacks in border areas the Smith régime finally agreed to the principle of majority rule. Rhodesia became the independent republic of Zimbabwe in April 1980.

People and towns

Plans to open all land in Zimbabwe to anyone regardless of race, were being considered early in 1977. Traditionally the country had been divided into European and African zones of almost equal area. The European zone, with under 4% of the population, included the best farming land. The African zone with 96% of the population, comprised Tribal Trust Lands and Purchase Areas (of which there are over 200 mostly located in the Middle and Low Veld) and special townships attached to cities (in which about one third of Africans live). About 40% of Europeans live in Harare, central Africa's largest city. Founded in 1890, the capital is an important commercial centre, particularly for tobacco. Bulawayo (373,000) is the country's main industrial city and hub of the rail network. The third largest town, Gwelo (62,000), is the manufacturing centre of the Midlands.

Industry

As a result of sanctions there has been an increase in the production of previously imported consumer goods such as textiles, food, beverages and furniture. Heavy industry is also expanding since Zimbabwe has adequate supplies of coal, iron ore, limestone and power and is therefore not dependent on imports; there are iron and steel plants at Bulawayo, Redcliffe and Gwelo. Zimbabwe and Bulawayo together account for 80% of Zimbabwe industry; the remainder is located in Umtali and the Midlands (Gwelo, Que, Que, Hartley, Redcliffe, Gatooma).

Agriculture

Sanctions made Zimbabwe diversify its agriculture and aim at self-sufficiency in food production. Maize, grown on 75% of all cultivated land, is the staple crop and a surplus is exported. Tobacco, largely from the northeastern parts of the High Veld, is the main crop. Other major crops, for both domestic and export markets, are: citrus (produced near Inyanga and Harare and on irrigated estates in the south-east), cotton (from the Hartley-Gatooma region), sugar (grown under irrigation in the Low Veld) and tea (from the Umtali region). Except in the north and northwest, Zimbabwe is free of the tsetse fly and livestock is important. Beef cattle predominate in the dry southwest, while the chief dairying region is along the Bulawayo-Harare railway. The country is self-sufficient in meat and dairy products and meat is a significant export. Fishing is centred on L Kariba. In spite of sanctions, Zimbabwe manages to export its main commodities.

Mining

Mining makes a major contribution to the economy and provides Zimbabwe with its chief exports. High-quality asbestos is the country's most valuable mineral resource: it is mined in the Shabani area and also about 100 km northwest of Harare. Next in importance are: chrome (obtained near Sinoia and Selukwe), copper (also mainly produced in the Sinoia region), nickel (occurring near Bulawayo, Gwelo, Gatooma and Bindura), gold from scattered deposits near Gwanda, Bulawayo, Gwelo, Fort Victoria, Que Que, Gatooma and Harare, and tin from Wankie. More than twenty other minerals are worked in Zimbabwe, among them several which form the basis of local industries. These include iron ore (Que Que), iron pyrites (Bindura) and limestone (Que Que and south of Bulawayo near the Botswana border). Also of vital importance to industry are Zimbabwe's coal fields; these are mainly located in the southeast and west and are unexploited except for the Wankie field.

Transport

The main railway runs from Bulawayo, via Harare to Umtali with branch lines serving mining and industrial centres. As part of sanctions, road and rail links with neighbouring countries have been severed (except for South Africa). Losing access to the Mozambique ports of Beira and Maputo was particularly harmful to Rhodesian trade as all imports and exports now have to be shipped via South Africa which is a longer and more costly route.

Energy

Except for oil, Zimbabwe is self-sufficient in energy resources. Over 90% of the country's electricity is generated by hydro-power. The principal hydro-electric plant, at Kariba, supplies power to Harare, Bulawayo and the Midlands. Wankie coal is also used to produce electricity; the main thermal stations are at Harare, Bulawayo, Umtali, Umniati, Shabani and Wankie. Following sanctions, the oil pipeline from Beira was closed.

South Africa

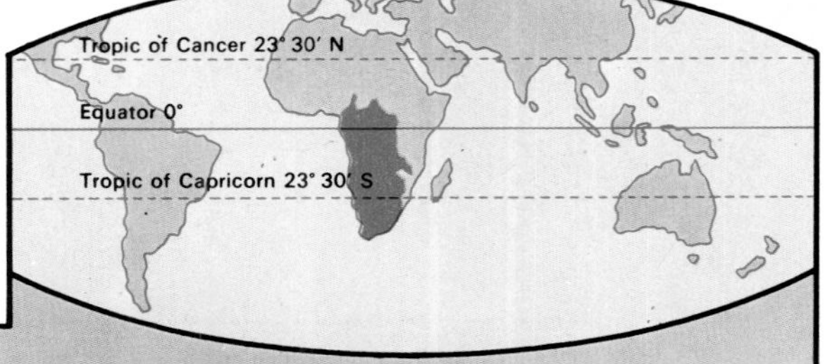

Area
1,221,042 km²/471,445 sq miles
Location
22°10′—34°55′ S
16°30′—32°55′ E
Population
29,526,000 (1981)
Population density
24 per km²/63 per sq mile
Administrative capital
Pretoria: 528,000 (1980)
Legislative capital
Cape Town: 892,000 (1980)
Largest city
Johannesburg: 1,536,000 (1980)
Languages
Afrikaans, English
Major imports
machinery and transport equipment, manufactured goods, chemicals, metals, foodstuffs, oil
Major exports
gold, diamonds, copper, other minerals, fruit, iron and steel, maize, wool, sugar, hides and skins
Currency
rand (1 rand = 100 cents)
Gross National Product
81,840 million US dollars (1981)
Status
republic

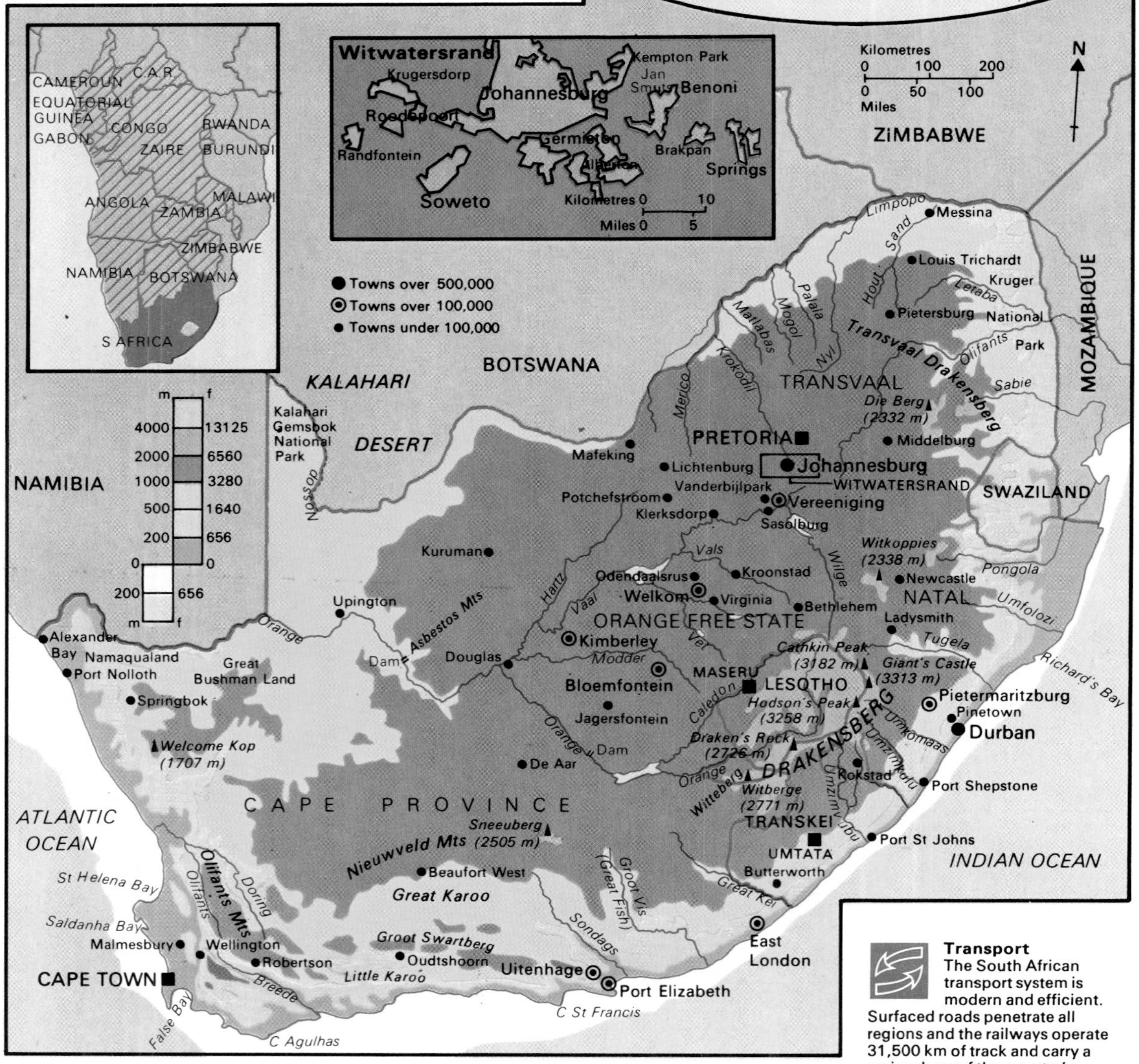

● Towns over 500,000
◉ Towns over 100,000
• Towns under 100,000

Kilometres 0 100 200
Miles 0 50 100

Physical features
South Africa's dominant feature is its height: most of the country is over 1,000 m and only the narrow coastal plain lies under 300 m. From the coast, the land rises steeply to the great escarpment encircling the interior plateau; this mountain rim is highest in the east where the Drakensberg reach 3,300 m. In the south, minor ranges enclose the arid basins of the Little and Great Karoo ('Karoo' comes from a Hottentot word meaning dry or bare). The plateau, over 1,200 m high, is like a huge saucer: from the escarpment rim the land slopes inwards down to the Kalahari desert in the north. Vast featureless plains with scattered low ridges and shallow river valleys characterize the landscape. The country's main river, the Orange, fed by the Caledon and Vaal, flows 2,250 km westwards to the Atlantic.

Climate
South Africa has a relatively temperate climate because of latitude, altitude and proximity to the sea (nowhere more than 800 km away). Mean annual temperatures in the north and south are remarkably uniform: 17°C for both Cape Town and Pretoria. The west coast, subject to the cold Benguela current is cooler (Port Nolloth: 13°C); the east coast, with the warm Mozambique current, is hotter (Durban: 20°C). Over most of the country, rain occurs as summer thunderstorms; amounts decrease from east to west: Durban has 100 cm annually, Bloemfontein has 55 cm and Port Nolloth only 6 cm.

Towns
Johannesburg, founded in 1886 as a gold-mining camp, is now South Africa's largest city and leading industrial and commercial centre. The republic's second largest city, Cape Town, dates from 1652 when Jan van Riebeeck built a fort at Table Bay for the Dutch East India Company; as the legislative capital it contains the Houses of Parliament. Durban (851,000) is the third largest city.

Agriculture
As much of South Africa is arid or mountainous, only 10% of the land is cultivated. The main food crops are maize, sorghum, groundnuts, potatoes and wheat. A wide variety of deciduous, citrus and tropical fruit is grown in the western Cape Province and fresh and canned fruit is the top agricultural export—it is also a major wine-producing area. Other exports are sugar, tobacco and flowers. About 70% of the country is used for grazing. With 40 million sheep, South Africa is the world's fifth wool producer: 60% of the wool comes from Cape Province; karakul sheep, prized for their pelts, are found in the dry northwest. Angora goats are kept in the extreme south and the republic ranks as the world's third producer of mohair. Beef and dairy cattle predominate in the east and north. Fishing is important with 90% of the catch (anchovy, pilchard, crayfish, mackerel and hake) coming from the cold waters off the west coast. Cape Town is the main fishing port. Forests cover less than 1% of the total area.

Mining
South Africa has immense mineral wealth. It supplies 70% of the world's gold, 65% of its diamonds, 45% of vanadium and is a leading producer of platinum, uranium, manganese, chrome, iron ore, asbestos, antimony and vermiculite. About 40 other minerals are also exploited. The republic's seven goldfields form a 500 km arc across the centre, extending from Evander in the east through Johannesburg and Klerksdorp to Welkom and Virginia. The main diamond mines are at Kimberley, Jagersfontein, Finsch and Pretoria; alluvial diamonds are found in the Vaal and Orange and on the west coast at Namaqualand. Large coal deposits occur in Transvaal and Natal.

Tourism
In the last decade, the number of tourists visiting South Africa has doubled and is expected to reach one million by 1980. The country's main attractions are its unspoilt beaches, magnificent scenery, game reserves and its sun: Cape Town has twice as much sunshine as London or Paris.

Energy
Of the electricity generated on the African continent, 57% is produced in South Africa, mostly by coal-fired thermal stations in Transvaal, Natal and the Orange Free State. Hydro-power is being developed: the giant Orange River Project, to be completed by the year 2000, includes 20 hydro-electrical plants. The country's first nuclear station, using Transvaal uranium, will operate from 1978.

Industry
The chief industries are: food-processing (canned fruit and vegetables, refined sugar, meat and fish products); wool and cotton textiles; chemicals (oil from coal at Sasolburg, fertilizers, pharmaceuticals); iron and steel (Pretoria, Vanderbijlpark, Newcastle) and engineering. Manufacturing is concentrated in four main areas: southern Transvaal (47% of total industrial output), Durban/Pinetown (14%), western Cape (11%) and Port Elizabeth/Uitenhage (8%). The republic is Africa's most industrialized state.

Transport
The South African transport system is modern and efficient. Surfaced roads penetrate all regions and the railways operate 31,500 km of track and carry a major share of the country's freight. There are 4 main ports: Durban (handling 60% of all cargo), Cape Town, Port Elizabeth and East London (the only river port). SAA (South African Airways) flies overseas and internally and Johannesburg is the chief airport.

Apartheid
South Africans are divided into four groups: Whites (17% of the population), Coloured (10%), Asian (3%) and Bantu or Blacks (70%). Of the nine homelands for the Bantu (covering 13% of the land) Transkei has been made independent. About 50% of the Bantu live in townships attached to the industrial cities.

Transkei
The Transkei republic home of 1.7 million Xhosa, is an enclave of 36,900 km² on the southeast coast. Farming is the main activity and irrigation projects, using streams from the Drakensberg, are increasing the cultivable area. Maize is grown for food, while cash crops include flax and tea; cattle grazing and forestry are also important. Industry is centred on Umtata, the capital, and Butterworth.

Indian Ocean Islands 1

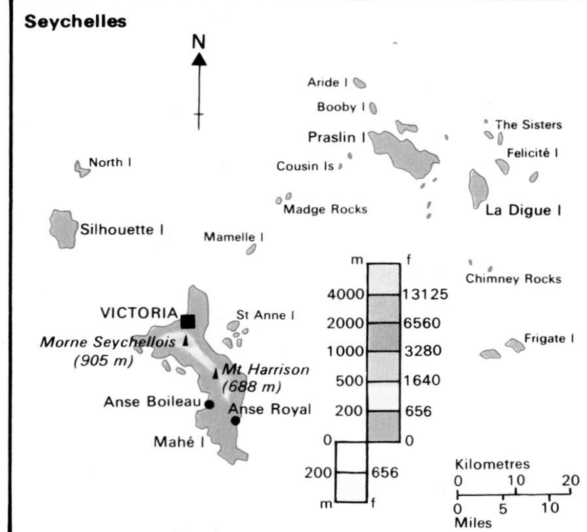

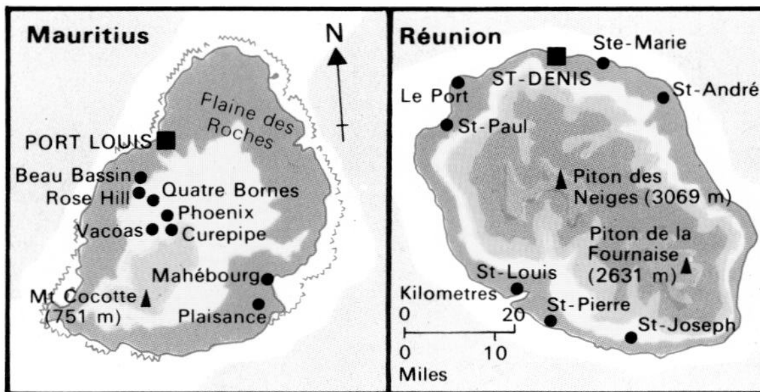

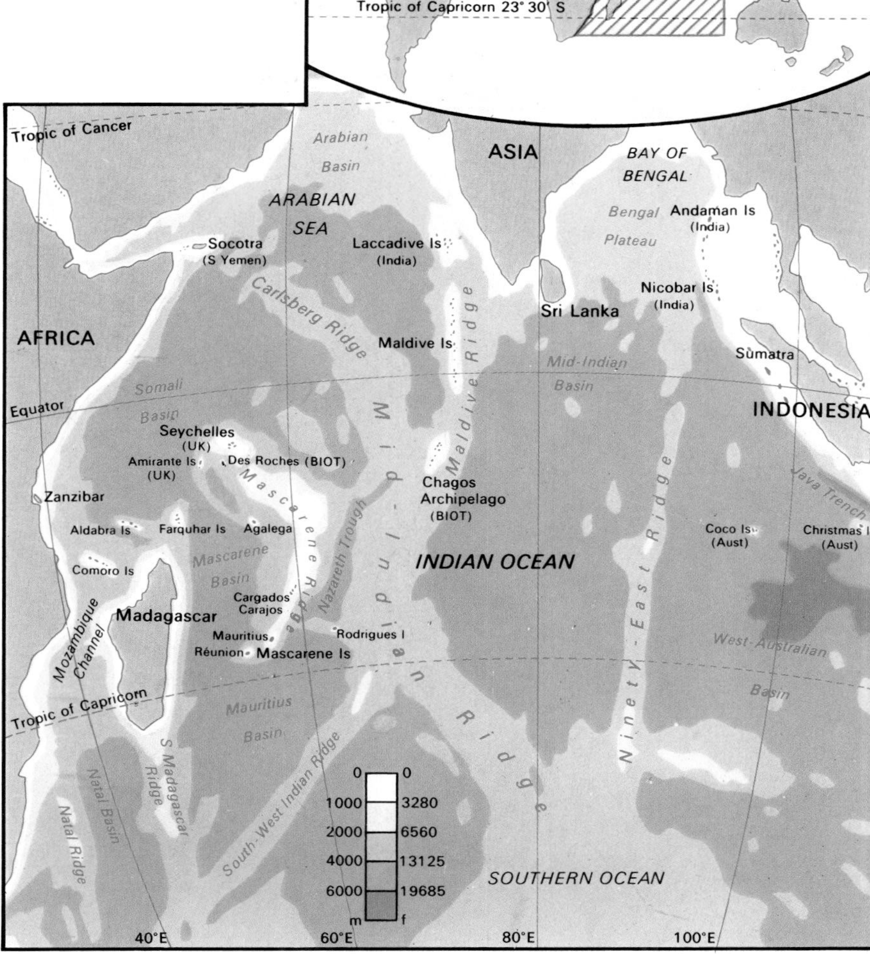

Seychelles
Area
277 km²/107 sq miles
Location
4°30′ S; 55°40′ E
Population
63,000 (1981)
Population density
227 per km²/589 per sq mile
Capital and largest city
Victoria: 23,000 (1980)
Language
English
Major imports
foodstuffs, petroleum products, vehicles
Major exports
copra, cinnamon bark and oil, guano, fish
Currency
rupee (1 rupee = 100 cents)
Gross National Product
110 million US dollars (1981)
Status
republic

Seychelles: the land
The Seychelles, lying 1,000 km northeast of Madagascar, consist of some 85 granitic and coralline islands. The granitic islands, with mountainous interiors up to 900 m, are all situated within 60 km of the principal island, Mahé (148 km²), and include Praslin (41 km²), Silhouette (15 km²) and La Digue (10 km²). The scattered coral islands are low-lying atolls and reefs. The wet season, from December to April, is hot (29°C) and humid with up to 250 cm of rain. The rest of the year is slightly cooler (24°C). Most of the islanders are either African or Afro-French (the Seychelles were first colonized by France): 80% of the population lives on Mahé.

Seychelles: economy
The Seychelles have an unbalanced economy and exports (mainly copra and cinnamon bark) pay for only a quarter of the massive import bill. As well as copra, the palms growing on the fertile volcanic soils of the granitic islands provide coconuts, coconut oil and coir. Other export products are vanilla, patchouli, tortoiseshell, fish and guano (phosphate-rich topsoil formed from bird droppings and used for fertilizer). Tea cultivation has been introduced. The islanders' staple diet consists of rice (mostly imported), lentils and fish. In the last few years, tourism has been developed and visitors to the islands increased from 500 in 1970 to 80,000 in 1976. Inter-island links are by boat and plane; there is an international airport on Mahé.

BIOT
The British Indian Ocean Territory (BIOT) was formed in 1965 to link, politically, some small, widely scattered coral islands and atolls. The Territory, with a total land area of 453 km², consists of the Chagos Archipelago and the islands of Aldabra, Farquhar and Des Roches. Copra and guano are the main products. Except for imported labour on the Chagos Archipelago copra plantations, the islands are uninhabited. The largest island in the Chagos Archipelago, Diego Garcja (28 km²), is a US defence base. Aldabra island, northwest of Madagascar, is famous for its giant tortoises and rare birds and is leased to the Royal Society for research.

Mauritius
Area
1,865 km²/720 sq miles
Location
20°15′ S; 57°30′ E
Population
971,000 (1981)
Population density
521 per km²/1,349 per sq mile
Capital and largest city
Port Louis: 147,000 (1982)
Languages
English, French
Major imports
rice, petroleum products, machinery
Major exports
sugar, molasses, tea
Currency
rupee (1 rupee = 100 cents)
Gross National Product
1,230 million US dollars (1981)
Status
independent Commonwealth nation

Mauritius: the land
Mauritius, 880 km east of Madagascar, is a hilly, volcanic island fringed by coral reefs. The central plateau, 600 m high consists of craters from which lava flowed down to form a fertile coastal plain. Basalt mountain blocks rise to over 800 m in the southwestern part of the plateau. The climate is hot and humid: average temperatures range from 24°C in August (the coolest month) to 30°C in February (the hottest). During the wet season (December to June), the southeast trade winds bring 500 cm to upland areas, but under 100 cm to some coastal districts. The heavy rains have cut deep gorges on the plateau. Cyclones occur frequently during the wet season damaging crops and houses

Mauritius: economy
Sugar dominates the economy, accounting for 90% of exports, 90% of cultivated land and 28% of the workforce. The chief secondary crops are tea, grown in the Curepipe area, tobacco and aloe (used in fibre manufacture). Subsistence farming is small-scale, so food makes up 25% of imports. Industry is based on agriculture: products include refined sugar, molasses, rum and aloe fibre. Power comes from hydro-electric plants and from the re-cycling of sugar by-products. Tourism is being developed.

Mauritius: transport
There is a good network of surfaced roads and regular bus services cover all areas. There are no railways. Port Louis has a modernized harbour and, 22 km away at Plaisance, there is an international airport.

Dependencies
Rodrigues, Agalega and Cargados Carajos are all dependencies of Mauritius. Rodrigues (104 km²) lies 585 km east of Mauritius and comprises a central volcanic ridge, a coastal plain and an encircling coral reef. The 26,000 islanders live by fishing and livestock farming: live animals and salted fish are sent to Mauritius. The coral islands of Agalega and the Cargados Carajos group have a combined area of 71 km² and a total population of 400. The main products are copra (from Agalega), salted fish and guano (from Cargados Carajos); all trade is with Mauritius.

Réunion
Area
2,512 km²/970 sq miles
Location
21°10′ S; 55°30′ E
Population
534,000 (1981)
Population density
213 per km²/551 per sq mile
Capital and largest city
St-Denis: 105,000
Language
French
Major imports
rice, pharmaceuticals, machinery vehicles
Major exports
sugar, rum, essences, vanilla
Currency
franc (1 franc = 100 centimes)
Gross National Product
2,050 million US dollars (1981)
Status
French overseas department

Réunion: the land
Réunion, situated 780 km east of Madagascar, is a mountainous island of volcanic origin—its highest peak is Piton des Neiges (3,069 m). The climate is tropical with heavy rainfall between December and March and high temperatures (from 23°C to 27°C).

Réunion: economy
The island's economy depends on sugar cane. Grown on plantations covering 20% of the territory, the cane is processed at St-Denis, St-Pierre and St-Paul; the chief products are sugar, rum and molasses. Other cash crops include vanilla, tobacco, tea and perfume plants for essences. Maize and manioc are the staple foods. There is one major road and a railway which follow the coast and link all main towns.

Indian Ocean Islands 2

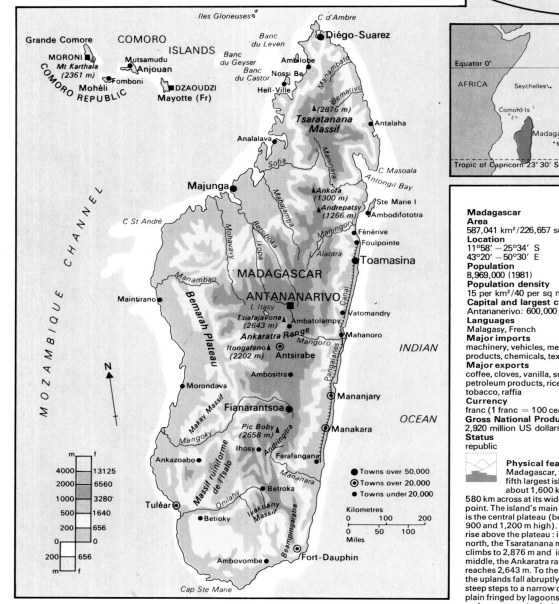

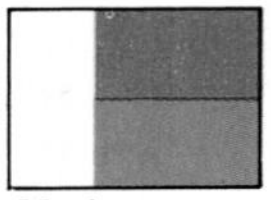
Madagascar

Comoros

Tropic of Cancer 23° 30′ N
Equator 0°
Tropic of Capricorn 23° 30′ S

Equator 0°
AFRICA
Seychelles
Chagos Is
INDONESIA
Comoro Is
INDIAN OCEAN
Madagascar
Mascarene Is
Tropic of Capricorn 23° 30′ S

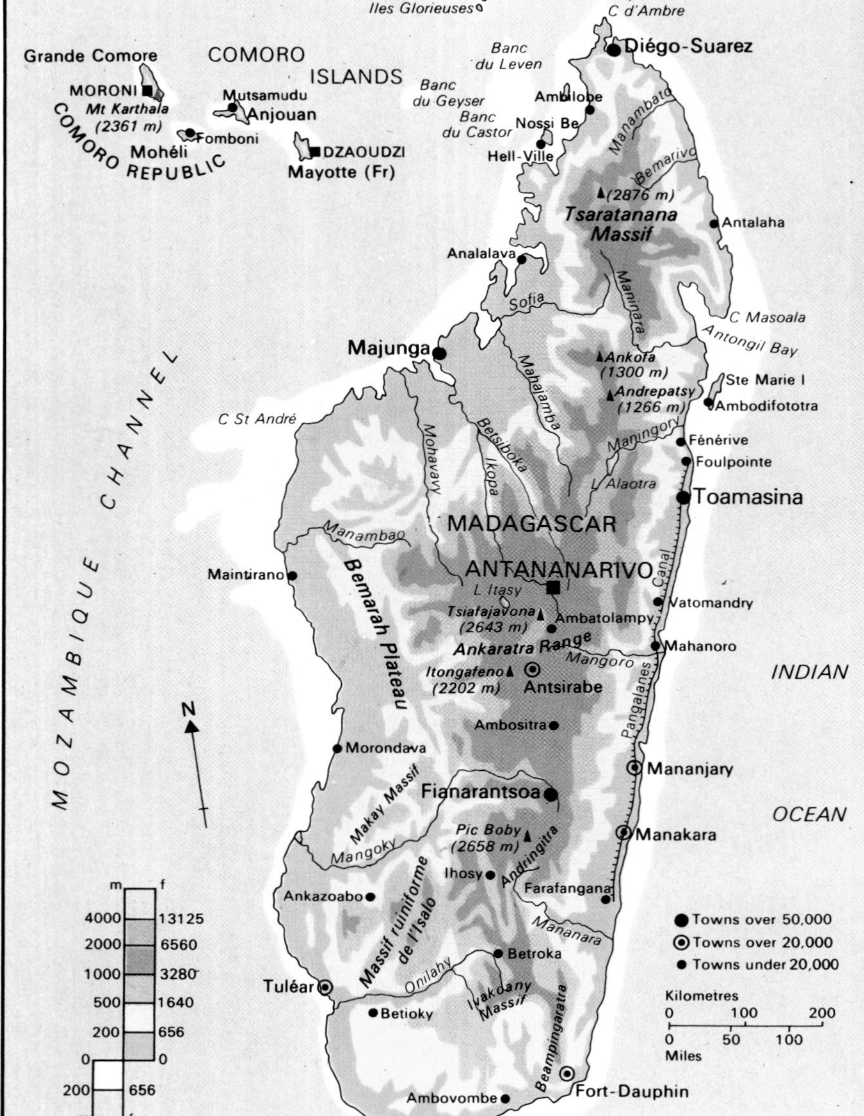

Madagascar
Area
587,041 km^2/226,657 sq miles
Location
11°58′ – 25°34′ S
43°20′ – 50°30′ E
Population
8,969,000 (1981)
Population density
15 per km^2/40 per sq mile
Capital and largest city
Antananerivo: 600,000 (1982)
Languages
Malagasy, French
Major imports
machinery, vehicles, metal products, chemicals, textiles
Major exports
coffee, cloves, vanilla, sugar, petroleum products, rice, tobacco, raffia
Currency
franc (1 franc = 100 centimes)
Gross National Product
2,920 million US dollars (1981)
Status
republic

Physical features
Madagascar, the world's fifth largest island, is about 1,600 km long and 580 km across at its widest point. The island's main feature is the central plateau (between 900 and 1,200 m high). Two ranges rise above the plateau : in the north, the Tsaratanana massif climbs to 2,876 m and in the middle, the Ankaratra range reaches 2,643 m. To the east, the uplands fall abruptly in steep steps to a narrow coastal plain fringed by lagoons and reefs ; westwards, the land descends in terraces to a 150 km wide alluvial plain. The west coast is characterized by mangrove swamps and offshore islands. The central highlands act as a watershed : the short, swift rivers in the east cut deep gorges while the longer, western rivers flow through broad fertile valleys. Tropical rain forest occurs along the wet east coast, savanna covers the plateau while elsewhere scrub and grass-lands predominate. Animal life includes crocodiles in the west and most of the world's lemurs, which are indigenous.

Climate
Coastal temperatures range from 23°C in the south and east to 27°C in the north and west. The plateau is cooler (18°C). Rainfall is heavy on the east coast (over 250 cm) but decreases westwards to 140 cm on the plateau and to under 50 cm in the west and south. During the summer (from January until April), cyclones are common in the north and east.

Agriculture
About 30% of the island is cultivated and half this area is used for rice, the staple food. The western coastal swamps and river valleys are the main rice-producing regions. Other subsistence crops are cassava, maize, millet and potatoes. Coffee, grown near the east coast, is the chief cash crop and accounts for 30% of exports. Vanilla, cloves, tobacco, sugar and pepper are also important commercial crops (Madagascar ranks as the world's leading vanilla producer). Livestock is important and cattle outnumber people 2 to 1. Cattle are raised on the plateau and western plain while sheep are grazed in the south.

Mining & industry
Madagascar's minerals are only partially developed. Sizeable amounts of graphite and chromite and smaller quantities of mica and beryl are exported. There is also some production of iron ore and alluvial gold. Deposits of coal, bauxite and nickel have yet to be exploited. The island's isolated position has encouraged industrial development. As well as traditional activities based on agriculture (such as rice milling, meat packing, oil-seed crushing and brewing) the industrial sector now includes vehicle assembly, oil refining, textiles, chemicals and cement.

Transport
The steep gradients from the coast to the plateau make communications difficult, particularly in the east. The main railway runs from Tamatave to Antananarivo. The 38,000 km road network is mostly dryweather and travel is arduous during the wet season (November-April). In the west, the rivers are navigable for up to 160 km while in the east, the 640 km Pangalanes canal runs parallel to the coast between Farafangana and Foulpointe. The chief ports are Tamatave, Majunga and Diego-Suarez. There is an international airport near Antananarivo and Air Madagascar flies overseas and internally.

Towns
Antananarivo, 'city of a thousand warriors', stands high on the plateau. It is linked by rail to Antananarivo (77,000), the chief port. The second city and second port, Majunga (67,000) serves the northwest—especially the Betsiboka valley.

Comoros
Area
2,274 km^2/878 sq miles
Location
11°20′ – 13° S
43°15′ – 45°20′ E
Population
358,000 (1981)
Population density
157 per km^2/408 per sq mile
Capital and largest city
Moroni: 22,000 (1982)
Language
French
Major imports
rice, consumer goods, petroleum products, vehicles
Major exports
ylang-ylang, copra, vanilla, essences, cloves
Currency
franc (1 franc = 100 centimes)
Gross National Product
110 million US dollars (1981)
Status
the islands were French colonies; now, Grande Comore, Mohéli and Anjouan form the Comoro Republic but Mayotte (53,000) remains, by choice, under French rule.

The land
The Comoro archipelago, lying 300 km off the Mozambique coast, comprises the volcanic islands of Grande Comore (1,147 km^2), Anjouan (424 km^2), Mayotte (400 km^2) and Mohéli (290 km^2), plus numerous coral islets and reefs. The four main islands are mountainous and thickly forested ; Grande Comore is dominated by Mt Karthala (2,361 m), an active volcano. The climate is tropical : summers (November to April) are wet and hot (27°C), while winters are dry and cooler (23°C).

Transport
Settlement is concentrated along the coasts and boats are widely used. Roads, totalling 750 km, also follow the coast. Inter-island links are maintained by boat (between Moroni, Fomboni, Mutsamudu and Dzaoudzi) and by air. The republic's airline, Air Comores, also flies to Kenya, Tanzania and Madagascar.

The economy
There is no mining or industrial activity and the archipelago's undeveloped economy depends solely on agriculture. Most islanders are engaged in subsistence farming, using primitive methods on over-exploited land. Output of basic crops (rice, cassava, sweet potatoes and maize) is insufficient and food accounts for 50% of imports. There is some livestock ; lobster and shrimp fishing is being developed off Mayotte. Plantations, occupying a third of land area, produce commercial crops : the chief products are copra, vanilla, essential oils for perfumes (from ylang-ylang, lemon grass, jasmine, orange flower and tuberose), sisal, cocoa, coffee, cloves and cinnamon. Together, ylang-ylang (the base of 90% of French perfumes), copra, vanilla and cloves provide over 90% of all exports. Small quantities of timber, from the forested interior of Grande Comore, are also exported.

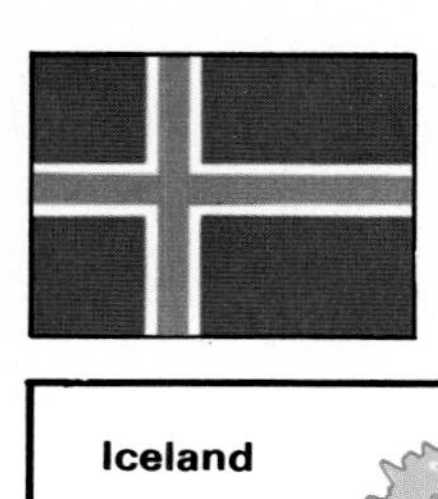

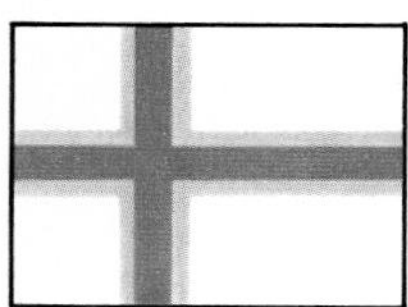

Iceland and the Faeroes

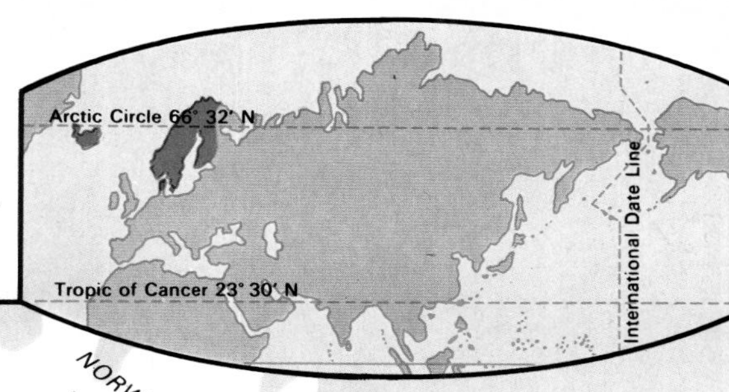

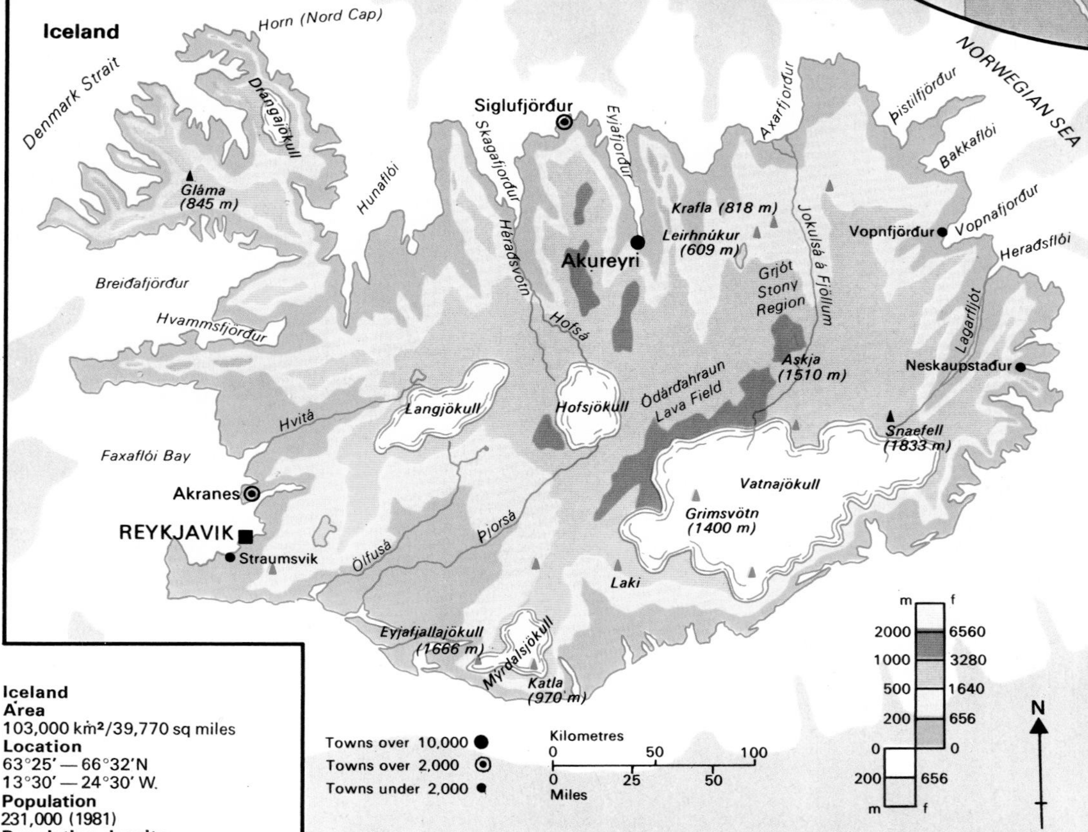

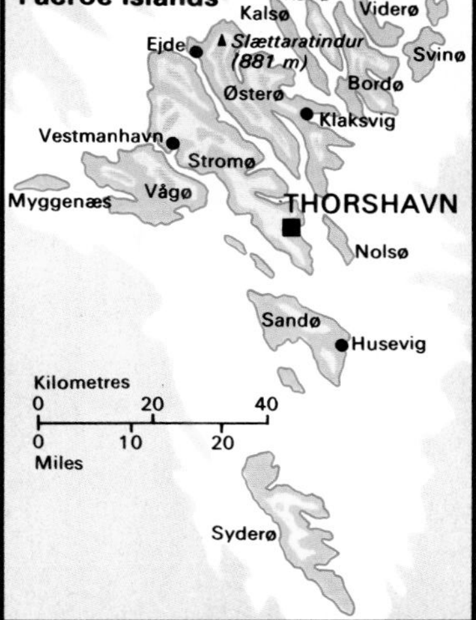

Iceland
Area
103,000 km²/39,770 sq miles
Location
63°25' — 66°32'N
13°30' — 24°30' W.
Population
231,000 (1981)
Population density
2 per km²/6 per sq mile
Capital and largest city
Reykjavik: 85,000 (1981)
Language
Icelandic
Major imports
transport equipment, fuel oil, foodstuffs, aluminium ore
Major exports
fish, fish products, aluminium
Currency
krona (1 krona — 100 aurar)
Gross National Product
2,970 million US dollars (1981)
Status
independent republic

Physical features
In spite of its name, Iceland is one of the world's major geological hot-spots. Nearly all of the island—a bare plateau over 600 m high—has been built by volcanic activity and one third of the country is still actively volcanic with an average of one eruption every five years. The active zone lies north-south along the Mid-Atlantic Ridge and contains many types of volcanoes from snow-capped Hekla (a lava volcano) to Askja (a complex volcano with an 11 km wide crater). Some of these volcanoes are perpetually under ice as 12% of Iceland is covered by glaciers, the largest being Vatnajökull (8,400 km²). Volcanic activity also produces the many hot springs, steam vents and mudpots.

Climate
The climate of Iceland is influenced by wind and sea. Arctic waters bring fog and ice to the north coast, but the Gulf Stream gives mild winters and cool summers. South-west winds bring heavy rain and snow in the south: as much as 380 cm a year. In contrast, the north has only 33 cm.

Fishing
Iceland is a one industry state and that industry is fishing. It accounts for over 80% of exports and so pays for most imports. As Iceland has no coal, valuable minerals or timber and very little agriculture, all necessities have to be imported and hence its dependence on fishing. The country has about 900 fishing vessels which catch mainly cod and herring on the continental shelf surrounding the island. The total catch landed by Icelanders represents only half the fish taken from the Icelandic shelf: foreign fishermen carry home the rest. Intensive fishing by foreign fleets has reduced stocks alarmingly: catches have decreased, younger fish are being caught and spawning has decreased through the reduction in mature fish. Faced with the destruction of its fishing banks (and consequently its economy) Iceland extended its fishing limit to 320 km in 1975.

Energy
With thousands of hot springs and steam fields, it was natural that Iceland should pioneer the use of geothermal energy for heating. Today, half the population lives in houses heated by natural hot water. Geothermal power is also used to heat greenhouses and to power a small electricity plant. The other electricity plants are hydro-electric—harnessing the energy from Icelands waterfalls, especially on the rivers Thjórsá and Ölfusa. A cement plant at Akranes, a fertilizer factory at Reykjavik and an aluminium reduction plant at Straumsvik are powered by electricity.

Agriculture
Mountains, glaciers, lava flows, lakes and bogs (which are all unproductive) make up 80% of Iceland. Only 1% of the surface is cultivated: hay, potatoes and turnips are grown along the coast and in the valleys. The rest is rough grazing land, mainly for sheep which outnumber cattle 12 to 1. Agricultural produce, including hothouse grown fruit, vegetables and flowers, is processed and marketed co-operatively: dairies, meat-packing stations and slaughter-houses are also joint concerns.

Transport
When, about a thousand years ago, the Vikings settled in Iceland they brought their horses with them. Until recently, these unique, sturdy animals only 13 hands high were the Icelanders' sole means of transport. The internal combustion engine has since eased the horse's load and Iceland's roads were improved by British and American troops during the Second World War. There are no railways but domestic air services are well developed.

Reykjavik
Reykjavik (or 'smoking bay') was the name given by Iceland's first settler, a Norseman called Arnarson, who was fascinated by the smoke coming from hot-springs near his home on the edge of Faxaflói bay. That was in 874. Today, Reykjavik is Iceland's main port and commercial centre with shipbuilding, textile and fish-processing industries. The second largest town is Akureyri.

Faeroe Islands
Area
1,400 km²/540 sq miles
Location
61°26'—62°24' N
6°15'—7°41' W
Population
44,000 (1981)
Population density
28 per km²/73 per sq mile
Capital and largest city
Thorshavn: 11,000 (1977)
Language
Faeroese and Danish
Major imports
food, machinery, fuels, textiles
Major exports
fish and fish products
Currency
krona (1 krona = 1 Danish krone)
Gross National Product
490 million US dollars (1981)
Status
self-governing community within the kingdom of Denmark

Agriculture
In the Faeroes, three days out of five are wet (annual rainfall is over 150 cm), fogs are frequent and temperatures are low (3°C in January, 10°C in July). Climate, together with infertile soil, restricts vegetation and produces conditions which do not favour agriculture. Less than 4% of the surface is cultivated—the main crop being potatoes. Much of the uncultivated land, especially the heaths, is used for grazing sheep. Sheep rearing is a traditional Faeroese activity with early records showing that the islands were originally called *Faereyiar* which means 'sheep islands'.

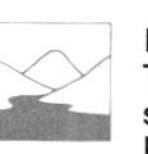

Physical features
The Faeroe Islands, situated mid-way between the Shetlands and Iceland, are of volcanic origin. Formed by Tertiary eruptions, they consist of layers of basaltic lava and volcanic ash with a thin covering of glacial deposits. Glaciation left a rugged landscape with steep cliffs, ravines and mountains—the highest of which is Slættaratindur (881 m) on the island of Østerø.

Economy
As agricultural conditions are poor, the Faeroese, who inhabit 17 of the islands, are forced to earn their living from the sea. The islanders fish off Newfoundland, Greenland and in their own coastal waters and the catch, which is principally herring and cod, is the basis of the Faeroese economy. There is a hydro-electric power station at Vestmanhavn on the island of Strømø which, as well as satisfying domestic requirements, powers the local industries. These include fish-processing (frozen, salted, canned and dried) and fish products (such as fish meal and cod liver oil). Industry is also concerned with the fishermen's needs such as ropes, nets and reels as well as ships. There are eight shipyards on the island. Fish and fish products account for 95% of exports. The main port is the capital of Thorshavn on Strømø. The one airport is on Vågø.

Finland

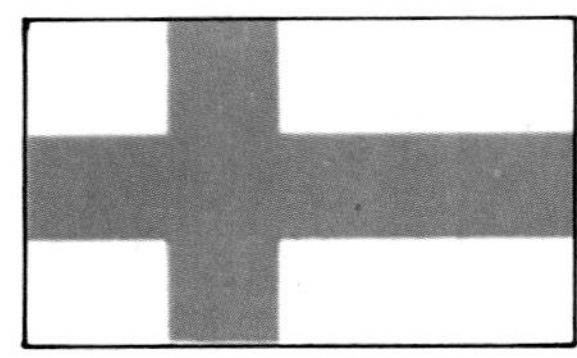

Area
337,032 km²/130,128 sq miles
Location
59°30′—70°05′ N
19°07′—31°35′ E
Population
4,801,000 (1981)
Population density
14 per km²/37 per sq mile
Capital and largest city
Helsinki: 490,000 (1982)
Languages
Finnish and Swedish
Major imports
machinery, transport equipment, fuels, chemicals, food
Major exports
forest products, engineering products, textiles
Currency
markka (1 markka = 100penniä)
Gross National Product
51,270 million US dollars (1981)
Status
independent republic

Physical features

Finland is a low-lying country covered with forests and lakes (its Finnish name, *Suomi*, means 'lakeland'). There are about 60,000 lakes which cover 10% of the country's total area. These are Ice Age souvenirs: severe glaciation left the land stripped of soil, scattered with rock ridges (like the Salpausselkä) and pitted with hollows. These water-filled hollows are concentrated in the densely forested central plain 100 m above sea-level known as the Lakes Plateau. They include the Saimaa, Päijänne and Näsijärvi. To the north of this plateau is a harsh region of swamp, fells and forest stretching [illegible] Circle. To [illegible] coastal pla[illegible]ngly fertile clay so[illegible] o[illegible]-shore, some 30,000 islands: the two most important groups are the Turku archipelago and the Åland islands.

Climate

In Finland, the winter snow lasts for seven months in the north and for three months in the south with lakes, waterways and ports frozen over. Winter is also cold: minimum temperatures are as low as —30°C. In contrast, the short summer (two months long in the north and four in the south) is warm, partly because of the Gulf Stream. Maximum temperatures reach 30°C. As in all countries with an Arctic (or Antarctic) zone, northern Finland experiences the midnight sun: on the 70th parallel there are 73 days of uninterrupted light in summer and 51 days of darkness in winter.

Agriculture

Farming in Finland is a fight against terrain and weather. Except in the south, land for cultivation has to be carved out of forest or reclaimed from swamps. The result is isolated smallholdings covering only 9% of the country. In northern Finland climate limits crop production but farmers do grow potatoes, oats and barley and keep cattle up to 250 km north of the Arctic Circle. On the central plateau, most smallholders also own some woodland which provides both winter work and extra income. Finland's main farming area is the fertile coastal plain where wheat, rye and cattle predominate. Butter and cheese are exported.

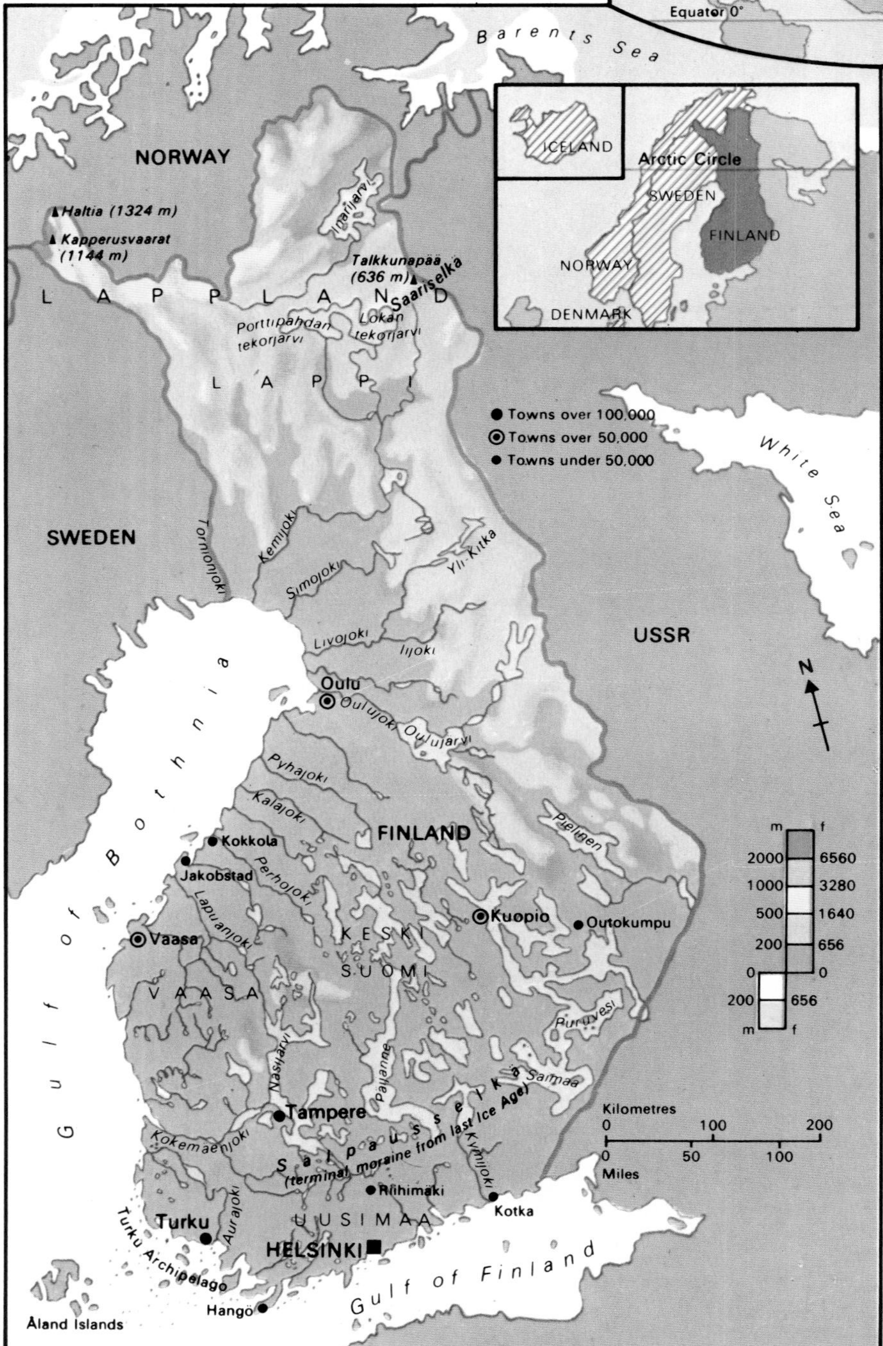

Forestry

For centuries Finland has lived off its forests. Although the metal and engineering industries have recently assumed equal importance at home, wood and wood products are still Finland's leading export—providing 57% of total export income. The forest, mostly privately owned, covers 70% of the land giving Finland the third largest area in Europe after the USSR and Sweden. The main trees grown are pine and spruce (which are used principally for pulp) and birch (used in plywood manufacture). To increase production, improvements such as swamp drainage, the use of fertilizers, and the replacement of slow-growing species are being made. Road construction, especially in the north-east, has opened up new areas. Much of Finland's timber is still floated—the 41,600 km of floatable waterways carry timber (placed on the ice before the spring thaw) to lakeside sawmills and processing plants. Each plant is usually a complex of factories that process a variety of products including pulp, paper, board, plywood and veneers of which approximately 80% is exported.

Nordic co-operation

Finland works closely with the other Scandinavian (Nordic) countries (consisting of Denmark, Iceland, Norway and Sweden) through a co-ordinating body called the Nordic Council. The results of this co-operation are numerous. For example, laws have been harmonized, citizens of member states can travel within the Nordic area without passports, it costs no more to send a letter from one country to another than within one of the countries, and the power grids of Denmark, Finland, Norway and Sweden are interconnected. Many radio and television programmes are jointly produced and Nordic citizens may work in any member country without restrictions—like the 200,000 Finns at present working in Sweden.

Industry

Many of the rivers plunging over the 180 m high Salpausselkä have been harnessed for hydro-electricity, as have rapids in the north. Thermal stations, using imported oil, also help supply Finland with energy. Much of this power is consumed by the country's main industrial sector—the metal and engineering industries—concentrated at Tampere, Helsinki and Turku and accounting for 27% of total exports. In the engineering field, which includes shipbuilding at Helsinki and Turku, Finland has drawn on its own experiences to produce such items as paper-making machines, forest tractors, ice-breakers, oil rigs, car ferries and other special ships.

Mining

Copper is Finland's most abundant metal and is used, for example, on roofs and in kitchen utensils. Mined at Outojumpu, copper is essential to the expanding electrical industry where it is used in wires and cables. Other metals mined include zinc, cobalt, nickel, lead and, most important, vanadium (used in special steels). Finland is the world's fourth largest producer of vanadium. Also of commercial importance are clay and sand. Clay is essential to the brick, tile and porcelain industries (the Arabia factory at Helsinki is Europe's largest china works). Sand is the basis of the glass industry centred on Riihimäki and Lahti. Finland has no fuels except peat.

Shipping

With 4,600 km of coast and 6,600 km of navigable lakes, rivers and canals, water transport is important—especially for trade with other countries (including neighbouring Sweden which has a different railway gauge to Finland). Almost 90% of Finland's trade is done by sea and over half of this is in Finnish vessels. Because the Gulfs of Bothnia and Finland are both low in salinity and nearly tideless, ice once blocked most ports during the winter months, but now these harbours are, kept open by ice-breakers. Helsinki is the largest port, but others of importance are Kotka (timber), Hangö (dairy produce) and Turku which is Finland's main link with Sweden.

Helsinki

Helsinki is, after Reykjavik in Iceland, the world's most northerly capital at a latitude of 60°10′ N. One Finn in five lives there, either in the city proper or in the suburbs which lie to the north (the sea surrounds Helsinki in all other directions as it is built on a peninsula). Its coastal position has made Helsinki Finland's leading port—its five harbours handle more than half the country's imports, but only 10% of exports (some of which are manufactured in the capital itself). As the centre of Finnish industry, Helsinki specializes in food processing, printing, textiles and metal goods. Because many of the main official buildings are painted in very light colours, Helsinki is known as the 'white city of the north'. It is a relatively modern city which has developed rapidly since it was made the capital in 1812.

Norway

Area
323,797 km²/125,018 sq miles
This does not include the Arctic territories of Spitsbergen and Jan Mayen Island, nor Peter I Island, Bouvet Island and Queen Maud Land in the Antarctic.
Location
57°57′—71°11′ N
4°30′—31°10′ E
Population
4,100,000 (1981)
Population density
13 per km²/33 per sq mile
Capital and largest city
Oslo: 452,000 (1981)
Languages
bokmal ('book language') and nynorsk (Neo Norwegian)
Major imports
machinery, transport equipment, metals, fuels, textiles, food and chemicals
Major exports
fish, forest products, ores, ships, electro-chemical and electro-metallurgical products
Currency
kroner (1 kroner = 100 øre)
Gross National Product
57,640 million US dollars (1981)
Status
constitutional monarchy

Climate
Norway's climate is influenced by latitude, topography (high mountains, deep valleys) and its proximity to the sea. Winter temperatures range from 1°C at Bergen to —14°C at Hammerfest. Summer temperatures at the same places average 15°C and 9°C. The amount of rain and snow is even more varied. The prevailing onshore winds are the main cause of the heavy rainfall typical of western Norway, but inland areas are drier: Bergen has over 300 cm of rain a year, but Oslo only 100 cm. The coast is also subject to severe storms and in winter force 9 gales are quite common.

Communications
Fjords, mountains and inclement weather make railways and roads difficult to build and costly to maintain. Railways corkscrew up and down mountains, or tunnel through them; roads are a sequence of hairpin bends that follow the chasm's edge and only 15% of them are hardsurfaced. Travelling by public transport often means using two, if not three, forms of transport: buses pick up where trains stop and ferries link one road to another. Water transport is the most used with almost 700 vessels operating across fjords and between coastal and island towns. Norway shares an airline with Sweden and Denmark (SAS) and has seven international airports.

Forestry
About 76% of Norway is unproductive consisting of bog and mountain. The remainder is mostly forest, making forestry a major Norwegian activity. Two-thirds of the forest (mainly spruce) belongs to farmers with the rest owned either by the government or by industry, but all forest areas are under government supervision. The industry is being increasingly mechanized. Cutting is done with power saws and the lumber is transported by truck, funicular or winch to road and rail heads. Woodpulp and paper are the main exports while timber is now aimed more at the home market.

Physical features
Stretching down the western edge of the Scandinavian peninsula, Norway is the fifth largest country in Europe and, after Iceland, the least populated. Its peaks and high plateaux are generally uninhabitable and settlement is confined to the deep valleys cut by glaciers in the Ice Age and to the sides of fjords. Fjords are a characteristic of Norway's coastline. They are narrow valleys carved by glaciers and subsequently flooded by the rising sea level. The longest fjord is Sognefjorden with a length of 203 km. Islands are another characteristic of Norway's coastline: some 50,000 of them lie offshore, the most famous being the archipelagos of Lofoten and Vesteralen. The mountains of the Scandinavian peninsula rise sharply in the west and slope down gently towards the Gulf of Bothnia in the east. They are highest in the vicinity of the Swedish-Norwegian border and especially in the southwest where the Dovrefjellen, Jotunheimen and Hardangervidda ranges form a central mass. Norway's highest peak is Glittertind (2,470 m) in the Jotunheimen range.

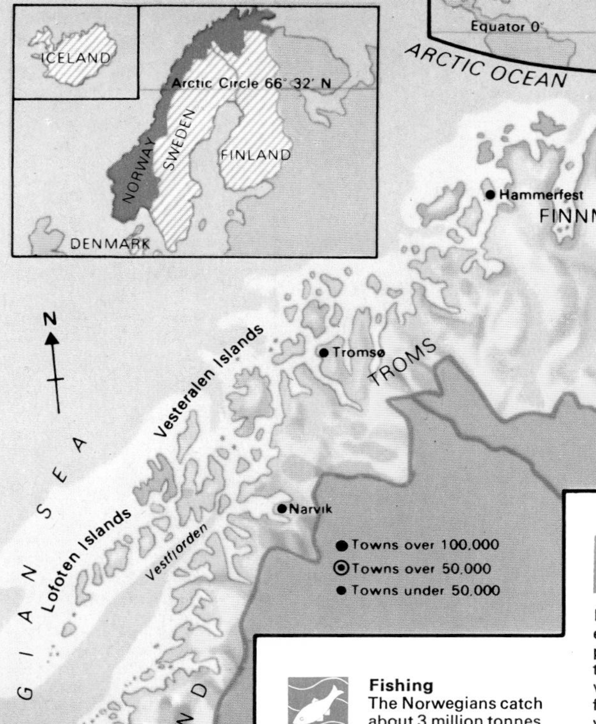

Fishing
The Norwegians catch about 3 million tonnes of fish annually—exceeding that of any other European nation. Cod, capelin, herring and mackeral are the major varieties. Until recently, Norwegian fishing was predominantly coastal with fish-farmers going out in their own motorboats. Now, the emphasis is placed on ocean fishing with modern steel vessels. Herring are caught off More og Romsdal, cod off the Lofoten islands and, further afield, both cod and herring off Greenland and Iceland. Norway only uses between 10 and 15% of the catch. The rest is exported in one form or another (fresh, frozen, canned, salted, smoked, as fish-meal or oil). Of the various processing industries, freezing is now the most important with 235 plants and a fleet of factory freezer trawlers. Alesund (40,000) is the largest fishing port and a sealing base for operations off Newfoundland and Greenland.

Farming
Barren, mountainous Norway is not easily farmed and, of the total area, only 3% is under cultivation. This cultivated land is largely concentrated into two areas: one in the Oslo region, the other centred on Trondheim. The farms, cramped in valleys or alongside fjords, are small; so small that 65,000 farmers (just over half) get their main income from elsewhere. By the coast farmers are often fishermen; inland, lumbermen. But they invariably own their own farms and do all the work themselves—Norwegian farms are highly mechanized. About 65% of the agricultural area is given over to hay and pasture where cattle, sheep, pigs and poultry are the main livestock groups. The corresponding products of cheese, milk, beef, pork, eggs, poultry and wool are marketed through cooperatives. The rest of the land is used for crops—mainly barley, oats and potatoes. Often, extra income is earned through fur farming.

Energy
Heavy rain and snow plus high, steep mountains form the basis of one of Norway's main assets: hydro-electricity. If all the water-power resources were developed, the estimated annual production would be 135,000 million kWh. So far, only 50% has been exploited, yet the amount of electricity produced is, per head of population, greater than in any other country. The largest output is in the Rjukan area where there are six plants. Cheap and plentiful power was the beginning of the electro-chemical and met[illegible]al industries and now [illegible]orters—using [illegible]ry's electricity. [illegible]ning 55% meets other demands at home and abroad. Norway supplies Sweden with about 5,000 million kWh annually. In turn, when water levels are low, power is imported from Sweden.

Merchant shipping
Norway's merchant fleet is the world's fourth largest (after Liberia, Japan and the UK). As 97% of the fleet operates between foreign ports, earnings from freight are a major source of national income. This foreign-going traffic consists mostly of tankers, bulk carriers and liners. The other 3% (by weight) of the fleet includes cargo and passenger vessels working along Norway's coasts as well as fishing boats. Norwegian shipping is in the hands of some 300 private companies, each owning or managing anything from one to 50 ships. These ships are generally modern—older ones are exported before becoming obsolete. New vessels are imported, mainly from Sweden and Japan, but about a quarter of the fleet is built in Norway itself. The most important shipyards are at Stavanger (85,000) which is also the centre of the fish-canning industry.

Oslo
Oslo is situated at the head of Oslofjord. It is surrounded by forested hills which are maintained as recreational areas. Much of the city's economic importance comes from its position: Oslo harbour is the largest and busiest in Norway and handles much of the country's trade.

Sweden

Arctic Circle 66° 32′ N
Tropic of Cancer 23° 30′ N
Equator 0°

Area
449,800 km²/173,665 sq miles
Location
55°20′—69°05′ N
11°—24°10′ E
Population
8,324,000 (1981)
Population density
19 per km²/48 per sq mile
Capital and largest city
Stockholm: 1,387,000 (1980)
Language
Swedish
Major imports
machinery, fuels, food, textiles, chemicals
Major exports
engineering products, forest products, transport equipment, iron and steel
Currency
krona (1 krona = 100 øre)
Gross National Product
123,770 million US dollars (1981)
Status
constitutional monarchy

Physical features

Sweden occupies the eastern part of the Scandinavian peninsula and is almost 1,600 km long. It divides into two main regions: Norrland and the southern-central region. From the mountains of Norway, the broad Norrland plateau slopes eastwards to the Gulf of Bothnia. This plateau, forested and unpopulated, is crossed by many rivers which, in their upper reaches, spread into lakes. In all, Sweden has 96,000 lakes covering 9% of the country. The largest of them, Vänern, Vättern, Malaren and Hjälmaren, are in central Sweden. Central Sweden, like the south, is mainly lowland. The Baltic and Bothnian coasts are edged with archipelagos resulting from land uplift—as great as 1 cm a year in the north.

Climate

The Gulf Stream of the north Atlantic makes Sweden's climate mild for its latitude. In July, the average temperature for most of the country is 15 to 17°C; in January it varies from —1°C in the south to —14°C in the north. Rain is heaviest in the mountains: the Sarek mountains in the north receive over 200 cm a year. Continental influences on the eastern side cause hotter summers and colder winters and at the head of the Gulf of Bothnia coastal ice lasts for nine months.

Agriculture

Agriculture involves only 8% of Sweden's land area. In the north, where winters last at least six months, farms are generally small concentrating on fodder plants and pasture for cattle and pigs. The west and south, however, influenced by the warm Gulf Stream, are more suited to cultivation. Farms are bigger and major crops include cereals, sugar beet and potatoes. Fishing also presents a varied pattern. The 7,600 km long shoreline plus over 38,000 km² of lake water provide ample fishing space, but other factors are missing. For example, moraine lakes in forests give poor nutriment and the Baltic's low salinity means small fish and few varieties. Also, 200 days of ice a year in the Arctic Circle restricts fishing methods. Off the west coast, however, conditions are better and herring fishing is particularly important.

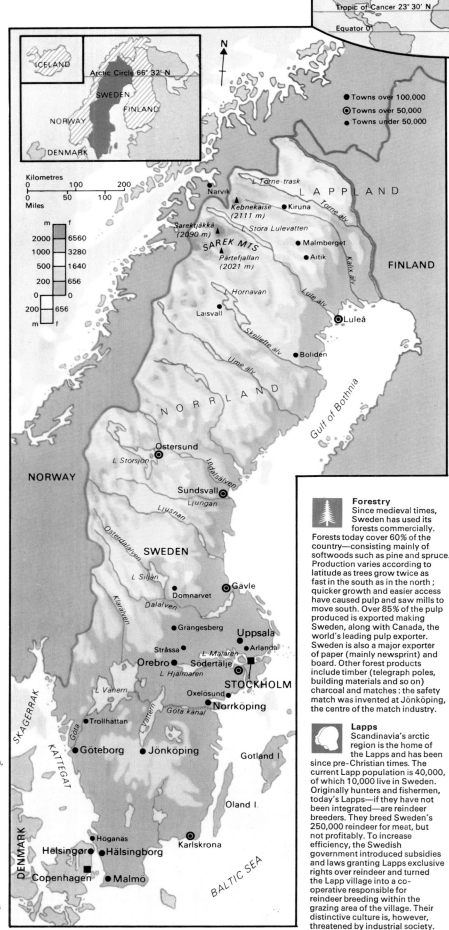

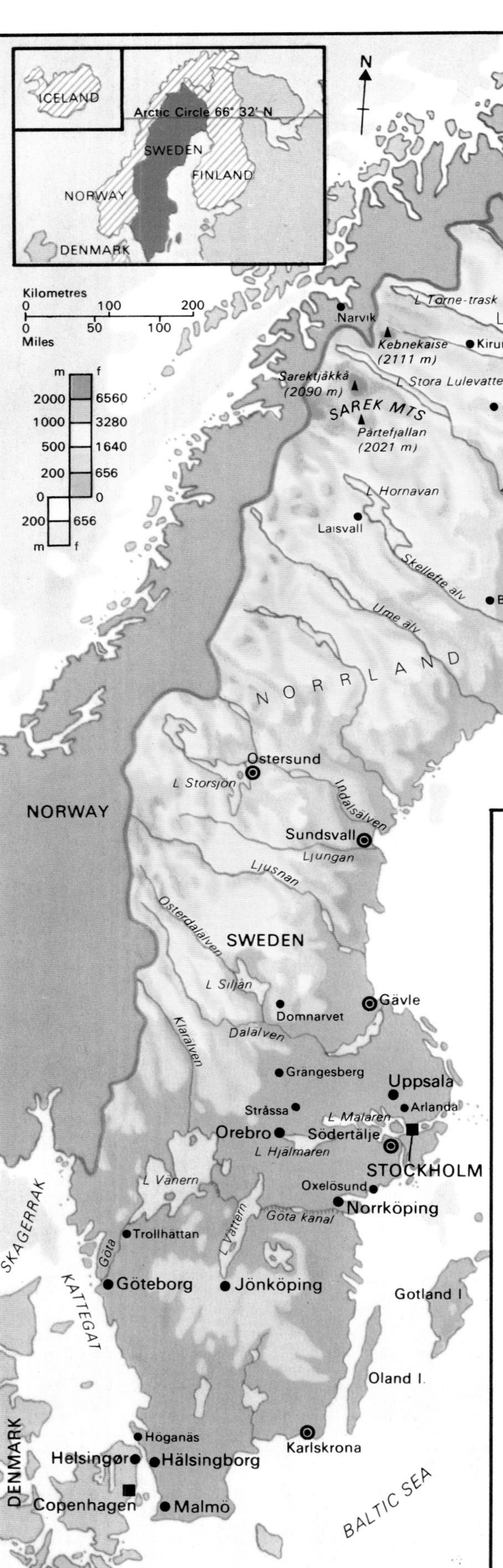

Forestry

Since medieval times, Sweden has used its forests commercially. Forests today cover 60% of the country—consisting mainly of softwoods such as pine and spruce. Production varies according to latitude as trees grow twice as fast in the south as in the north; quicker growth and easier access have caused pulp and saw mills to move south. Over 85% of the pulp produced is exported making Sweden, along with Canada, the world's leading pulp exporter. Sweden is also a major exporter of paper (mainly newsprint) and board. Other forest products include timber (telegraph poles, building materials and so on) charcoal and matches: the safety match was invented at Jönköping, the centre of the match industry.

Lapps

Scandinavia's arctic region is the home of the Lapps and has been since pre-Christian times. The current Lapp population is 40,000, of which 10,000 live in Sweden. Originally hunters and fishermen, today's Lapps—if they have not been integrated—are reindeer breeders. They breed Sweden's 250,000 reindeer for meat, but not profitably. To increase efficiency, the Swedish government introduced subsidies and laws granting Lapps exclusive rights over reindeer and turned the Lapp village into a co-operative responsible for reindeer breeding within the grazing area of the village. Their distinctive culture is, however, threatened by industrial society.

Mining

The growth of steel industries in Europe has created a demand for ores: in meeting this demand Sweden has become the world's fifth largest iron-ore exporter. About 90% of Swedish iron-ore comes from Kiruna and Malmberget. This area, which also has Sweden's biggest copper mine, Aitik, is linked to two ports: Luleå (ice-bound in winter) and Narvik (in Norway). Sweden's two other mining districts are between Boliden and Laisvall (sulphide ores) and Grängesberg and Stråssa in central Sweden, where iron and sulphide ores are shipped via Oxelösund. Mining also includes limestone quarrying (for use in the cement industry) and coal extraction near Höganäs.

Industry

One factor leading to the industrialization of Sweden was water-power. Hydro-electricity compensates for the scarcity of coal and oil deposits, providing about 75% of Sweden's electrical energy. Industry is concentrated mainly in the centre and south: the steel industry, noted for high quality steel, is based at Domnarvet and heavy engineering is concentrated around Stockholm, Göteborg and Malmö. Allied to these basic industries is the manufacture of telephones, ball-bearings, sewing machines, cutlery and so on. The chemical industry is also important, producing fertilizers, explosives paints and pharmaceuticals.

Transport

For every car on the road 20 years ago there are now ten and Sweden has the most cars per head in Europe. In the same period, rail passenger traffic fell but freight transport increased. The busiest line from Narvik in Norway to Luleå carries iron ore from the Kiruna-Malmberget region. Other materials, such as stone, pyrites and petroleum, are often moved by ship. There are 186 coastal ports and some canals (such as the Trollhättan and the Södertälje) take sea-going vessels. During the winter, ice-breakers hold open Baltic and lake ports. To meet the demand of growing air traffic, a new airport has been built at Malmö and facilities extended at Göteborg and Arlanda (Stockholm). Future projects include a bridge-tunnel between Malmö and Copenhagen and a Hälsingborg-Helsingør tunnel.

Shipbuilding

Sweden comes second after Japan in shipbuilding. Of the tonnage launched by Swedish yards (concentrated between Göteborg and Malmö) 75% is exported, and half of this to Norway. Many of the ships are tankers, but ore and paper carriers are also produced to meet the needs of Swedish industry. Over 80% of Sweden's merchant fleet trades between foreign ports. The leading port and second largest city in Sweden is Göteborg (693,000). With its deep, ice-free harbour, shipbuilding and shipping are the main activities.

Denmark

Area
43,070 km²/16,630 sq miles
Location
54°34'—57°45' N
8°05'—15°12' E
Population
5,122,000 (1981)
Population density
119 per km²/309 per sq mile
Capital and largest city
Copenhagen: 654,000 (1980)
Language
Danish
Major imports
machinery, metals, fuels, transport equipment, textiles
Major exports
machinery, meat, live animals, dairy produce, eggs, fish and fish products
Currency
krone (1 krone = 100 øre)
Gross National Product
67,190 million US dollars (1981)
Status
constitutional monarchy

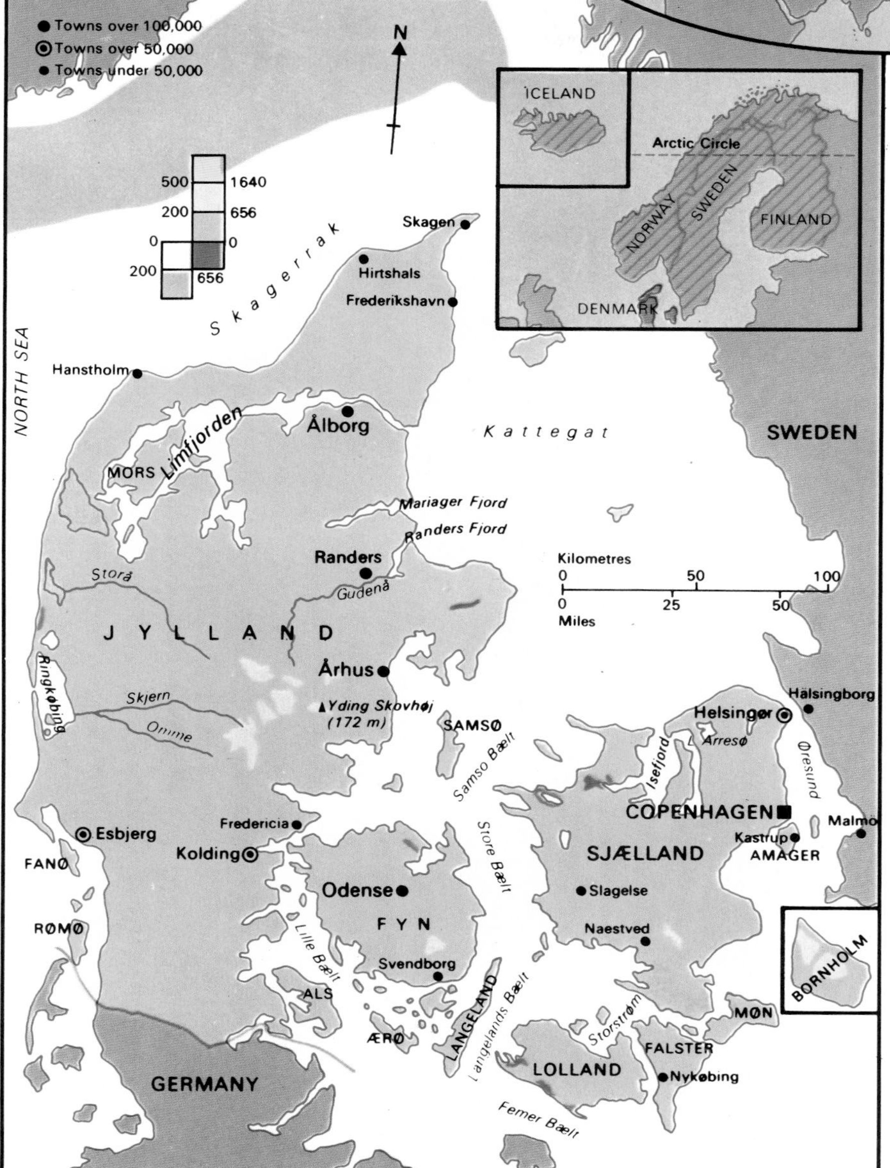

Climate

Generally Denmark's climate is moderate: the average temperature of the coldest month, February, is just below freezing, and that of the warmest, July, 17°C. Winter is tempered by the surrounding seas: to the west, the North Sea and the warming current of the Gulf Stream; to the east, the Baltic which, separating Denmark from the continental land mass, acts as a heat reservoir. But, on the rare occasions when ice closes the Baltic, cold air from the east spreads over Denmark causing very harsh weather. On one such occasion in 1940, the temperature fell to a record —31°C. Conversely, in summer the same easterly air-stream may hold off the westerly sea winds and cause a heat wave: the highest temperature recorded was 36°C. Rainfall varies from 80 cm a year in south-west Jylland to about 40 cm in the Store Bælt area.

Fishing

With sea on all sides (except for its 67 km frontier with Germany) Denmark enjoys excellent fishing conditions. The 10,000 vessels of the Danish fishing fleet are mostly privately owned. A third of them are rowing boats, but increasingly, steel vessels over 200 tonnes are replacing the smaller types. The catch consists of herring, cod, plaice and mackerel from the North Sea and the Skagerrak, and eel and shrimp from the Baltic. Esbjerg (79,000), with canning and processing factories, is the main fishing port followed by Skagen, Hirtshals and the new port of Hanstholm.

Porcelain

One of Denmark's traditional manufactures is porcelain using kaolin from Bornholm and also the UK. The most famous centre is the Royal Copenhagen Porcelain Manufactory. It was founded in 1775 as a private company with royal support—the Queen herself supposedly suggested the factory's trade mark, three blue wavy lines symbolizing the Lille Bælt (Little Belt), Store Bælt (Great Belt) and the Oresund (Sound). Four years later, the factory was taken over by the King and for nearly 100 years remained a royal possession before reverting to private ownership. Its products are exported all over the world.

Physical features

Denmark almost forms a land bridge between the continent of Europe and the Scandinavian peninsula and separates the North and Baltic Seas. Its land area is divided between Jylland (Jutland: 29,650 km²) and 406 islands (of which 97 are inhabited) which are mostly concentrated at the Baltic entrance. The largest of these islands are Sjælland (Zealand), Fyn (Funen), Lolland, Falster and, in the south Baltic, the granite island of Bornholm. The country is low-lying with Denmark's highest point, Yding Skovhøj in east Jylland, only 172 m above sea level. Glacial moraine deposits cover the surface to form undulating plains alternating with low hills and lakes. The biggest lake is Arresø (41 km²). Jylland's west coast is characterized by dunes, the north is swampy while the east coast is broken up by inlets leading back into valleys. Denmark's longest river, the Gudenå (157 km), follows a series of such valleys, formed by glacial melt water.

Cities

Copenhagen, or Merchants' Harbour, was founded in 1167 and became Denmark's capital in 1417. The city centre is the medieval Raadhuspladsen (Town Hall Square) with Strøget, the main shopping street now open to pedestrians only, leading off it. Built opposite Malmö on the east of Sjælland and the north of Amager, Copenhagen lies at the entrance to the Baltic. Its position led to its commercial, and later industrial, importance: for centuries Copenhagen controlled trade in the Baltic and today is its leading port. More than 35,000 ships visit Copenhagen annually, handling 60% of Danish imports, but only about 30% of exports (since trade in dairy produce and bacon with the UK is dealt with by Esbjerg on the west coast of Jylland). The second largest city is Århus (245,000) in east Jylland, followed by Odense (170,000) on Fyn. Although three out of four Danes live in urbanized areas, there are few major towns apart from these.

Industry

There is no coal, iron, oil or water power in Denmark, but there is an enormous output of agricultural produce. One of Denmark's main industries is food processing which ranges from meat packing to pharmaceuticals (Denmark is the world's principal supplier of insulin). Another major industry using a domestic raw material, chalk, is cement. Ålborg in Jylland has the world's largest rotary cement kiln. The second biggest industrial sector, employing 36% of the total labour force and using imported materials, is engineering and electronics. Products range from ships and their engines (one diesel-powered vessel in three is fitted with an engine built either in Denmark or under Danish licence) to car components (but not cars) and hearing aids. The other main sector, employing imported materials, is textiles. About 80% of Danish firms employ less than 50 people and many of these small units specialize in high quality craft goods.

Agriculture

Drainage and reclamation schemes plus fertilizers have made 90% of Denmark's land surface available for agriculture. Although less than one tenth of this is for permanent grazing (barley, oats, sugar-beet and green forage are grown on most of the remaining land) farming is mainly concerned with cows and pigs and the major part of the harvest (about 90%) is used for feeding animals. There are over a million dairy cattle in the country; the most popular breed is the Red Danish which can produce 5,000 litres (8,750 pints) of milk a year. Milk is collected from farms in tankers and taken to co-operative dairies where it is processed into butter, cream and cheese. The by-products, such as skimmed milk, butter milk and whey, are sold back to the farmers as pig feed. The pigs are all of the Danish Landrace breed which is well suited for bacon. Increasing demand for meat and meat products had led to concentrated and efficient pig raising systems without the use of battery farming techniques. Each year, about 12 million animals are slaughtered and 80% of the resulting meat is exported. Denmark is the world's biggest exporter of pigmeat, second biggest exporter of butter and the third largest exporter of cheese. Although only 8% of Danes work in agriculture, they produce enough animal-based foodstuffs to feed over 15 million people. This is about three times the total population of Denmark and the reason why Denmark is able to export two-thirds of its farm produce. (It is exported to over 140 countries.) Another major animal-based export is mink skin. Danish breeders produce about 3.5 million mink pelts annually of which about 95% are exported. This makes Denmark the world's third biggest mink producing nation. Mink auctions are held five times a year in Copenhagen. Market gardening is also important and one of the main production areas which supplies Copenhagen is Amager.

Transport

Apart from the Jylland peninsular, Denmark consists of a number of small islands which require a combination of land and sea communications. Ferry and steamer services between islands co-ordinate with rail and bus networks overland. For example, trains from Jylland to Copenhagen cross the Store Bælt (between Fyn and Sjælland) by ferry. A feature of the road and rail networks is the number of bridges involved: the largest is Storstrøm bridge, a 3 km link between Sjælland and Falster. Denmark has a large merchant fleet, mainly serving overseas trade and earning about 2,000 million kroner (about 350 million US dollars) in foreign currency. International air transport is handled by SAS and Copenhagen airport (Kastrup) is the fourth busiest in Europe. From Copenhagen there are domestic flights to nine provincial airports.

West Germany

Area
248,600 km²/95,980 sq miles
Location
47°12′—54°55′ N
6°—12° E
Population
61,666,000 (1981)
Population density
248 per km²/642 per sq mile
Capital
Bonn: 288,000 (1980)
Largest city
Berlin (West): 1,896,000 (1980)
Language
German
Major imports
foodstuffs, metals, chemicals, fuels, textiles
Major exports
engineering products, electrical goods, chemicals, road vehicles
Currency
Deutsche Mark (= 100 Pfennige)
Gross National Product
829,600 million US dollars (1981)
Status
independent republic

Physical features

The Federal Republic, consisting of 10 *Länder* (states), divides into three physical zones: the Alpine region, the Central Uplands and the north German plain. The Alpine region in the extreme south comprises the Bavarian Alps—a continuation of the main Alpine system which contains Germany's highest peak, the Zugspitze (2,962 m). The undulating foreland, which extends to the Danube, has numerous lakes and peat bogs. The Central Uplands is a region of ancient plateaux and ranges. The main highland masses are the Harz, Fichtelgebirge and Bohemian Forest in the east, the Schwäbische and Fränkische Alb in the south, the Hohe-Rhön and Vogelsberg in the centre and, bordering the Rhine, the Schwarzwald (Black Forest), Odenwald, Taunus, Westerwald, Sauerland, Eifel and Hunsrück. Between these highlands and the coast lies the north German plain. In the south this is covered by fertile loess but, further north, infertile sand, clay and moorlands predominate. The low-lying marshy coast is fringed by the East Friesian Islands. With the exception of the Danube, the main rivers flow into the North Sea.

Climate

In the coastal regions of Germany, the climate is affected by the North and Baltic Seas with cold (but not severe) winters and warm summers. At Emden, winter and summer temperatures are 1°C and 17°C respectively. In the southern interior the climate is more continental with hotter summers and colder winters: January and July averages for Munich are —2°C and 18°C. Rain is heaviest in highland areas: the Alps receive over 200 cm a year, the Central Uplands have 75 cm and the lowlands only 50 cm.

Energy

Thermal stations generate 90% of Germany's electricity. Half of these are fired by coal, the rest by lignite (brown coal), oil and natural gas. Hydro-electric plants, mostly situated in the south, produce 8% and nuclear power stations only 2%. About 90% of Germany's oil requirement has to be imported as well as 40% of natural gas.

Agriculture

Although 54% of the country is farmed, agriculture accounts for only 4% of the GNP and employs under 9% of the workforce. It does, however, provide 75% of the nation's food. Almost half the cultivated land is used for wheat, barley, rye, oats, potatoes and sugarbeet. The main arable regions are the northern plain (the loess belt is West Germany's best farmland and sandy regions are heavily fertilized), the 'Cologne bay' (a fertile lowland area at the northern end of the Rhine gorge) and valleys in the Central Uplands. Between Basel and Mainz, the Rhine flows through a broad rift valley. Here, summers are warmer and maize, tobacco, fruit and vines are grown. Federal Germany is Europe's fourth largest wine-producing country. Hops are cultivated near Munich. Livestock is mainly located on the reclaimed marshlands in the north, but there are also pastures in upland areas. Forests, covering 29% of the country and largely coniferous, are concentrated in the south. About 50% of Germany's fish requirement is covered by domestic production mainly caught in distant Atlantic waters. Bremerhaven is the main fishing port.

Mining

About 90% of German coal comes from the Ruhr with the remainder from Saarland and the Aachen district. Lignite is worked west of Cologne and in Hessen and Bavaria. Oil production, centred on the northern plain, meets 7% of Germany's needs. Natural gas is also obtained from the oil-fields. Mines in Lower Saxony, Hessen and Baden-Württemberg yield 60% of the world's potash of which half is exported. Other mineral resources are limited. Iron ore, mined mainly at Salzgitter, is of low quality and meets only 7% of domestic requirements. Some lead and zinc are mined in the Harz mountains.

Transport

Transport in Federal Germany is highly developed. The Autobahn (motorway) network is the longest in Europe with secondary roads and the rail network coming second. Germany also has Europe's busiest waterway, the Rhine, which, with its tributaries, serves the east, centre and south. The North Sea is connected to the Baltic by the Kiel canal and will be linked to the Black Sea by the Main-Danube canal now under construction. Hamburg is the main seaport, followed by Bremen, Bremerhaven, Emden, Wilhelmshaven and Lübeck. The airline, Lufthansa, operates domestic and overseas flights.

Industry

Since the Second World War, German industry has made a dramatic recovery and Germany is now a leading industrial nation. Of the world's top ten companies, five are West German. The Ruhr, the most concentrated industrial zone in Europe, produces 70% of West Germany's steel. The main steel and engineering centres are Dortmund, Bochum, Essen, Duisburg and Düsseldorf. Other industries established in the Ruhr are textiles at Wuppertal, Krefeld, Mönchengladbach and Rheydt, and chemicals at Cologne, Leverkusen and Rheinport. Steel is also produced at Neunkirchen and Saarbrücken in Saarland and at Salzgitter and Bremen. Frankfurt is the hub of another manufacturing region with engineering, textile, chemical and food-processing industries. Other major industrial zones include Aachen, Munich (München), Nürnberg, Stuttgart and the Braunschweig-Wolfsburg-Hannover-Salzgitter area. Important Rhine towns are Mainz, Mannheim and Karlsruhe. Federal Germany is the world's third largest producer of automobiles and ships. Shipyards are located in Hamburg, Bremen, Bremerhaven, Emden and Kiel.

Cities

The federal capital, Bonn—a university town on the Rhine and Beethoven's birthplace—is an administrative centre. The largest city and leading industrial centre is West Berlin isolated 150 km inside East Germany. The second largest city as regards size and industry is Hamburg (1,645,000) on the Elbe. The third largest city is Munich (München: 1,299,000) in Bavaria where brewing is a traditional industry. Cologne (Köln: 977,000) is an industrial and communications centre. Essen (648,000) is the leading Rhur town and Frankfurt am Main is the country's financial capital.

The Netherlands

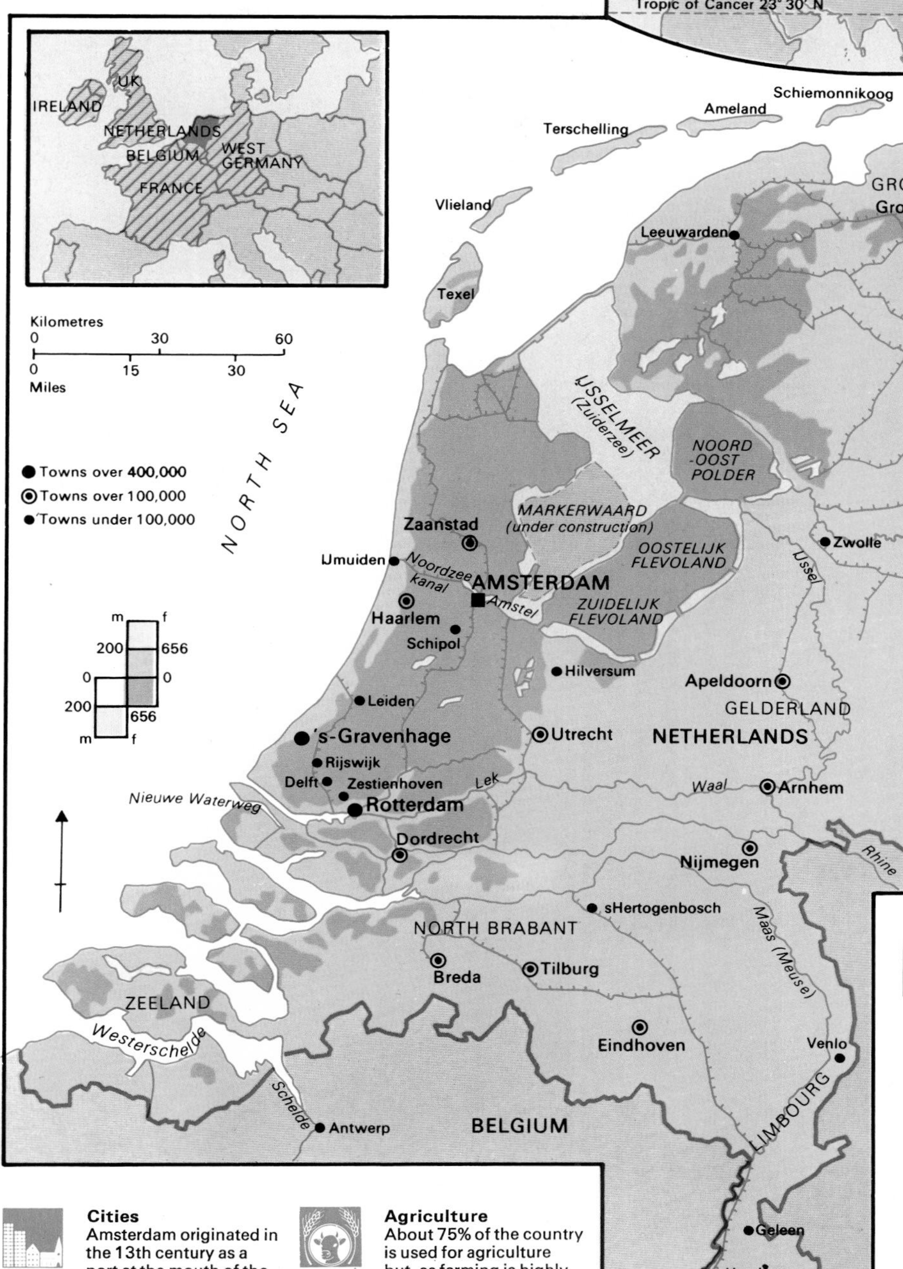

Area
36,946 km²/14,265 sq miles
Location
50°45'—53°30' N
3°20'—7° E
Population
14,246,000 (1981)
Population density
386 per km²/999 per sq mile
Capital and largest city
Amsterdam: 719,000 (1979)
Language
Dutch
Major imports
petroleum, chemicals, textiles, iron and steel, metal products and machinery
Major exports
machinery, transport equipment, chemicals, petroleum products, agricultural produce, textiles
Currency
guilder (1 guilder = 100 cents)
Gross National Product
167,980 million US dollars (1981)
Status
constitutional monarchy

Physical features

The world's most densely populated country, the Netherlands is situated on the North Sea at the estuaries of three rivers: the Rhine, Maas and Schelde. Popularly known as Holland, this small state, which has a maximum length and breadth of 312 km and 120 km respectively, is very flat: most land lies below 30 m and half the total area is below sea level. Sand dunes fringe the coast; the dune barrier has broken to form the Friesian Islands in the north and, in the south, the Maas-Rhine delta islands. Behind the dunes are the polders—reclaimed tracts of land surrounded by dykes. Eastern Holland, lying above sea level, consists of a sandy plain with stretches of pine forest and peat bog. The country's highest point, Vaalseberg (322 m), is in the Limburg district near Maastricht. Apart from the Maas, the main rivers draining the country are the IJssel, Lek and Waal.

Climate

The Netherlands has a marine-type climate with cool summers and mild winters. The average temperature in July is 17°C and in January —1°C. In winter, snow is common and frosts are sufficiently severe to freeze canals, lakes and small rivers; skating is a traditional pastime. Rainfall is moderate (between 60 and 80 cm a year) and occurs throughout the year, but summer is the wettest season. The prevailing westerly and south-westerly winds are strongest along the coast where they sometimes reach storm force.

Mining

The Netherlands has no metal ores and few minerals. Salt is mined at Hengelo and Delfzijl in the east and 60% of output is exported. Coal used to be worked in south Limburg, but production ceased as oil and natural gas became increasingly important. The Schoonebeek and Rijswijk oilfields yield two million tonnes annually, enough to supply 10% of domestic needs. Gas from Slochteren, the world's largest natural gas field, is piped throughout Holland and exported to W Germany, France and Belgium.

Cities

Amsterdam originated in the 13th century as a port at the mouth of the Amstel river on the old Zuiderzee. Over the centuries, it spread on to adjacent swamp land: hence its many canals, its 800 bridges and its houses built on piles. Today, despite the closure of the Zuiderzee, it ranks as the world's 15th largest port having canal links to both the North Sea and Rhine. Industrial suburbs extend along the Noordzeekanaal to IJmuiden. Although Amsterdam is the capital, it is not the seat of government: parliament, ministries and foreign embassies are located in the third largest city, 's-Gravenhage (the Hague: 458,000). The Netherlands' second city, Rotterdam (582,000) has the world's largest port. 75% of cargo handled is transit trade. Access to the North Sea is by a deep ship canal, the Nieuwe Waterweg. Near its mouth is the new Europoort, built to take large ships. The conurbation formed by Amsterdam, Rotterdam, the Hague and Holland's fourth city, Utrecht (236,000)—accounts for 46% of the population.

Agriculture

About 75% of the country is used for agriculture but, as farming is highly intensive and mechanized, it only employs 6% of the labour force. Livestock is kept on 63% of agricultural land, especially on the rich polder pastures. Dairy farming is important and the main products exported are butter, cheese (Edam and Gouda) and condensed milk. The Netherlands is the world's leading cheese exporter. Other exports include meat, bacon and eggs. Arable farming, covering 31% of agricultural land, predominates in Zeeland and Groningen. The main crops are wheat, barley, sugarbeet and potatoes. Horticulture occupies the remaining 6% of farmland. The leading sector is bulb growing, which is concentrated between Leyden and Haarlem, and millions of bulbs (tulips, hyacinths and daffodils) are exported annually. Most vegetables, especially tomatoes, cucumbers and lettuces, are grown in glasshouses just south of the Hague and there are orchards in Gelderland, North Brabant and Limburg.

Land from water

The first polders were created in the 13th century. Since then, the Dutch have gradually won more and more land from rivers, lakes and the sea. Two major schemes are currently in progress. In the Delta project, all the Rhine-Maas-Scheldt delta estuaries are being closed except the Waterweg and the Westerschelde to allow access to Rotterdam and Antwerp. This scheme, designed to protect the area from flooding, will reclaim 150 km² of land and create a 520 km² fresh-water lake. The Zuiderzee project involves a 30 km dam. The Zuiderzee is being turned into five polders, totalling 2,260 km², and a 1,200 km² reservoir, the IJsselmeer.

Transport

The flatness of the country facilitates all forms of transport. The Netherlands has 3,150 km of railways (with 50% electrified)—radiating from Utrecht; 70,000 km of roads; 7,000 km of cycleways and, most important, 5,700 km of navigable rivers and canals. About 60% of freight is carried by water and half the traffic on Holland's waterways is international. The two main airports, Schipol (Amsterdam) and Zestienhoven (Rotterdam) are the only airports in the world below sea level. Schipol is the base of KLM, the world's oldest civil aviation company.

Industry

Industry employs 42% of the workforce and accounts for 70% of all exports. The leading sector—metallurgy and engineering—uses imported raw materials and is therefore mainly located near the coast: there are works at Amsterdam, Rotterdam, IJmuiden and Dordrecht; at Arnhem and Nijmegen (both river ports) and in Limburg, near the old coalfield. The food and tobacco industry ranks second. Activities such as cheese manufacture, gin distilling, sugar refining and vegetable canning are based on Dutch produce; other manufactures, like chocolate and cigars, process imported materials. The electro-technical industry is dominated by Holland's biggest firm, Philips, based at Eindhoven. Other major industries include chemicals, textiles, tourism and, in Amsterdam, diamond cutting.

Belgium

Area
30,514 km²/11,780 sq miles
Location
49°30′—51°30′ N
2°35′—6°25′ E
Population
9,861,000 (1981)
Population density
323 per km²/837 per sq mile
Capital and largest city
Bruxelles: 1,000,000 (1981)
Languages
French, Flemish (Dutch), German
Major imports
fuels, metals, iron and steel, chemicals
Major exports
engineering goods, steel products, textiles, chemicals, foodstuffs
Currency
franc (1 franc = 100 centimes)
Gross National Product
117,510 million US dollars (1981)
Status
constitutional monarchy

Languages
There are basically two linguistic groups in Belgium: the French speaking Walloons in the south (32% of the population) and the German/Dutch speaking Flemings in the north (56% of the population). The 'border' between these tv·o groups lies just south of Kortrijk, Ronse, Bruxelles, Leuven and Tongeren. At times there has been considerable friction between these two communities—especially during the First World War when their differences were exploited by the occupying German army.

Physical features
Although Belgium is small, it offers a varied landscape. The 66 km long coast is marked by a line of broad dunes backed by polders. This belt of reclaimed land (about 10 km wide) runs into the Flanders plain—a sandy lowland drained by the Schelde and its tributary, the Lys. Kempenland in the north is similar with an undulating sandy plain, but with stretches of heath, bog and pine forest. Central Belgium, lying between the Sambre-Meuse and the Schelde, is a low fertile plateau from 40 to 200 m in height and drained by the Demer, Dijle, Senne and Dender (all tributaries of the Schelde). In the south-east lie the Ardennes. The foothills consist of limestone valleys and forested sandstone ridges with an average altitude of 300 m. Behind these lies the Ardenne plateau, formed over 250 million years ago. It is a region of forests and moorlands between 300 and 600 m high. In the north-east is Belgium's highest point, Botrange (694 m). The winding rivers of the Ardennes—the Meuse and its tributaries, the Semois, Ourthe and Vesdre—flow through deep valleys.

Climate
Belgium has a temperate climate with damp mild winters and cool summers. Bruxelles averages 2°C in January and 17°C in July. Atlantic air masses cause variable weather and the prevailing westerly winds brings frequent rain: most of the country has between 80 and 100 cm a year. Regional differences in climate are determined by altitude and distance from the coast. In the Ardennes, for instance, temperatures are lower (January, —4°C), rainfall is heavier (140 cm) and snow lies for between 35 and 50 days (less than 10 days on the coast).

Energy
Belgian coal is now in competition with oil and natural gas. Oil is mostly imported, but there is some exploitation of the North Sea reserves. Natural gas is piped from Holland. Blast-furnace gas, a by-product of steel manufacture, is used in industrial areas. Many of the power stations are coal-fired and located in the Kempenland region. There are a few small hydro-electric power stations in the Ardennes.

Mining
Belgium's mineral resources are limited to coal, sand, limestone and clay. Coal, located in the Sambre-Meuse valley and in the Kempenland region, is the most significant. The Sambre-Meuse deposits, which led to the industrialization of Mons, La Louvière, Charleroi, Namur and Liège, are now nearly exhausted and yield only 20% of total production. The remaining 80% comes from Kempenland, centred on Genk, Beringen and Zolder. Sand, worked near Charleroi and in Kempenland, is the basis of an important glass industry.

Industry
Belgium is highly industrialized with mechanical engineering the most important industry accounting for 20% of total industrial output. Products range from ships and bridges to bolts and screws. Other major industries include steel manufacture (Belgium produces over 10% of the EEC output), chemicals, glass (products range from large plate glass to Val St-Lambert crystal), textiles (including traditional linen, tapestries and lace) and non-ferrous metals (Belgium is the world's leading processor of cobalt and radium). Oil refining, food processing, cement, paper manufacture and sugar refining are also important industries. Belgium's chief port, Antwerpen, is a major diamond-cutting centre. Approximately 40% of Belgium's industrial output is exported.

Agriculture
Although only 52% of the total area is farmed, Belgian agriculture meets 80% of the country's food requirements. Wheat, barley and sugarbeet are grown on the fertile loess and loam soils of central Belgium; barley, potatoes, flax and hops predominate on the Flanders plain while some fodder crops are grown on the polders and in the lower Ardennes. The high Ardennes, Kempenland and most of the polders are used for dairy farming. Market gardening and glasshouse cultivation are located on the polders and near major cities: horticultural products, such as asparagus, endives, roses and orchids are exported. About 80% of Belgian farms are less than one hectare (2.5 acres) in area and much of the work is done by women and children as the men are often employed in industry. Fishing, in the North Sea and Atlantic, meets 30% of domestic demand. Eight out of 10 Belgian trawlers are based at Oostende; the two other fishing ports are Zeebrugge and Nieuwpoort. Forests, mainly situated in the Ardennes, cover 19% of the country, but timber imports are still necessary.

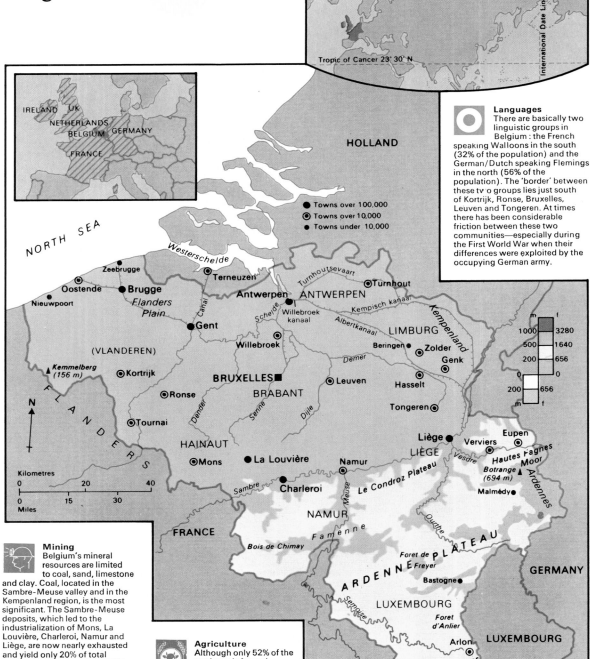

Transport
The 4,165 km Belgian rail network, radiating from Bruxelles, is one of the densest in the world. And for every 1 km of railway, there are 3 km of main roads, including sections of European expressways. There are over 1,500 km of navigable inland waterways and these are used for bulk freight transport. The major arteries are the Albertkanaal, linking Liège and Kempenland with Antwerpen; the Willebroek kanaal, joining the Schelde and Sambre via Bruxelles; and the two ship canals linking the ports of Brugge and Gent with the sea at Zeebrugge and Terneuzen (Holland) respectively. Antwerpen is Belgium's first (and the world's third largest) port. Other main ports are Brugge/Zeebrugge, Oostende, Gent and Bruxelles. The national airline is Sabena.

Cities
Bruxelles, by the river Senne, is Belgium's leading industrial, commercial and cultural city. It is also a major European centre—housing the headquarters of the EEC. Antwerpen (197,000), on the Schelde estuary, is the heart of an urban area containing half a million people. The port serves Flanders via the Schelde and the east via the Albertkanaal. Gent (244,000) is Belgium's second largest city and port. Traditionally a textile centre, it has developed new industries—many of them located along the ship canal. Both Gent and Brugge (119,000) have many ancient buildings and are popular with tourists. Around 25% of the population lives in the Sambre-Meuse region where the largest towns are Liège (224,000) and Mons (97,000).

Luxembourg

Area
2,586 km²/998 sq miles
Location
49°26′—50°10′ N
5°44′—6°31′ E
Population
364,000 (1981)
Population density
141 per km²/365 per sq mile
Capital and largest city
Luxembourg: 80,000 (1982)
Languages
French, German, Letzeburgesch
Major imports
mineral products, consumer goods, foodstuffs
Major exports
steel, chemical products (including plastic and rubber), textiles, machinery, wine
Currency
franc (1 franc = 100 centimes)
Gross National Product
5,790 million US dollars (1981)
Status
constitutional monarchy

Physical features
The Grand Duchy of Luxembourg, lying between Belgium, Germany and France, is the EEC's smallest member state: its maximum length is 82 km, and width, 57 km. The Grand Duchy divides into two regions. In the north is the Oesling, an extension of the Ardennes, covering about a third of the total area. These forested uplands contain the country's highest point: Bourgplatz, 559 m. The remaining 68% of the territory corresponds to the Bon Pays or Gutland (Good Land). This region, a continuation of the Lorraine scarplands, is less hilly than the north and has an average height of 228 m. The two main rivers are the Alzette and Sûre which, together with their tributaries, flow through deep, picturesque valleys. The Alzette and Sûre drain into the Sauer, a tributary of the Moselle. The Moselle, Sauer and Our flow along the 135 km border with Germany.

Climate
Prevailing south-westerly and north-westerly winds have a moderating influence. As a consequence, Luxembourg has warm summers and cool winters: in the capital, July averages 19°C, January, 2°C. Mean temperatures in the Oesling are about two degrees lower. Rainfall occurs throughout the year, but is heaviest in winter when it often falls as snow. Amounts vary from 70 cm in the Moselle valley to 100 cm in the northern hills.

Mining and Energy
Industry in Luxembourg is based on the country's iron ore deposits. These deposits, which correspond to the northern tip of the Lorraine iron ore field, are worked in opencast mines near Dudelange, Esch and between Rodange and Differdange. Annual production amounts to some 3 million tonnes; a further 12 million tonnes has to be imported. There is some stone and slate quarrying. The main sources of energy are imported coal and oil, electricity and, since 1972, natural gas from the Netherlands. 60% of electricity is generated thermally, using blast furnace gas—a by-product of the steel industry. The remainder is produced by hydro-electric plants on the Sûre, Moselle and Our.

Transport
The Grand Duchy's 5,000 km of roads radiate from the capital; the main international routes are to Germany (via Echternach), to France (via Frisange), and to Belgium (via Steinfort). The rail network totals only 271 km. Luxembourg is a transit country for Belgian and Dutch railways to Switzerland and Italy. Over 50% of cargo handled by the river port of Mertert, on the Moselle, is connected with the steel industry. Luxembourg airlines, Luxair and Cargolux, operate from the international airport, Findel, located 6 km east of the capital.

Cities
In 963, Siegfried, Count of the Ardennes, built a castle high above the Alzette. In the course of time, the castle grew into a powerful fortress known as 'the Gibraltar of the North'. The development of the modern city began in 1867 when the fortress was dismantled. Today's city, an urban agglomeration of nearly 80,000 people, houses several European institutions including the Court of Justice and the Monetary Fund. The Grand Duchy's other leading towns are in the south-western industrial zone: Esch (26,000), Differdange (17,000) and Dudelange (14,000).

Languages
Luxembourg is a linguistic puzzle: French, German and Letzeburgesch are all official national languages. Letzeburgesch, a Germanic dialect, is used in conversation, German is popularly used for written communication, while French is the language of government. In this way, a parliamentary debate is conducted in Letzeburgesch; the report of that debate, for general circulation, is printed in German; the law resulting from that debate is drawn up in French. To cope with this situation, children are taught all three languages at school.

Agriculture
Around 50% of the country is under cultivation and this area divides almost equally into arable land and pasture land. Livestock farming predominates in the Oesling where the soils are thin and infertile. In contrast, the Bon Pays, with its limestone, sandstone and clay, supports mixed farming. The main crops are barley, potatoes, oats and wheat; both dairy and beef cattle are kept as well as poultry and some pigs. In the south, there are also orchards, market gardens and, along the Moselle valley, vineyards. White wines are produced and about 50% of output is exported, mainly to Belgium and the Netherlands. Most farms are small: one in three is under 10 hectares. Every year the total number of farms and that of agricultural workers decreases by about 4%. This is due to the amalgamation of small units and to mechanization. Agriculture contributes less than 5% to the national income and employs only 9% of the workforce.

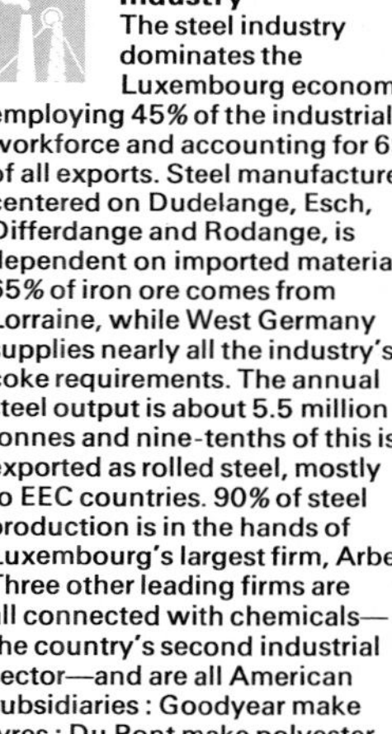

Industry
The steel industry dominates the Luxembourg economy employing 45% of the industrial workforce and accounting for 69% of all exports. Steel manufacture, centered on Dudelange, Esch, Differdange and Rodange, is dependent on imported materials: 65% of iron ore comes from Lorraine, while West Germany supplies nearly all the industry's coke requirements. The annual steel output is about 5.5 million tonnes and nine-tenths of this is exported as rolled steel, mostly to EEC countries. 90% of steel production is in the hands of Luxembourg's largest firm, Arbed. Three other leading firms are all connected with chemicals—the country's second industrial sector—and are all American subsidiaries: Goodyear make tyres; Du Pont make polyester foils and Monsanto, synthetic fibres. Traditional chemical manufactures include fertilizers, dyes and explosives.

Tourism
Tourism is playing an increasingly important role in the Luxembourg economy. The Grand Duchy's assets as a tourist country include varied landscape, relatively sparse population, industry concentrated in the south-western corner and scope for outdoor activities such as sailing, climbing and riding. The main problem encountered by the developing tourist industry is the short duration of the season, July-August. Most visitors come from Belgium and the Netherlands.

Benelux
1944 saw the creation of Benelux, an economic union of Belgium, the Netherlands and Luxembourg. As a result of the union, goods, people and capital now circulate freely within the three member states. The Benelux countries also have agreements on postal and transport rates, on welfare systems and on overseas trade policies.

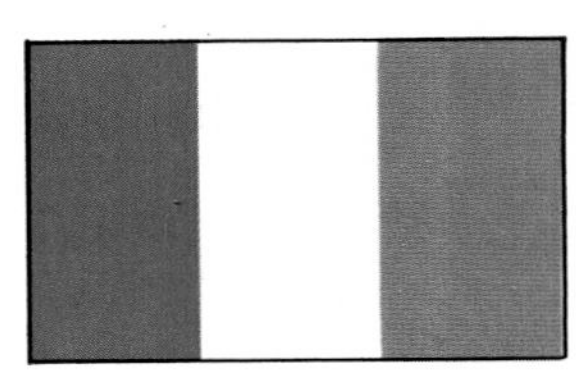

France

Area
551,000 km²/212,750 sq miles
Location
42°20′—51°5′ N
5°55′—8°10′ E
Population
53,963,000 (1981)
Population density
98 per km²/254 per sq mile
Capital and largest city
Paris: 2,300,000 (1975 census)
Language
French
Major imports
fuels, metals, chemicals, machinery, foodstuffs
Major exports
machinery, transport, iron and steel, cereals, dairy produce, wine, textiles, soap
Currency
franc (1 franc = 100 centimes)
Gross National Product
657,560 million US dollars (1981)
Status
independent republic

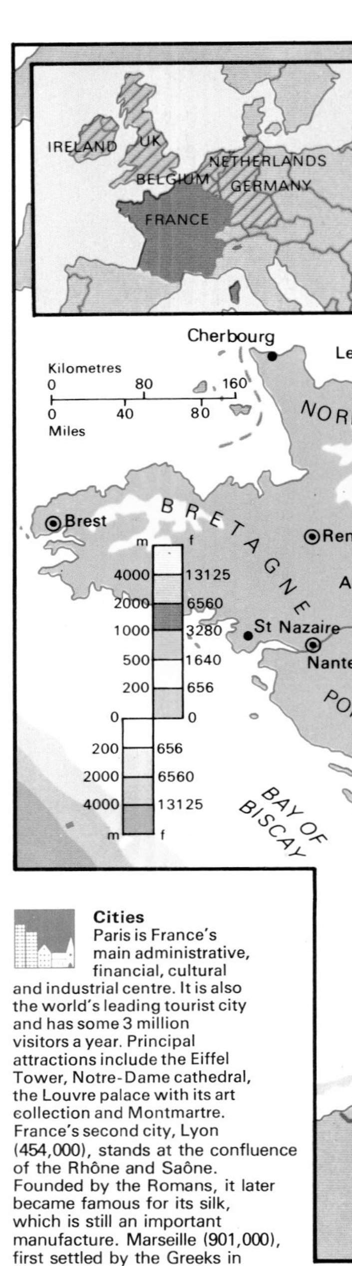

Physical features
The USSR apart, France is Europe's biggest state. Although it contains the highest point in western Europe—Mont Blanc, 4,807m—60% of the country lies below 250m. There are three main lowland areas, each drained by a major river. The largest is the Paris basin. In the south-west is Aquitaine, drained by the Garonne, while the third area corresponds to the Rhône-Saône valley. These lowlands are bordered by mountains and plateaux. In the south and west, high ranges—the Pyrénées, Alps and Jura—separate France from her neighbours: Spain, Italy and Switzerland. The less rugged plateaux comprise the Vosges, the Ardennes, Armorica and the Massif Central, which covers 15% of the total area and has an average height of 1,000 m. With the exception of the Rhône and its tributaries, the main rivers—including the longest, the Loire—drain into the Atlantic.

Climate
Because of the Atlantic and the Gulf Stream, most of France has a temperate, oceanic cimate which is mildest in the west. January averages 7°C in Brest and 2°C in Strasbourg; respective July temperatures are 17°C and 20°C. Although the rain-bearing winds are westerly, many eastern areas are wetter than the west because of altitude: average annual rainfall in Besançon is 110 cm, but only 66 cm in Rennes.

Mining and energy
Coal, iron and bauxite constitute the major part of France's mineral wealth. Coal, from the north and east, meets 70% of domestic needs. France is the world's third largest producer of iron ore—main deposits are in Lorraine and Normandy—and is also a leading producer of bauxite (named after the village of Lex Baux, in Provence, where it was first mined in 1882). Other minerals worked include uranium, gold and potash. Most oil has to be imported, as domestic output, chiefly from Parentis, is low. In contrast, natural gas, from Lacq and other smaller fields, supplies 32% of demand. 59% of electricity is of thermal origin, 40% hydroelectric and 1% nuclear.

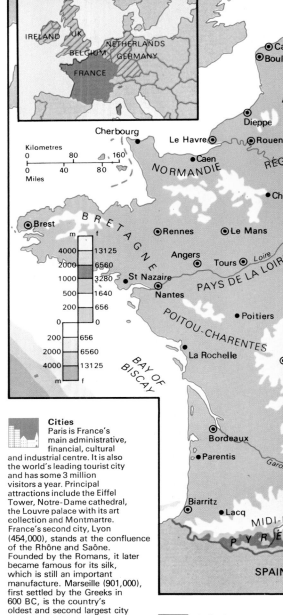

Cities
Paris is France's main administrative, financial, cultural and industrial centre. It is also the world's leading tourist city and has some 3 million visitors a year. Principal attractions include the Eiffel Tower, Notre-Dame cathedral, the Louvre palace with its art collection and Montmartre. France's second city, Lyon (454,000), stands at the confluence of the Rhône and Saône. Founded by the Romans, it later became famous for its silk, which is still an important manufacture. Marseille (901,000), first settled by the Greeks in 600 BC, is the country's oldest and second largest city as well as being its chief port. Lille (171,000), at the heart of the industrial north, is a major textile centre.

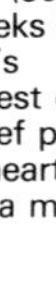

Transport
Paris is the centre of France's transport system: it has three airports, is a major river port and serves as the hub of the country's dense road and rail networks. Trains—the fastest in Europe—and lorries carry the bulk of freight. A further 25% is transported on the 8,600 km of inland waterways. The Seine, Rhine and Rhône are particularly important; chief river ports are Strasbourg, Rouen and Paris. Marseille is France's first, and Europe's third, seaport, followed by Le Havre, Dunkerque, Nantes and Bordeaux. The national carrier, Air France, is the world's third, and Europe's second largest airline. It has various subsidiaries, including Air-Inter which operates internally.

Industry
France is a major industrial nation. The iron and steel industry, formerly concentrated in the north and east near coal and iron reserves, has gravitated to the coast—at Dunkerque and Fos-sur-Mer—in order to take in imported fuel and ore. Of the various sectors using steel, the automobile industry, centred on Paris, is the most important. Throughout the world, one car in ten is French. The chemical industry is located in Paris and Lyon and on the coalfields; petro-chemicals are associated with the oil-refineries at Dunkerque and on the lower Seine in the north, and at Etang de Berre in the south. Textiles, including synthetic fibres, are important in Lyon, Paris and the Lille-Roubaix-Tourcoing conurbation. The tourist season is year-long: the most popular holiday areas are the Alps in winter, and the coasts in summer.

Agriculture
After the USSR, France is Europe's leading agricultural nation and is largely self-sufficient; agricultural products account for 20% of total exports. Wheat, grown extensively in the Paris basin, is the chief cereal followed by barley and maize. Two other leading crops are potatoes and sugar-beet, cultivated in Brittany and the north. Fruit and vegetables are grown in Brittany, the Rhone and Loire valleys, and near Paris. France is the world's leading wine-producer; major production areas are Languedoc, Burgundy, Bordeaux, Champagne, the Loire and Alsace. Livestock is important: cattle predominate in the north-west and north; sheep in the Massif Central and southern Alps. With over 300 varieties, France is the world's second largest cheese manufacturer. The fishing industry is concentrated in Brittany and the north-west; Boulogne is the main fishing port.

Corsica
Corsica (8,722 km²), situated in the Mediterranean 170 km south-east of Nice, is part of France. Except for the low-lying east coast, the island is mountainous, rising to 2,710 m in Monte Cinto. Tourists—about half a million a year—and sheep are basic to the economy. Cheese from sheep's milk accounts for 75% of exports. Fruit and vegetables are grown on the coastal plain and olive oil, citrus, almonds and wine are exported. 33% of the total population of 269,800 lives in Bastia—the largest town and chief port—and in Ajaccio, the capital and Napoleon's birth-place. Industry is small-scale.

Great Britain

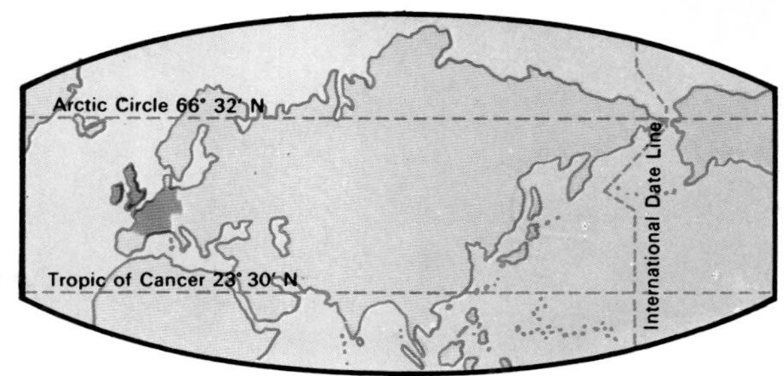

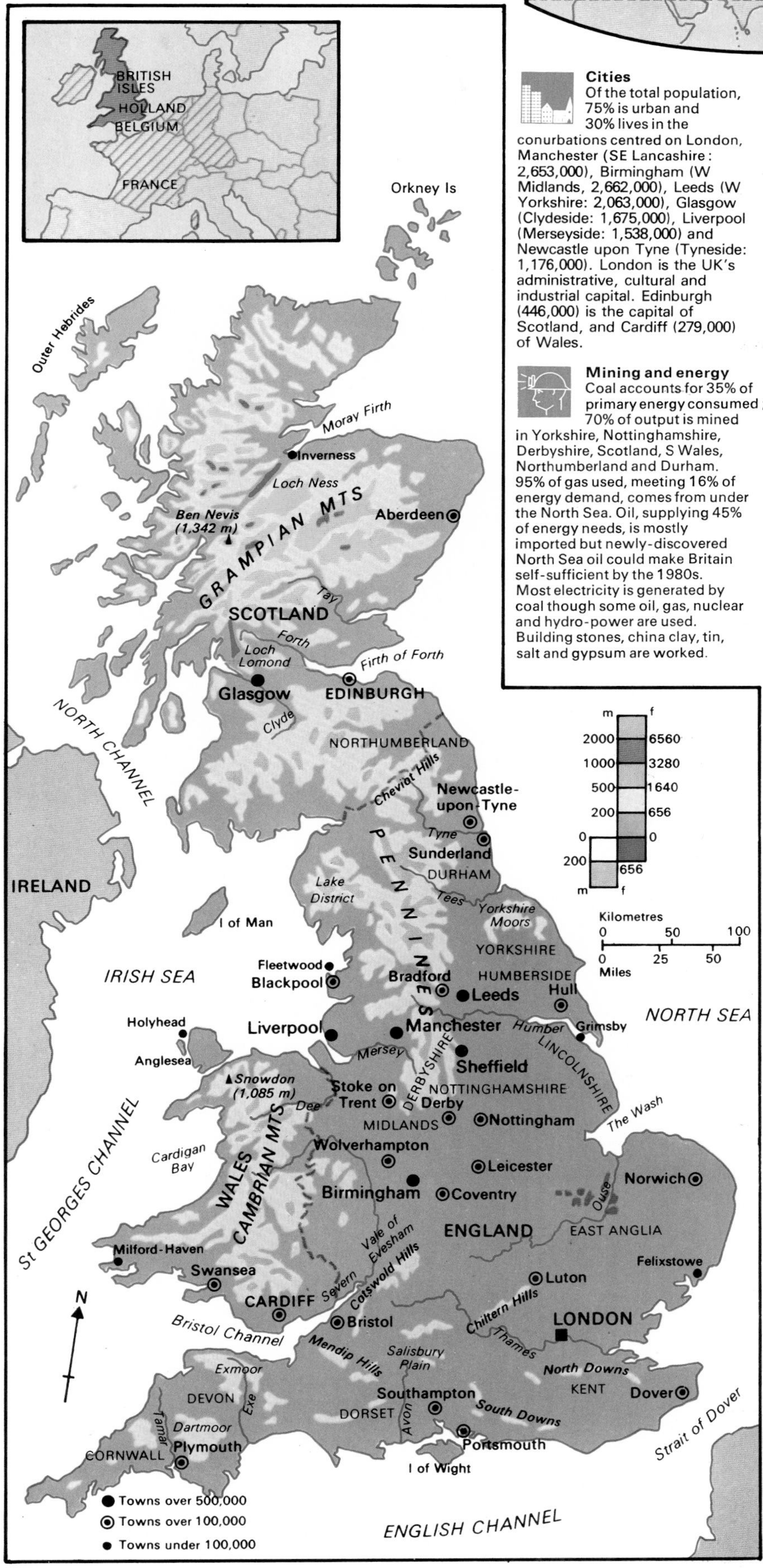

The United Kingdom

Area
(including Northern Ireland)
244,021 km²/94,217 sq miles
Location
49°10'—60°50' N;
1°45'E—8°10' W
Population
56,005,000 (1981)
Population density
230 per km²/594 per sq mile
Capital and largest city
London: 6,696,000 (1981)
Languages
English. Welsh and Gaelic used by minorities in Wales and Scotland respectively.
Major imports
fuels, machinery and transport equipment, foodstuffs, metals and ores, chemicals
Major exports
engineering products, chemicals, metals, foodstuffs, textiles
Currency
pound (£1 = 100 pence)
Gross National Product
510,310 million US dollars (1981)
Status
constitutional monarchy
Statistics refer to whole of UK. Text excludes N. Ireland.

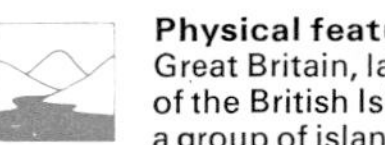

Physical features

Great Britain, largest of the British Isles—a group of islands lying off northwest Europe—divides into highland and lowland areas. Lowland Britain, situated south and east of a line from the mouth of the river Tees to the mouth of the river Exe, consists of a series of chalk and limestone hills—such as the Cotswolds, Chilterns, North and South Downs—separated by broad clay valleys. Highland Britain, over 300m and lying to the north and west, comprises Scotland, the Lake District, Wales, the central upland known as the Pennines and the south-western peninsula of England. The highest point in the British Isles—Ben Nevis, 1,342 m—is in the Grampians in Scotland. Britain's longest river, the Severn, 354 km, rises in central Wales and flows in a wide arc to the Bristol Channel.

Climate

Britain has a mild, temperate climate. The changeable weather is largely determined by a series of depressions brought in from the Atlantic by the prevailing south-westerly winds. The average temperature in the coldest months, January and February, is 4°C, and in the warmest, July and August, 16°C. Rain, occurring throughout the year, averages 70 cm in the lowlands and 250 cm in highland areas; annual rainfall on Snowdon (1,085 m) and Ben Nevis is between 400 and 500 cm.

Islands

Most of the smaller islands round the British coast—such as the Isle of Wight, Scilly Isles, Orkneys and Shetlands—are part of the UK. There are two exceptions: the Isle of Man (588 km²; pop: 56,000) and the Channel Isles (194 km²; pop: 125,000) which are Crown dependencies. Manx is spoken in addition to English in the Isle of Man, while French is still the official language of Jersey, the biggest of the Channel Isles.

Cities

Of the total population, 75% is urban and 30% lives in the conurbations centred on London, Manchester (SE Lancashire: 2,653,000), Birmingham (W Midlands, 2,662,000), Leeds (W Yorkshire: 2,063,000), Glasgow (Clydeside: 1,675,000), Liverpool (Merseyside: 1,538,000) and Newcastle upon Tyne (Tyneside: 1,176,000). London is the UK's administrative, cultural and industrial capital. Edinburgh (446,000) is the capital of Scotland, and Cardiff (279,000) of Wales.

Mining and energy

Coal accounts for 35% of primary energy consumed; 70% of output is mined in Yorkshire, Nottinghamshire, Derbyshire, Scotland, S Wales, Northumberland and Durham. 95% of gas used, meeting 16% of energy demand, comes from under the North Sea. Oil, supplying 45% of energy needs, is mostly imported but newly-discovered North Sea oil could make Britain self-sufficient by the 1980s. Most electricity is generated by coal though some oil, gas, nuclear and hydro-power are used. Building stones, china clay, tin, salt and gypsum are worked.

Agriculture

British agriculture, employing 3% of the workforce, produces over half of domestic food requirements. 79% of land is used for agriculture and crops are grown on 38% of this area. Arable farming predominates in East Anglia, Kent, Lincolnshire, Humberside and the coastal lowlands of east Scotland. Main crops are wheat, barley, oats, potatoes and sugarbeet. Dairying is widespread but is most concentrated in southwest Scotland, western England and southwest Wales. Beef-cattle and sheep are kept in upland regions, while pigs are important in lowland areas. The chief fruit-growing regions are Kent and East Anglia. Apples make up 65% of the harvest.

Fishing and forests

Britain is almost self-sufficient in fish. 82% of the catch is white-fish—notably cod, haddock and plaice—taken in distant waters such as the W Atlantic and the Barents Sea, and in coastal areas. Herring, from Scottish waters, and shellfish are also important. 45% of fishing vessels come from Scotland. The main fishing ports are Grimsby, Hull, Aberdeen and Fleetwood. Forests cover less than 8% of Great Britain and production meets only 8% of demand.

Industry

Britain is highly industrialized: over 80% of exports are manufactured goods, 55% of the workforce is employed in industry and it ranks as the world's fifth steel-producing nation. Metallurgy and engineering employ 50% of the industrial workforce and account for over half total exports. The chemical in[illegible]try supplies 13% of exports; expanding sectors inclu[illegible] plastics, petrochemicals pharmaceuticals. The tex[illegible] industry provides 6% of e[illegible]rts; high-quality woollens a[illegible] synthetic fibres are important. The food industry also accounts for 6% of exports: major items are whisky, confectionery and biscuits. Other leading industries include cement, rubber, glass, paper, leather and footwear. The chief manufacturing regions are London, the Midlands, Yorkshire, Humberside, NW and NE England Wales and central Scotland.

Transport

In Great Britain, 90% of passengers and 64% of freight travels by road. The 345,400 km road network includes some 2,000 km of motorways; a further 1,000 km are being built. There are 18,170 km of railways. Only 17% of the 4,000 km of navigable waterways are used commercially; Manchester is the chief inland port. The British merchant fleet is the world's third largest. London is the leading port followed by Southampton. Other major ports include Liverpool (exports), Dover (passengers), Milford-Haven (oil) and Felixstowe (containers). There are some 150 airports; Heathrow (London) is the world's busiest.

Ireland

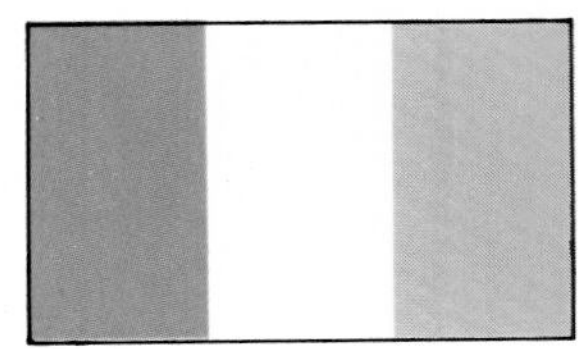

Republic of Ireland (Eire)
Area
70,282 km²/27,136 sq miles
Location
51°27′—55°25′ N
6°—10°30′ W
Population
3,440,000 (1981)
Population density
49 per km²/127 per sq mile
Capital and largest city
Dublin: 525,000 (1981)
Languages
Irish and English
Major imports
machinery, foodstuffs, transport equipment, metals, chemicals, petroleum
Major exports
meat, live animals, dairy products, textiles and clothing, engineering goods, pharmaceuticals
Currency
pound (1 pound = 100 pence)
Gross National Product
17,990 million US dollars (1981)
Status
independent republic

The following text includes Northern Ireland (14,139 km²; pop: 1,547,000).

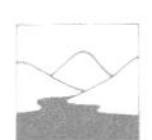

Physical features

Ireland, the second largest island in the British Isles, consists of a broad limestone plain ringed by coastal highlands. The central lowland, mostly under 100 m, is covered with glacial deposits of clay and sand, extensive bogs and numerous lakes. The most spectacular scenery lies in the southwest where a series of east-west sandstone ranges are separated by drowned valleys. The island's highest point, Carrantuohill, 1,040 m, towers over the lovely Killarney lakes. In the southeast, the rounded Wicklow mountains, rising to 926 m in Lugnaquilla, form the largest granite mass in the British Isles. Granite also predominates in the Mourne Mountains—which include N. Ireland's highest point: Slieve Donard, 852 m—and in the desolate western uplands. Of the many lakes, the biggest are Lough Neagh, 396 km², Lough Corrib, 168 km² and Lough Erne, 137 km².

Climate

Ireland, lying in the path of moisture-laden southwesterly winds and the warm waters of the Gulf Stream, has a mild wet climate. As the island is small, with no part more than 112 km from the sea, temperatures are uniform throughout the country. Average temperatures in January and February are between 4°C and 7°C, and in July and August, between 14°C and 16°C. Annual rainfall ranges from 150 cm in the western hills to 75 cm on the east coast.

Tourism

In the Republic, tourism is a leading industry. The eight million visitors who come to Ireland annually are attracted by the varied scenery—particularly in the southwest—the unspoilt countryside, the traffic-free roads and the relaxed way of life. In the 1960s and 70s tourism in Northern Ireland has been adversely affected by the political unrest.

Transport

Throughout Ireland, people and goods travel mainly by road and most areas are served by buses and freight services. Road transport has developed at the expense of rail. The main line in the North runs from Londonderry via Belfast to the border and then to Dublin. In the South, there are rail links from Dublin to Sligo, Galway, Limerick, Tralee, Cork, Waterford and Rosslare. Major ports are Belfast Larne, Dublin, Cork, Dun Laoghaire, Rosslare, Waterford, Limerick, Foynes and Whiddy Island (oil). The Republic's airline, Aer Lingus, operates from international airports at Shannon, Dublin and Cork. Flights from Belfast also go to the UK.

Agriculture: arable

In Northern Ireland, crops like hay, barley, oats and potatoes are of minor importance and are mainly for the farmer's own use. In the Republic, only 7% of the land is used for crops, compared with 63% for livestock. Arable farming is concentrated in the southeast, particularly in County Wexford where oats, barley and wheat are grown. Some fodder crops, such as turnips, potatoes oats and barley, are produced in Counties Carlow, Kilkenny and Waterford: market gardening is important on the coastal plain near Bray. Sugar-beet is grown in the southwest and some fodder crops in the midlands. Productivity is hampered by the small size of farms.

Cities

Dublin had its beginnings in a Viking fortress built on high ground at the mouth of the River Liffey. The modern city owes its development to the growth of the port and trading activities in the 17th century. Today, the port and its outport of Dun Laoghaire are vital to Dublin's role as the country's leading commercial and industrial centre. Industries include food-processing, brewing, engineering, clothing and electrical goods. Cork, on the River Lee, originated as a seventh-century monastery. Now the Republic's second-largest city (136,000) and second port, its industries range from oil refining and chemicals to steel manufacture and flour-milling; trans-Atlantic trade is handled at the outport of Cobh. A third of N. Ireland's people live in the capital, Belfast (298,000), in the east.

Agriculture: livestock

Agriculture, employing 27% of the workforce and accounting for 45% of total exports, is vital to the Republic's economy. 80% of agricultural output consists of livestock and livestock products. Beef cattle are reared on the wet pastures in the midlands and along the fertile Nore, Barrow and Suir valleys in the southeast. Dairy farming predominates in the south and southwest, especially in the Golden Vale of Limerick and Tipperary. The milk is sent to co-operatives for cream, butter and cheese manufacture. Skimmed milk is returned to farms and fed to pigs. The main pig-farming areas are the southwest and southeast; there are bacon and ham-curing factories at Limerick and Cork. Sheep are grazed on the Wicklow mountains and in the west. In Northern Ireland livestock farming also dominates agriculture and accounts for 20% of total exports. Beef cattle are concentrated in Armagh and Co. Down; dairy farming is important in Fermanagh and parts of Antrim and Co. Down; sheep are grazed on the Mourne Mountains, the Antrim Hills and the highlands of Donegal.

Mining and energy

Ireland lacks mineral resources. In N. Ireland, some limestone, sand, gravel, basalt, chalk and clay are worked but the fuels and minerals needed for industry have to be imported. Electricity generating stations use coal and oil. The Republic has valuable deposits of lead, silver and zinc at Tynagh and Silvermines; copper, silver and mercury at Gortdrum; copper and pyrites at Avoca. Other minerals exploited include barytes, gypsum, marble, building stone and some low-quality coal. Peat, from the central plain and the western coast, is used as a domestic fuel and to fire seven generating plants producing 33% of the country's electricity. A further 33% is generated by coal, the remainder is hydro-electric.

Industry

In the Republic, food and drink manufacture is a leading industry. Creameries, flour-mills, beet-sugar refineries, distilleries, breweries and bacon factories all process local produce. Textile and light engineering are also important. With the aim of promoting industrial development, the Government provides financial incentives to help Irish industrialists expand and to attract overseas firms to Ireland. Many of the foreign factories—largely British, American and German—are on industrial estates in Galway, Waterford and at Shannon airport. N. Ireland's industry, concentrated in Belfast, is based on imported raw materials. The main industry is engineering, especially shipbuilding and aircraft manufacture. The chief shipbuilding firm, Harland and Wolff, has the world's largest shipbuilding berth. N. Ireland is also a major textile centre—traditionally famous for its linen produced since the 13th century.

Switzerland

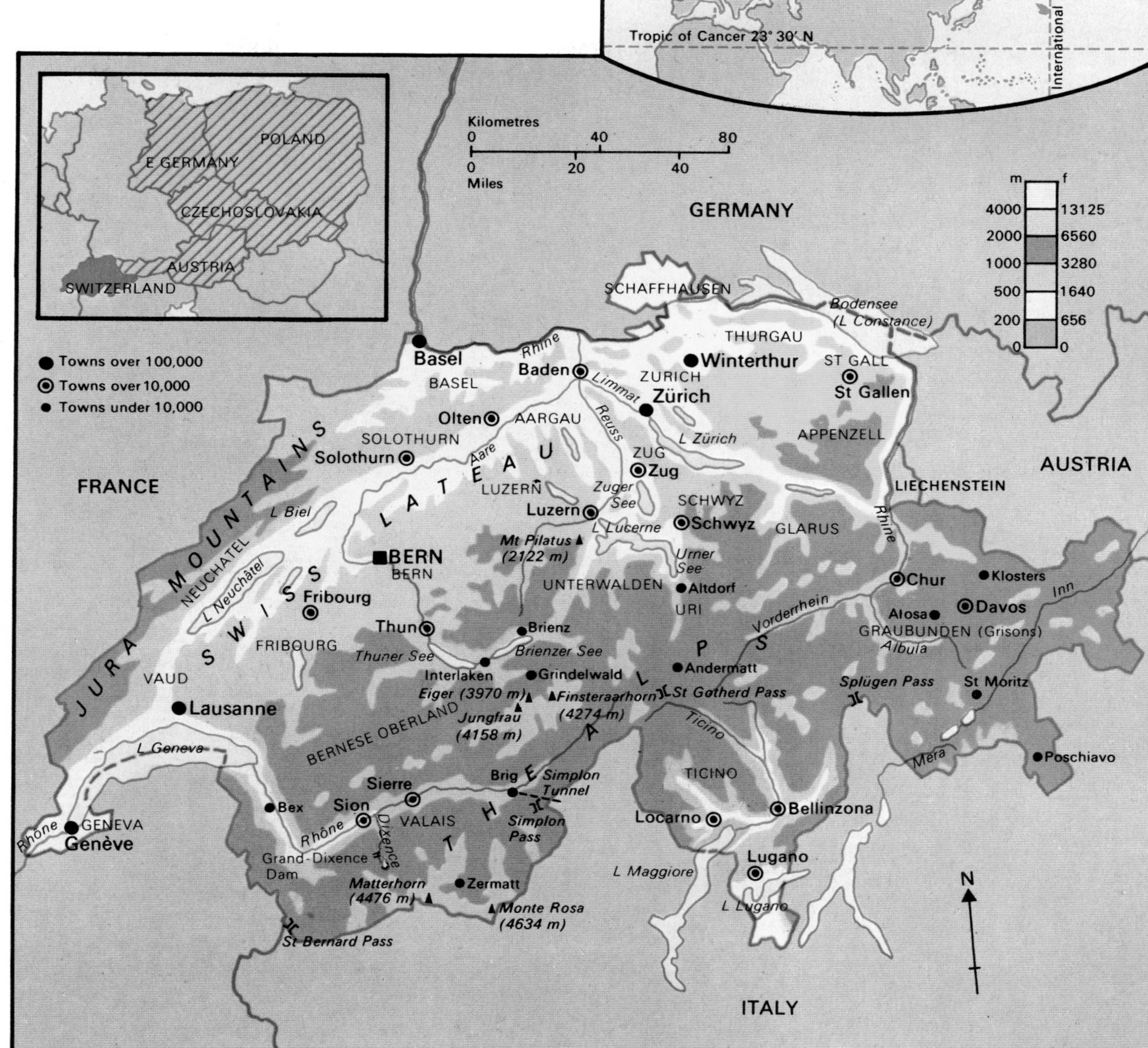

Area
41,287 km²/15,941 sq miles
Location
45°50'—47°54' N; 6°—10°30' E
Population
6,473,000 (1981)
Population density
157 per km²/406 per sq mile
Capital
Bern: 145,000 (1982)
Largest city
Zürich: 375,000 (1982)
Languages
German, French, Italian, Romansch
Major imports
industrial raw materials, fuel, foodstuffs
Major exports
machinery, chemicals, watches, textiles, cheese, chocolate
Currency
franc (= 100 centimes/Rappen)
Gross National Product
112,850 million US dollars (1981)
Status
independent republic

Physical features

Landlocked, mountainous Switzerland divides into three regions: the Jura, the Alps and the plateau. The Jura mountains, rising to 1,800 m, stretch along the French border and consist of limestone ridges and deep forested valleys. The frontiers with Italy, Austria and Liechtenstein are formed by the Alps, comprising two northeast-southwest ranges separated by the Rhine and Rhone valleys. The southern mass contains Switzerland's highest peak, Monte Rosa (4,634 m) and the Matterhorn (4,476 m); the northern chain, the Bernese Oberland, includes the Finsteraarhorn (4,274 m), the Jungfrau (4,158 m) and the Eiger (3,970 m). The Alps act as a giant watershed: the Rhine flows to the North Sea, the Rhone to the Mediterranean; the Ticino runs via the Po to the Adriatic while the Inn meanders eastward to the Danube and the Black Sea. Between the Jura and the Alps lies the Swiss plateau, a region of rolling hills stretching from Lake Geneva to Lake Constance. There are 1,484 lakes in Switzerland; the biggest are Lakes Geneva and Constance.

Climate

Switzerland has a central European climate modified by altitude. Winter is cold with widespread and heavy snowfall; January averages 0°C in Zürich, —6°C in Davos and 2°C in Lugano. Summer is wet and warm; the average July temperature is 17°C in Zürich, 11°C in Davos and 21°C in Lugano. About one-seventh of the country is permanently under snow and ice.

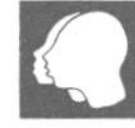

Languages

The Swiss Confederation is a union of 22 cantons —miniature states, each with its own history, culture and dialects. These dialects are used locally; nationally, there are four official languages. 65% of the population speaks German; 18%, French; 12%, Italian and less than 1%, Romansch. The remainder, mostly immigrant workers, belong to other language groups. French predominates in the west, Italian in Ticino, while the Romansch-speaking minority is located in Graubünder.

Mining and energy

Switzerland lacks minerals. Mining activity is limited to salt—from the Rhine valley above Basel and the Rhone valley near Bex—and to iron ore, worked in Gonzen and the Fricktal. Some peat, cut on the moors and former lake bottoms, is used locally for fuel. However, Switzerland does have one great natural asset: water. Several thousand hydro-power plants transform the energy of alpine torrents and rivers into electricity. There are 44 artificial lakes and the Grande-Dixence dam in Valais is the world's second highest (284 m). Water-power generates 90% of the country's electricity; the rest is of thermal or nuclear origin. Yet electricity meets only 20% of Swiss energy requirements; imported oil supplies the remainder.

Tourism

Switzerland is one of Europe's major tourist centres. Its attractions include the beautiful mountain and lake scenery, facilities for sports—especially mountaineering, walking and sailing, and thermal springs. It is equally popular with visitors in winter: as well as skiing, provision is made for skating, curling and ice-hockey.

Agriculture: livestock

A quarter of Switzerland consists of unproductive rocks, glaciers, rivers and lakes. A further 25% is forested, leaving just half the country for agriculture. 87% of this area is used for livestock. Dairy farming is important and is the basis of 3 major exports: cheese (Gruyère and Emmenthal), condensed milk and milk chocolate. In the Jura and Alps, cattle are still-fed in winter and grazed on mountain pastures in summer. There are also some sheep in mountain areas. Both cattle and pigs are kept on the plateau; the pigs are fed on skimmed milk, a dairy by-product.

Agriculture: arable

Mixed farming predominates on the plateau—the main agricultural region. Crops include wheat, rye, barley, potatoes, sugar-beet and vegetables. Some fodder crops—hay and lucerne—are also grown in mountain valleys. Orchards on south-facing slopes in the valleys and the midlands yield apples, pears, cherries and plums. Fruit and fruit products, such as jam and pectin, are exported. There are vineyards on the south-facing slopes above Lake Geneva, Neuchatel, Biel and Zürich and in Graubünden and Ticino.

Forestry

Swiss forests, covering a quarter of the country, are located in the Jura and on the lower slopes of the Alps. The timber is used for fuel, chalet construction, furniture manufacture and for wood-carving. In the Alps, the forests also protect settlements from avalanches.

Industry

Almost all raw materials have to be imported, yet Swiss industry—specializing in quality goods for export—is highly developed and employs 50% of the workforce, compared with 7% engaged in agriculture. The 5 major industries are engineering, watches, textiles, chemicals and food-processing. 70% of Swiss engineering products, ranging from marine diesel engines to sewing machines, are exported. Watchmaking, dating from the 16th century, is traditionally located in the Jura. Textile manufacture is centred on the cantons of St Gall and Zürich. The chemical industry, based at Basel, accounts for 20% of total exports, chiefly drugs and dyes. With the exception of the building trade, the food industry has the largest labour force. Swiss cheese, chocolate, condensed milk and preserved foods are world-famous.

Transport

In spite of the many mountains, railways reach all parts. The 3,417 km-long network incorporates over 5,000 bridges and 612 tunnels—including Europe's longest, the Simplon: 19.8 km. In the mountains there are also some 400 cog railways, funiculars and aerial cableways. The 18,511 km road network is supplemented by 3,680 km of mountain post roads served by postal buses. Of the 25 major Alpine passes, the St Bernard, St Gotthard and Simplon are the most important. Apart from traffic on the Rhine, water transport is limited to lake steamers. There are 43 airfields and 4 international airports.

Cities

The 5 main cities—Zürich, Basel, Genève, Bern and Lausanne—house 1 in 4 of the population. Zürich, the home of Swiss banking, has textile and engineering industries. Basel (183,000) handles 50% of Swiss foreign trade through its port. Genève (157,000), famous for international meetings, is the seat of the International Red Cross and various UN agencies. The capital, Bern, is noted for engineering and watchmaking. Lausanne (127,000) is the centre of French-speaking Switzerland.

Austria

Area
83,850 km²/32,375 sq miles
Location
46°30′—49°N ; 9°30′—17°E
Population
7,554,000 (1981)
Population density
90 per km²/233 per sq mile
Capital and largest city
Vienna: 1,504,000 (1981)
Language
German
Major imports
manufactured goods, fuel, foodstuffs, raw materials
Major exports
machinery, steel, chemicals, textiles, paper, electricity
Currency
schilling (=100 groschen)
Gross National Product
72,120 million US dollars (1981)
Status
independent republic

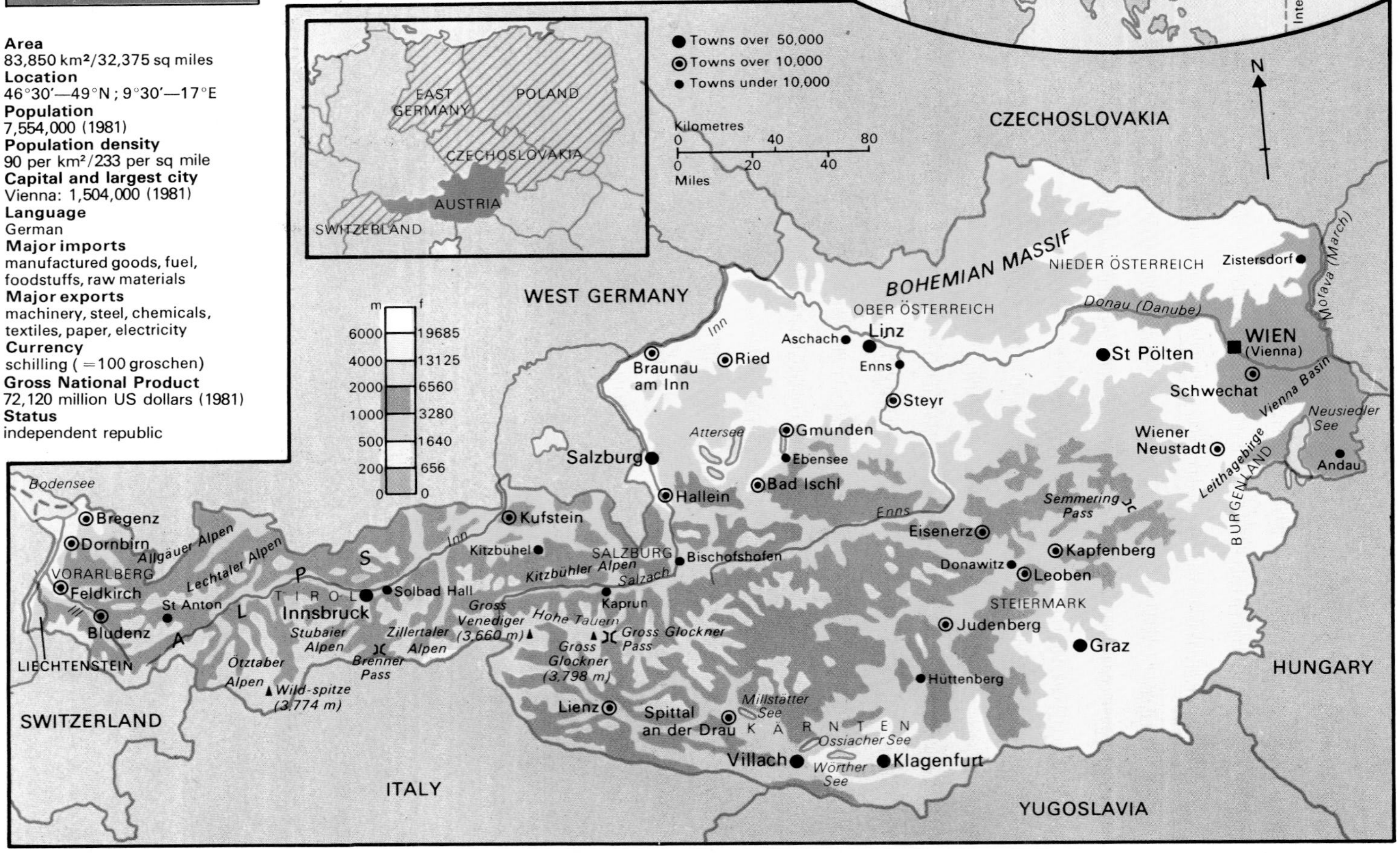

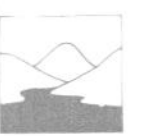

Physical features

Austria, one of Europe's most mountainous states, falls into three main regions. The largest, covering 70% of the country, consists of the Alps—two parallel ranges divided by the east-west sections of the Inn, Salzach and Enns river valleys. The more southerly range is the highest and contains Austria's tallest peak, Gross Glockner (3,798 m). North of the Alps are the Danube lands. The Danube or Donau, flows for 352 km across northern Austria, and its tributaries drain most of the country. From the German border to Linz, the river rushes through a narrow gorge, flanked by the rolling hills of the Alpine foreland to the south and by the forested Bohemian massif to the north. Below Linz, the valley broadens and enters the third region, the Vienna basin. The Leithagebirge mountains separate the Vienna basin from Burgenland, a steppe-like plain.

Climate

Austria has a central European climate with cold winters and hot summers moderated by altitude in many areas. In winter, snowfall is heavy and temperatures often remain below freezing, with a January average of —2°C in Salzburg and —1°C in Andau. The Vienna basin and Burgenland are the warmest parts in summer, Wien (Vienna) and Andau averaging 20°C in July and Salzburg 18°C. Rainfall, heaviest in summer, increases from east to west and coincides with rising heights—Andau receives 57 cm of rain a year, Salzburg 137 cm.

Agriculture

Although only 20% of the total land surface is used for arable farming and 20% for livestock, Austrian agriculture supplies 84% of the country's food needs. Cattle predominate in the Alps and Alpine foreland and dairy produce exported includes dried milk, butter and cheese. Arable farming is most important in the Vienna basin and Burgenland where the main crops are potatoes, sugarbeet, wheat, barley and maize. Stock-raising, dairying and pig-farming are also practised in these areas and beef and pork are exported. Orchards and vineyards are sited on south-facing terraces in the Leithagebirge and in the lower Donau valley. North of Wien, the Weinviertel (wine district) is famous for its vineyards. Arable farming extends up to 2,000 m above sea-level and in Alpine valleys some wheat, maize, fruit, vines and tobacco are grown.

Forestry

Forested areas, covering 38% of the country, largely correspond to the Alpine provinces, where conifers predominate, and to the Bohemian massif. The industry is most developed in the provinces of Steiermark and Karnten. Forest products include fuel, construction timber, pulp, matches resin and turpentine. Paper mills are located in the valleys and much of their output is exported. An important timber fair is held annually in Klagenfurt, capital of Karnten.

Mining

Austria's chief mineral resources are iron ore, graphite and oil. Opencast mines near Erzberg in Steiermark produce 75% of the iron ore output. The remainder is mined at Huttenberg in Karnten. Austria is a leading world producer of graphite and magnesite and is one of Europe's major oil-producing countries. Oilfields are located in Zistersdorf and between the rivers Inn and Enns in Ober Osterreich province. The refinery at Schwechat near Wien handles domestic output as well as imported oil pumped by pipeline from the Adriatic port of Trieste. Natural gas from the same fields is piped direct to factories and power stations. There is also some production of copper, lead, zinc, salt, bauxite and lignite.

Energy

One of Austria's greatest natural resources is water. Hydro-power plants, sited on the Donau and on fast-flowing Alpine rivers such as the Ill, Inn, Salzach and Enns, generate 80% of the country's electricity. The highest station, 2,036 m above sea-level, is at Kaprun in Salzburg province, while the 1,700,000 kW Aschach installation on the Donau, producing 10% of Austrian hydro-electricity, is the largest in Europe outside the USSR. Thermal stations are fired by coal, oil or natural gas. Electricity is exported via international power lines to neighbouring countries, particularly West Germany and Czechoslovakia.

Industry

The iron and steel and engineering industries account for 35% of industrial production. Steel manufacture, using Erzberg ore, is based on Donawitz, Judenburg and Kapfenberg and on Linz where ore is imported via the Donau. Steel is the basis of the construction industry, and of the engineering industry whose products range from turbines to bicycles. The second main industry, food-processing, includes dairy products, sugar, canned fruit, beer and confectionery. The chemical industry, centred on Lenzing (synthetic fibres), Linz (fertilizers) and Schwechat (petro-chemicals) is expanding. Textile manufacture is next in importance. Vorarlberg specializes in lace and cotton ; Wien and the Inn valley in wool. The traditional glass industry has developed to include optical instruments. Industrial goods make up 70% of total exports.

Tourism

In Austria, tourism contributes more to the gross national product than in any other European country. Tirol is the main holiday province both in summer and winter, St Anton, St Christoph and Kitzbuhel all being major skiing resorts. Salzburg, another Alpine province, ranks second in popularity, followed by Karnten which is noted for lakes such as the Worther See, the Ossiacher See and the Millstatter See. Wien is also a leading tourist centre.

Transport

Centrally situated, Austria has become a bridge for traffic between eastern and western Europe. Wien, in particular, is the focus of several major routes—to Germany via the upper Donau, to eastern Europe and the Black Sea via the lower Donau, to Poland and the Baltic via the Morava valley, and to Italy and the Adriatic via the Semmering Pass. The railways, stretching 5,891 km, are almost 50% electrified. The extensive road network covers 32,000 km, including some 600 km of motorways. The Donau provides a means of water transport, coal, coke and oil making up 65% of freight carried. Six airports—Wien, Salzburg, Innsbruck, Linz, Graz and Klagenfurt—serve the national airline, Austrian Airlines.

Cities

One Austrian in four lives in Wien, the country's economic centre. Main industries include engineering, food-processing, printing and clothing manufacture. Wien's magnificent past and its active tradition of music and theatre attract many foreign visitors. Austria's second largest city is the old cathedral and university town of Graz (249,000) where industry has been developed using Alpine hydro-power. Linz (203,000) dating from Roman times, is a leading industrial centre and major river port. Salzburg (129,000), Mozart's birthplace, and Innsbruck (115,000) are both tourist centres.

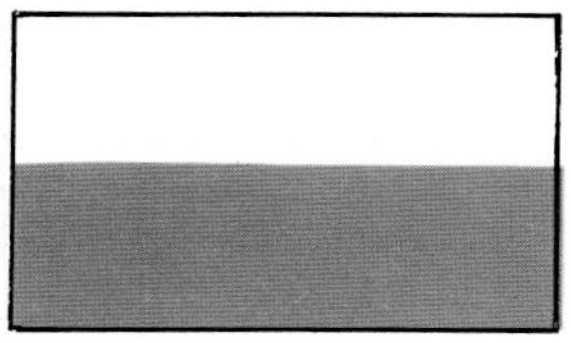

Poland

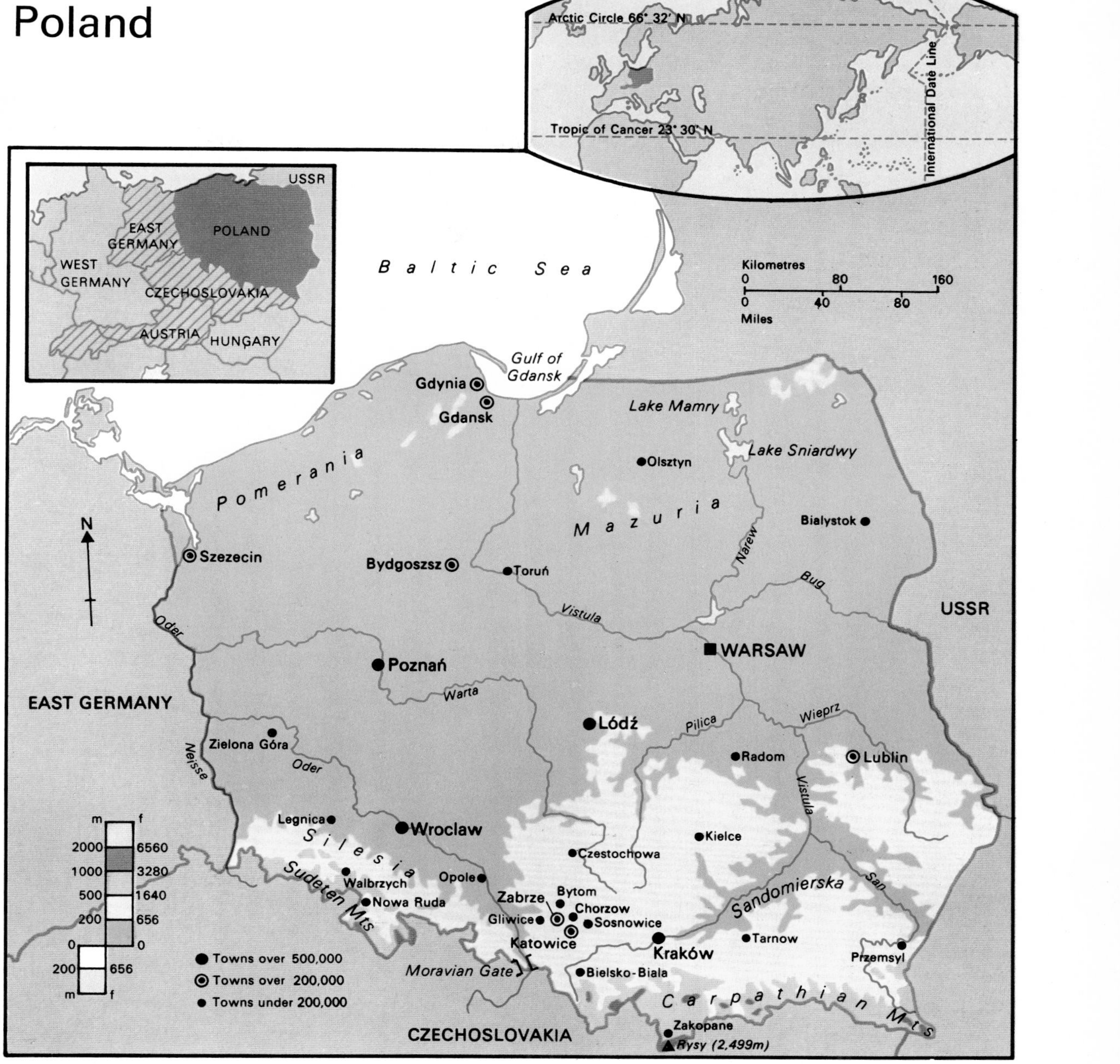

Area
312,677 km²/120,725 sq miles
Location
49°—54° N ; 14°07′—26°08′ E
Population
35,902,000 (1981)
Population density
115 per km²/297 per sq mile
Capital and largest city
Warsaw: 1,500,000 (1979)
Language
Polish
Major imports
machinery, ores, petroleum, cereals, chemicals
Major exports
engineering products, coal, foodstuffs, textiles, sulphur
Currency
zloty (1 zloty = 100 groszy)
Gross National Product
not available
Status
independent republic

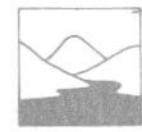

Physical features
Poland is predominantly low-lying ; 90% of the country is under 300 m. In the north, the Baltic coast areas consist of shallow, sandy beaches backed by dunes, marshes and lagoons. Further inland lies a belt of morainic hills, rising to over 300 m in places and containing thousands of lakes : the two largest are Sniardwy (114 km²) and Mamry (104 km²). Southwards, the lake zone gives way to the central plain. This gently undulating lowland has large areas of infertile glacial sands and, in the east, bogs. The plain is separated from the mountainous southern rim by uplands enclosing the loess-covered basins of Silesia and Sandomierska. Two major ranges, divided by the Moravian gate, line the Czech border : in the west the Sudetens, in the east the Carpathians, which include the Tatra mountains and Poland's highest peak, Rysy (2,499 m). The country is drained by the Vistula (961 km) and Oder (512 km) and their tributaries notably the Narew, Bug, San and Warta.

Climate
Poland's climate varies from oceanic to continental. The west and Baltic coast, affected by the proximity of the Atlantic and the warm Gulf Stream, are relatively mild. In contrast the east, subject to continental air masses, is more extreme, with colder winters and hotter summers. Temperatures in the south are modified by altitude. January averages 0°C in Gdansk and —5°C in Zakopane ; respective July temperatures are 17°C and 15°C. Rain, falling mostly in summer, is heaviest in the mountains : Szczecin (Stettin) has 56 cm per year ; Zakopane 112 cm. In the mountains, winter precipitation falls as snow.

Forestry
Forests, covering 27% of Poland, are located in the Sudetens. 82% of these are coniferous, with pine trees in the lowlands, spruce in the mountains. Forestry production consists of timber plus by-products such as resin, dye barks, Christmas trees, fruit (bilberries in particular), mushrooms, herbs and game. Both mushrooms (dried, salted or pickled) and bilberries are significant export items.

Mining
Poland is a major producer of coal, copper and sulphur. 90% of all Polish coal comes from Upper Silesia near the Moravian Gate ; there is also some production at Walbrzych ana Nowa Ruda. Half the total annual output of 150 million tonnes is exported. Lignite, mined in the Turoszow and Konin regions, is less important. Copper production is centred on Glowgow and Boleslawiec, while sulphur deposits, among the world's largest, are worked near Tarnobrzeg. Lead and zinc, from Bytom, Chrzanow and Olkusz, are also exported. Low quality iron ore, worked near Czestochowa and Kielce, meets only 10% of Polish industry's needs. Other minerals exploited include nickel, salt, kaolin and building stone. Oil production from fields east of Krakow is small, but natural gas reserves, mainly in the Lubaczow region, are extensive.

Energy
Thermal stations, using coal and lignite, generate over 90% of all Poland's electricity. A further 3% comes from hydro-electric plants in the Sudetens and Carpathians. Other stations are fired by oil or gas imported by pipeline from the USSR.

Agriculture
Agriculture, employing 25% of the workforce, covers two-thirds of Poland. Only 20% of farm-land is state-owned ; the remainder is worked privately by peasants. In the lake belt and central plain, dairying and pig-farming are important and, despite infertile soils, some oats, rye, potatoes and sugar-beet are grown. In contrast, the loess-soils of Silesia and areas further east give high yields of wheat, barley, sugar-beet and potatoes : the potato crop is the world's second largest. Cattle and sheep graze on the lower slopes of the Sudetens and Carpathians. Fruit and vegetables, mainly cabbages, onions, apples, pears and plums, are grown near Warsaw. Farm exports include bacon, butter, eggs and sugar.

Fishing
The fishing industry, conducted by the state, by co-operatives and by private individuals, is based at Gydnia, Swinoujscie and Szczecin. Poland has developed a fleet of deep-sea trawlers and factory ships and 70% of fish landed—mainly cod, herring, sprat and haddock—comes from distant Atlantic waters. About 14% of the catch is exported.

Industry
Engineering, including electrical engineering, is Poland's leading industry, accounting for 30% of total industrial production. Products range from combine harvesters and computers to rolling-stock and radios. Ship-building is important, in particular fishing vessels such as factory trawlers. Steel production is centred on Upper Silesia but there are also plants at Szczecin, Warsaw and Czestochowa. Total steel output will almost double when the new mill at Katowice comes into operation. Food-processing is the second most important sector, providing 17% of industrial production. The chemical industry, based on domestic reserves of coal, salt, sulphur and natural gas, is expanding rapidly. Leading products are sulphuric acid, fertilizers and synthetic fibres, but plastic production is insufficient for domestic needs. Other major industries include textiles (cotton and woollen manufactures and clothing) wood and paper. The traditional home of Polish industry is the Upper Silesian coalfield, near Gliwice, Zabrze, Bytom, Sosnowiec, Katowice and neighbouring towns towns of Krakow and Opole.

Transport
Railways, with a total length of 26,717 km, carry 25% of Poland's freight traffic, mostly coal, coke, ores, metals and stone. Road transport, operating over 140,576 km, has recently been developed and is now more important than rail, accounting for two-thirds of both freight and passenger traffic. Navigable waterways, totalling 6,907 km, transport only 6% of freight, in particular sand, gravel and fertilizer. 60% of waterway traffic is on the Oder between Silesia and the Baltic. Szczecin is the leading sea-port, followed by Gdansk and Gydnia. The national airline, LOT, provides both overseas and domestic services.

Cities
Warsaw, originally a 13th-century trading centre on the Vistula, was totally devastated during the Second World War but has since been rebuilt in its former style. Lodz (832,000), the second largest city is the centre of Polish textile manufacture. The country's third town and former capital, Krakow (705,000) was founded in the 9th century, on a hill by the Vistula. Its proximity to the Silesian coalfield led to industrialization.

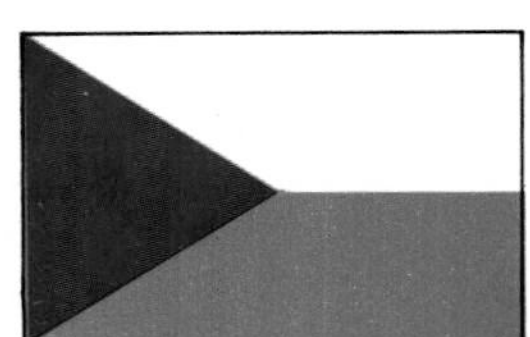

Czechoslovakia

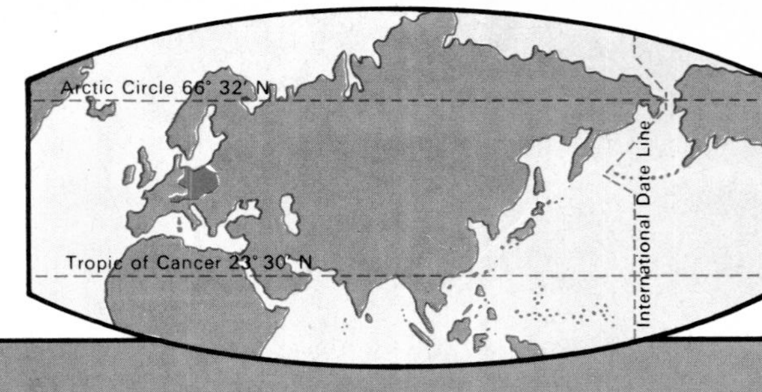

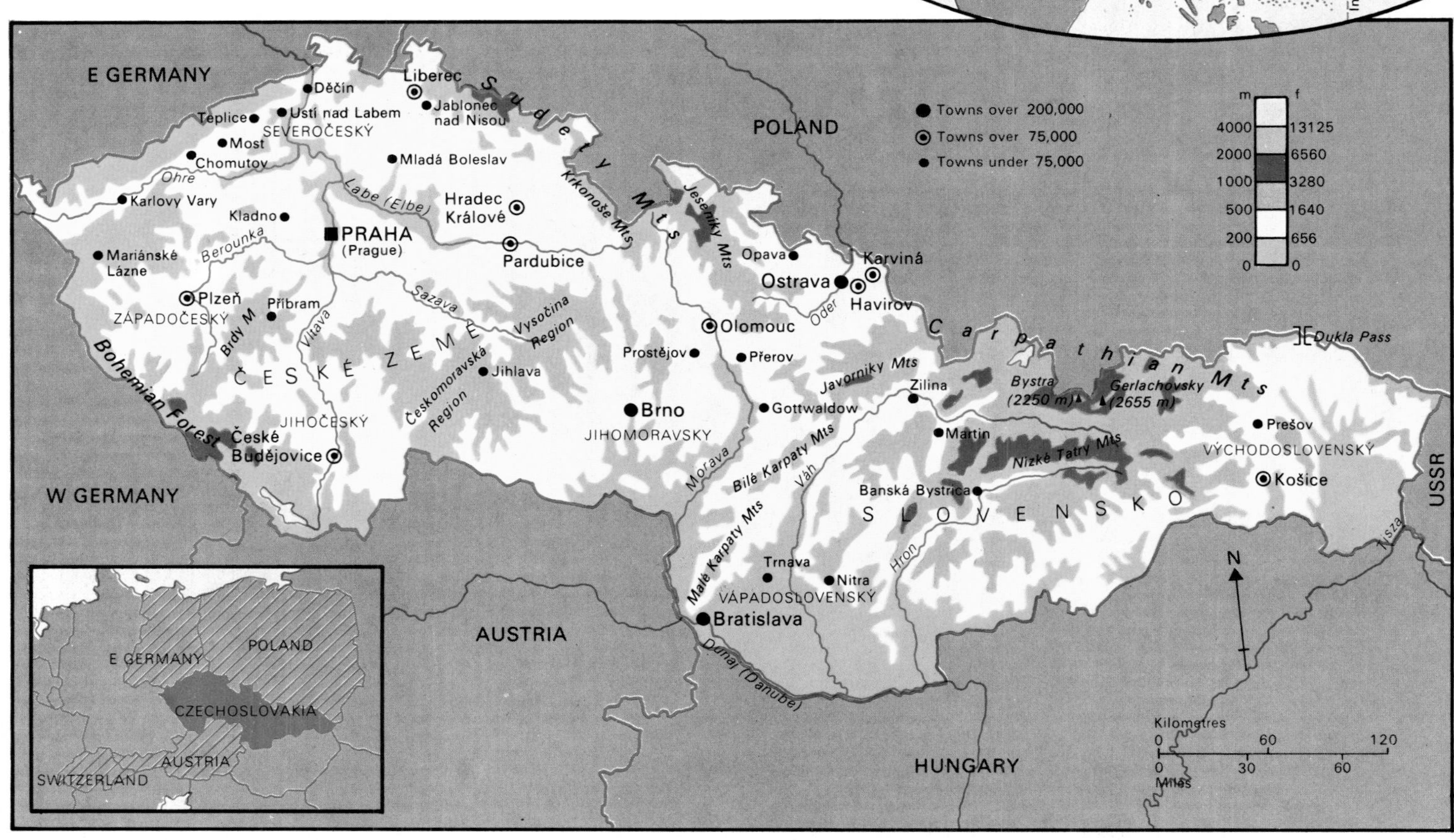

Area
127,877 km²/49,373 sq miles
Location
47°43'—51°03' N
12°05'—22°34' E
Population
15,314,000 (1981)
Population density
120 per km²/310 per sq mile
Capital and largest city
Prague: 1,100,000 (1981)
Languages
Czech, Slovak
Major imports
fuels, ores, metals, machinery, chemicals, cereals and livestock products
Major exports
machinery, sugar, transport equipment, forest products, textiles, shoes, glass
Currency
koruna (1 koruna = 100 hellers)
Gross National Product
not available
Status
federal republic

Cities
Czechoslovakia is a federal republic made up of two nations: the Czech and the Slovak Socialist Republics. The federal capital, Prague, is also the Czech capital. Situated on the Vltava, Prague is the only city in Czechoslovakia with over a million inhabitants and is a leading industrial and commercial centre. Brno (369,000), also in the Czech Republic, is the country's second largest city with important engineering works and textile factories. The third largest town, Bratislava (368,000), a major river port on the Danube, is the Slovak capital. Karlovy Vary is world famous for its mineral waters.

Physical features
Czechoslovakia stretches 758 km along the highlands of central Europe. Bohemia, in the west, consists of a central basin ringed by mountains: Sudetens, Moravian Heights, Bohemian Forest, Ore Mountains and Giant Mountains. This mountainous rim is broken in the north-west by the Labe (Elbe) gorge with its sheer sandstone cliffs. Central Bohemia comprises rugged uplands in the south and, in the north, the Polabi plain, covered with fertile loess and alluvium. The region is drained by the Labe (396 km) and its tributaries: the Ohre and Vltava. Moravia corresponds to the undulating lowlands of the Morava (352 km) and Oder river valleys. Slovakia, in the east, is dominated by the Carpathians, which include the High Tatras and Czechoslovakia's highest peak: Gerlachovasky (2,655 m). Southwards, lower ranges give way to the Dunaj (Danube) plain. Slovakia is drained by tributaries of the Dunaj, notably the Vah (433 km).

Climate
Czechoslovakia has a central European climate. Summers are hot (20°C in July) and stormy; winters are cold and dry, but milder in the west due to moderating Atlantic winds. January averages 0°C in Prague, —3°C in Kosice. Rainfall, with a July maximum, varies according to altitude: lowlands receive 40-60 cm a year; highlands, up to 200 cm, including heavy snow in winter. Relief also modifies temperature: in the High Tatras, January temperatures fall to —40°C.

Forests
Woodland, mostly state-owned, accounts for 35% of the country. Spruce predominates in the Bohemian highlands and in the Carpathians; beech, pine and some oak cover central Slovakia and low hills in Bohemia and Moravia. As forests are in mountainous regions, the timber industry and associated manufacture benefit from local hydro-electric power. Products include lumber, cellulose, pulp, paper, matches, furniture and toys. Timber, paper, cellulose and matches are exported.

Agriculture
Farmland covers two-thirds of the country and 75% of this agricultural area is arable. In the most fertile regions—the alluvial Polabi plain, the Moravian lowland and the Danube plain—the main crops are wheat, barley, sugar-beet and potatoes with some maize, flax, hops, tobacco and hemp in southern Slovakia and in Moravia. Highland areas are less fertile and rye, oats and potatoes are the principal crops grown along mountain valleys and on lower slopes. In central Slovakia, south-facing slopes support orchards and vineyards. Dairy farming is important in lowland Moravia and Slovakia; beef cattle are reared in the Bohemian foothills while sheep-grazing predominates on the mountain pastures of Slovakia; pigs are kept in most lowland zones. Czechoslovak agriculture is almost totally socialized and state farms and co-operatives account for 86% of farmland and 70% of agricultural production.

Mining
Coal is Czechoslovakia's most important mineral asset. 85% of hard coal output comes from Ostrava-Karvina; smaller fields are sited at Kladno, Plzen, Trutnov and Rosice. Most brown coal and lignite is mined in north-west Bohemia at Chomutov and Sokolov. Reserves of other minerals are less significant. Iron ore is worked in central Slovakia and the Berounka valley; copper and manganese in central Slovakia; kaolin at Plzen and Karlovy Vary; glass sand at Jablonec. There is also some production of uranium, tin, antimony and building stone. Oil and natural gas is largely imported from the USSR but small amounts are obtained from the Hodonin field.

Transport
The 13,293 km rail network, centred on Prague and Bratislava, is vital to Czechoslovakia's transport system and carries most long-distance heavy freight such as coal, ores, building materials, cereals and sugar beet. So far, only 16% of lines are electrified. Since 1947, the road network has been substantially improved and now totals 73,400 km. Public bus services are important: some 6,000 routes over 234,000 km. There are 473 km of navigable rivers but winter ice and spring floods limit their use. The Labe (giving access to the North Sea), the Vltava and the Dunaj (leading to the Black Sea) account for most waterway traffic. CSA (Czechoslovak Airlines) operate international flights from Prague, while Brno, Bratislava, Olomouc and Kosice also have airports.

Energy
Over 95% of electricity is generated in thermal stations. Two-thirds of these are fired by brown coal and lignite. The remainder use oil and, to a lesser extent, natural gas; both fuels are imported via pipeline from the USSR: oil comes from the Vloga area, gas from Siberia. Hydro-electric installations on the Vltava and Vah produce under 5% of the country's electricity.

Industry
Czechoslovak industry is highly developed and is based on natural resources supplemented by imports of fuel and ores from the USSR and other Comecon countries. Engineering accounts for 25% of total industrial output and 50% of exports. Major steel plants and engineering works are located in Prague, Plzen, Ostrava and Kosice; Brno, Kladno and Chomutov are also engineering centres. Leading products range from rolling mills and locomotives to machine tools and looms. Food-processing comes next in importance and includes flour-milling, meat-canning, cheese and butter manufacture, sugar-refining and brewing; main products exported are ham, sausages, sugar and beer—Plzen (Pilsen) is the traditional brewing town. The expanding chemical industry, based on coal from the Chomutov and Ostrava fields, and on imported oil at Bratislava, produces fertilizers, sulphuric acid, synthetic fibres and plastics. Footwear production is important and the Bata shoe factories at Gottwaldov are the world's largest.

Hungary

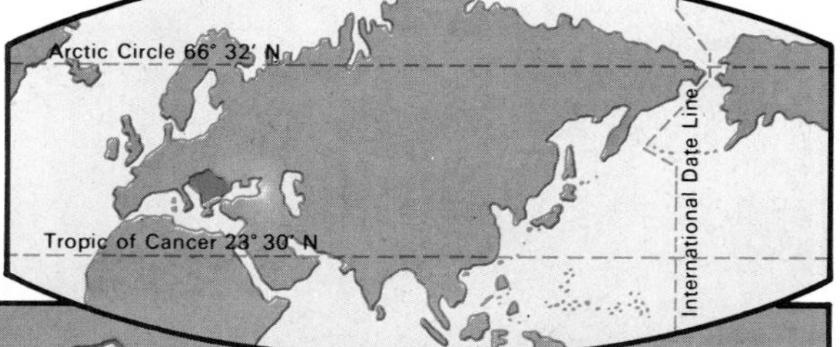

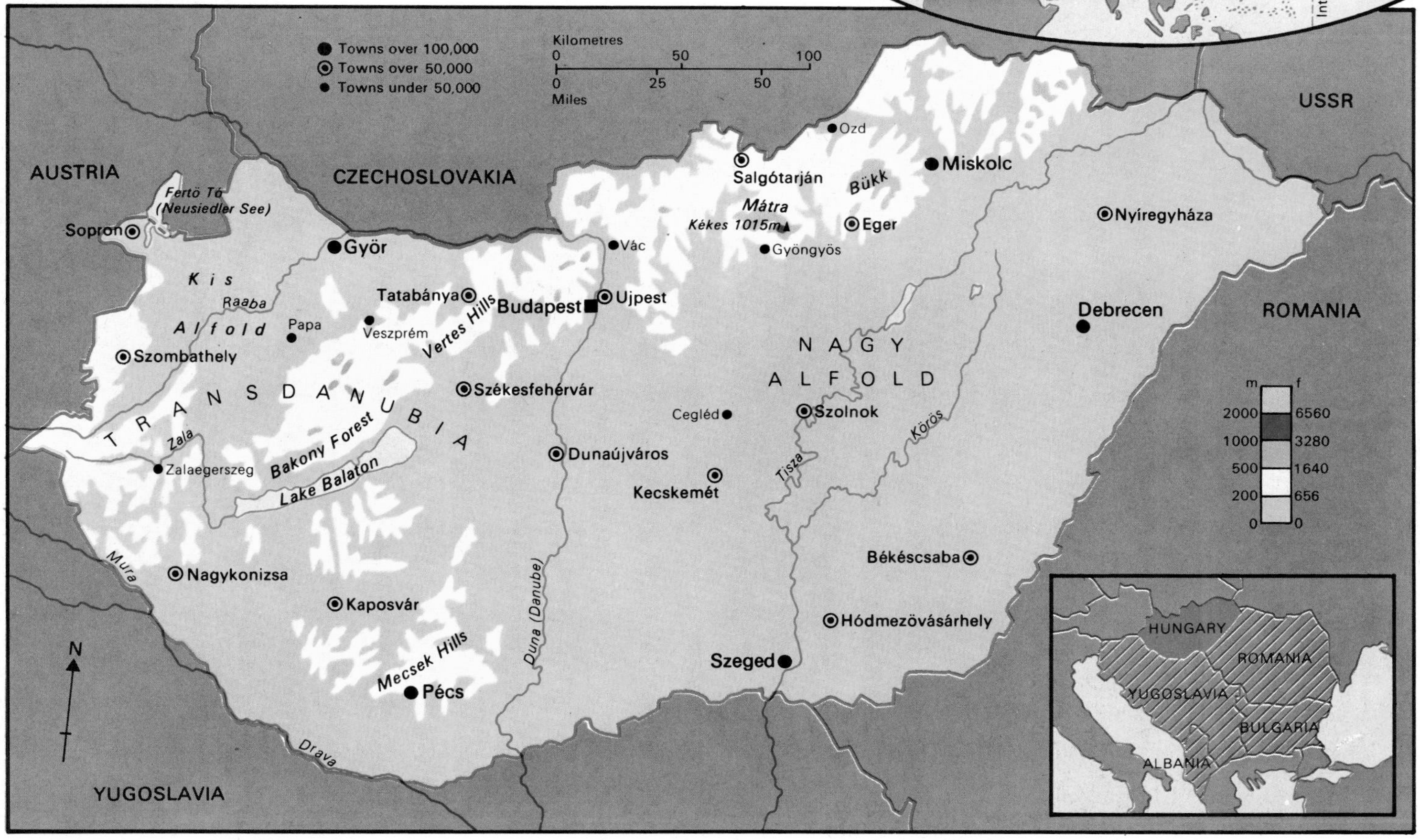

Area
93,032 km²/35,911 sq miles
Location
45°48'—48°40' N
16°05'—22°55' E
Population
10,712,000 (1981)
Population density
115 per km²/298 per sq mile
Capital and largest city
Budapest: 2,093,000 (1979)
Language
Hungarian
Major imports
fuels, iron ore, machinery, foodstuffs, cotton, timber
Major exports
vehicles, pharmaceuticals, bauxite, alumina, steel
Currency
forint (= 100 fillers)
Gross National Product
22,550 million US dollars (1981)
Status
independent republic

Mining

Hungary's underground resources are limited. Bauxite, mined in the Bakony Forest and Vertes Hills, is the most important mineral and the only one to be exported in significant quantities—mostly to the USSR and Poland. Iron ore output, centred on Miskolc, meets only 15% of requirements; imports come primarily from the USSR. Coal deposits consist mainly of low quality brown coal at Ozd, Miskolc, Salgotarjan, Tatabanya and Ajka. Supplies of hard coal, mined at Pecs, are supplemented by imports from other Comecon countries. Small amounts of oil are drilled near Zalaegerszeg, and some natural gas is produced east of the Tisza near Hortobagy and Bekescsaba.

Climate

Hungary's continental climate is moderated by Atlantic and Mediterranean influences: although summers are hot and winters cold, temperatures are seldom extreme. In Budapest, January averages —1°C and July 22°C. As the country is sheltered by the Carpathians and the Alps, rainfall is slight: Transdanubia and the northern hills receive only 30 cm of rain a year, while the Nagy Alfold has even less. The summer months are particularly arid. The Danube, frozen in winter, often floods in spring.

Physical features

The Danube, flowing 417 km from north to south across Hungary, divides the country roughly in half. East of the river lies the Nagy Alfold, the Great Plain, a flat, monotonous lowland less than 200 m above sea level. Loess covers most of the plain, but there are stretches of infertile sand and, in the river basins, of marsh-land. The Nagy Alfold is drained by the Tisza (579 km) and its tributaries. To the north, the Great Plain is bordered by the Carpathian foothills which contain Hungary's highest point, Kekes (1,015 m). The landscape west of the Danube (Transdanubia) is more varied. In the north-west is the flat, and sometimes, swampy Kis (Little) Alfold. Central and southern Transdanubia consist of rolling upland broken by the Bakony and Mecsek highlands, both rising to over 700 m. These two ranges are separated by Europe's largest natural lake, Balaton (596 km²).

Agriculture

Three-quarters of Hungary is agricultural land and 65% of this area is used for arable farming. Maize is the chief crop and is grown extensively in the Nagy Alfold. Other crops on the Great Plain include wheat, sugar-beet, sunflowers, rye (on sandy stretches) and rice in the irrigated valleys of the Tisza and Koros. Rye, oats, potatoes and sugar-beet predominate in lowland Transdanubia. Sandy soils between the Danube and Tisza and in the north-east favour fruit-growing. Vineyards near Pecs, Lake Balaton, Eger and Tokaj produce world-famous wines. There are some 8 million pigs, mostly swill-fed, and over 40 million hens. The 2 million cattle are largely stall-fed but there is some grazing for both sheep and cattle on infertile grasslands in the Nagy Alfold and on upland pastures in Transdanubia. State and collective farms account for 95% of agricultural land.

Energy

Hungary's energy resources do not meet demand and 42% of fuel is imported. Coal accounts for 40% of primary energy consumption, oil 35% and natural gas 17%. Three-quarters of the country's oil needs are imported via pipeline from the USSR; another pipeline brings gas from Romania. Electricity is largely generated in thermal stations but there is a major hydro-power plant near Vac. Production does not meet internal needs so 30% of electricity used is imported, mainly from the USSR.

Forestry

Much of Hungary's woodland has been cleared but 17% of the country is still tree-covered. The forests, located on the upper slopes of the Transdanubian and northern hills, consist mainly of oak and beech. Timber production does not meet the requirements of the construction, furniture and paper industries and substantial imports, especially of softwoods, are necessary.

Industry

Industry, employing 36% of the work-force, accounts for 87% of exports. Iron and steel production relies on ore and coke imports from the USSR; major plants are located at Miskolc, Ozd and Dunaujvaros. Hungary's metallurgical industry also includes aluminium: bauxite is exported to the USSR and Poland for smelting and aluminium ingots are then imported; Szekesfehervar is the main aluminium centre. The Ikarus bus factory in Budapest—Europe's largest—makes 10,000 buses a year, 80% of them for export. Other engineering products include diesel engines, TV sets and machine tools. In the last 15 years Hungary's chemical industry has grown rapidly and produces fertilizers, pesticides, plastic, pharmaceuticals, and synthetic fibres. Textile manufacture is also expanding; cotton, wool and silk fabrics, clothing and, in particular, shoes, are exported. The food industry processes domestic produce and exports salami, canned fruit and vegetables, wine and jam.

Transport

Budapest is the focal point of Hungary's transport system and both road (29,700 km) and rail (8,600 km) networks radiate from the capital to all parts of the country. Lorries and buses are gaining ground at the expense of trains: 55% of goods and passengers travel by road compared with 40% by rail. Although the country has two major rivers, the Danube and Tisza, water transport is insignificant. The national airline, Malev, operates international flights from Ferihegy (Budapest) airport; domestic services were discontinued in 1969.

Cities

Just over a hundred years ago the capital was still two separate towns—Buda, lying among the hills on the west bank of the Danube, and Pest, built on the east bank lowland. Today, eight bridges link the two parts of the city. Budapest is Hungary's cultural, commercial and industrial centre, having 70% of the country's factories and accounting for 40% of industrial output. Other Hungarian cities are all much smaller than the capital. Miskolc (212,000), the second largest town, is heavily industrialized; Debrecen (200,000), in the Nagy Alfold, is a cultural centre with some manufacturing; in spite of its rapid industrialization Pecs (171,000) has retained its historic character; Szeged (178,000), a cultural and commercial centre on the Tisza, is noted for its paprika.

Yugoslavia

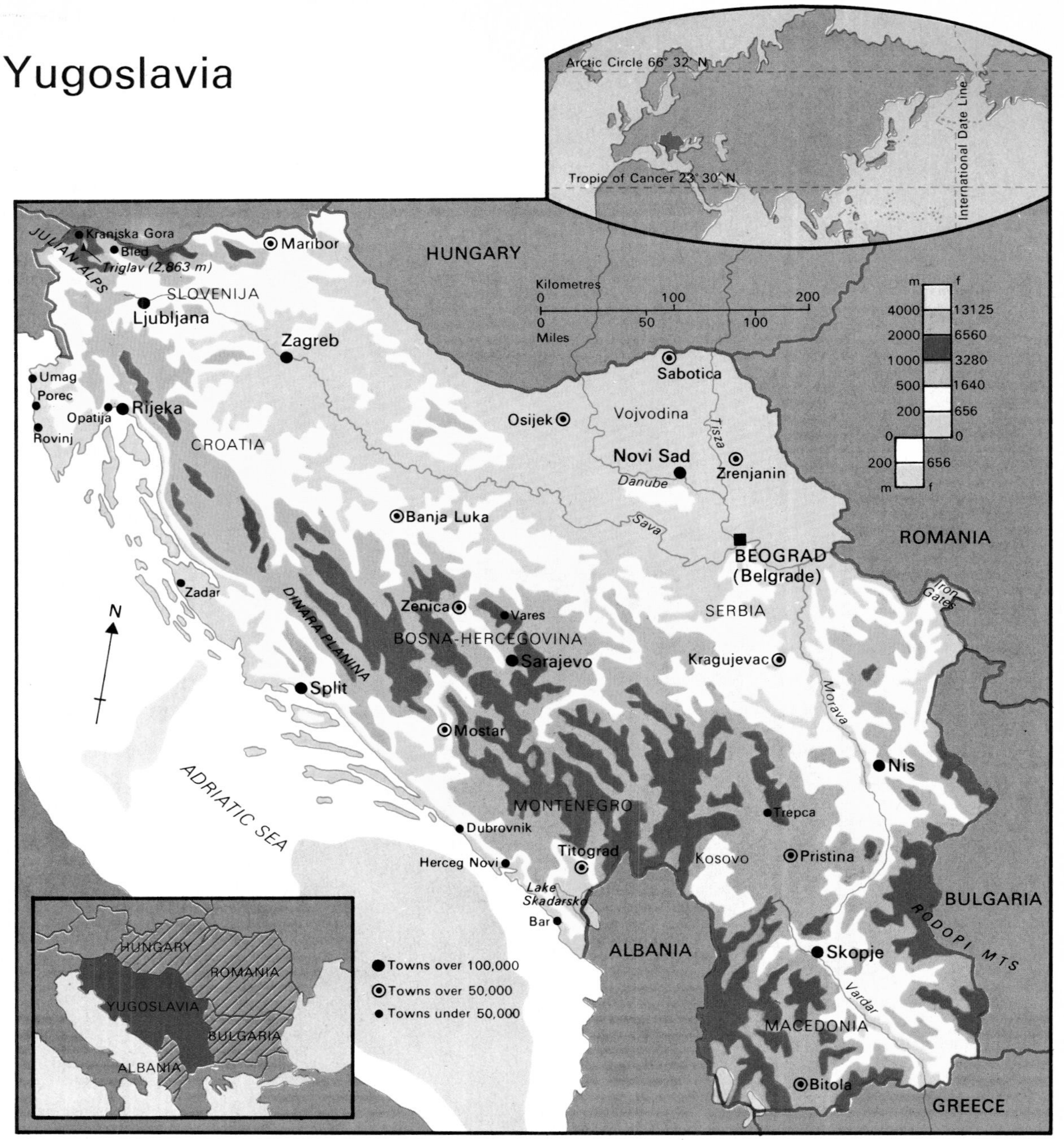

Area
255,804 km²/98,725 sq miles
Location
40°51'—46°53' N
13°23'—23°02' E
Population
22,516,000 (1981)
Population density
88 per km²/228 per sq mile
Capital and largest city
Belgrade: 1,300,000 (1980)
Languages
Serbo-Croatian, Macedonian
Slovenian
Major imports
petroleum, coal, fertilizers, iron and steel
Major exports
machinery, vehicles, electrical goods, ships, minerals, metal products, timber, food
Currency
dinar (1 dinar = 100 paras)
Gross National Product
62,930 million US dollars (1981)
Status
federal republic

Peoples
Yugoslavia is composed of 6 republics: Bosna-Hercegovina, Montenegro (Crna Gora), Croatia (Hrvatska), Macedonia (Makedonija), Slovenija and Serbia (Srbija: containing the 2 autonomous provinces of Vojvodina and Kosovo). It has the most diverse population in Europe outside the USSR. There are 5 major nationalities, all Slavs: Serbs, Croats, Slovenes, Madeconians and Montenegrins. In addition, there are important Albanian and Hungarian communities and some 15 other minority groups. Serbo-Croat is the most widely used language, but has equal status with Macedonian and Slovenian, which together involve 2 alphabets: Latin and Cyrillic.

Physical features
Mountains, covering 75% of Yugoslavia, stretch from the extreme north-west to the southeast of the country. The Julian Alps, with steep ridges and deep valleys, occupy the northern area; they rise to 2,863 m in Triglav, Yugoslavia's highest peak. A series of parallel ridges, the Dinaric range (Dinara Planina), extends south-eastwards to Lake Skadarsko. Forest covers the northern Dinarics, but further south barren limestone plateaus, drained by underground rivers, predominate. A narrow lowland strip separates these highlands from the island-fringed Adriatic coast. In the southeast, the Rodopi massif extends from Bulgaria into Makedonija and Serbija. A depression, drained by the Morava and Vardar, lies between the Rodopi and Dinarics. North-eastwards, the Dinarics give way to the plains of eastern Slovenija, Croatia and Vojvodina.

Climate
Yugoslavia has 3 climatic regions. The coast has a typical Mediterranean climate with hot drysummers (24°C) and warm, wet winters (7°C); annual rainfall averages 75cm. In the mountains, summers are cool and short, winters, long and cold with heavy snow; precipitation ranges from 200-500 cm. A continental climate prevails in the northeast with January and July averages of —1°C and 27°C and 80 cm of rain.

Agriculture
Agriculture, employing 49% of the population, accounts for 20% of overall exports. Farmland covers half the total area and is largely concentrated on the low-lands of the Danube (Dunav) and its tributaries. Maize and wheat are the main cereals and Yugoslavia is self-sufficient in grains. Industrial crops include hemp, sugar-beet, potatoes and sunflowers; tobacco is important in Makedonija. Orchards and vineyards are located on the foothills and along the coast; tree crops include apples, plums, olives, figs and walnuts. Livestock is kept in highland areas and Kosovo. Meat, fruit, wine and tobacco are exported. Only 20% of cultivated land is socialized; the remainder (in units of 10 ha or less) is held by peasant farmers.

Forestry
A third of Yugoslavia is wooded. 85% of the forests are deciduous with beech and oak predominating. Conifers, mainly fir, grow on the higher slopes. The timber-processing industry is most developed in Slovenija, Bosna, Croatia and Makedonija. Sawn timber, fuel, veneer, pulp and cellulose are all exported.

Mining
Yugoslavia has extensive mineral resources and is a leading world exporter of lead, bauxite and copper. Antimony, chrome, mercury and zinc are also exported in significant quantities. Trepca (Kosovo) is the main lead-zinc centre; copper is mined chiefly at Bor (Srbija); bauxite is exploited in the southern Dinarics. The Dinarics also have deposits of salt, lead, zinc, barite, asbestos, copper, nickel and chrome. The principal iron ore mines are in western Makedonija and at Vares and Ljubija in Bosna. Coal comes from Bosna and Srbija; oil and natural gas from Vojvodina.

Cities
Beograd stands at the confluence of the Danube and Sava. It is a major route centre and handles 50% of Yugoslav foreign trade; the rivers Danube, Sava and Morava provide access to the Black Sea, Adriatic and Aegean. With engineering, chemical and textile works, Beograd accounts for 10% of the country's industrial output. Yugoslavia's main industrial centre and second largest city is Zagreb (700,000). Zagreb is the capital of Croatia.

Energy
Many rivers in the Julian Alps, the Dinarics and the Rodopi have been harnessed and hydro-power supplies 60% of Yugoslav electricity. There is also a major installation, part Romanian, at the Iron Gates gorge on the Danube. Thermal stations are sited near lignite deposits in Slovenija, Bosna and Srbija. The country's first nuclear plant is under construction in Slovenija.

Industry
Yugoslavia is one of Europe's least industrialised states and development is based on domestic resources: minerals, agricultural produce and timber. Industry is invariably located near the materials used: there are sugar refineries, breweries and canneries in Vojvodina, copper works at Bor, cigarette factories in Makedonija, iron and steel mills at Skopje and near Sarajevo, lead and zinc foundries in Kosovo and aluminium plants at Mostar and Titograd. Textile wood-working, engineering (industrial and agricultural machinery, motor vehicles, machine tools), electrical and chemical industries are also important.

Transport
The road and rail networks are most developed in the north-west, but measures have been taken to improve facilities in the south and south-west. These improvements include the Beograd-Bar railway and the Adriatic highway from Rijeka to Skopje. There are almost 2,000 km of navigable waterways; the most important are the Danube, Sava and Tisza. The main seaports are Dubrovnik, Split, Rijeka, Zadar and Bar; ferries link the mainland to the Adriatic islands. There are 13 international airports; the JAT national airline operates both domestic and overseas services.

Tourism
60% of the 6 million foreign tourists who visit Yugoslavia each year stay in Croatia which contains the main Adriatic resort such as Herceg Novi, Dubrovnik, Opatija, Porec, Rovinj and Umag. Tourism is also being developed in inland Yugoslavia. Many mineral spring spas have been established in the mountains of Slovenija and northern Croatia. Mountain zones also offer winter sports; ski centres include Bled, Kranjska Gora and Jahorina.

Romania

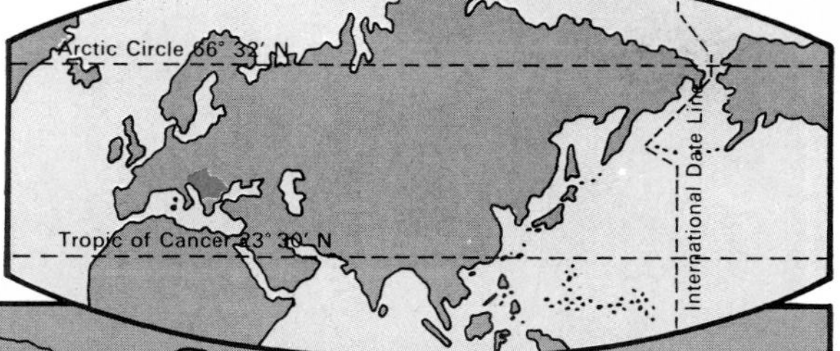

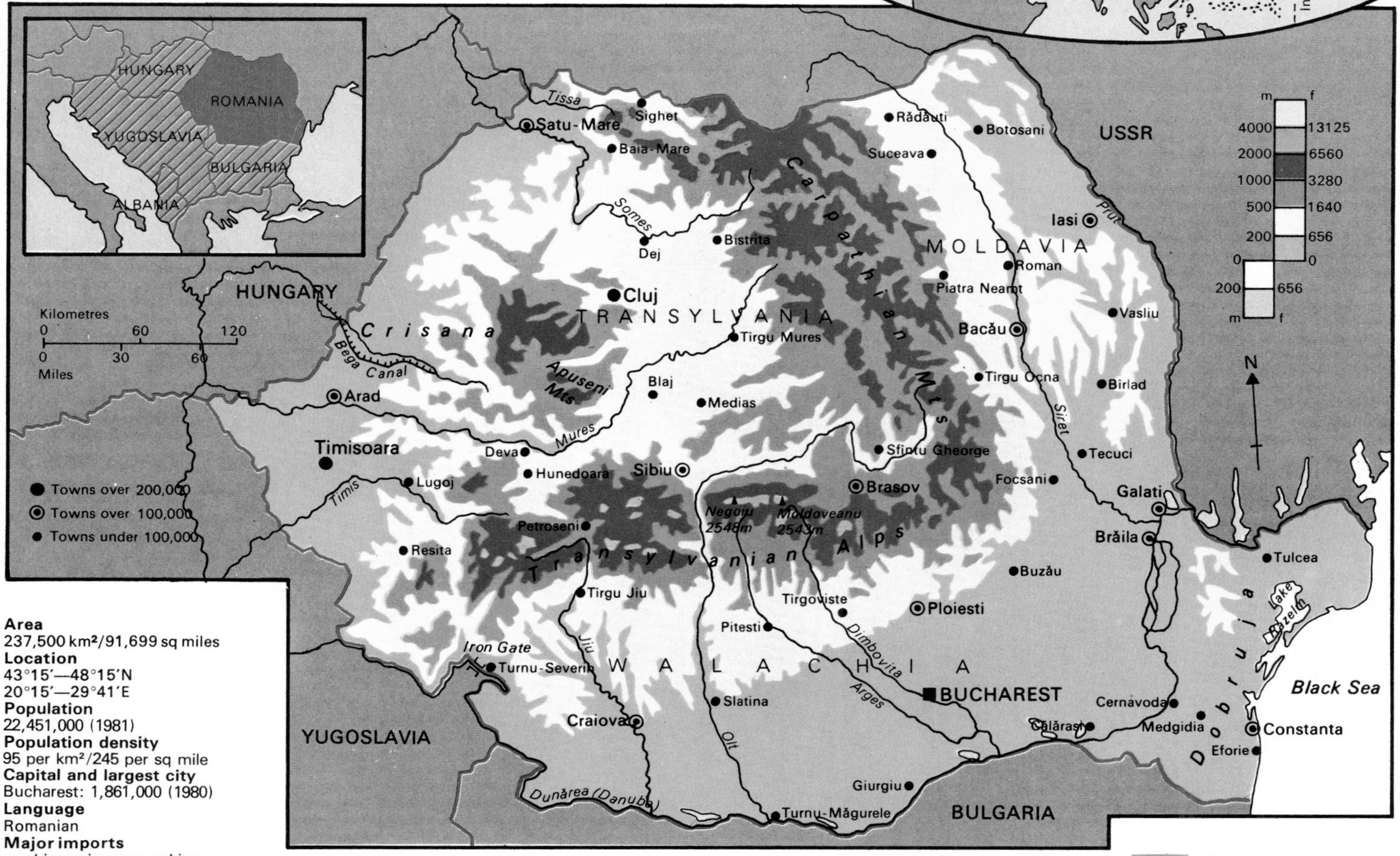

Area
237,500 km²/91,699 sq miles
Location
43°15'—48°15'N
20°15'—29°41'E
Population
22,451,000 (1981)
Population density
95 per km²/245 per sq mile
Capital and largest city
Bucharest: 1,861,000 (1980)
Language
Romanian
Major imports
machinery, iron ore, coking coal, metals, vehicles
Major exports
engineering products, oil, foodstuffs, chemicals
Currency
leu (1 leu = 100 bani)
Gross National Product
57,030 million US dollars (1981)
Status
independent republic

Mining and Energy

Romania's leading mineral resource is oil: the annual output of 14 million tonnes is the highest in Europe outside the USSR. The chief oilfields are Ploiesti, Bacau, Pitesti, Craiova and Tirgu-Jiu. Romania also ranks as the world's fifth producer of natural gas, with production mainly centred on the Cluj-Tirgu-Mures area. Although there is a lack of high-grade coal, there are major deposits of lignite near Rovinari, Motru and Oradea and low-grade coal at Petroseni. Output of iron ore, mined in the western Carpathians, does not meet industrial requirements. However, there are adequate reserves of other minerals: the western Carpathians, notably the Apuseni mountains, are rich in copper, lead, zinc, chromium, gold, silver, bauxite and mercury. Salt is worked near Ploiesti and Turda. Thermal stations, fired by lignite, oil and gas, account for 80% of electricity. Hydro-power is being developed: the most important installation, half-owned by Yugoslavia, is at the Iron Gates gorge. A nuclear station under construction uses uranium from the Apuseni range.

Physical features

At the heart of Romania lies the Transylvanian Basin, a hilly tableland some 400 to 500 m high. This is enclosed by the Carpathians which are greatest in the south, where the Transylvanian Alps rise to over 2,000 m and include Romania's highest peak: Negoiu (2,548 m). The country's major lowland is in Walachia and corresponds to the broad, loess-covered Danube valley. The lowlands in the extreme west are also loess-covered; in contrast Moldavia in the east and Dobruja in the south-east are both rock plateaus. Romania's rivers—such as the Somes, Mures, Jiu, Olt, Arges, Dimbovita, Siret and Prut—rise in the Carpathians and drain directly or indirectly into the Danube. The Danube enters the Black Sea via three channels which enclose Europe's largest delta, a marshy area covering over 3,750 km².

Climate

Romania has a central European climate with a mean annual temperature of 11°C in the south and 8°C in the north. In the highlands, snow lasts for up to 3 months. The eastern plain, exposed to north-easterly winds from Russia, is subject to severe cold in winter and burning heat in summer: Bucharest averages —5°C in January and 24°C in July. Rainfall decreases from west to east and is heaviest in the mountains: the Transylvanian Alps have about 130 cm annually but Dobruja has less than 40 cm.

Agriculture

70% of Romania is used for agriculture and a third of this area is arable land. Wheat and maize are the chief cereals and are grown in the Transylvanian Basin, Walachia, the western lowlands and Moldavia. Other crops include sunflowers and sugar-beet in Walachia and the west; barley, oats and potatoes in the Transylvanian Basin, hemp near Oradea and tobacco in Walachia. Terraces in the Carpathian foothills support orchards and vineyards. Moldavia is also a major wine-producing area. There is intensive market gardening near large cities such as Bucharest and Timisoara. Livestock is reared in the Carpathians and Dobruja and on the Danube marshlands. Crop production has been increased by drainage in the Danube lands and by irrigation in the south-east. Agriculture is 90% collectivized.

Forestry and fishing

Forests, covering 27% of the country, consist mainly of beech, spruce and fir. Commercial exploitation is centred on the Carpathians and major processing plants (producing timber, plywood and furniture) are sited at Blaj, Pitesti, Dej, Tirgu-Jiu, Oradea, Caransebes and at the ports of Braila and Constanta. Fish is an important food source: trout predominate in mountain streams, carp in larger rivers. Sturgeon are caught in the Danube delta and caviar (from the roe or eggs) forms a valuable export.

Industry

Romania is the most industrialized country in South-East Europe. The iron and steel industry is well established: some plants, like those at Resita and Hunedoara, use domestic ore and coal, while others, on the lower Danube, rely on Russian imports. 60% of steel produced comes from Romania's biggest iron and steel combine at Galati. Steel is the basis of an engineering industry which accounts for 30% of industrial output and 25% of total exports. Products range from oil refinery equipment and ships to tractors and lathes. The chemical industry, using local oil, gas, coal and salt, has expanded dramatically and now provides 8% of exports; reeds from the Danube delta supply the Braila cellulose plant. Since the 1960s consumer industry has developed and some goods—shoes and clothing—are exported.

Tourism

Some four million foreigners visit Romania annually, making tourism an important sector of the economy. The principal tourist regions are the Black Sea coast with modern resorts such as Mamaia and Eforie; the Carpathians, equally popular in summer and winter; Poiana Brasnov, the main ski resort; northern Moldavia, famous for 15th-century monasteries with exterior frescoes; and the Danube delta, the home of over 300 bird species and the only place in Europe where pelicans breed.

Transport

In the Carpathians, numerous valleys and depressions facilitate communication between the Transylvanian Basin and the lowlands, and 12 railway lines and over 30 trunk roads cross the mountains. Although the roads, totalling 76,304 km are being modernized, the 10,370 km rail network (used for long-distance freight) is still the most important feature of Romania's transport system. The Danube is a major highway but winter shipping is hampered by ice. Galati, Braila, Giurgiu and Turnu-Severin are the main river ports. Cross-Danube ferry services are important as there are only three bridges: at Giurgiu Giurgeni and Cernavoda (rail). The state airline, TAROM, links 17 cities and operates international flights from Bucharest and Constanta.

Cities

Bucharest, on the Dimbovita, was founded in 1459 and became the national capital four centuries later. Romania's urban population doubled between the 1950s and mid-1970s and besides Bucharest there are 13 other towns with over 100,000 inhabitants. Among these are Cluj (274,000) a 2,000-year-old cultural and manufacturing centre; Timisoara (281,000), a commercial town on the Bega canal; Iasi (262,000) in Moldavia and industrial Brasov (299,000). Galati (253,000), located at the confluence of the Danube, Siret and Prut, is noted for its steel and shipbuilding industries.

Bulgaria

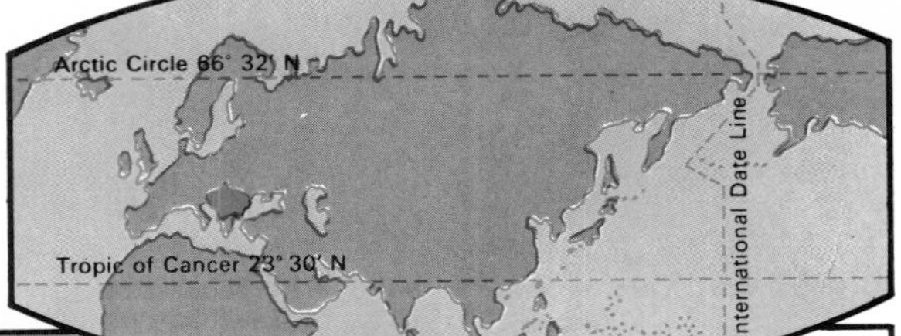

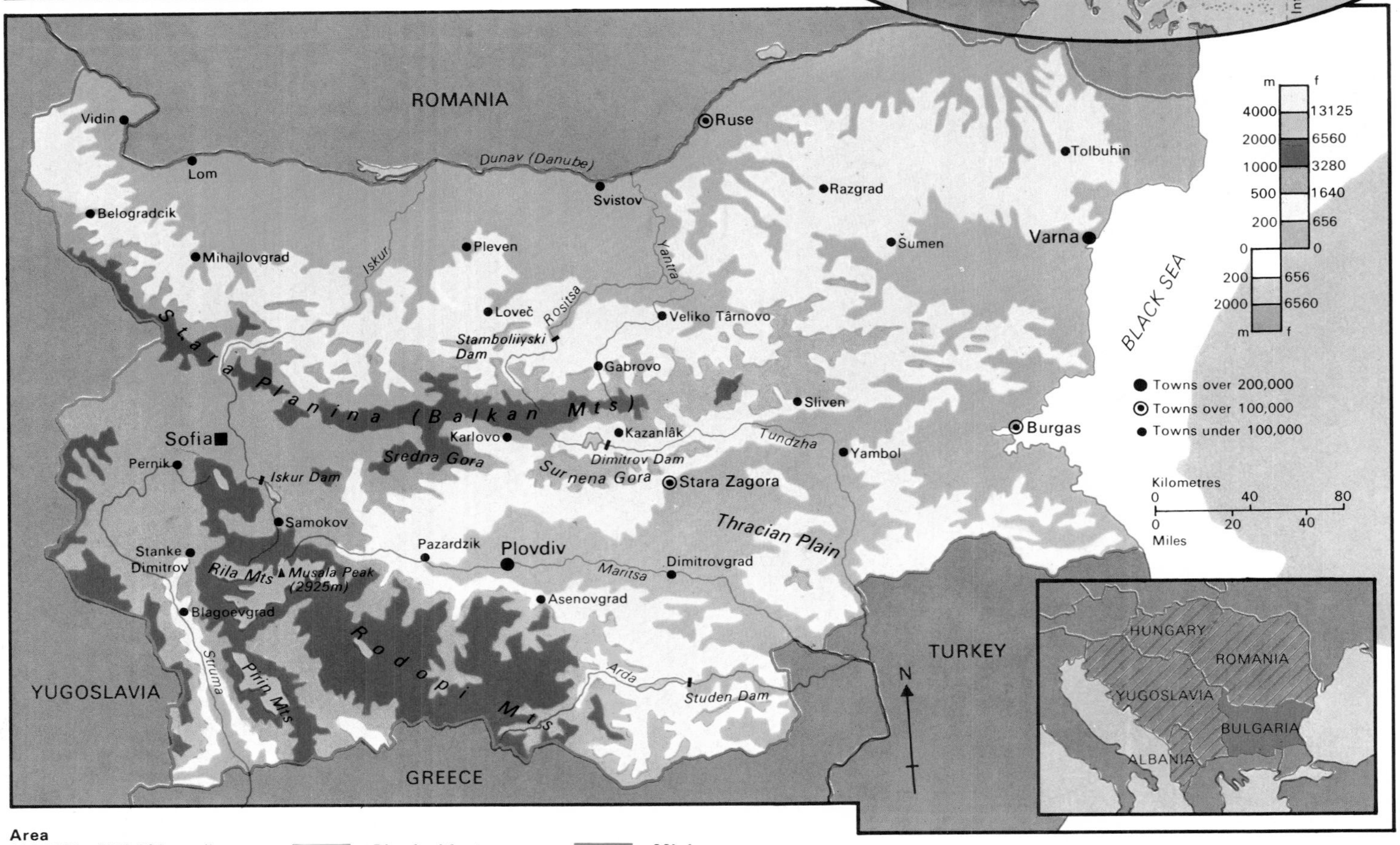

Area
110,912 km²/42,823 sq miles
Location
41°15′—44°10′N
22°20′—28°25′E
Population
8,890,000 (1981)
Population density
80 per km²/208 per sq mile
Capital and largest city
Sofia: 1,057,000 (1980)
Language
Bulgarian
Major imports
fuel, machinery and transport equipment, chemicals
Major exports
food products, tobacco, metals textiles, rolling stock
Currency
lev (1 lev = 100 stotinki)
6,500 million US dollars
Gross National Product
not available
Status
independent republic

Cities
Sofia, on the banks of the Iskur at the foot of the Rodopi mountains, is Bulgaria's cultural, commercial and industrial centre. Plovdiv (307,000), the second largest town, is on the Maritsa. Its food-processing and textile industries are based on the rich agriculture of the Thracian plain. The port and resort of Varna (258,000) has become industrialized, with shipbuilding, oil-refining and petro-chemicals. Ruse (173,000) the leading Danube port, has a bridge link with the Romanian town of Giurgiu. Bulgaria's main port, Burgas (168,000), is also a leading tourist centre. Stara Zagora (136,000), of Roman origin, is famous for its archaeological and architectural treasures.

Physical features
Mountainous Bulgaria divides into a series of east-west zones. In the north lies a platform some 100 m high which ends in a steep cliff fall to the Danube. Southwards, the Danubian platform rises gently to the Balkan Mountains (Stara Planina), which have an average height of 870 m. This massif is separated from a parallel and more southerly range—the Sredna Gora—by a series of depressions extending from Sofia in the east to Sliven in the west. South of the Sredna Gora is the Thracian plain—a broad alluvial lowland drained by the Maritsa. South-west Bulgaria is dominated by the majestic Rodopi mountains which rise to 2,925 m in Musala Peak, the highest point in the Balkan Peninsula. The main rivers are the Danube, Maritsa, Iskur, Struma, Arda, Tundzha and Yantra.

Climate
Bulgaria has a temperate continental climate with hot summers and cold winters, Pleven averaging —4°C in January, 23°C in July. There are distinct regional differences. The Danubian platform, with summer rainfall, is subject to seasonal extremes of heat and cold brought about by north-easterly winds from Russia. The southern border has a Mediterranean climate with winter rain and summer drought. The central region is transitional between these two climatic types, while the Black Sea coast has mild winters but cooler summers.

Mining
Bulgaria has few energy minerals and is largely dependent on Russian imports for supplies of high-grade coal, oil and gas. Small quantities of oil and natural gas are produced at Dolni Dabnik Tjulenovo and off-shore near Varna. There are, however, major lignite deposits at Pernik and Stara Zagora. Lead and zinc are mined in the eastern Rodopi range and in the western Balkan mountains; copper comes from the western Balkans and near Burgas; manganese is worked in the Varna area and north of Sofia; iron ore is extracted near Sofia, in the Maritsa basin and at Belogradcik.

Transport
With the growth of industry the Bulgarian transport system has been modernized. Roads, covering a total of 30,800 km, have developed at the expense of rail and now account for 80% of freight and passengers carried. The 6,000 km rail network is centred on Sofia. Although the increase in road traffic has caused inland shipping to decline, the Danube is still important. Ruse is the leading river port, followed by Lom, Vidin and Svistov. Burgas, the main seaport, handles a large share of Bulgarian exports; it also has an oil refinery. Varna, the second Black Sea port, is equipped with modern shipyards. The state airline, Balkan, links 14 cities and operates international flights from Sofia, Varna and Burgas.

Agriculture
With almost 50% of the land used for arable farming, Bulgaria ranks as South-East Europe's leading agricultural state. The main cereals, grown on the Danube platform and in the Sofia basin, are wheat, maize and barley. Farming is most intensive on the fertile, alluvial soils of the Thracian plain, where the emphasis is on fruit and industrial crops such as cotton, tobacco, sunflowers and sugar-beet. The Black Sea coast, the lower slopes of the Stara Planina and river valleys in the south-west are also fruit-growing areas; plums are a Bulgarian speciality. Market gardening is important in the Maritsa and Sofia basins and on the coastal lowlands. Petals from the world's largest rose gardens near Kazanluk are used to make the famous Bulgarian attar of roses, a perfume base. Livestock—cattle, sheep, pigs and poultry—is widespread. 90% of farmland is collectivized.

Forestry and fishing
Forests cover a third of Bulgaria and are largely concentrated in highland regions. Deciduous trees predominate on the plains and lower slopes: chestnut and walnut on the Thracian plain and oak and beech in the Balkan mountains. The higher slopes of the Rodopi range are forested with conifers. Fishing is mainly in the Black Sea, but some boats go out to the Mediterranean.

Energy
Thermal stations, predominantly fired by lignite, produce 90% of Bulgaria's electricity. The remaining 10% is provided by about 100 hydro-electric installations. A new 800,000 kw nuclear power station will generate a quarter of the country's requirements. Other nuclear and hydro plants are under construction.

Industry
Since the Communist take-over of 1947, the Bulgarian economy has been transformed. Industry has has been developed round local raw materials: iron ore (steel), lignite and oil (chemicals), ores (metallurgy), cotton (textiles), timber (wood and paper), agricultural produce (food-processing). Food-processing is the main industry, accounting for 25% of industrial output; products exported include jam, canned fruit and sugar. Engineering is next in importance, followed by chemicals and metallurgy. The country's two steelworks at Pernik and Kremikovci form part of the major industrial zone centred on Sofia-Pernik. The region—producing 25% of industrial output—also contains important engineering, chemical and textile plants. Other leading industrial centres are Plovdiv, Dimitrovgrad, Stara Zagora, Varna and Burgas. The tourist industry based on the Black Sea coast, is also expanding at several modern resorts.

Albania

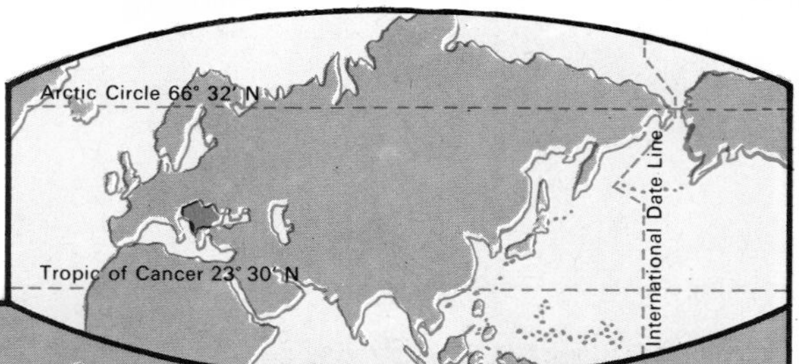

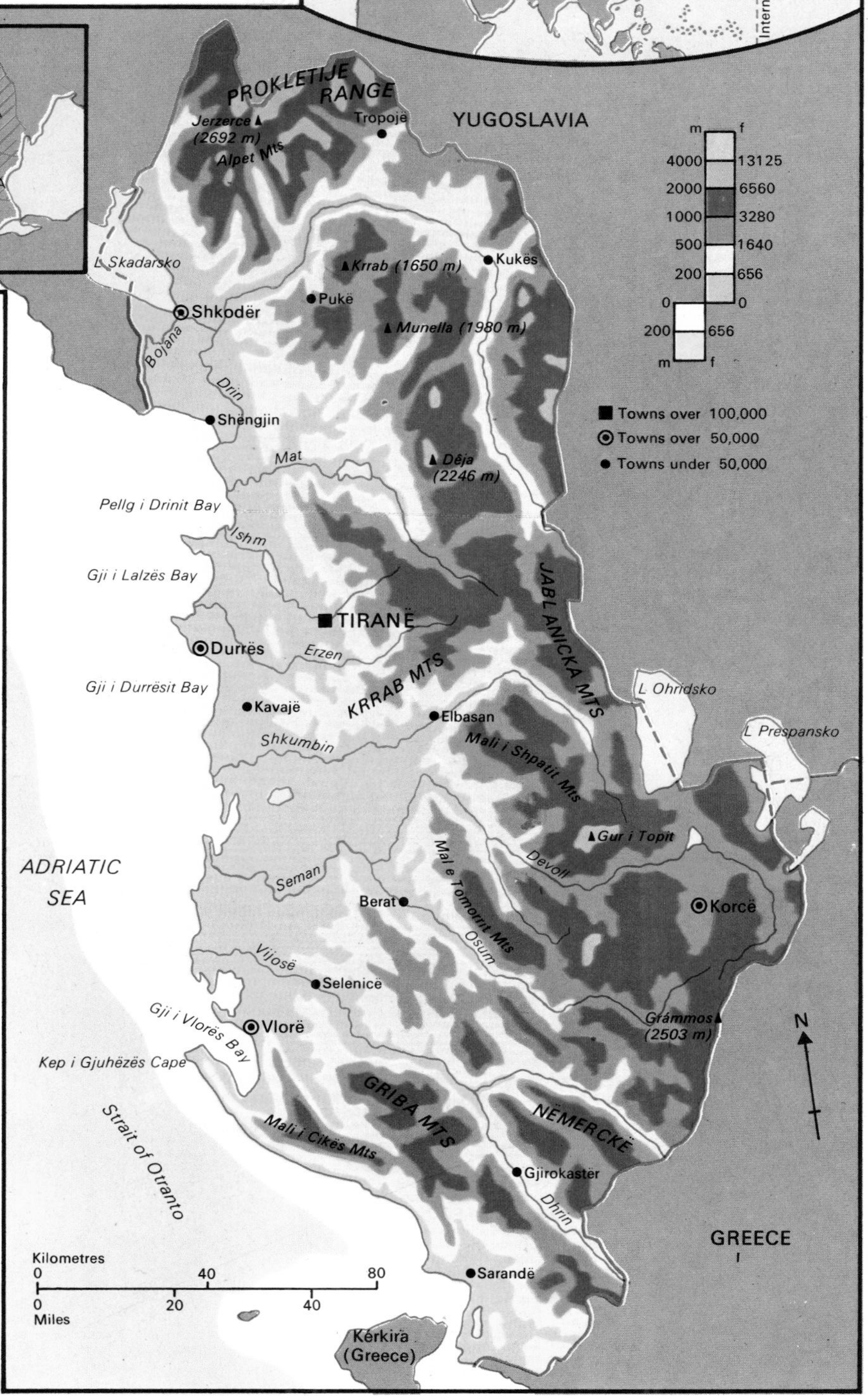

Area
28,748 km²/11,100 sq miles
Location;
39°40′—42°40′ N
19°15′—21°5′ E
Population
2,795,000 (1981)
Population density
97 per km²/252 per sq mile
Capital and largest city
Tiranë (Tirana): 200,000 (1980)
Language
Albanian
Major imports
iron and steel, fuels, machinery, transport equipment, chemicals
Major exports
fruit and vegetables, wine, tobacco, copper products, wood, crude oil, bitumen, chrome ore
Currency
lek (1 lek = 100 quintars)
Gross National Product
not available
Status
independent republic

Physical features

Albania, on the west coast of the Balkan peninsula, is eastern Europe's smallest country, in both area and population. Highlands, covering the interior and extending to the coast in the south, account for 70% of the territory. In the northeast, the limestone Prokletije rise to over 2,500 m; the mountains, dissected by steep gorges and often impenetrable, continue southwards and include the Korab, Jablanica, Griba and Nëmerckë ranges. Lowland Albania is confined to the north and central coast. In the north, the coastal strip is narrow, but further south it widens into a triangular plain between Durrës, Elbasan and Vlorë. This plain is largely composed of fertile alluvium interspersed with swampy tracts and low scrub-covered hills. The main rivers, notably the Drin, Mat, Shkumbin, Seman and Vijosë, are swollen in winter and spring with rain and meltwater, but almost dry in summer. In its upper course, the Drin flows from south to north, draining Lake Ohridsko; to the south-east is another lake, Prespansko.

Climate

Coastal Albania has a Mediterranean climate with hot dry summers and mild, wet winters; in January, the average temperature is 8°C and in July, 25°C. Inland, altitude causes a decrease in temperature and an increase in rainfall; in the northeast, January averages −1°C and July, 21°C. Precipitation, occurring mostly in winter, ranges from 109 cm a year at Vlorë to over 260 cm in the Prokletije.

Flora and fauna

Characteristic Mediterranean scrub, or maquis, predominates on the coastal lowlands. The mountainous interior is forested: oak grows on the lower slopes and is succeeded by mixed forest, mainly composed of elm and beech; pine is the principal species in higher zones. In all, woodland covers 47% of Albania. Wild animals—mainly wolves, boars and deer—are found in remote forest and mountain areas.

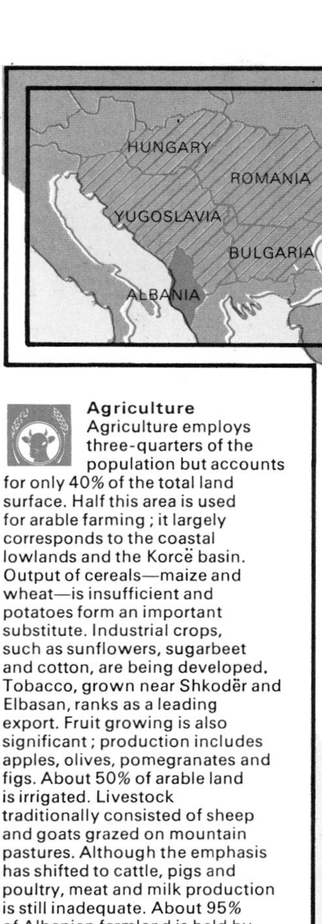

Agriculture

Agriculture employs three-quarters of the population but accounts for only 40% of the total land surface. Half this area is used for arable farming; it largely corresponds to the coastal lowlands and the Korcë basin. Output of cereals—maize and wheat—is insufficient and potatoes form an important substitute. Industrial crops, such as sunflowers, sugarbeet and cotton, are being developed. Tobacco, grown near Shkodër and Elbasan, ranks as a leading export. Fruit growing is also significant; production includes apples, olives, pomegranates and figs. About 50% of arable land is irrigated. Livestock traditionally consisted of sheep and goats grazed on mountain pastures. Although the emphasis has shifted to cattle, pigs and poultry, meat and milk production is still inadequate. About 95% of Albanian farmland is held by state farms and co-operatives.

Mining

Although Albania has a wide range of minerals, commercial exploitation is a recent development. Chromium and copper are the two most important minerals and are both found in the north: chromium near Tropojë, copper near Pukë and Kukës. Bitumen is extracted at Selenicë and salt mined near Vlorë. Deposits of iron, nickel, lead, zinc, bauxite and sulphur are also worked. Low-grade coal is mined near Tiranë but bituminous coal is lacking. The main oilfield, at Kucovë, has a pipeline link to Vlorë; natural gas is also produced. The main mineral exports are chromium, copper and iron-nickel.

Industry

Industry, developed with Russian and later Chinese aid, is based on domestic raw materials. Food-processing is important and includes flour-milling, olive-pressing, sugar-milling, tobacco-processing and vegetable-canning. The chemical industry, centred on oil and gas, and metallurgy, using chromium, copper, iron and nickel, are expanding. The steelworks at Elbasan is supplied by Albanian iron ore but for coal is dependent on imports. Timber-processing is also important and wood is exported. Engineering works have been established but, as yet, the range of products is limited. Heavy industry has developed at the expense of light manufacturing, but textile, clothing and shoe production is increasing. Albanian industry, which is totally nationalized, is concentrated on the Adriatic coastal plain; Tiranë is the chief manufacturing centre.

Energy

Power production has been a major priority of the Communist government and by 1971 every Albanian village had been supplied with electricity. The fast-flowing streams, characteristic of the mountainous interior (particularly in the north and south), are suitable for generating power and several hydro-electric installations have been built; others are under construction. Thermal stations are fired by coal and natural gas. A plant with a capacity of 400 MW, under construction in 1976, was to be the largest in the country.

Transport

The Communist government has developed transport, since the previously inadequate system hindered economic expansion. Roads now serve agricultural regions, industrial centres, mining zones and forested areas. The network is 3,100 km long, but many northern mountain districts remain inaccessible to motor traffic. Railways, totalling 150 km and centred on Durrës and Vlorë, have been established since 1947. Durrës is the main port, followed by Vlorë, Sarandë and Shëngjin. The country's only airport is near Tiran.

Cities

Tiranë, originally a sixth-century fortress, became the capital in 1920. About 32 km inland, on the Ishm river, the city is at the heart of an agricultural region where maize, olives and vines are grown. Under the Communists, who came to power in 1945, Tiranë has become increasingly industrialized. It is linked by rail to Durrës, the principal port. The country's other main industrial towns are also former agricultural centres. They include Shkodër (63,000), Durrës (61,000), Vlorë (58,000), Korcë (51,000) and Elbasan (51,000).

Greece

Fishing
Greece, with its long coastline and numerous islands, has a well-established fishing industry and fish is an important item in the national diet. The eastern Mediterranean, however, has limited fish stocks (except for mullet, squid, sardines and tunny) and, as a result, Atlantic fishing is increasing in significance.

Mining and energy
The mountains contain a wide range of minerals including bauxite, iron ore, magnesite, copper, chromite, lead-zinc, sulphur and barite, but in most cases reserves are limited. Bauxite is the most notable exception: some 2 million tonnes are mined yearly, mostly near Elevsís, making Greece one of Europe's main bauxite producers. The island of Náxos is the world's chief supplier of emery and Greek marble is world-famous. With lignite the only energy mineral found in significant quantities, Greece is largely dependent on imported fuels; 75% is used for electricity production. Hydro-electric power currently generating 30% of electricity, is being developed in the Pindhos mountains.

Cities
Athínai, encircled by mountains, is situated 8 km inland. The heart of the city is the Acropolis with world-famous monuments such as the Parthenon—the shrine of the goddess Athena. On becoming the capital of modern Greece in 1833, Athínai expanded rapidly. It has now merged with the port of Piraievs and forms the country's main industrial region inhabited by a third of the Greek population. The second largest city, Thessaloníki (800,000), is the only major industrial centre outside Athínai.

Area
131,944 km²/50,943 sq miles
Location
34°50′—41°45′ N
19°20′—28°15′ E
Population
9,707,000 (1981)
Population density
74 per km²/191 per sq mile
Capital and largest city
Athens: 3,300,000 (1981)
Language
Greek
Major imports
machinery, transport equipment, iron, steel, petroleum, meat, dairy products, pharmaceuticals and textiles
Major exports
tobacco, fresh and processed fruit and vegetables, olive oil, aluminium, cotton, minerals and handicrafts
Currency
drachma (1 drachma = 100 lepta)
Gross National Product
42,890 million US dollars (1981)
Status
republic

Climate
Most of Greece has a Mediterranean climate with warm wet winters and hot dry summers—especially the Pelopónnisos and the islands. In Athens (Athínai), January temperatures average 14°C, in July 27°C. Continental extremes in temperatures prevail in Thrace (Thraki) and Mecodonia (Makedhonia). Thessaloníki averages 6°C in January, 29°C in July. Throughout the country, rainfall occurs in winter and is heaviest west of the Pindhos mountains: Corfu (Kérkira) receives 130 cm of rain a year while Athínai receives only 30 cm per year.

Transport
The mountainous interior has hindered development of land transport and both road and rail networks are poor although they are being modernized. Roads, totalling 36,000 km, are 50% unpaved. New highways link Athínai to Thessaloníki and to Igoumenitsa via Patrai. Greece is a seafaring nation; shipping is the main foreign-currency earner and the merchant fleet is one of the world's largest. Piraeus (Piraievs), near Athínai, is the chief port, followed by Thessaloníki and Pátrai. There are regular steamer services to the islands. The privately owned Olympic Airways operates domestic and international flights.

Tourism
The expanding tourist industry, catering for over 3 million visitors a year, is a major source of income. The country's main assets are its climate, its archeological wealth and its many beaches (no point is more than 130 km from the sea). Popular historical sites include Mycenae, Olympia and the Acropolis (which means 'city at the top') in Athínai.

Agriculture
Agriculture is still basic to the Greek economy: it employs half of the population and provides over 50% of exports. Rough pastures cover 40% of the country and arable land (mostly in Thessalía and Makedhonia) less than 30%. Wheat is the chief cereal and sufficient is grown for some to be exported. Greece is a leading exporter of tobacco, cultivated mainly in Makedhonia, Thraki and Thessalía. Cotton is also a valuable lowland crop; others include sugarbeet and rice. Vines are particularly important in the Pelopónnisos and on the islands and the chief products are currants, raisins and sultanas—Greece is a major supplier of dried fruits. The principal tree fruit is the olive and Greece is the world's third largest producer of olive oil. Citrus production is also significant with oranges, lemons and mandarines exported. Apples, peaches, apricots and vegetables are also cultivated. Farm output is being increased by reclamation and irrigation schemes and by the use of fertilizers. Livestock consists largely of sheep and goats.

Industry
Traditionally, Greek industry is concerned with processing agricultural produce (wheat, tobacco, grapes, olives, tomatoes and so on) but in the last decade there has been considerable growth in the chemical, textile and metallurgical sectors. Industrial development is still in its early stages but recently completed projects include a giant refinery and petro-chemical complex at Diavata, iron and steelworks at Elevsís, an aluminium smelter near Delphi., shipyards at Elevsís and an automobile plant at Pátrai. Most industry is concentrated in the Athínai-Piraievs and Thessaloníki conurbations, but manufacturing is being established in other centres such as Iráklion (Kríti), Lárimna, Vólos, Ptolemaïs and Kavalla. With the growing tourist industry, handicrafts have increased in significance and typical products range from lace, carved knives and icons to alabaster ware, hand-woven carpets and pottery.

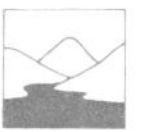

Physical features
Greece occupies the southern extremity of the mountainous Balkan peninsula. The barren limestone Pindhos chain, running northwest-southeast and rising to 2,500 m, constitutes the principal mountain axis. Other ranges run from this highland spine to the coast where they project as rocky promontories, then continue as islands. Lowlands consist of mountain-enclosed areas such as the plain of Thessaloníki and the Thessalía basin. The range separating these two major lowlands contains Greece's highest peak, Olympus (Ólimbos: 2,917 m). In the south lies the Pelopónnisos, a rugged peninsula joined to the mainland by the isthmus of Corinth. Kriti (8,331 km²) is the largest of the Greek islands and an extension of the Pelopónnisos ranges. Greece has almost 500 islands accounting for 20% of its area. There are relatively few rivers as the limestone causes water to flow underground. The longest river is the Aliákmon (256 km).

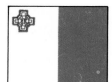

Cyprus and Malta

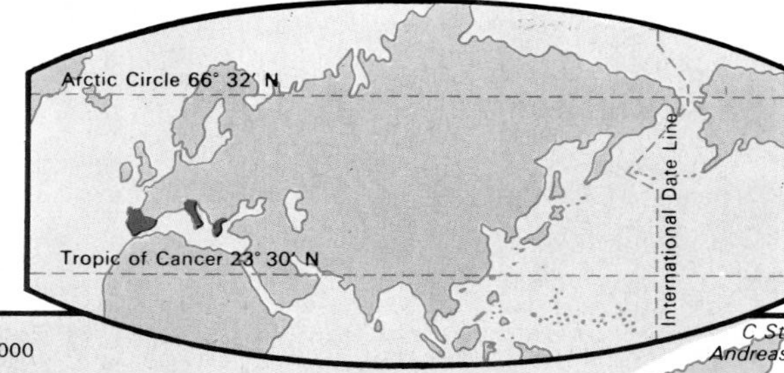

Cyprus
Area
9,251 km²/3,572 sq miles
Location
34°33' –35°41' N
32°17' –34°35' E
Population
623,000 (1973)
Population density
67 per km²/174 per sq mile
Capital and largest city
Nicosia: 121,000 (1982)
Languages
Greek and Turkish
Major imports
food, textiles, fuels, machinery, transport equipment
Major exports
citrus, potatoes, copper products, wine, asbestos, iron pyrites
Currency
pound (1 pound = 1,000 mils)
Gross National Product
2,330 million US dollars (1981)
Status
independent republic

Cyprus

The populations quoted are pre-1974 figures. Since the Turkish invasion of summer 1974 an estimated 200,000 Greek Cypriots have been displaced from and 30,000 mainland Turks imported to the northerly 40% of the island now occupied by the Turkish army.

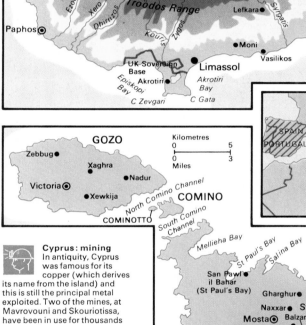

● Towns over 50,000
◉ Towns over 10,000
• Towns under 10,000

Kilometres 0 25 50
Miles 0 15 30

m 2000 1000 500 200 0 200 — f 6560 3280 1640 656 0 656

MEDITERRANEAN SEA

Cyprus: the land

Cyprus, the third largest island in the Mediterranean, has a maximum length of 240 km and a maximum width of 96 km. The island consists of two mountain systems separated by a central plain, the Mesaöria. The Kyrenia range, rising to 1,000 m, runs along the north coast and the Troödos massif covers the south-west and includes the island's highest peak, Mt Olympus (1,953 m). The wide Mesaöria lowland has fertile soils. Summers are hot and dry and winters wet and mild. Nicosia averages 29°C in July, 9°C in January. Annual rainfall ranges from 40 cm on the plain to over 100 cm in the mountainous districts.

Cyprus: agriculture

Agriculture, employing 35% of the total workforce, is the basis of the Cypriot economy and provides almost 80% of total exports. About half the island is farmed and most arable land lies in the Mesaöria plain. Here, the chief crops are wheat, barley, potatoes, carrots, vegetables, melons, tobacco, almonds, carobs and olives. The major cash crop is citrus, grown in coastal areas often under irrigation. About 80% of citrus production (oranges, mandarins, lemons, grapefruit) is exported, accounting for 40% of exports. In the southern mountains, orchards and vineyards cover the terraced hillsides; Paphos and Limassol are both noted for their wines. Livestock consists mainly of sheep and goats grazed on upland pastures. Forests of pine and cypress cover the higher mountain slopes and supply 30% of the island's timber needs.

Cyprus: industry

Cypriot industry is traditionally based on agricultural produce: flour-milling, brewing, fruit and vegetable canning, wine-making, distilling, biscuit manufacture, tobacco processing and so on. Since independence, other light industries have been developed including clothing, shoes, carpets, cement, bricks, furniture, animal feeds and pharmaceuticals. Tourism is growing in importance with over half a million people visiting Cyprus annually.

GOZO — COMINO — MALTA

Kilometres 0 5
Miles 0 3

Malta

● Towns over 10,000
◉ Towns over 5,000
• Towns under 5,000

Cyprus: mining

In antiquity, Cyprus was famous for its copper (which derives its name from the island) and this is still the principal metal exploited. Two of the mines, at Mavrovouni and Skouriotissa, have been in use for thousands of years. There are also important deposits of asbestos, iron pyrites and chromite, mostly in the Troödos range. Minerals, handled by the ports of Limassol, Vasilikos, Limni, Xeros and Karavostasi, account for 20% of total exports.

Cyprus: Nicosia

Nicosia, some 5,000 years old, is situated on the Pedieos river in the Mesaöria plain. The city's light industry includes food-processing, cigarette manufacture, clothing and footwear. The capital has good road links with the port of Famagusta.

Cyprus: transport

The island's 9,200 km road network is 50% unsurfaced and there are no railways. Up to 1974, Nicosia was the only civil airport but this has since been closed. Larnaca is now being developed for international flights. The main port of Famagusta (43,000) is also closed. Other ports include Limassol (54,000), Larnaca (21,000), Paphos (10,000) and Kyrenia (4,000). Oil is discharged at Larnaca and, in smaller quantities, at Akrotiri, Moni and Vasilikos.

Malta: agriculture

Agriculture employs 16% of the workforce but two thirds of these also have part-time jobs in industry. Farmland, accounting for 30% of the country, is located on the plain and in the valleys which are intensively terraced. The chief crops are wheat, vegetables and fruit, including grapes and wine. Production is mostly consumed locally but potatoes, onions, tomatoes and flowers are exported. Livestock consists mainly of sheep, goats and pigs; meat and dairy products are imported. The Maltese fishing fleet operates off the coast with the bulk of the catch landed between May and November.

Malta: industry

The shipyard, formerly the British naval base, is a vital source of income. The yard, employing 5% of the workforce, undertakes repairs, new building and tanker cleaning. Processing agricultural produce ranks next in importance: products include bacon, margarine, tomato purée, potato crisps, frozen peas, wine and cigars. Other established manufactures are textiles, clothing and footwear. New industries include light engineering (machine tools and electrical), car assembly and chemicals. With the development of tourism, traditional crafts such as jewellery, lace and filigree work have been encouraged.

Malta
Area
316 km²/122 sq miles
Location
35°48'–36° N
14°10'–14°35' E
Population
364,000 (1981)
Population density
1,152 per km²/2,984 per sq mile
Capital
Valletta: 14,000 (1981)
Largest city
Sliema: 22,000 (1981)
Languages
Maltese and English
Major imports
machinery, transport equipment, foodstuffs, fuels, metals, metal products, textiles
Major exports
clothing, fabrics, rubber and plastic goods, electrical apparatus, potatoes
Currency
pound (= 100 cents = 1,000 mils)
Gross National Product
1,310 million US dollars (1981)
Status
independent republic

Malta: the land

Situated in the middle of the Mediterranean, the Maltese archipelago comprises Malta (246 km²), Gozo (67 km²), Comino (2 km²) and two uninhabited islets, Cominotto and Filfla. The main island, Malta, is a maximum 27 km long and 14 km wide and consists of a limestone block which has been tilted eastwards resulting in 250 m high cliffs on the west coast and drowned valleys in the east. The northern part of the island is characterized by east-west ridges and alluvial valleys; a clay-covered plain lies to the south. There are no rivers or mountains. The climate is Mediterranean with mild winters (14°C) and hot summers (23°C) tempered by sea breezes. Some 50 cm of rain falls annually, mostly between September and April.

Malta: Valletta

In the 16th century, Malta was ceded to the Knights of St John who subsequently built a new capital and named it after the Grand Master of the Order, Jean de la Valette. Valletta stands on a rocky promontory between two harbours: Marsamxett and Grand Harbour. Grand Harbour is the country's main port and handles nearly all domestic and transit trade. The capital has bus links to all parts of the island; there are no railways. The international airport is Luqa (6 km southwest).

Spain

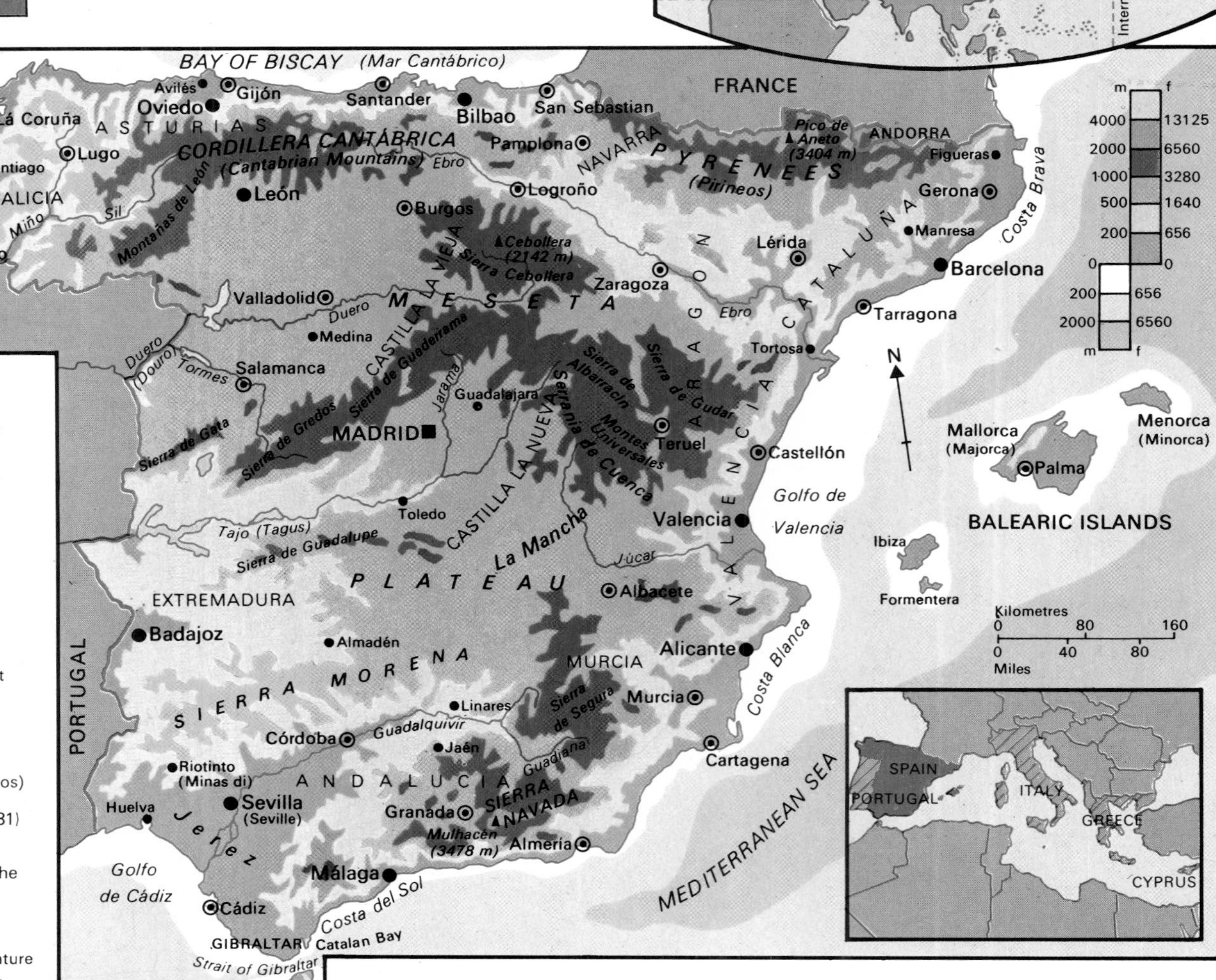

Area
510,000 km²/197,000 sq miles
Location
36°—43°47′ N
9°20′ W—4°20′ E
Population
37,973,000 (1981)
Population density
74 per km²/193 per sq mile
Capital and largest city
Madrid: 3,520,000 (1978)
Language
Spanish
Major imports
machinery, fuels, chemicals, foodstuffs, transport equipment
Major exports
citrus and other fruits, olive oil, vegetables, fish, wine, cotton textiles, minerals, ships
Currency
peseta (1 peseta = 100 centimos)
Gross National Product
214,300 million US dollars (1981)
Status
Monarchy
The Canaries are included in the statistics but not in the text.

Physical features

Spain's dominant feature is the central Meseta, a vast plateau some 600 m high, which is crossed by a series of east-west ranges (the Gata, Gredos and Guaderrama mountains). The Meseta is bounded by the Cantabrian mountains in the north, the Serrania de Cuenca in the east and by the Sierra Morena in the south. West of the Cantabrian chain is Galicia, a region of green hills and *rias* (drowned river valleys). The Cuenca ranges are separated from the Pyrenees by the broad basin of the river Ebro, while in the south another great depression (drained by the Guadalquivir) lies between the Sierra Morena and the Sierra Navada which contains the country's highest peak, Mulhacén (3,478 m). The Meseta tilts slightly towards Portugal so that its main rivers, the Duero, Tajo (Tagus) and Guadiana, drain westwards. Spain's 4,000 km coastline is mostly cliffed and rocky with long sandy beaches. The Balearic islands (5,014 km²) lie off the east coast.

Climate

The northwest coast is mild and wet: in Lá Coruña, January averages 9°C, July 18°C. Rainfall, in all seasons, is over 100 cm. The mediterranean coast is warmer and drier: Valencia has 10°C in January, 24°C in July and 25 cm of rain, mostly in winter. The interior has a continental climate: Madrid records 4°C in January, 26°C in July with 40 cm of rain falling mostly in spring and autumn.

Mining and energy

There are two main mining areas. In the north, the Cantabrians contain coal and high-quality iron ore. In the south, the Sierras Morena and Nevada yield mercury (Almadén), copper pyrites (Riotinto), lead, zinc, sulphur and manganese. Spain is the world's leading producer of mercury and third producer of pyrites. Other deposits include tungsten and tin in the extreme northwest, potash and bauxite in the northeast and uranium in the northeast and near Jaén. Minerals are exported via Bilbao and Huelva. In contrast, Spain has to import fuels (coal and petroleum) as domestic supplies are inadequate. About 50% of electricity is generated by hydro-electric plants, mostly in the northeast. Nuclear power is being developed.

Transport

Madrid is the hub of both road (150,000 km) and rail (18,000 km) networks. Roads are 50% unsurfaced and still used by mules and donkeys in many rural areas. Buses cover the country and carry more passengers than trains. Spain has some 200 ports of which the main ones are Bilbao, Barcelona, Cartagena and Cádiz. There are 33 cities with airports, mostly in tourist areas. Iberia is the national airline.

Cities

Madrid, at the heart of Spain, is primarily administrative and it is Barcelona (1,810,000) which acts as the country's industrial and commercial capital. Although industrialized, Valencia (713,000), Sevilla (589,000) and Zaragoza (547,000) are all centred on important agricultural regions.

Agriculture

Low rainfall and poor soils predominate, but Spain is primarily agricultural. The Meseta is the main cereal region: wheat is in the lead, followed by barley, oats and rye. Maize is grown in the northwest and rice, under irrigation, in the Ebro delta and Valencia. Potatoes, sugarbeet and vegetables are also important. The most fertile zone is the irrigated Mediterranean coast. Citrus, a major export, is the chief fruit in the Valencia area. Other tree crops include apples and pears in the northwest; dates figs and almonds in the south and Balearics; peaches and apricots in the southeast; olives in Andalucia. Spain is the world's leading producer of olives and olive oil and also ranks as the third wine-producing country. Vines are cultivated in the upper Ebro valley, La Mancha, the Mediterranean coastlands and Jerez (sherry). Livestock consists of cattle in the northwest and sheep and goats on the Meseta plateau and the Balearic islands.

Forests and fishing

Most of Spain was once forested but now only mountain areas are wooded and timber imports are necessary. There are, however, extensive cork oak forests in the southwest and Spain is second only to Portugal in cork production. Fishing is widespread but is most important on the Atlantic coasts where the chief centres are Vigo and Lá Coruña. The catch, consisting mainly of sardine and anchovy, is Europe's second largest (after Norway). Galician boats fish cod in the Atlantic waters off Newfoundland.

Industry

Although still not as advanced as other European countries, Spain is rapidly becoming industrialized. Most industry is concentrated in the north and northeast. The north accounts for 80% of steel production: major centres include Avilés (60% of the country's steel output), Gijón, Santander and Bilbao. Engineering (in particular, ship-building) is also important in the north. Barcelona and surrounding Cataluña is noted for textiles (supplying 80% of total production), chemicals and vehicle assembly. A third industrial zone with metallurgical, chemical and ceramic works is growing round Madrid. The food-processing industry includes flour-milling on the Meseta, olive-oil refining in Andalucia and fish-canning in Galicia.

Tourism

Tourism accounts for 75% of foreign currency earnings and ranks as Spain's leading export industry. The tourist boom is also benefitting other industries such as building, handicrafts and transport. Most of the 35 million foreigners who visit Spain each year are attracted to the Mediterranean coasts, in particular the Costa del Sol, the Costa Brava and the Balearic islands of Mallorca and Ibiza.

Gibraltar

Gibraltar, 6 km² in area, is a narrow peninsula jutting out from the southernmost tip of Spain into the Mediterranean. The peninsula consists of a limestone block north-south for almost 5 km; in the north it is over 400 m high but slopes down to 30 m at Europa Point. The climate is mild with average temperatures of 15°C in January and 27°C in August. Rain (80 cm a year) falls in winter. Most of the 29,000 inhabitants live in Gibraltar City, situated on the wet side; Catalan Bay, a village on the east side, is the only other settlement. Rocky, infertile Gibraltar has no agriculture, little livestock and no mineral resources. In addition to a small ship-repair yard there is some light industry such as clothing manufacture, beer bottling and watch assembly, but the economy is largely dependent on the British naval base and tourism.

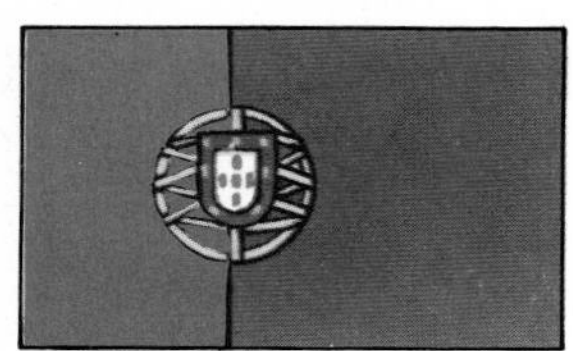

Portugal

Area
88,500 km²/34,170 sq miles
Location
37°—42°15′ N
6°20′—9°30′ W
Population
9,826,000 (1981)
Population density
111 per km²/288 per sq mile
Capital and largest city
Lisbon: 812,000 (1981)
Language
Portuguese
Major imports
vehicles, foodstuffs, fuels, iron and steel, textile fibres
Major exports
wine, cork, wood and wood products, sardines, cotton textiles, minerals, fruit
Currency
escudo (1 escudo = 100 centavos)
Gross National Product
24,750 million US dollars (1981)
Status
independent republic
This information does not include Madeira and the Azores, both part of Portugal.

Physical features
Portugal, a rectangular country about 560 km long and 220 km wide, consists of the western margin of the Spanish Meseta and an extensive coastal plain. Highland Portugal lies north of the river Tejo (Tagus) and is characterized by mountains, plateaux and the deep narrow valleys of the Douro and its tributaries. In the centre, the Serra da Estrêla rises to 1,993 m, the country's highest point. Southern Portugal consists of the flat Alentejo plain, the wide alluvial valleys of the rivers Tejo and Sado, and, in the extreme south, the Serra do Caldeirão. The coast, 830 km long, is low and sandy and along the Algarve is fringed by dunes and lagoons. Portugal's main rivers, the Minho, Douro, Tejo and Guadiana, rise in Spain.

Forests
Woodlands, covering 28% of the country, are vital to the Portuguese economy. Cork oak accounts for a quarter of the forested area and predominates in the Tejo valley and in western Alentejo. Portugal is the world's leading producer and exporter of cork (most of the cork is exported crude, but processing plants are being developed). A third of the woodland consists of pine, particularly in the north and pine lumber, pulp, resin and turpentine are all exported. The other main species grown in Portugal's forests are holm oak, chestnut and eucalyptus.

Fishing
Fishing is one of Portugal's chief industries. The main sector is sardine fishing, based at Matozinhos, Setúbal, Portimão and Olhão. Most of the catch is tinned in home-produced olive oil and exported. The tunny fisheries, centred on Vila Real, are also important. The fish are caught in the early summer as they enter the lagoons to spawn. Anchovy is the other main species taken in coastal waters. Every spring the cod fleet leaves for Newfoundland and Greenland and returns in the autumn, but the catch does not meet demand and dried cod has to be imported.

Climate
Southern Portugal has hot dry summers and mild winters: January averages 10°C in Lisboa (Lisbon), 12°C in Faro; corresponding August temperatures are 22°C and 24°C. Lisbon has 75 cm of rain a year, Faro 45 cm. The wettest period is October to March. The mountainous north is wetter and cooler with temperatures of 4°C in winter rising to 20°C in summer. On the Serra da Estrêla, annual rainfall reaches 250 cm and snow lasts from November to April. Winter fogs are common along the north coast.

Agriculture
Portugal is largely agricultural. Farmland covers over half the country—the main areas being the coastal lowlands, the Douro, Tejo, Sorraia and Sado valleys, the Alentejo and the Algarve. The north is characterized by very small farms and polyculture (beans, potatoes, maize and rye) while the Alentejo has vast estates and monoculture of wheat. Rice is grown in the Sorraia and Sado basins. But cereal production is inadequate and imports are necessary. Tree crops, such as olives, figs, almonds and citrus predominate in the Algarve. There is market gardening north of Lisboa. Vines are the leading crop in value and the chief vineyards, producing port wine for export, are on the terraced slopes of the Douro valley. Olives, grown in the south and the Douro valley, are also important; olive oil is both exported and used in fish canning. Irrigation is being developed in the south. Livestock consists of cattle in the north, sheep and goats in the south and pigs (reared on acorns) in the widespread oak forests.

Industry
Traditional industries (cork manufacture, wine, olive oil processing and fish canning) are based on domestic raw materials. The long established textile industry, centred on Porto and Braga, uses imported cotton. New industries are being developed, mostly in the Lisboa and Porto areas, and include steel production (Seixal), shipbuilding (Lisboa and Leixões), engineering (Porto, Setúbal and Lisboa), chemicals (Barreiro, Setúbal, Estarreja and Porto) and motor-vehicle assembly (Lisboa, and Azambuja). a major factor contributing to industrial expansion is increased power production. About 80% of electricity is generated by hydro-electric plants and there are major installations on the Tejo, Cavado, Douro and Zezere.

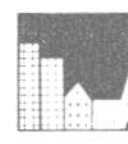

Cities
Lisboa, on the north side of the Tejo estuary 14 km from the Atlantic is dominated by the medieval castle of São Jorge. Most of the other old buildings were destroyed by one of the world's worst earthquakes which wrecked the city in 1755. The industrial zone lies south of the Tejo and is expanding towards Setúbal (50,000). The world-famous port wine takes its name from Porto (330,000), on the north bank of the Douro. The wine trade is based in nearby Vila Nova de Gaia (50,000). Other leading towns are Coimbra and Braga.

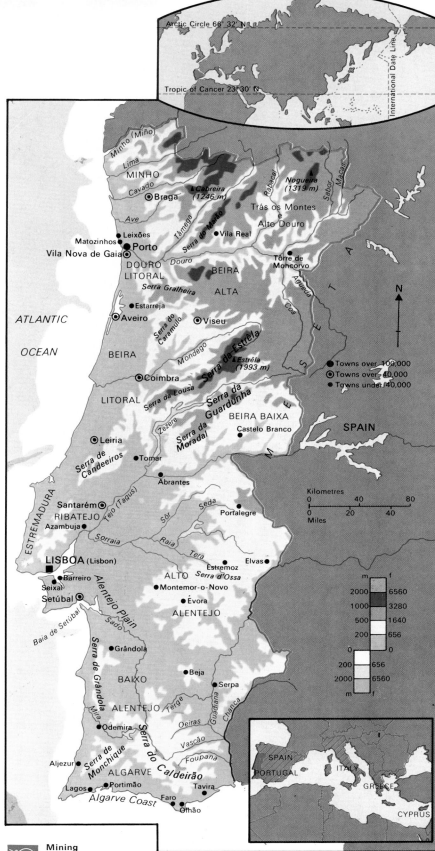

Mining
Portugal's mineral resources are limited and, in many cases, not fully developed. The most significant commercially is tungsten, mined in the north; Portugal ranks as the world's third largest exporter of tungsten. Copper pyrite, mostly from Beja, is also exported. There are iron ore deposits at Torre de Moncorvo, Montemor-o-Novo and in the Guadiana valley. Small amounts of manganese and tin are also produced. Fuels are lacking except for a little coal near Porto.

Transport
Lisboa-Coimbra-Porto is the principal axis of the road and rail networks. There are also several main road links with Spain and major rail routes via the Douro and Tejo valleys. Shipping is vital to the economy: the two leading ports, Lisboa and Leixões handle 80% of Portuguese trade. The national airline, Tap, operates overseas flights from Lisboa, Porto and Faro.

Tourism
Portugal's thriving tourist industry was badly hit by the overthrow in 1974 of the Caetano dictatorship and the ensuing political unrest. As tourism played a major part in the economy, the Government is now trying to re-establish the industry. Previously, four million people visited Portugal annually; the most famous resorts lying on the Algarve coast.

Italy

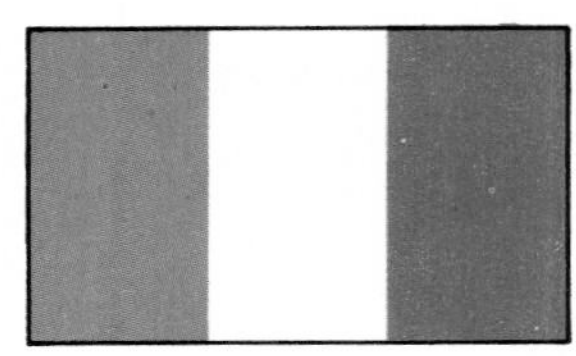

Area
301,054 km²/116,237 sq miles
Location
36°40′—47°05′ N
6°33′—18°30′ E
Population
56,223,000 (1981)
Population density
187 per km²/484 per sq mile
Capital and largest city
Rome: 2,900,000 (1980)
Language
Italian
Major imports
metal ores, fuels, cereals, meat, iron, steel, machinery, timber and paper
Major exports
fruit, vegetables, metal goods, machinery, fabrics, footwear, vehicles, chemicals
Currency
lira
Gross National Product
391,440 million US dollars (1981)
Status
independent republic

Physical features
The main mountain systems are the Alps and the Apennines. The Alps sweep across northern Italy and are highest in the north-west where Monte Rosa rises to 4,638 m. Alpine lakes, such as Garda (370 km²), Maggiore and Como, are of glacial origin. The Apennine chain extends from the western Alps to the southern tip of the mainland; Monte Corno (2,914 m) is its highest peak. The principal lowland is the fertile northern plain formed by Italy's longest river, the Po (652 km) and its tributaries. In the peninsula there are smaller lowlands such as Campania, Campagna, Maremma, Tavoliere della Puglia and Salentina. Peninsula rivers like the Tiber (Tevere), Arno and Volturno, have a seasonal flow. The two main islands are Sicily (Sicilia: 25,707 km²) and Sardinia (Sardegna: 24,089 km²). Mountainous Sicilia (an extension of the Apennines) is dominated by Etna (3,322 m)—Europe's largest active volcano. Sardegna consists of a desolate plateau broken, in the south, by the Campidano plain.

Climate
Italy divides into two climatic zones. The northern plain has a modified central European climate with long warm summers and short cold winters. Milano averages 25°C in July, 1°C in January. In contrast, a Mediterranean climate prevails in peninsula Italy and the islands with hot summers and mild winters. Palermo averages 27°C in July, 12°C in January. In the north, rain falls throughout the year but is heaviest in autumn; the plain receives about 80 cm a year, the Alps over 125 cm. The south has less than 60 cm of rain a year.

Energy
Hydro-electric power stations in the Alps, central Apennines and Calabria supply 35% of electricity; geothermal power (in Larderello, using steam of volcanic origin), 6%; nuclear plants, 5%; the remainder is generated thermally. As domestic oil production meets only 4% of Italy's energy needs, natural gas 10% and coal only 13%, fuel imports are high.

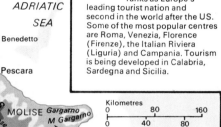

Agriculture
In spite of industrial growth, agriculture is still important and provides 25% of total exports. Farmland covers 67% of the country. The most fertile area is the Po plain, but other regions with a high turnover from agriculture are Piemonte, Lazio, Campania and Puglia. Wheat, the main cereal, is grown throughout lowland Italy; other cereals include rice (Piemonte, Lombardia) and maize. Italy produces 25% of the world's wines with Piemonte, Veneto, Toscana, Lazio and Sicilia the main vine growing areas. Olives are important, especially in Puglia, Calabria, Sicilia and Toscana. Other tree crops are apples, peaches and pears from the north and citrus fruits from Calabria and Sicilia. The main industrial crops are sugar beet, tobacco and hemp. Dairying is concentrated in Lombardia and Emilia; products include Gorgonzola and Parmesan cheese. Emilia is the chief pig-breeding zone; sheep and goats predominate in the south.

Forests and fishing
Forests, covering 20% of the country, are mostly in the Alps, Abruzzi and Gargano. Deciduous woods grow to 1,000 m then give way to conifers. The timber industry is particularly important in Alto Adige. Thousands of small boats operate off the 8,500 km long coast. Of the seas around Italy, the Adriatic is richest in fish; consequently the chief fishing ports (Chioggia, Fano, San Benedetto, Pescara and Molfetta) are along its coast. The catch includes sardines, anchovies, mullet, octopus, tunny.

Mining
Although Italy has a variety of minerals, deposits are usually small and often unworkable. The principal mining regions are Sicilia (sulphur, potash), Toscana (mercury, salt, pyrites), Sardegna (lead-zinc), Piemonte (asbestos, manganese) and Lombardia (asbestos). Some iron is mined in Valle d'Aosta and on Elba and there is bauxite in Abruzzi. Low quality coal comes from Sardegna and the Alps and lignite from Toscana. Natural gas is produced in the Po basin and oil at Gela in Sicilia. Marble quarrying is important: the Toscana centres of Versilia (Massa, Carrara and Garfagnana) form the world's largest source.

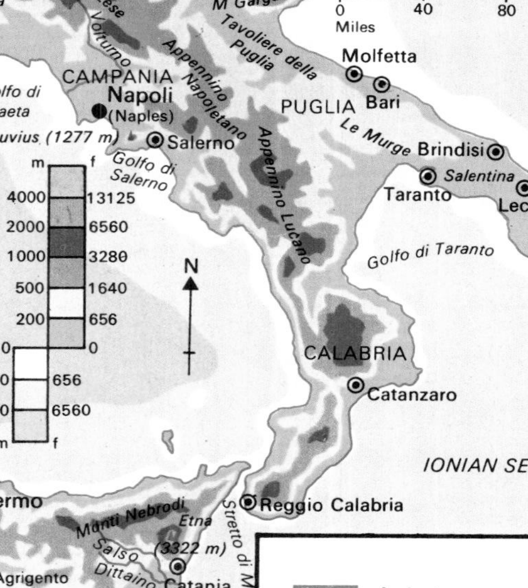

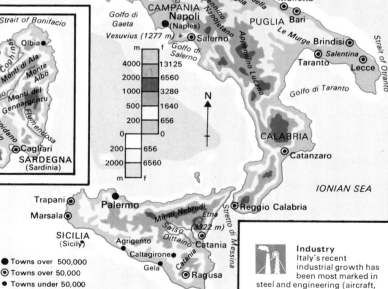

Transport
Railways total 20,000 km and consist of 4 main lines: Ventimiglia-Reggio Calabria, Padova-Lecce, Milano-Roma and Torino-Trieste. The 300,000 km road network includes Europe's second longest motorway system—the most famous being the 1,250 km Autostrada del Sol from Milano to Reggio Calabria. Inland shipping is mainly concentrated on Lakes Garda, Maggiore, Como and Iseo. The main sea ports are Genova, Venezia, Trieste, Palermo, Napoli, Savona, Livorno and Ancona and Italy has the world's eighth largest merchant fleet. There are 30 major airports in Italy served by the national airline, Alitalia.

Cities
Roma was founded on the Palatine hill in 753 BC and within 400 years had spread to 6 other hills on the south bank of the Tiber (Tevere). As one of the greatest historical and religous cities in the world, Roma's main source of income is tourism. Milano (1,600,000), a major route centre, is Italy's industrial, commercial and financial capital. Napoli (1,200,000) is the only major industrial city in the south and is backed by Vesuvius, the mainland's one active volcano. The fourth largest city, Torino (1,000,000), is dominated by Europe's leading car producer, Fiat, which has some 20 plants in or near the city.

Tourism
With 40 million foreign visitors a year, Italy ranks as Europe's leading tourist nation and second in the world after the US. Some of the most popular centres are Roma, Venezia, Florence (Firenze), the Italian Riviera (Liguria) and Campania. Tourism is being developed in Calabria, Sardegna and Sicilia.

Industry
Italy's recent industrial growth has been most marked in steel and engineering (aircraft, rolling stock, vehicles, machine tools). This heavy industry is concentrated in the Milano-Torino-Genova triangle, but there are also steel plants and engineering works at Piombino, Napoli and Taranto. Genova and Trieste are major ship-building centres. The chemical industry is located in the ports, the Alps (using hydro-electricity) and Torino, Milano, Mantua, Ferrara and Ravenna. Textile manufacture in cotton, silk, wool and artificial fibres is also concentrated in the north (Lombardia and Veneto) but with some production in Napoli and Salerno. Food processing is the only industry evenly distributed throughout the country: exports include cheese, wine, pasta and canned vegetables. Tourism has increased the demand for traditional craft products such as glass (Venezia) and onyx (Siena).

Small European States

Andorra

Monaco

Liechtenstein

San Marino

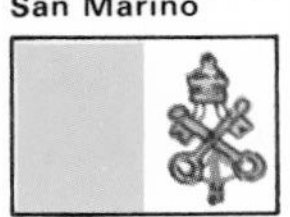
Vatican City

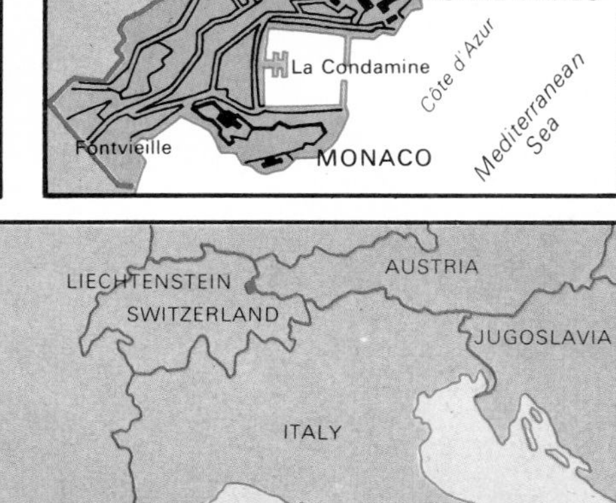

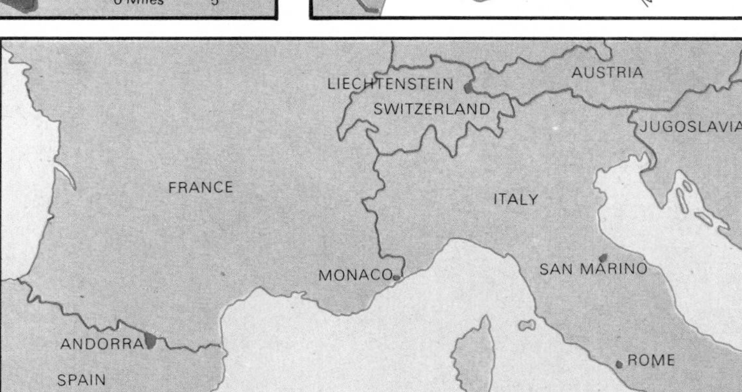

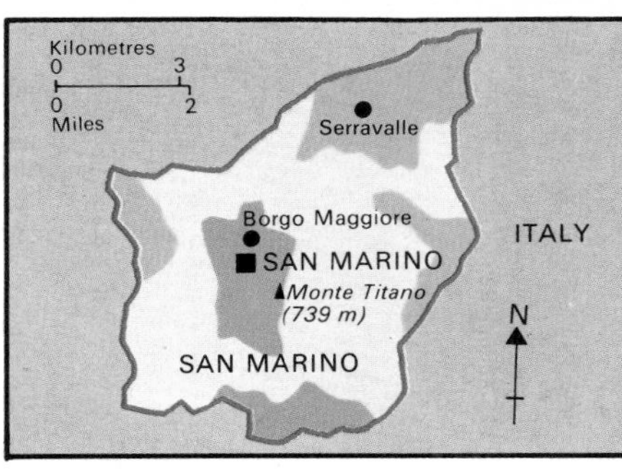

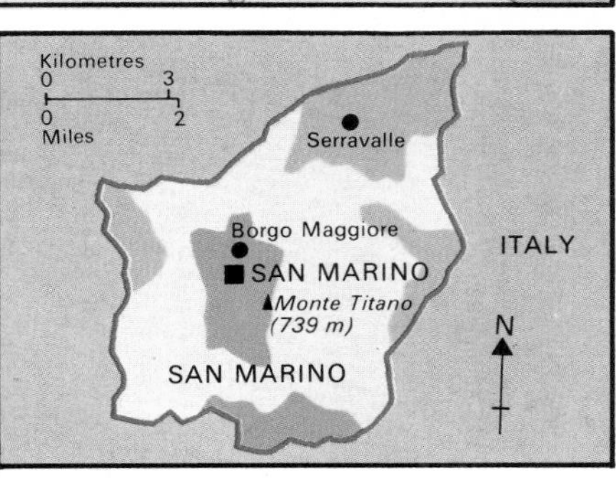

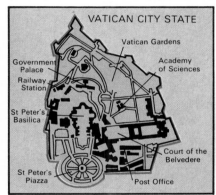

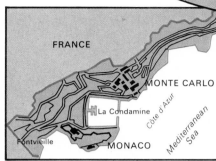

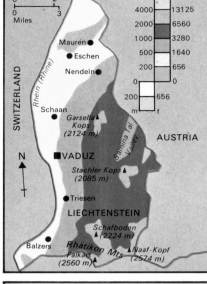

Andorra
Area
465 km²/180 sq miles
Population
38,000 (1981)
Capital
Andorra la Vella: 11,750 (1980)
Language
Catalan
Exports
dairy products, timber, stamps and furniture
Currency
Spanish peseta, French franc
Status
co-principality

Monaco
Area
1.9 km²/0.7 sq miles
Population
26,000 (1981)
Capital
Monaco-Ville: 1,700 (1979)
Language
French
Currency
French franc
Status
principality

Liechtenstein
Area
160 km²/62 sq miles
Population
26,000 (1981)
Capital
Vaduz: 5,000 (1980)
Language
German
Exports
manufactured goods, dairy products, wine and stamps
Currency
Swiss franc
Status
principality

San Marino
Area
61 km²/24 sq miles
Population
22,000 (1981)
Capital
San Marino: 3,000 (1981)
Language
Italian
Exports
wine, manufactured goods, stamps
Currency
Italian lira
Status
republic

Vatican City State
Area
0.44 km²/0.17 sq miles
Population
740 (1981)
Languages
Italian, Latin
Currency
lira
Status
ecclesiastical state

Vatican City
Vatican City, the headquarters of the Roman Catholic Church, is the smallest independent state in the world. Situated in north-west Rome near the west bank of the Tevere (Tiber) it is dominated by St Peter's basilica, the world's largest Christian church. The adjacent palace, containing over 1,000 rooms, includes the Sistine chapel with Michelangelo's ceiling, museums, libraries and catacombs. The Pope is the head of state and most citizens are Vatican employees, many of them priests and nuns. The city has its own flag, radio station (broadcasting in 30 languages), bank, army, telephone exchange, railway station, daily newspaper (*L'Osservatore Romano*), and a rarely-used prison. It also issues its own coins (accepted throughout Italy), postage stamps and car licences.

Monaco
Monaco lies at the foot of the Alps on the Mediterranean coast about 10 km on the French side of the border between France and Italy. Sheltered from cold winds by the Alps, Monaco has a mild climate: winter averages about 12°C. summer 23°C. The whole territory is built up and consists of four districts: Monaco-Ville (the old city standing on a rocky promontory), the sophisticated capital of Monte Carlo, La Condamine (the port area) and Fontvieille (an industrial zone partly constructed on land reclaimed from the sea). The economy is based on tourism: some of Monaco's major attractions are its luxury yacht harbour, the Casino, international events such as the Monte Carlo Rally and the oceanographic museum. Other sources of income are taxes on gambling and the sale of postage stamps. The industrial sector is growing rapidly with products such as fish preserves, textiles, electronic apparatus, plastics and pharmaceuticals.

San Marino
San Marino, the world's smallest republic, is entirely surrounded by Italy. It is located in the northeast Apennines and, for the most part, consists of Monte Titano (739 m). The capital, San Marino town, perches high on the mountain's west side; its main suburb, Borgo Maggiore, stands below. Serravalle, an agricultural and industrial centre, is the only other town. Because of its height, a modified Mediterranean climate prevails: temperatures rise to 26°C in summer, but fall to —7°C in winter. Three roads connect San Marino with Italy and there is a helicopter link with Rimini in summer. A funicular runs from Borgo Maggiore to San Marino town. The republic's economy is based on manufacturing, tourism, agriculture and the sale of postage stamps. Industrial development is recent and includes woollen textiles, ceramics, tiles, paints, varnishes and furniture. Tourism is important: some 3 million tourists visit San Marino annually, mostly on day-trips. The volcanic soil of Monte Titano is very fertile: vineyards cover the lower slopes and red wine is a leading export. Wheat, maize and barley are grown on the encircling lowlands and there is also a limited amount of dairy farming.

Liechtenstein
Liechtenstein occupies a small section of the Rhine valley between Austria and Switzerland. In the east, the Rhätikon foot-hills rise to over 2,500 m while the western part of the country (the most densely populated) consists of an alluvial lowland along the right bank of the Rhine. Because of its sheltered position, Liechtenstein has a relatively mild climate. There are bus links with Switzerland and Austria and the Paris-Vienna railway crosses the north of the country. In the last 30 years, Liechtenstein has developed a wide range of light industries such as pharmaceuticals, textiles, precision instruments, ceramics and food-processing. Agriculture also makes a contribution to the economy. Stock raising and dairying, based on the rich alpine pastures, are important. Arable farming is concentrated on the Rhine plain where wheat, maize, potatoes and fruit (plums, apples, pears and cherries) are produced. Vineyards grow on the terraced hill sides. The tourist industry, centred on Vaduz, is expanding. Frequent issues of postage stamps are another source of income. There are several hydro-electric power stations and some of the electricity generated by these power plants is exported to Switzerland.

Andorra
Andorra, situated high in the eastern Pyrenees between France and Spain, consists of mountain peaks rising to between 2,000 and 3,000 m and steep valleys. No point is below 900 m. Winters are severe, but summers are hot and dry. Most settlements, including the capital Andorra la Vella, lie in the valley of the river Valira. There are bus services to France and Spain, but in winter the main road is often snow-bound near the French border. Traditionally, Andorra is a pastoral country: in summer, livestock is grazed on the mountain slopes; in winter, cattle are stall-fed while sheep are taken to lower pastures in France. Arable farming is confined to the terraced sides of the valleys where potatoes, maize, oats, rye and the main cash crop, tobacco, are grown. Forests, notably pine, still cover much of the country. Industry, based on local raw materials, consists of cigar and cigarette manufacture, food-processing and furniture-making. The mainstay of the economy is, however, tourism. Apart from scenic beauty, Andorra offers its 3 million visitors a year ideal conditions for fishing, riding, walking and, in winter, skiing. Other attractions include tax free shops, thermal springs and colourful stamps.

German Democratic Republic

Area
108,178 km²/41,768 sq miles
Location
50°10′—54°41′N;
9°54′—15°2′ E
Population
16,736,000 (1981)
Population density
155 per km²/401 per sq mile
Capital and largest city
East Berlin: 1,153,000 (1980)
Language
German
Major imports
fuels, metal products, foodstuffs, textiles
Major exports
machinery, chemicals, transport equipment, minerals
Currency
Mark (1 Mark — 100 pfennige)
Gross National Product
not available
Status
independent republic

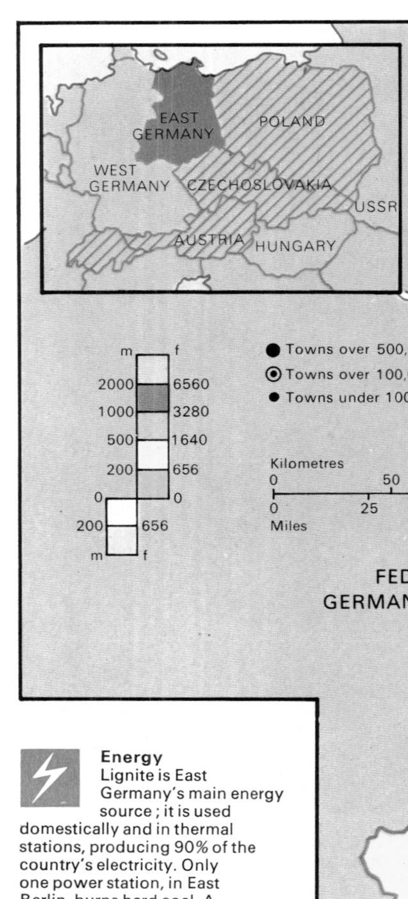

Physical features

Most of the German Democratic Republic (GDR) forms part of the north European plain. The largely infertile central area consists of morainic ridges separated by broad, shallow marshland valleys. In the north, low undulating clay hills with numerous lakes back the Baltic coast, which is characterized by swamps and sandbars. The southern margin of the plain is marked by a wide belt of loess. Beyond this fertile zone lies a plateau over 1,000 m high. These highlands include the granite Harz mountains, the thickly-wooded Thuringian Forest and the Erz Gebirge, with the country's highest point, Klinovec: 1,244 m. Steep, gorge-like valleys cut into the mountain blocks. East Germany is drained by the Elbe and its tributaries; the Oder and Neisse form the eastern border with Poland.

Climate

East Germany's climate is transitional between oceanic and continental. Winters are relatively mild and damp, but increase in severity towards the east—the Oder is frozen for almost three months —while summers are warm and stormy. January averages—1 °C in both Greifswald and Dresden; corresponding July temperatures are 17 °C and 19 °C. In the lowlands, rainfall is fairly evenly distributed: Schwerin has 51 cm of rain a year, Berlin 57 cm. The southern highlands are considerably wetter: on west-facing slopes, annual precipitation ranges between 150 and 200 cm, although sheltered basins can be arid.

Mining

East Germany has vast reserves of lignite and potash: the 250 million tonnes of lignite mined annually account for 35% of world output. Most of it comes from the Lusatian field, north-east of Dresden, and the Halle-Leipzig field lying west of the Elbe. Vast potash beds are worked open-cast on the eastern edge of the Harz near Halle, giving an annual output of 2.5 million tonnes. Small quantities of hard coal are mined in the Karl-Marx-Stadt-Zwickau area. There is some iron ore production in the Harz and in Thuringia, copper at Mansfeld and uranium in the Erz Gebirge.

Energy

Lignite is East Germany's main energy source; it is used domestically and in thermal stations, producing 90% of the country's electricity. Only one power station, in East Berlin, burns hard coal. A further 5% is generated in oil-fired stations; the remainder is derived from hydro-electric installations—in the Harz, Thuringia and the Erz Gebirge—and from the GDR's one atomic power station. Electricity output is insufficient for the country's needs and oil is piped from the USSR to be refined at Schwedt.

Cities

Following war destruction, East Berlin was rebuilt and industry reconstructed; the capital is now the GDR's leading industrial city with electrical and mechanical engineering, textiles, chemicals and food-processing. Leipzig (563,000), at the confluence of the Weisse Elster, Pleisse and Parthe, is a major industrial and commercial town. Dresden (516,000), on the Elbe, was devastated in the war but has been restored and is an industrial, cultural and tourist centre. The famous Dresden china is made nearby at Meissen.

Forestry and fishing

Forests, mostly coniferous, cover 27% of the country. Spruce predominates in the Harz, Thuringer Wald and the Erz Gebirge, while fir, Scotch pine and larch grow on sandy areas in the central plain and coastal region. The production of lumber, pulp and paper is most important in the southern highlands. Demand exceeds output, however, and timber has to be imported. Fish must also be imported as catches, often from distant Atlantic waters, do not meet domestic needs. The deep-sea fleet is based at Rostock.

Agriculture

Agriculture, organized collectively and consisting of state farms and co-operatives, accounts for 58% of the land surface, and almost three-quarters of this area is used for arable farming. The most fertile region corresponds to the southern loess belt which gives high yields of wheat, barley and sugar-beet. Rye and potatoes are grown throughout the rest of the northern plain, with some sugar-beet and fodder crops on the semi-fertile clays near the coast. Livestock is less widespread: beef and dairy cattle and pigs are kept in the Baltic region; dairy farming is important on drained pastures south and west of Berlin; cattle are stall-fed in the loess belt and both cattle and sheep are grazed in the southern highlands. Market gardening is important near most major towns, particularly in the industrial south. Although crop yields are fairly high, the GDR still has to import much of its food.

Transport

The 14,384 km rail network basically serves the industrial south, where it links the principal cities and connects the region with Berlin and the Baltic ports of Rostock and Stralsund. 70% of freight is carried by rail and only 25% by road. Like the railways, the 45,570 km road network is dense in the south, but less developed in the north; it includes the incomplete motorway (autobahn) system which radiates from Berlin. As the inland waterways, totalling 2,546 km, do not connect with the south, they transport less than 5% of freight; tourist traffic, however, is expanding. The main navigable routes are the Elbe, Saale, Havel and Oder plus east-west linking canals. Rostock has been enlarged to include a deep-water harbour, modern shipyards and oil terminal and is now the GDR's leading port; it also serves the Czechoslovak hinterland. The national airline, Interflug, operates overseas and internally.

Industry

The GDR is Eastern Europe's leading industrial country. Natural resources are the basis of the main industrial regions: Halle-Leipzig (lignite, potash); Zwickau-Karl-Marx-Stadt (coal); Lusatia (lignite). Engineering leads in importance and accounts for 40% of total exports, which include machine tools, vehicles, electrical goods and precision instruments. The major centres are Leipzig, Halle, Magdeburg, Karl-Marx-Stadt, Zwickau and Dresden. The chemical industry, ranking second, is located in the Halle-Leipzig area and is based on lignite, potash and oil. Chemical products, making up 17% of exports, range from fertilizers, plastics and artificial fibres to drugs, paints and explosives. Food-processing is third in importance, followed by textile manufacture; imported wool and cotton are being replaced by home-produced synthetic fibres. The expanding metallurgical industry includes several steelworks and an aluminium smelter.

USSR 1

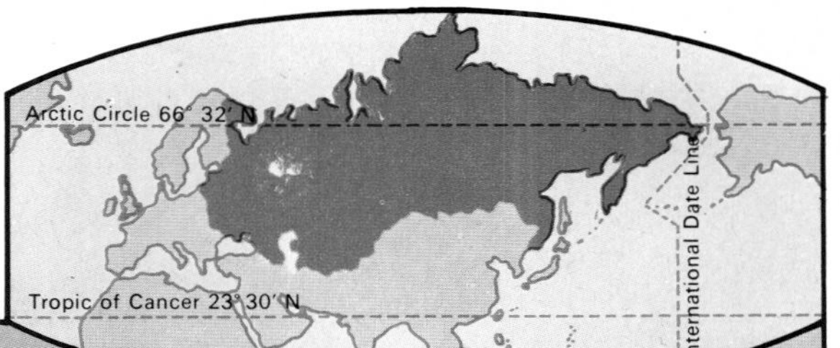

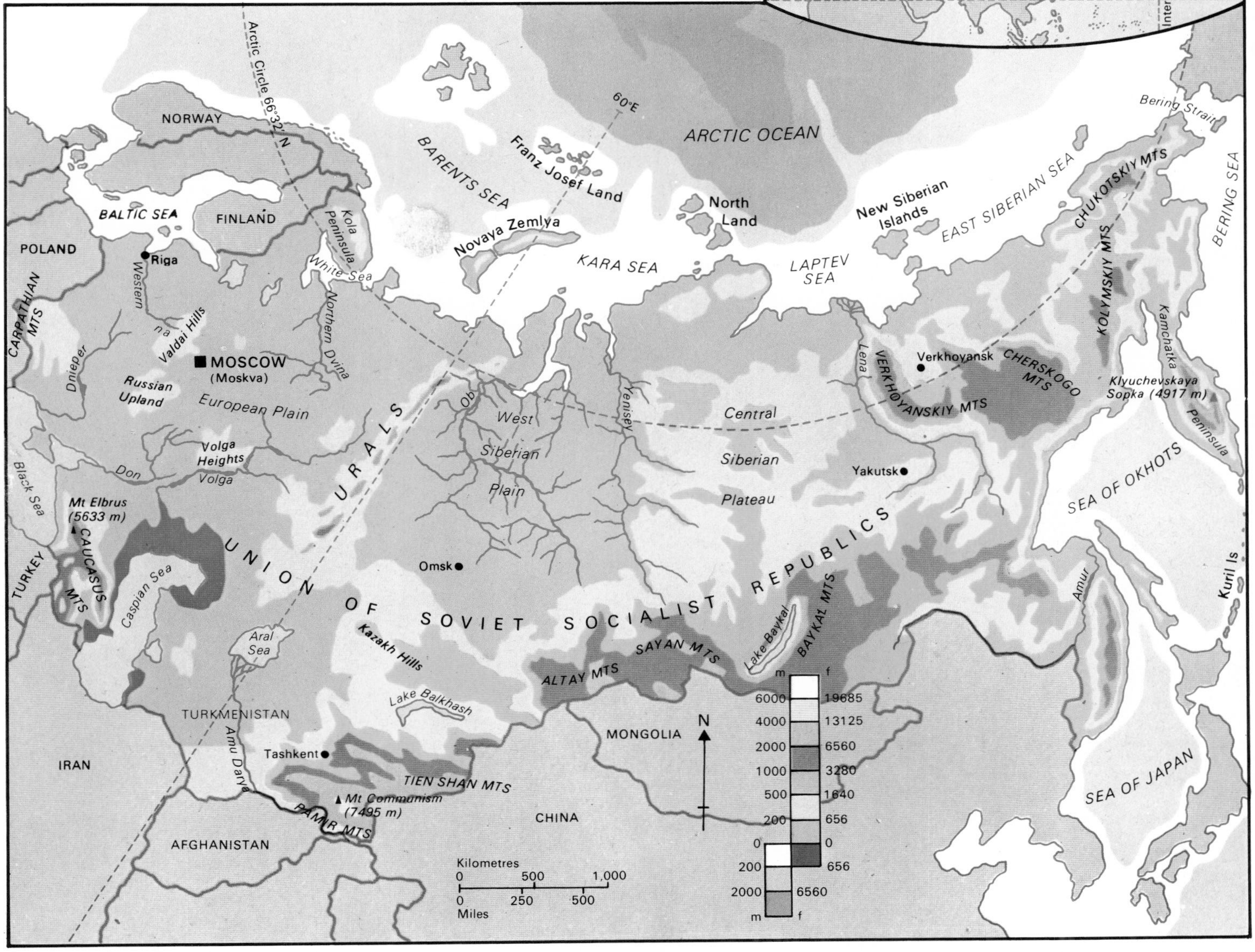

Area
22,402,200 km²/8,649,500 sq miles
Location
35°10′—77°45′ N
19°40′ E—169°40′ W
Population
267,967,000 (1981)
Population density
12 per km²/31 per sq mile
Capital and largest city
Moscow: 8,203,000 (1981)
Language
Russian
Major imports
machinery, fuel and raw materials, foodstuffs, consumer goods
Major exports
crude oil, coal, iron ore, paper, lumber, cotton, vegetable oil, motor vehicles, clocks, watches
Currency
rouble (1 rouble = 100 kopeks)
Gross National Product
not available
Status
federal union of republics

Each of the 15 republics comprising the USSR is the home of a major ethnic group. The largest and most important republic, which contains 75% of the total area and over 50% of the total population, is the Russian Soviet Federated Socialist Republic.

Physical features
The USSR is the largest country in the world: twice the size of China, three times as big as Australia, it stretches across Europe and Asia and covers 17% of the world's land surface. There are two main divisions: lowlands, largely corresponding to the plains west of the Yenisey river, and highlands which are concentrated in peripheral zones. The European plain, west of the Urals, is bordered by the Baltic, White and Barents Seas in the north, the Carpathian mountains to the west and the Caucasus mountains and the Black and Caspian Seas in the south. The Caucasus has Europe's highest peak, Mt Elbrus (5,633 m). The lowland is broken by the Valdai hills, the Central Russian Upland, the Volga Heights and the Kola Peninsula mountains. The region is drained by the Northern Dvina, flowing to the Arctic, the Western Dvina to the Baltic, the Dnieper and Don to the Black Sea and by the Volga (Europe's longest river, 3,690 km) which flows into the Caspian. The Urals, with an average height of between 500 and 800 m, form the traditional barrier between Europe and Asia.

The West Siberian Plain extends 3,200 km eastwards from the Urals to the Yenisey river and is one of the largest lowlands in the world. This region is mainly drained by the Ob. East of the Yenisey lies the Central Siberian Plateau which stretches to the Lena. The plateau has an average height of 600 m, but is rimmed by the Baykal and Sayan ranges (2,000 to 3,000 m) in the south. Two principal Asian rivers, the Amu Darya and Syr Darya, flow to the Aral Sea through the semi-arid depression separating the Urals from the Kazakh hills. These hills, up to 1,000 m high, stretch southwards to Lake Balkhash and the high mountain mass: the Pamir, Tien Shan and Altay ranges. The Pamir range includes the USSR's highest peak: Mt Communism, 7,495 m. The area between the Lena and the Pacific is mountainous, containing the Verkhoyanskiy, Cherskogo, Kolymskiy and Chukotskiy ranges. The Kuril islands are an extension of the volcanic Kamchatka peninsula which contains Asia's highest active volcano, Klyuchevskaya Sopka (4,917 m). Lake Baykal (33,000 km² and 1,940 m deep) is the world's biggest freshwater lake.

Climate
The USSR has a continental climate. Winters are long and harsh: January temperatures in most parts are below freezing. Conditions are most severe in the north-east where rivers are frozen for eight months and the land is snow-covered for six. In the west, the Baltic, Black and Caspian Seas have a moderating influence. Average January temperatures are: Riga —5°C, Tashkent —5°C, Moscow —10°C, Omsk —19°C and Yakutsk —40°C. At Verkhoyansk, —72°C has been recorded. In contrast, summers are warm: the hottest area is Turkmenistan where 32°C is not uncommon; the coolest zone is the Arctic coast, but here prolonged sunshine raises the temperature to 10°C. July averages are: Riga 17°C, Moscow 18°C, Tashkent 26°C, Omsk 19°C and Yakutsk 18°C. Rainfall, occurring in spring and summer, is generally moderate and light and most of the country receives less than 60 cm a year. The wettest areas are the Black Sea coast (250 cm) and the south Pacific coast (75 cm). Central Siberia has under 25 cm, Turkmenistan under 10 cm.

Flora and fauna
Distinct vegetation zones, related to latitude, extend from east to west in great broad belts. In the extreme north is the tundra. Only mosses and lichens grow on the waterlogged soils of this treeless plain where the subsoil is permanently frozen. Tundra wildlife is limited to reindeer, lemmings, Arctic foxes and migrating birds. Southwards, the tundra merges into the taiga, a belt of coniferous forest some 1,000 km wide. This is the world's most extensive forest zone with spruce, pine, fir and larch. Wolves, brown bears, squirrels, foxes and rabbits inhabit this area. The mixed forest belt of oak, ash, birch and fir is widest in European Russia where animal life has been depleted through clearance. In the east, however, leopards, tigers and black bears are found. The forest gives way to the steppes—treeless grasslands with rich, black soil. Cultivation has driven away much of the wildlife, but wolves and foxes remain. South of the steppes are desert areas. Peripheral mountains are largely forested and inhabited by goats, snow leopards and ibexes.

USSR 2

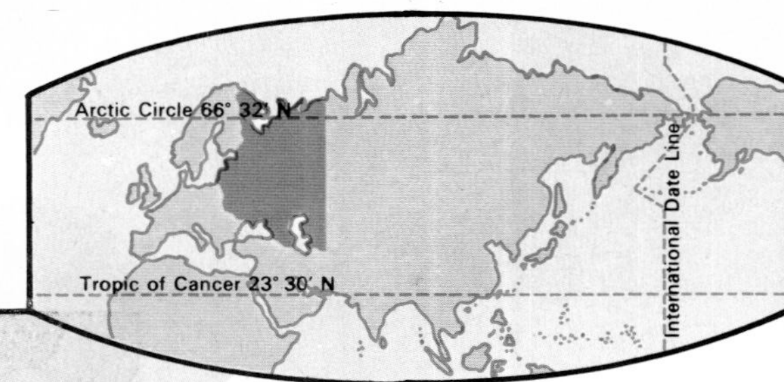

Agriculture

In the last 50 years, the USSR has evolved from an agricultural to an industrial nation. About 46% of the population, however, is still rural and a third of the total labour force is employed in farming. Only 25% of the country is used for agriculture, including grazing. Less than half this area is under cultivation and roughly corresponds to the triangle between Leningrad, the Black Sea and Lake Baykal: this takes in the mixed forest zone and the steppes with their rich black earth. Almost 70% of farmed land lies in European USSR.

Farm organization

The USSR has two types of farm: the collective farm, *kolkhoz*, and the state farm, *sovkhoz*. A collective farm, covering an average of 30 km² and grouping some 440 families, is worked as a co-operative. Most of the output is sold to the state and the proceeds are used to buy equipment, fertilizer etc., or to improve cultural amenities. Each household has a private plot and the fruit and vegetables grown on this land may be consumed or sold by the owner as he wishes. There are about 33,000 collectives, mainly situated in traditional farming areas, and together they produce 92% of the country's sugar beet, 76% of its cotton and 54% of its grain. The 15,500 state farms, each with an average of 60 km² and 600 workers, are mostly located in newly developed agricultural regions. These farms are highly mechanized, state owned establishments and the workforce consists of state employees. They provide 75% of the USSR's meat.

Crops

Over 30% of the land under cultivation is used for wheat and another 30% for rye, oats, barley, rice and maize. The main wheat zones are the black earth belt, western Siberia and Kazakhstan. Rye, oats and barley predominate in the northwest, maize in the steppes and the Caucasus and rice in Soviet Central Asia and Kazakhstan. Other major crops are sugar beet, grown in the black earth belt, Soviet Central Asia and western Siberia; flax, potatoes and vegetables in the western steppes and northwest; sunflower (the most important oil plant) in the southeast steppes, the Caucasus and western Siberia; and cotton, grown under irrigation in Soviet Central Asia and in Transcaucasia. The sub-tropical conditions in western Transcaucasia also favour tea, citrus fruits and tobacco. Deciduous fruits and grapes are grown in eastern Transcaucasia, Moldavia and Central Asia.

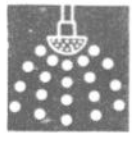

Irrigation

Approximately 120,000 km² of land is irrigated and further schemes are under construction. Wheat, rice, cotton and fruit are the main crops grown in these irrigated areas. They are largely concentrated in Kazakhstan and Soviet Central Asia where water is available in summer from snow melting in Pamir, Tien Shan and Altay ranges.

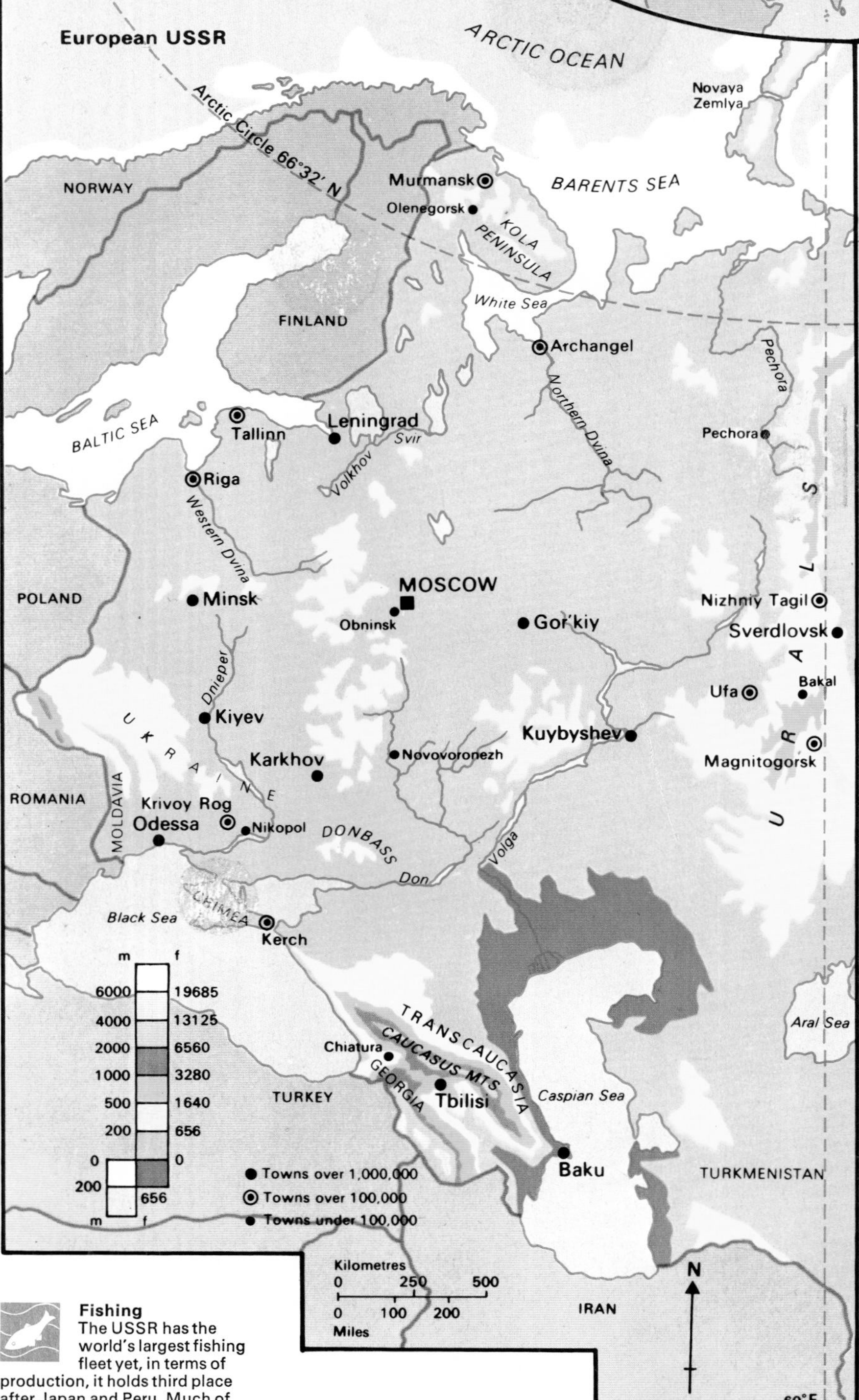

Livestock

In spite of measures to develop livestock, such as importing new stock and expanding fodder sources. meat and dairy production is still below national requirements. Cattle, pig and poultry farming, based on fodder crops, are practised extensively in the mixed forest and steppes zones, particularly west of the Volga. Dairy herds predominate in the north, beef cattle in the south. Sheep and goats are grazed in the Caucasus, the mountains of Soviet Central Asia and southern Siberia and in the desert zone south of the Urals. There are some 140 million sheep and their wool is the basis of the world's largest woollen textile industry. Reindeer herding takes place in the tundra. Natural pasture is used in the steppes east of the Volga and the Lena valley.

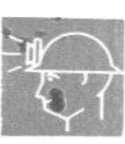

Coal

With an annual output of 700 million tonnes, the USSR is the world's leading coal producer. About 33% of production comes from the Donbass field in the Ukraine, 16% from the Kuzbass in western Siberia, 5% from Karaganda in Kazakhstan, and 3% from Pechora in the north. These four fields are important as output exceeds local demand and the surplus is sent to other parts of the country. The Moscow and Ural fields consist largely of lignite suitable only for generating electricity. At present, scattered mines in eastern Siberia and the Far East yield only 12% of total production, but vast reserves are known to exist, particularly in the Tunguska and Lena basins. Peat is used in European USSR.

Oil and gas

An annual production of 500 million tonnes makes the USSR the world's second largest oil producer. About 70% of the country's petroleum comes from the Ural-Volga area which has been developed since 1940. Before that, 80% of oil came from the Baku and North Caucasus fields; today, these yield only 15% of the total output. The remainder mainly comes from recently discovered fields in western Siberia and Kazakhstan. The USSR exports 20% of its oil. Natural gas production is also expanding rapidly with 50% of output linked to oil-fields in the Ural-Volga, Baku and North Caucasus. There are new gas fields east of the Urals: one of the largest is at Gizli in Uzbekistan.

Other minerals

In terms of world production, the USSR holds first place for manganese and phosphate and second place for potash, copper and zinc. Manganese production, accounting for 50% of the world's supply, is centred on Nikopol, Ukraine, and on Chiatura, Georgia. The Urals and Kazakhstan are major mineral-producing areas. The Urals have deposits of gold, copper, bauxite, platinum and potash. Chrome, copper, lead, zinc, bauxite, sulphur and phosphate are worked at Kazakhstan. Eastern Siberia is noted for gold and diamonds.

Fishing

The USSR has the world's largest fishing fleet yet, in terms of production, it holds third place after Japan and Peru. Much of the Soviet catch comes from distant waters in the Atlantic and Pacific. Coastal fishing is most important in the northwest and eastern seas. The two leading ports in the northwest are Archangel and ice-free Murmansk; principal varieties caught are cod, haddock and flatfish. Vladivostok is the main eastern fishing port and base of the Soviet whaling fleet. Salmon and crab are important and, in arctic areas, whales, walruses and seals. The Baltic catch, largely landed at Riga, includes cod, salmon, lamprey and sprat. Sturgeon from the Caspian and Black Seas are the source of caviar.

Forestry

The USSR has more forested area than any other country in the world. Forests cover 40% of the total land surface—mainly in the east and north-west. The eastern forests yield 17% of the country's timber. Saw and pulp mills are sited on the Trans-Siberian railway, on the Pacific coast and on the Yenisey. A further 13%, mostly spruce and pine, comes from the northwest. Archangel, with over 150 sawmills, has become the country's main lumber port—logs are floated down the Northern Dvina. Riga is a leading Baltic lumber port.

Iron ore

The USSR claims 41% of the world's iron ore reserves. Half of this comes from Krivoy Rog in the Ukraine. Other high grade deposits are worked at Bakal, Magnitogorsk and Nizhniy Tagil in the Urals, at Kerch in the Crimea, Atasu and Gornaya Shoriya in Kazakhstan, and at Orlenegorsk in the Kola peninsula. Low grade reserves are situated in the northern Urals and Kazakhstan. The USSR is also the world's leading iron ore producer.

USSR 3

Population

The bulk of the Soviet population lives in the European USSR where the average density is 30 per km², but cities and major industrial zones have higher levels: the Ukraine, with only 3% of the total area and 19% of the population, has a density of 81 per km². In contrast, Siberia and the Far East, covering 50% of the area, has only 10% of the population—a density of 2 per km². Due to the mechanization of agriculture and the creation of new urban-industrial complexes, the urban population is increasing. At the moment, however, approximately 50% of the total population lives in an urban environment.

Water transport

The USSR has over 144,000 km of inland waterways. The network is most extensive on the European plain where rivers and canals link the White, Baltic, Black and Caspian Seas. The Volga alone carries 50% of water freight, serving the industrial areas of Moscow, the Urals and Donbass. Coastal shipping is hampered in winter when the major ports of Riga, Vladivostok, Archangel and Leningrad are frozen. Murmansk, however, remains ice-free and Odessa and other Black Sea ports are also free during the year.

Other transport

In a country as vast as the USSR, transport is vital. The 140,000 km rail network carries 70% of freight and 45% of passenger traffic. It is most extensive in the European USSR where Moscow is the heart of the network. In the Asiatic sector, the famous Trans-Siberian route (Moscow to Vladivostok) is now supplemented by other lines to serve new industrial areas. Less than 33% of the 1,500,000 km road network is surfaced and only 7% of freight travels by road—usually to the nearest railhead. In remote regions, air transport is important. The Soviet airline, Aeroflot, operates domestic and international flights.

Energy

The role of traditional fuels (coal, lignite and peat) is decreasing. These now supply only 36% of the USSR's energy, as against 59% supplied by oil and gas. Gas directly supplies 40% of domestic needs; it is also piped to industry and, along with coal and oil, is used in thermal power stations. About 80% of Soviet electricity is still generated thermally in spite of vast hydro-electric projects. Initially, hydroelectric stations were centred in European USSR, on the Don, Dnieper and Volga, but recently plants have been built east of the Urals, notably on the Ob, Yenisey and Angara. The world's largest station is at Krasnoyarsk on the Yenisey. It has a kilometre-long dam and produces 6,000 MW. There are nuclear power stations at Obninsk, Novovoronezh and Byeloyarskaya. It is hoped to establish a national power grid by 1980. It has been estimated that approximately 70% of the electricity generated in the USSR is used by industry.

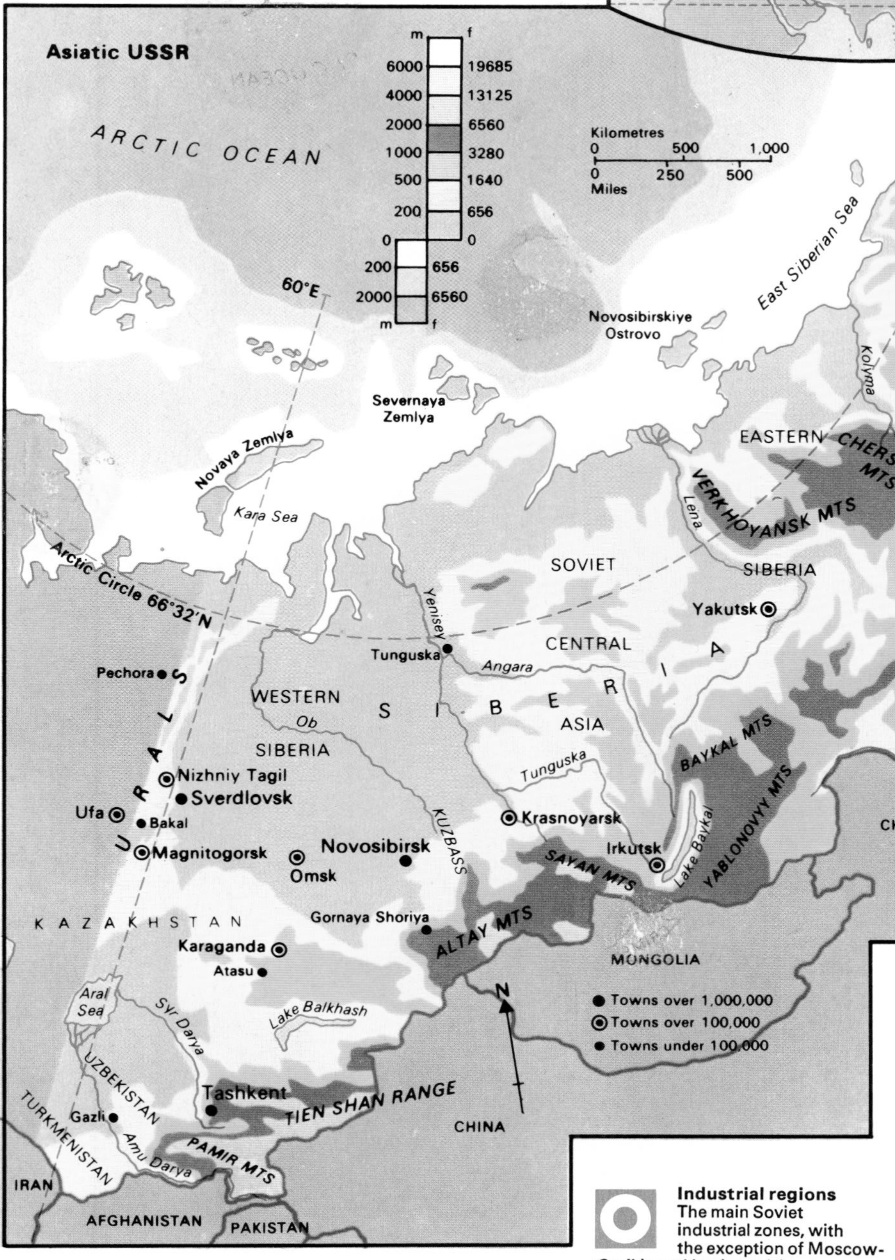

Heavy industry

Fifty years ago, the USSR was industrially backward, but today it is a major industrial power and, in many sectors, rivals the USA. The USSR is the world's leading producer of steel and pig-iron. About 40% of steel and 50% of pig-iron are produced in the Ukraine. A further 30% of both comes from the Urals. Other branches of the metallurgical industry are similarly developed, especially aluminium and copper. Engineering, which employs 30% of the Soviet industrial work-force, is centred in the Ukraine, Urals, Leningrad and the Moscow-Gor'kiy region. The USSR leads the world in the production of diesel locomotives and tractors. Engineering products are exported to East European countries. The chemical industry, traditionally based on minerals such as salt, phosphate and sulphur, now includes major installations using oil and natural gas.

Consumer industry

During the initial stages of Soviet industrialization, development was uneven with the emphasis being placed on heavy industry at the expense of consumer goods industry. In recent years, however, a stimulus has been given to these lighter manufactures and the Soviet people are consequently enjoying a higher standard of living. The USSR's traditional textile centre is Moscow, and the Moscow-Gor'kiy region still accounts for 80% of cotton textiles. The textile industry is also being developed in cotton-growing and sheep-grazing areas. Food-processing is based on urban centres such as Moscow, Leningrad and Kuybyshev as well as growing areas: for instance, fruit canning factories in Transcaucasia, flour mills and sunflower oil extraction in the Ukraine and fish-processing plants in Vladivostok. Cameras, clocks and watches are exported.

Industrial regions

The main Soviet industrial zones, with the exception of Moscow-Gor'kiy and Leningrad, have developed around sources of fuel and raw materials. The leading industrial region is the Ukraine based on Donbass coal, iron ore from Krivoy Rog and Kerch, Nikopol manganese and hydro-electric power from the Dnieper and Don. The Urals owe their industrial importance to extensive mineral wealth and to natural gas at Ufa and Berezovo. Oil is brought in from the Volga fields, while Karaganda and the Kuzbass supply coal. Industry in the Volga lands developed with the discovery of petroleum and the construction of hydro-electric power stations on the river; local phosphate, sulphur and salt are significant. Caucasian industry is also based on oil at Baku and on manganese deposits at Chiatura. The industrial growth of the Moscow-Gor'kiy and Leningrad regions stems from these major urban centres where fuel and raw materials have to be imported. Kazakhstan is the main manufacturing zone in Asiatic USSR with coal and iron ore.

Cities

Moscow was founded as a fortress on the river Moskva in 1147. At that time, the entire settlement was contained within the walls of the citadel, or Kremlin. The modern city (inhabited by 3% of the Soviet population) has spread far beyond the old walls, but the Kremlin remains and is now the centre of government. As well as being the leading cultural city, Moscow has developed as a major industrial centre specializing in textiles, engineering, food-processing and chemicals. The former capital, St Petersburg, is now known as Leningrad (4,676,000), and is the second largest city. Built by Peter the Great in 1713 at the mouth of the Neva, St Petersburg was the principal outlet of Russia to Western Europe. Its industry relies on raw materials supplied by the rest of the USSR and on hydro-electricity from plants on the Volkhov and Svir. The city builds 75% of Soviet ships, particularly ice-breakers. The USSR's third city (and the Ukraine's first) is Kiyev (2,144,000), a major engineering centre on the Dnieper. Completely rebuilt since the Second World War, Kiyev is noted for its parks which cover 33% of its area. Other Soviet cities that have over a million inhabitants include: Tashkent (1,780,000), Baku (1,550,000), Kharkov (1,444,000), Gor'kiy (1,367,000), Novosibirsk (1,343,000), Sverdlovsk (1,239,000), Minsk (1,276,000), Tbilisi (1,066,000) and Odessa (1,046,000).

Mongolia

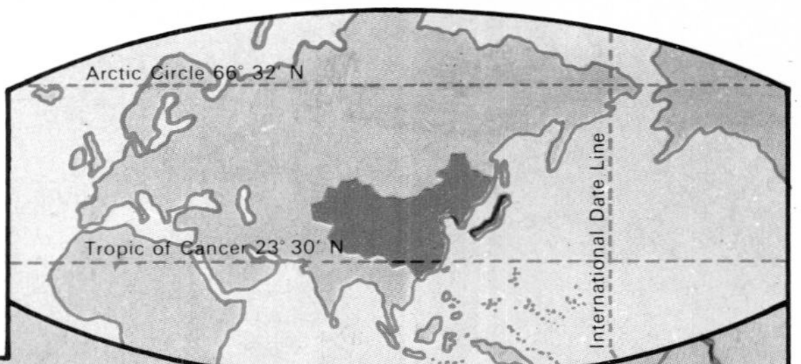

Arctic Circle 66° 32' N
Tropic of Cancer 23° 30' N
International Date Line

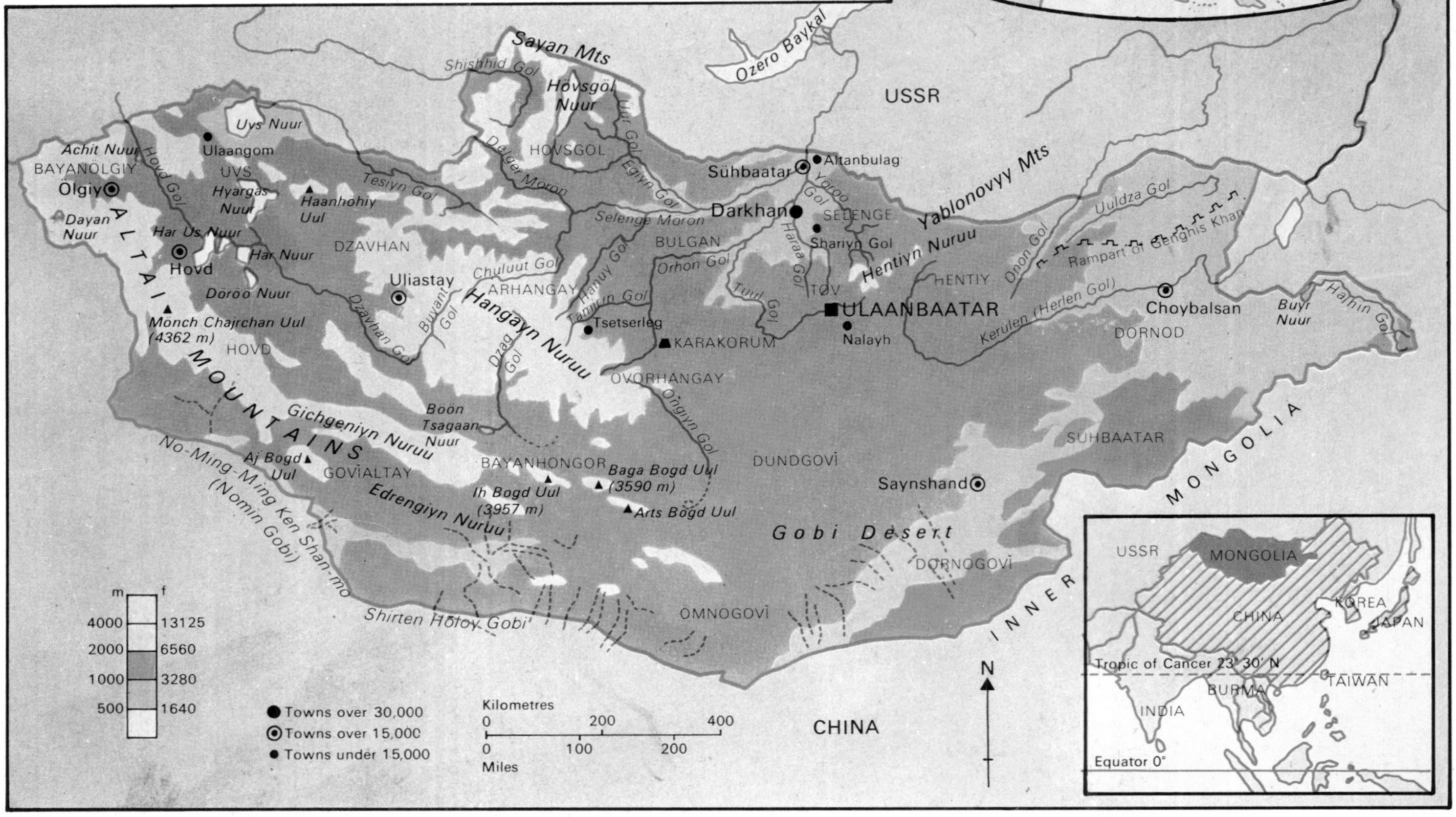

Sayan Mts
Ozero Baykal
USSR
Shishhid Gol
Hövsgöl Nuur
HÖVSGÖL
Uvs Nuur
Achit Nuur
BAYANÖLGIY
Ölgiy
Ulaangom
UVS
Hyargas Nuur
Haanhohiy Uul
Tesiyn Gol
Delger Mörön
Egiyn Gol
Selenge Mörön
Sühbaatar
Altanbulag
Darkhan
SELENGE
Shariyn Gol
Yablonovyy Mts
Dayan Nuur
Har Us Nuur
Hovd
Har Nuur
DZAVHAN
BULGAN
Orhon Gol
Hentiyn Nuruu
HENTIY
Onon Gol
Uuldza Gol
Rampart of Genghis Khan
ALTAI MOUNTAINS
Döröö Nuur
Uliastay
Chuluut Gol
ARHANGAY
Hangayn Nuruu
Tsetserleg
KARAKORUM
Tuul Gol
TÖV
ULAANBAATAR
Nalayh
Kerulen (Herlen Gol)
Choybalsan
Buyr Nuur
Halhin Gol
DORNOD
Mönch Chajrchan Uul (4362 m)
HOVD
ÖVÖRHANGAY
Ongiyn Gol
Gichgeniyn Nuruu
Böön Tsagaan Nuur
SÜHBAATAR
Aj Bogd Uul
GOVĬALTAY
BAYANHONGOR
Baga Bogd Uul (3590 m)
DUNDGOVĬ
Saynshand
MONGOLIA
No-Ming-Ming Ken Shan-mo (Nomin Gobi)
Edrengiyn Nuruu
Ih Bogd Uul (3957 m)
Arts Bogd Uul
Gobi Desert
DORNOGOVĬ
INNER
Shirten Höloy Gobi
ÖMNÖGOVĬ
m f
4000 13125
2000 6560
1000 3280
500 1640
Towns over 30,000
Towns over 15,000
Towns under 15,000
Kilometres 0 200 400
0 100 200 Miles
CHINA
N
USSR
MONGOLIA
KOREA
CHINA
JAPAN
Tropic of Cancer 23° 30' N
TAIWAN
BURMA
INDIA
Equator 0°

Area
1,565,000 km²/604,247 sq miles
Location
41°30'—52°10' N
88°10'—119°40' E
Population
1,707,000 (1981)
Population density
1 per km²/3 per sq mile
Capital and largest city
Ulaanbaatar: 435,000 (1981)
Language
Mongolian
Major imports
machinery, petroleum, transport, equipment, consumer goods
Major exports
livestock and animal products (meat, wool, hair, hides), fluorspar, tungsten
Currency
tugrik (1 tugrik = 100 möngö)
Gross National Product
not available
Status
people's republic

Population
Mongolia is one of the world's most sparsely populated countries. Formerly, most Mongols were nomadic herdsmen but, under the present system, they have been encouraged to settle so that 48% of the people now dwell in towns and the remainder are mostly grouped in villages; only a few still live in the traditional round, felt-covered tents (*yurts*). Half the urban population is concentrated in the capital. Founded in 1649 as a monastery town, Ulaanbaatar is now the republic's industrial, commercial and cultural centre. Darkhan (30,000), which is on the main road and railway to the USSR, is the site of a major industrial complex.

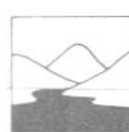

Physical features
The Mongolian People's Republic, the world's largest landlocked state, lies on a high plateau between 1,500 and 1,800 m above sea level. Mountains dominate the north and west: snow-capped peaks of the Altai rise to over 4,300 m and the parallel Hangayn range are almost as high. The Hangayn chain is separated from the northerly Hentiyn mountains by the fertile basin of the rivers Selenge, Orhon and Tuul. The Selenge-Orhon-Tuul system drains northwards into Lake Baykal (USSR); Mongolia's other major river, the Kerulen, flows east into China. Between the mountain blocks there are many large, deep lakes; among them is Hövsgöl with an area of 2,620 km² and a depth of 240 m. In the southeast, the plateau drops down to the Gobi desert which extends into China; the desert landscape features undulating sand seas as well as barren sheets of rock and stone.

Climate
Mongolia has a harsh, dry continental climate with short hot summers and bitterly cold winters; in Ulaanbaatar temperatures average 18°C in July and drop to —26°C in January. During the severe winter, lakes and rivers are frozen but there is little snow. Precipitation, varying from 30 cm in the northwest mountains to under 5 cm in the southeast desert, occurs mostly as heavy summer showers and often causes flooding. The country is exposed to frequent strong winds and dust storms and is also liable to earthquakes.

Flora & fauna
The southern fringe of the Siberian *taiga* (the great coniferous forest belt) covers the border lands of northern Mongolia. Except for this forested zone, the plateau is largely grassland steppe; towards the southeast, vegetation becomes sparser and is reduced to patches of tufted grass and scrub along the desert margins. The Gobi is the home of the wild camel, wild horse, wild ass, gazelle and dzeren (antelope); wildlife in the north includes bear, snow leopard, wolf, sable, beaver and ermine. Furs are a valuable export.

Agriculture
Traditionally, Mongols are herdsmen and, although crop growing is expanding, stockraising is still basic to the Mongolian economy and provides the bulk of exports (live cattle and horses, meat, wool, hair, hides, skins, butter). In all, there are 24 million animals: sheep account for 55% of the total and goats 20%; horses, cattle and camels make up the remainder. Some nomadic herding still occurs in the Gobi but stock-breeding has generally been collectivized and, like arable farming, is organized into co-operatives and state farms. In the last twenty years the arable sector has been substantially developed. The ploughing of virgin lands in the wetter north greatly increased the area under cultivation and Mongolia is now self-sufficient in flour; in addition to cereals, fodder, potatoes and vegetables are grown. Some fruit is cultivated under irrigation.

Mining & energy
Mining activity is being expanded with technical aid from the USSR and other Comecon countries. Fluorspar and tungsten are mined and exported and there is also some production of gold. Major deposits of copper and molybdenum are being developed and reserves of tin, lead, phosphates, silver, fluorite and uranium have been discovered. There are important coal fields at Nalayh and Shariyn Gol; the coal is supplied to industry in Ulaanbaatar and Darkhan and to a new thermal electricity plant at Darkhan which also serves the capital. There are some smaller thermal stations but in most provincial centres electricity is provided by diesel generators. Wood and dried dung are the main domestic fuels in rural areas.

Industry
Industrialization, based on Soviet assistance, is making some progress but is hampered by the lack of skilled labour, inadequate power supplies and limited domestic market. Manufacturing is still primarily concerned with processing agricultural products including woollen textiles, leather footwear, flour, butter and vodka. Light engineering is also important. About 50% of Mongolian industry is located in Ulaanbaatar; the other centres are Darkhan and Choybalsan. Economic plans emphasize the need for export-orientated industries to help reduce the country's chronic trade deficit. About 80% of trade is with the USSR and a further 15% with other Comecon states.

Transport
Modern transportation systems have been introduced as part of the country's economic development programme. Railways are particularly important, accounting for 70% of all freight and 30% of passenger traffic. The main route is the Trans-Mongolian line linking the capital with Moscow and Peking; there are spurs to the Nalayh and Shariyn Gol mines. Another line connects Choybalsan with the Trans-Siberian railway. The 9,000 km road network is surfaced in the Ulaanbaatar and Darkhan regions and at points along the Soviet border. In rural areas, oxen, horses and camels are still widely used. There are boat services on Lake Hövsgöl and the rivers Selenge and Orhon. The state airline, MIAT, flies to the USSR and operates internally.

People
The people belong to the Mongoloid race with such typical features as round face, straight black hair, small nose and 'almond eyes'. The Mongolian people are mostly *Khalkhas* (Mongols from the north) but about 5%, concentrated in the west, are Turkish-speaking *Kazakhs* and *Uighurs*. In the 13th century, under Genghis Khan, the Mongols adopted a form of lamaist Buddhism; 70 years ago, lamas and novices accounted for 15% of the population but, with the growth of Soviet influence, most people have abandoned their Buddhist traditions. The Mongolian language, quite unlike Russian or Chinese, is now written in a modified Cyrillic script.

China

Peoples Republic of China

Artic Circle 66°32'N
International Date Line
Tropic of Cancer 23°30'N
Equator 0°

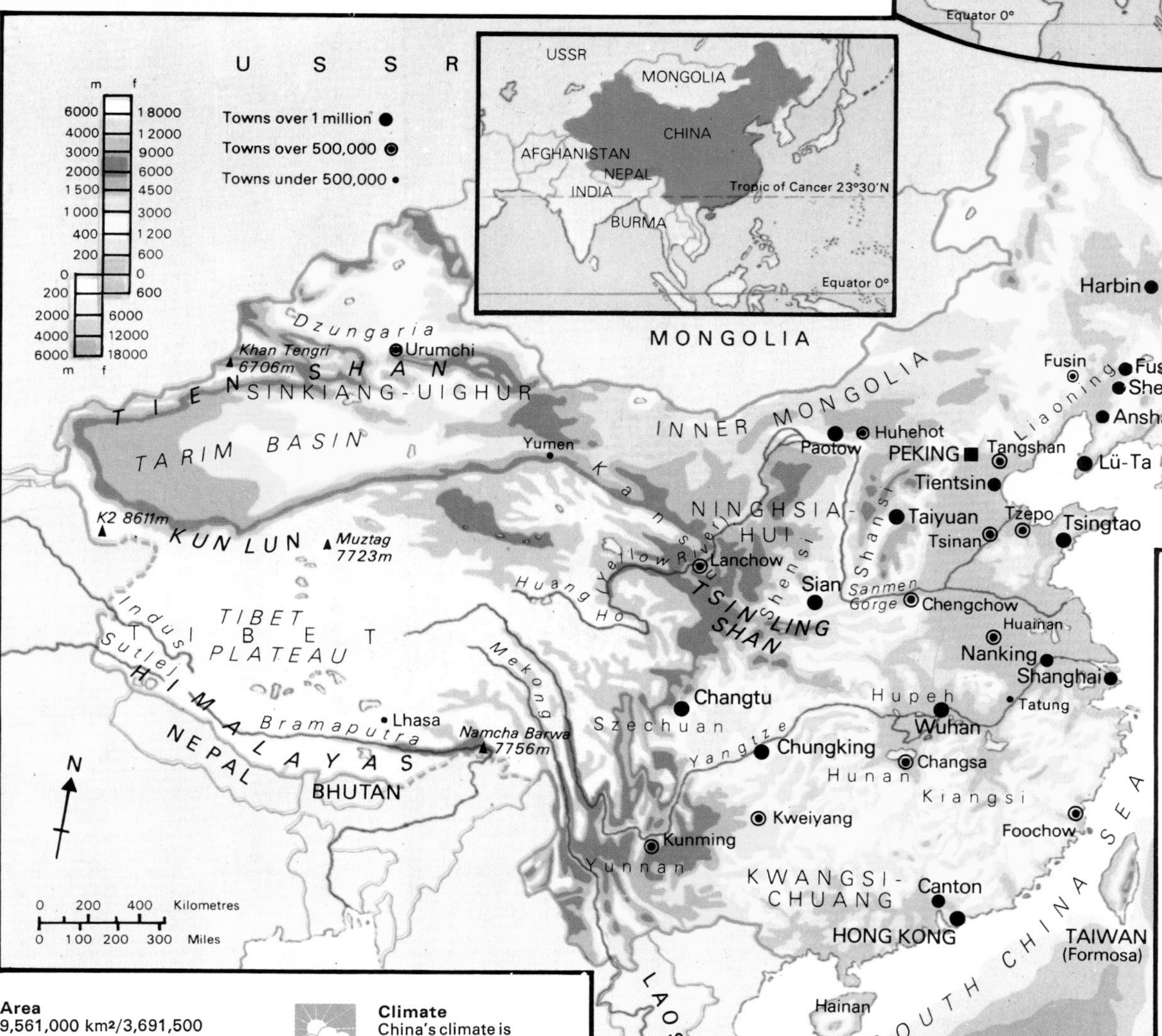

Autonomous regions
China is composed of 22 provinces and five autonomous regions. Originally, these five regions—Inner Mongolia, Sinkang-Uighur, Tibet, Ninghsia-Hui, Kwangsi-Chuang—were inhabited by national minorities but today the indigenous population has often been outnumbered by immigrant Han Chinese. Three of these regions—Tibet, Inner Mongolia and Sinkiang—are great interior lands on China's perimeter; the other two are in China proper. Kwangsi, in the Canton hinterland, is the home of eight million Chuangs—the largest of China's minorities. Ninghsia lies on the edge of loessland.

Inner Mongolia, part of the former Mongol empire created by Genghis Khan, is a 1000 m high plateau with an area of 1,177,500 km². The climate is dry with extreme differences in temperature between summer (21°C) and winter (—30°C). Agriculture predominates: cereals and sugar beet are grown in some areas; elsewhere the nomadic Mongols graze their animals. Industrial development, except for iron and steel at Paotow, is linked to agriculture: flour mills, sugar refineries and dairy plants. Huhehot is the capital.

Sinkiang, to the north of Tibet, has an area of 1,646,800 km². The region consists of two desert basins, the Tarim and the Dzungaria, separated by the Tien Shan mountains. In both basins oasis agriculture has been developed and crops include wheat, maize, rice, cotton and fruit. Livestock is kept on the less arid mountain slopes. Local oil, coal and iron has led to industrialization, centered on the capital, Urumchi.

Tibet consists of a high, bleak tableland, covering 1,177,500 km². Most of the two million Tibetans live in the south where they can grow maize, wheat, barley and potatoes in the Indus, Sutlej and Brahmaputra valleys. Livestock is also important. So far, there has been little industrial development, but some manufactures based on agriculture, such as leather factories, have been set up in Lhasa, the capital.

Area
9,561,000 km²/3,691,500 sq miles
Location
18°30'—55°N
70°—113°E
Population
991,300,000 (1981)
Population density
104 per km²/269 per sq mile
Capital
Peking: 8,706,000 (1980)
Largest city
Shanghai: 11,320,000 (1980)
Language
Mandarin, Cantonese and Hakka dialects
Gross National Product
299,770 million US dollars (1981)
Major imports
machinery, cereals, metals, chemicals, raw cotton
Major exports
agricultural products, textiles, minerals, manufactured goods, tea
Currency
100 fen = 10 Chiao = 1 yuan
Status
Independent republic

Forestry
Over the centuries, a shortage of fuel led to the widespread destruction of China's forests; today, only 10% of the land is forested. More than half this timber is located in the north-east uplands where there are extensive coniferous and deciduous forests. Other wooded areas, producing tung oil and teak, are situated along the south-east coast and in Yunnan and Szechuan.

Climate
China's climate is dominated by two air masses. From November to March, polar air moves south from Siberia, giving harsh winters in the north and west. Winter temperature differences between the north and south, which remains mild, range from 30°-50°C: in January, the coldest month, the average in Canton is 13°C and in Harbin, —19°C. From May to October tropical air from the Pacific brings warm, damp winds and 80% of the country's annual rainfall. Summer temperatures are more uniform: in July, the hottest month, the average in Canton is 27°C and in Harbin, 23°C. Rainfall is heaviest in the monsoonal south-east, where some areas receive over 250 cm a year, whereas the Mongolian plateau receives less than 10 cm.

Livestock
In a country where nearly all fertile land is used for crop production, there is little pasture. Farmers in the east limit their livestock to work animals, such as oxen and water buffalo, and to ducks, hens and pigs. Conversely, stock-raising predominates in the arid interior. In Inner Mongolia, where milk is basic to the economy, sheep, cows, camels and goats are all kept for their milk. Similar herds are grazed in Sinkiang while Tibet's animal, the yak, is kept for its milk, meat, skin and hair.

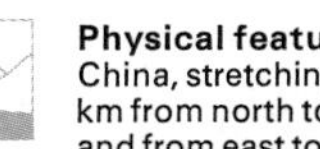

Physical features
China, stretching 5,000 km from north to south and from east to west, is one of the world's largest countries, second only to the USSR. More than half the surface area is made up of plateaux and mountains; these are highest in the west and descend gradually to the eastern plains. The highest region is the 4,800 m Tibet tableland in the far west which is enclosed to the south by the Himalayas and, to the north, by the Kun Lun range. North of Kun Lun lies the desert basin of Tarim which has as its northern edge another range of mountains the Tien Shan. South-east of the Tibet plateau is the slightly lower Yunnan plateau. A range of mountains north of Yunnan separate it from the fertile Szechuan basin—where the Yangtse river is joined by three major tributaries—known as the red basin because of its coloured sandstone. Continuing north, the Tsinling Shan range runs between Szechuan and loessland—an area covered with a 100 m layer of yellow silt and bounded to the north by the Mongolian plateau. China's two main rivers, the Yangtse (5,800 km) and the Huang Ho (4,845 km) both rise in Tibet. The Huang Ho flows through loessland; hence its name, the Yellow River.

Minerals
China is relatively rich in minerals and is the world's leading producer of tungsten, from Kiangsi, and of antimony, from Hunan. Two other minerals exported are tin, mined at Kochin (Yunnan), and molybdenum, in Liaoning. Main centres of iron ore production are at Anshan (Lianoning), Tayeh (Hupeh) and Bayin Obo (Inner Mongolia).

Energy
Coal supplies 90% of China's energy needs. Although almost all provinces have some coal, 80% of reserves are in Shensi and Shansi, but the most important basins are at Kailan, Fushun, Huainan and Tatung. An annual output of some 400 million tonnes makes China the world's third-largest coal-producing country. In the last 15 years oil production has rapidly increased and China now claims to be self-sufficient. Major oilfields are in Kansu (Yumen) and in Sinkiang (Karamai, Wusu). China has great hydro-electric power potential, but so far only 1% has been exploited—mostly in the north-east. The greatest potential, in the centre and south, is largely untapped because of inaccessibility.

Eastern China

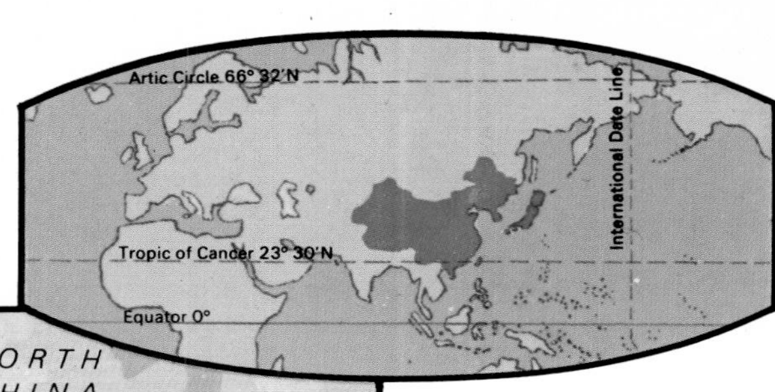

People

About 25% of the world's population lives in China, making it the most populous nation on earth. Exact population figures are hard to obtain: The UN estimated that it had passed the 1,000 million mark at the beginning of 1982. Of these vast numbers, 94% are indigenous, or Han Chinese; the rest are tribes whose territories have been absorbed. 90% of the population lives in the eastern part of the country which corresponds to 15% of the land area. In this region, rural population densities are high, 800 per km²; but in the interior they may be as low as 1 per km².

Communes

When the Communists came to power in 1949, radical land reforms were introduced. Initially, large private estates belonging to the rich were broken up and redistributed to the peasants who were encouraged to form mutual-aid teams. The second stage of communisation began in 1953 with the introduction of a larger unit, the producers' co-operatives. In 1958 a third stage saw the grouping of co-operatives into People's Communes. A commune, with an average of 4,600 families, is not just concerned with farming; it is also an industrial and social welfare unit and runs small factories, schools, etc. Although the commune has proved too large for some activities, it is ideal for major projects such as irrigation and afforestation.

Industry

After 1949, one of the Communists' first objectives was industrialisation. Today, there are major iron and steel plants at Anshan, Wuhan, Paotow, Chungking, Peking, Shanghai and Taiyuan. Steel is the basis of other developing manufactures, particularly agricultural machinery and transport equipment; main engineering works are sited at Shanghai, Shenyang and Tientsin. Another expanding sector is the chemical industry—plastics, synthetic fibres and fertilizers—based in Shanghai, Nanking, Tienstin and Lushun. As most light industry is concerned with processing agricultural produce such as cotton, tobacco and sugar, factories are located in the producing regions; 70% of industrial capacity, however, is concentrated in the north and north-east. Shanghai is the chief industrial city with iron and steel, textiles, engineering, chemicals and food processing.

Cities

According to current estimates, China has over 20 cities with over one million inhabitants. The biggest is Shanghai: its population of around 11 million makes it the world's largest city. Situated on the south bank of the Yangtse, Shanghai is the country's leading port and industrial city. Three other major cities are on the Yangtse; the former capital, Nanking (pop 2.4 m), 240 km from the sea, is an important textile centre; Wuhan (pop 4.43 m), the hub of the middle Yangtse basin, has iron and steel works; Chungking (pop 6.2 m), the largest settlement in the Szechuan basin, is a commercial and industrial city built on steep cliffs overlooking the river. Peking (pop 8.7 m), is the Republic's capital.

Silk

Silk production in China dates from 2700 BC and, over the centuries, Chinese silk became much coveted, especially in Imperial Rome. This trade gave rise to the Silk Road, the major land route out of China at that time. Silk is still being produced in China today, mainly as a cottage industry. Over 50% of the country's silk comes from the Tai Hu area in Kiangsu; the other two main silk regions are the Szechuan basin and the Canton delta.

Physical features

Eastern China is the country's lowest and most fertile area. The gently undulating Manchurian plain, hemmed in by mountains, is in the north-east. The basins of the Huang Ho and Yangtse rivers, separated by mountains in central China, merge nearer the coast to form an alluvial lowland 1,120 km long. The Nan Ling mountain system covers most of the area south of the Yangtse, except for the Canton hinterland where the rivers Tung, Peh and Si join to form the Pearl delta. Lying off the Luichow peninsula is the tropical island of Hainan. Although eastern China is mountainous in the centre, tropical produce such as coconuts and pineapples are grown in coastal areas. The coast is flat and smooth north of Shanghai, but to the south it is hilly, indented and island-fringed.

Water Transport

Some 170,000 km of navigable rivers and canals form a major transport system. The most important is the Yangtse which, together with its tributaries, accounts for 40% of China's waterways. This river, the world's fourth largest, is open to shipping as far as Ipin, in Szechuan, while ocean-going vessels can reach Wuhan. Other major networks are provided by the Pearl River, the Huang Ho and the Sungari. The Republic's main canal—and the world's longest artificial waterway—is the Grand Canal running 1,768 km from Peking to Hangchow. Coastal shipping is limited and tends to be divided into two zones, centered on Shanghai and on Canton. There are about 200 ships in China's ocean-going fleet and these are largely second-hand vessels from Europe and Japan.

Transport

Since 1949, steps have been taken to overcome the dual problem of size and relief and improve China's communications. There are now five times as many kilometers of roads as there were, while the total length of railways has been doubled. Enlarged road and rail networks have entailed considerable bridge-building. One of the most famous is the Yangtse brjge at Wuhan which is 1.6 km long and has two tiers: the upper one takes cars and pedestrians, the lower one carries trains. Railways are particularly important and handle 80% of all freight and passenger traffic. Fifteen main lines cover the country, even going as far West as Urumchi, in Sinkiang; the only region not accessible by rail is Tibet. Domestic air services are being developed and over 70 towns have airports; international flights operate from Peking, Shanghai and Canton.

Fishing

After Japan and Peru, China is estimated to be the world's third fishing nation. Fish is one of the main sources of protein and over one million Chinese exploit the seas off the coast, which are generally less than 200 m deep. These shallow waters make ideal fishing grounds for more than a thousand varieties of fish. In the north, where cod is the main catch, there are major fishing ports with processing plants at Chefoo and Tsingtao, both in Shantung, and at Luta, in Lianoning. Shanghai and Canton are the country's other two main fishing centres. One predominantly fishing region is the south-eastern coast where mountains and infertile soils have turned the population towards the sea. The traditional junk is still widely used and, recently, thousands have been motorised. Inland, many farming communities supplement their income by fresh-water fishing in rivers, ponds and rice fields.

Agriculture

In spite of growing industrialisation, China remains essentially an agricultural country and at least 70% of its people are engaged in farming. Only 13% of the land is under cultivation, mostly in the east. China is the world's leading rice-producer; the main growing area, yielding two or three crops a year, is south of the Yangtse. North of the Yangtse, wheat and millet are grown but, as consumption exceeds production, China has to import wheat from the West. Other crops include cotton, maize, millet and sugar beet in the north; sweet potatoes, potatoes, maize and fruit in the south; and, in the far south, citrus, sisal, rubber, tea and sugar cane. Primitive farming methods, like hand-sowing, are still widely used, but most communes now have a bulldozer, mini-tractors and water-pumps. Drainage, irrigation and afforestation schemes are being implemented to fight the Chinese farmer's traditional enemies: flood, drought and soil erosion.

North

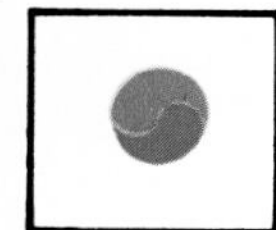

South

North and South Korea

North Korea
(Democratic Peoples Republic)

Area
121,247 km²/46,814 sq miles
Location
37°59'—43°1' N
124°3'—130°57' E
Population
18,699,000 (1981)
Population density
154 per km²/400 per sq mile
Capital and largest city
Pyongyang: 1,500,000 (1981)
Language
Korean (Hangul script)
Major imports
Chemicals, machinery, transport equipment, wheat, fuel
Major exports
Fresh fish, graphite, tungsten iron ore, copper, zinc and lead
Currency
Won (1 won = 100 chon (jun))
Gross National Product
not available
Status
independent republic

Industry
During the Japanese occupation of 1910-45, the north became established as the industrial centre of Korea. After the establishment of the People's Democratic Republic in North Korea, all industry was nationalized and land was distributed among the peasants. The north is rich in minerals, with large deposits of coal, iron, lead, copper, zinc, tin, silver and gold. Most gold comes from two mines at Unson and Suan. The richest anthracite coal mine in East Asia is near Pyongyang. Development has concentrated on heavy industry particularly iron and steel, electricity, heavy machinery, cement and chemicals. The Hwanghai iron works is the centre of iron and steel production and reached 4 million tonnes in 1973. Large scale automation in light industry increased production in the textile industry, centred around Pyongyang and Sinuiju, which produced over 600 million metres of natural and synthetic fibres. Industry relies mainly on hydro-electric power for which North Korea has great potential. Despite such advances, North Korea is turning increasingly towards the West for sophisticated machinery and technology.

Agriculture
Most arable land is concentrated in the relatively flat western provinces of Pyongyang and Hwanghai, with another area in the Hamyong province on the east coast, where the mountains extend almost to the sea. Paddy (rice) is the main crop, covering 27% of cultivated land, followed by maize, potatoes, pulses, millet, wheat and barley. Meat production, especially pigs and cattle, is generally more predominant than in China and Japan. Serious shortages of Agricultural labour made farm mechanization a high priority and a factory for agricultural machinery in South Hwangchai stared production in 1959. Successful programmes for farm mechanization plus recent irrigation schemes, including the construction of 40,000 km of canal, have meant that North Korea now produces a surplus for export.

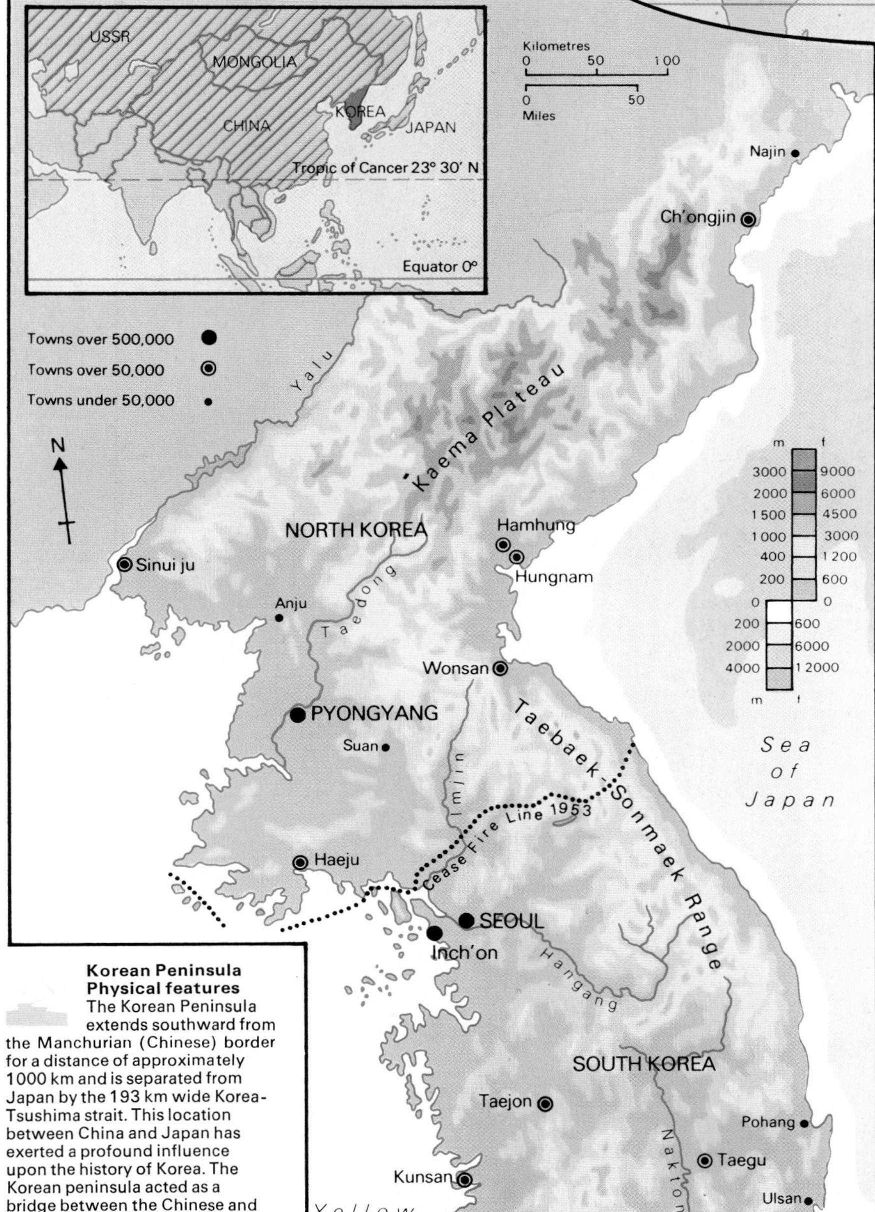

Korean Peninsula Physical features
The Korean Peninsula extends southward from the Manchurian (Chinese) border for a distance of approximately 1000 km and is separated from Japan by the 193 km wide Korea-Tsushima strait. This location between China and Japan has exerted a profound influence upon the history of Korea. The Korean peninsula acted as a bridge between the Chinese and Japanese cultures as well as a base from which Japan could launch military campaigns into the rich lands of Manchuria. The broad masses of highland determine the basic relief pattern. The Kaema Plateau in the north east forms the topographical roof of the peninsula combining, with other mountain ranges, to form a chain across the north from the south-west to the north-east which rises to over 1,829 m. A second major mountain range, called Taebaek-Sonmaek, runs the entire length of the peninsula parallel to the east coast. Thus the main lowland areas, which are also the areas of maximum cultivation and population density, are found in the south and west. Flowing away from the eastern highlands, the rivers of Korea drain mainly westward into the Yellow Sea. The valley plains of these rivers are major agricultural regions because of their relatively rich alluvial soils. The longest river is the Yalu, flowing south-west for 806 km. The south and west coasts are fringed with many islands and natural harbours.

Climate
The Korean Peninsula has a monsoon climate which is cold and dry in winter and hot and wet in the summer months when up to 70% of the annual rainfall falls. Mean temperatures in January range from —22°C in the northern interior to 2°C in Pusan on the south coast, and in August, from 20°C to 25°C respectively. The wider range in northern temperatures is produced by the continental influence. Rainfall also increases towards the south with 61 cm on the northern plateau and 140 cm on the south coast. Typhoons sometimes occur.

Vegetation
The natural vegetation of the Korean peninsula is temperate forest of mixed deciduous and coniferous trees. It resembles that of Japan, with pines, oaks and walnuts in the south and conifers and birch in the north. Forests once covered about 70% of the surface but the mountains of central and southern Korea have been severely deforested, resulting in flooding and soil erosion. There has been a considerable amount of afforestation but, nevertheless, the green valleys provide a marked contrast to the bare, eroded hills.

South Korea
(Republic of Korea)

Area
98,484 km²/38,025 sq miles
Location
33°0'—38°30' N
125°—130° E
Population
38,880,000 (1981)
Population density
345 per km²/893 per sq mile
Capital
Seoul: 8,367,000 (1980)
Language
Korean (Hanguk script)
Major imports
wood, wheat, petroleum, textiles, fabrics, machinery, raw cotton
Major exports
Textiles and clothing, plywood electrical machinery, fish
Currency
Won (1 won = 100 chun (jeon))
Gross National Product
66,090 million US dollars (1981)
Status
independent republic

Industry
Next to Japan and China, South Korea has the highest economic growth rate in Asia. In 1973 it reached the record level of 16.5%. All parts of the country are rich in mineral resources. The largest tungsten mine in the world is located near Songdong while the steel mill at Pohang is the centre of the iron and steel industry and capable of satisfying home demand entirely from domestic resources. Coal, gold, graphite, anthracite and fluorspar are also plentiful.
New manufacturing industries such as electronics, cotton and silk textiles, machine building, food processing, plywood, plastic goods and chemicals are increasingly the source of South Korea's economic strength. A petrochemical plant at Ulsan was completed in 1973—as was the largest shipyard in the world, which quadruples the annual ship-building capacity to 1.1 million gross tones. South Korea's exports totalled US $4,600 million in 1974, her major trading partners being the USA and Japan. Most of the exports pass through Pusan (population 1.5 million) in the south, the oldest and largest port of Korea, followed by Inch'on (550,000) near Seoul and Masan free export zone in the south. The silk industry has increased considerably in South Korea where climate and farm labour conditions are ideal for the production of high-quality raw silk at low cost. Ulsan, with its deep-sea fishing base and processing plants, is the centre of the fishing and sea culture industry which produces over US $100 million a year in exports.

Agriculture
In 1974, 50.4% of the working population was still involved in agriculture and fisheries. Rice accounts for two-thirds of all food-grain production, followed by wheat, barley, sweet potatoes and tobacco. The widespread use of chemical fertilizers, pesticides and improved, high-yield seed, together with the practices of double cropping, deep ploughing and intensified irrigation, have greatly increased agricultural production.

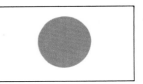

Japan

Area
377,484 km²/145,747 sq miles
Location
26°59'—45°31' N
128°6'—145°49' E
Population
117,645,000 (1981)
Population density
312 per km²/807 per sq mile
Capital and largest city
Tokyo: 11,648,000
Language
Japanese
Major imports
Oil, raw wool, iron ore, timber (raw materials, fuel, foodstuffs)
Major exports
Ships, motor vehicles, iron and steel, radios, synthetics
Currency
Yen (1 yen = 100 sen)
Gross National Product
1,186,430 million US dollars (1981)
Status
constitutional monarchy

Physical features

The four main islands of Japan—Hokkaido, Honshu, Shikoku and Kyushu—and its many smaller islands, lie off the east coast of Asia. The northernmost, Hokkaido, is about 1,300 km from Vladivostok in the USSR. Of the total area of Japan, 85% is mountainous and 580 of its peaks, many of which are volcanic, are more than 2,000 m high. Mount Fuji, now dormant, is the highest cone at 3,776 m. There are many active volcanoes today, including Mount Aso in Kyushu, and one of their by-products is numerous hot springs. Many fast-flowing streams cut through the mountains and provide good sources of hydro-electric power; the most important of these are the Teshio and Ishikari on Hokkaido, the Kitakami, Shinano and Tenryu in Honshu, and the Chikugo in Kyushu. The largest lake, Biwa-Ko in southern Honshu, covers 674 km². There is an acute shortage of cultivable lowland in Japan: the only lowland areas are formed by river deltas and flood plains. The largest is the Kanto plain (east central Honshu).

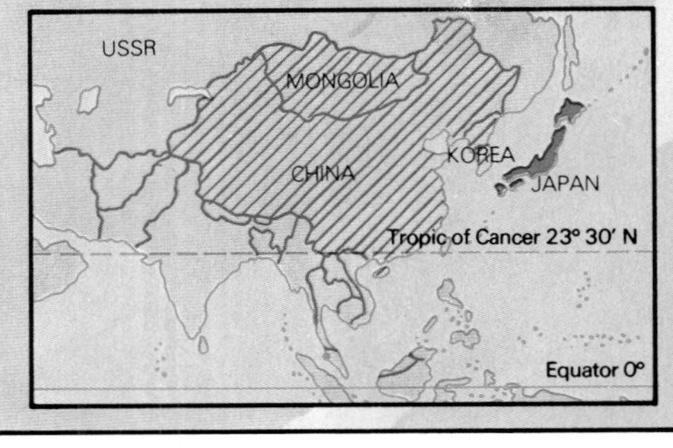

Climate

The winter monsoon (late September to early March) brings heavy rain and snow to the western parts of the islands, but the central mountains shield the east producing drier, windy weather. The summer monsoon, lasting from mid-April to early September, however, comes from the east and south and produces warm rainy weather throughout. The warm Kuroshio Current contributes to the warm temperatures on the east coast up to latitude 35° N, but causes dense sea fog when it meets the cold Oyashio Current off east Hokkaido and north-east Honshu. Minimum and maximum temperatures in Kagoshima in southern Kyushu are 7° and 27°C respectively, compared with —9° and 21°C in Asahikawa in north Hokkaido. Annual average temperatures for Tokyo are 15°C. The average annual rainfall varies from 94 to 400 cm but in most areas it is over 100 cm. Snow covers the whole of Hokkaido, and the interior of Honshu from November to April.

Agriculture

Only 15.6% of the land is arable, of which about 58% is paddy. Japan has therefore to import much of her foodstuffs, especially wheat, soyabeans, sugar and fodder grains. Agriculture accounts for less than 8% of the net national income (and its share in decreasing) and yet it involves more than 17% of the working population. The average size of a farm is still little more than three acres and much of the land consists of terraced hillsides which severely limits the use of machinery. The national output of rice in 1973 was over 12,000 million tonnes, but many farmers are responding to the increasing domestic demand for livestock, sugar and vegetables.

Forestry

About two-thirds of the Japanese archipelago is forested, providing an important source of building materials, paper-pulp and fuel. The most valuable timber forests are mixed conifer and deciduous and the most valuable trees are the Sugi (Japanese Cedar), Hinoki (Japanese Cypress) and Akamatsu (Red Pine). Japan now imports up to 56% of her timber requirements.

Transport

Japan has one of the most highly developed transport systems in the world. The Tokaido railway, linking Tokyo and Osaka, is capable of speeds up to 250 km per hour and is part of a total railway network of over 24,000 km. Japan's three major industrial cities, Tokyo, Nagoya and Kobe, are linked by modern expressways, part of a planned highway system of 7,600 km by 1985. Japan's three major ports; Kobe, Nagasaki and Yokohama, harbour a merchant fleet of over 30 million tonnes. Ships are an important means of transport between Japanese ports. There are two international airports, at Tokyo and Osaka, and a third is being built near Narita City about 40 km from Tokyo.

Fisheries

Japan is the chief fishing nation in the world after Peru, producing over 10 million tonnes of fish per year. This industry has, however, tended to slow down in recent years. About 250,000 individual households still produce about 40% of the catch, particularly in coastal fishing and shallow-sea culture (fish farming), which only require small boats or nets. Species raised include pearls and oysters, yellow-tail prawn and octopus. Offshore fishing is undertaken by slightly larger enterprises requiring boats from 10 to 100 tonnes while the really large companies are involved in long-distance deep-sea fishing, with large fleets and a mother ship handling the processing and packing on-the-spot. Their activities range from trawling off the African coast to whaling in the Arctic Ocean and salmon fishing in the North Atlantic. Ocean currents around Japan provide many varieties of fish.

Industry

After an unprecedented rate of growth, Japan is now one of the top three industrial nations in the world. The iron and steel industry, centred in northern Kyushu, produced over 220 million tonnes of steel in 1973 and made US $ 5,000 million in exports. Osaka is the centre of the largest shipbuilding industry in the world which, in all, comprises over 1,000 shipyards of which 28 produce over 90% of total output. Exports in 1973 amounted to US $ 3,819 million. In car production, Japan has an output of over 4.5 million vehicles per year—an export commodity worth over US $ 3,500 million. The petro-chemical industry is of growing importance with eleven major installations linked to refineries around the coast. Despite the recent shift in emphasis from light to heavy industry, Japan still exports US $ 1,600 million worth of textiles and clothing. Factories are to be found in Nagoya, Kyoto and many other industrial towns.

Energy

Japan has few indigenous energy resources and has, therefore, to rely heavily on imported oil. The demand is over 1.5 thousand million barrels per year which represents 70% of Japan's total energy consumption. This is met by importing US $ 6,000 million worth of crude oil —mostly from the Middle East. Attempts to diversify power sources include off-shore oil exploration and several nuclear power stations. Japan already ranks third after the USA and USSR in nuclear energy capacity. Small amounts of liquified natural gas have also recently been imported from Alaska. Japan is also developing her own oil refineries in the Middle East and Africa: 10% of oil supplies are already 'Yen Oil'. A joint project with the USSR is currently planned to develop resources in Siberia.

Cities

Japan's capital, Tokyo, on the main island of Honshu, is the centre of heavy industry as well as the seat of government. The thriving port of Yokohama is 34 km south of the capital. Another major industrial area is situated further south and contains Kyoto and the ports of Osaka and Kobe.

Hong Kong, Macao and Taiwan

left **TAIWAN** (Formosa)

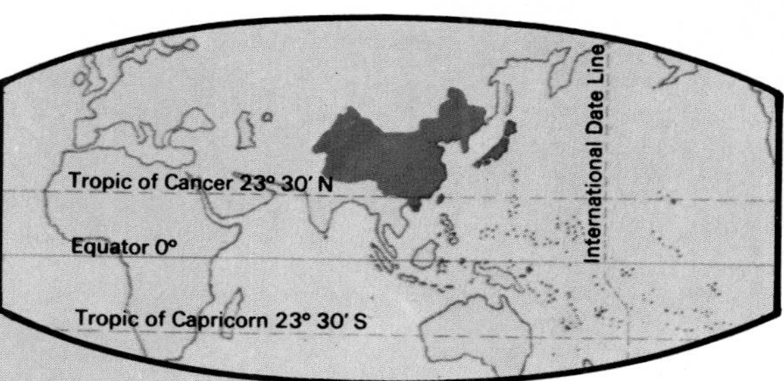

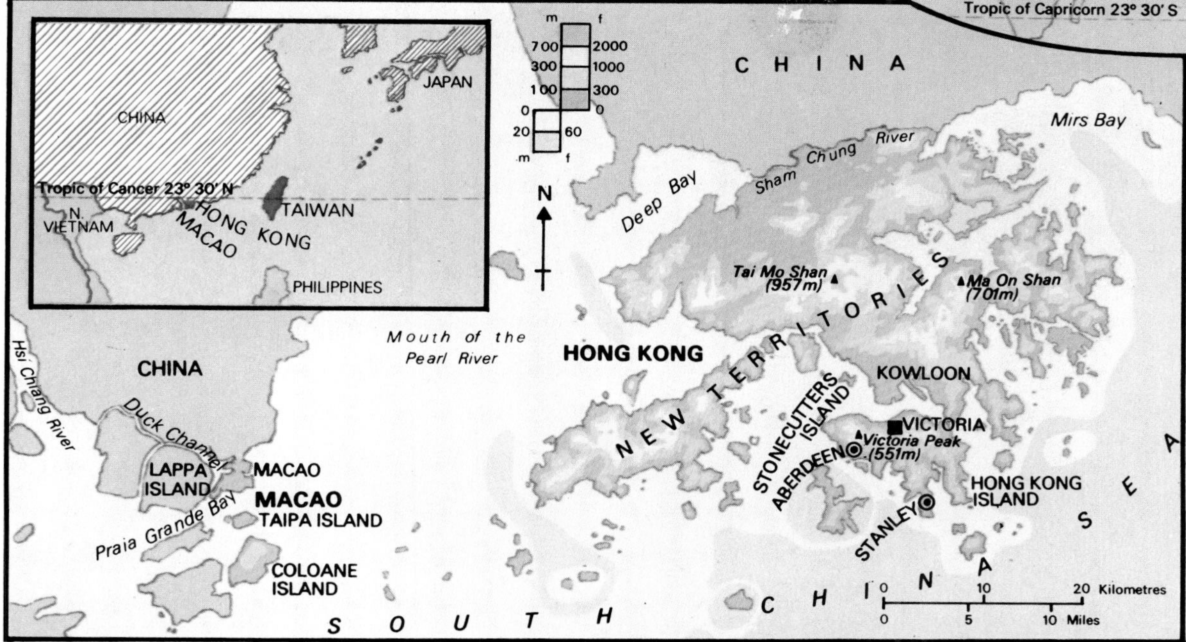

Hong Kong
Area
1046 km²/404 sq miles
Location
22°9′—22°37′ N
113°52′—114°30′ E
Population
5,154,000 (1981)
Population density
4,927 per km²/12,757 per sq mile
Capital
Victoria: 767,000
Language
English, Cantonese and Mandarin
Major imports
Food, raw materials
Major exports
Clothing, textiles, manufactured goods
Currency
Hong Kong dollar
Gross National Product
26,300 million US dollars (1981)
Status
British Crown colony

Physical features

Hong Kong is situated on the south east coast of China on the east side of the Pearl River estuary. The crown colony consists of Hong Kong island and islets (75 km²), the Kowloon Peninsula and Stonecutters Island (9.7 km²) and the New Territories (945 km²). The colony's main asset, the 44 km² Victoria Harbour, lies between Hong Kong and the mainland. Most of the land is volcanic rock with hills rising directly from the sea. The highest peak, Tai Mo Shan on the mainland, rises to a height of 957 m. The main agricultural area is north of the Kowloon ridge on the mainland, particularly around Deep Bay where the Sham Chun River, which forms the natural border with China, flows out to sea. The rest of Hong Kong is urban.

Climate

The subtropical climate brings hot, humid summers (28°C in July) and cool, dry winters (16°C in January). Over half the normal annual rainfall of 216 cm falls in the summer monsoon months of June to August. This is usually a period of bad weather with high winds and typhoons.

Population

The population of Hong Kong has grown from 600,000 to 5 million in 30 years, owing largely to the influx of Chinese from Communist China and South-East Asia. The Chinese form 98% of the population and of the remainder about 29,000 are of British origin. The government has undertaken huge housing projects, of which the largest, Tuen Wanr houses 400,000 of the population.

Agriculture

Only 13% of the total area is cultivated and this employs 4.5% of the work force. The traditional main crop is 'paddy' (or rice), but there is a shift towards land-intensive farming of vegetables (74% of total production value), fruit and flowers—also poultry and fish farming. The remaining land is either marsh, coarse grassland or eroded highland. Marine fishing, which employs 50,000 men, is a major industry and source of exports valued at about HK$ 137 million.

Industry

Hong Kong's exports of manufactured goods now account for 25% of total world industrial exports from developing countries. Its post-war economic expansion is based mainly on a large immigrant labour force, the import of cheap foodstuffs from China, a laissez-faire economy and, until recently the free trading advantages of a colony. The major industry and the source of 45% of exports is textiles and clothing manufacture. Total exports are worth nearly HK$ 23 billion (1974). Other light industrial products include plastics, optical and electronic equipment and watches. Heavy industries include shipbreaking and repairing. All the colony's raw materials are imported, as is much of its food. Invisible earnings come from tourism, shipping and new foreign investments. Nearly half of Hong Kong's goods go to the United States and Britain.

Towns over 500,000 ●
Towns over 50,000 ◎

TAIPEI, KEE-LUNG, Formosa Strait, Tan-Shui Ch'i, TAICHUNG, HUA-LIEN, TAIWAN, Cho-Shui Ch'i, CHUNGYANG SHANMO MOUNTAINS, CHIAYI, Yushan (3996m), TAINAN, PINGTUNG, KAO-HSIUNG, SOUTH CHINA SEA, PACIFIC OCEAN

m	f
3000	9000
2000	6000
1500	4500
1000	3000
400	1200
200	600
0	0
200	600
2000	6000
4000	12000

0 50 Kilometres
0 50 Miles

Macao
Area
16 km²/6.2 sq miles
Population
322,000 (1981)
Population density
20,125 per km²/52,124 per sq mile
Language
Portuguese, Cantonese
Major imports
Fabrics, yarn, food
Major exports
Clothing
Currency
1 pataca = 100 avos
Gross National Product
850 million US dollars (1981)
Status
Portuguese overseas province

Macao is situated 64 km west of Hong Kong on the mouth of the Pearl River. It consists of the Macao peninsula, and the islands of Taipa and Coloane. The capital of the province is Macao which is situated on the mainland peninsular. 98% of the population is Chinese and only 8,000 are Portuguese. Over 2 million tourists visit Macao annually from Hong Kong and about 60% of annual revenue derives from hotels, restaurants and gambling. The textile industry provides 60% of Macao's exports while much of her imports, (cheap food and clothing) come from China.

Taiwan/Formosa/ Nationalist China
Area
35,962 km²/13,885 sq miles
Location
21°45′—25°38′ N
120°—122° E
Population
18,000,000 (1981)
Population density
501 per km²/1,296 per sq mile
Capital and largest city
Taipei: 2,196,000 (1979)
Language
Mandarin (official), also Fukien, Hakka (mainland Chinese) and aboriginal dialects
Major imports
Timber, wheat, maize and cotton
Major exports
clothing, televisions, plastics
Currency
New Taiwan dollar
Gross National Product
46,260 million US dollars (1981)
Status
National republic

Land and climate

The Chungyang Shanmo mountains run from north to south and cover almost three-quarters of the island. In the east, they rise steeply from the coast, but in the west they slope gently down towards alluvial plains, the island's only arable land. The range includes many peaks over 3,000 m, the highest being Yushan (3,996 m). The main rivers are the Tan-Shui Ch'i flowing north and the Cho-Shui Ch'i flowing west. The climate is subtropical in the north and tropical in the south but is strongly affected by ocean currents such as the warm Kuroshio current from Japan. Summer temperatures average 20° to 30°C and winter temperatures about 15°C. The summer monsoons bring floods.

People and places

Apart from 150,000 aborigines, the 15.7 million Taiwanese are all descended from Chinese settlers from the Fukien and Kuomintang provinces. About 45% of the people live in rural areas and are engaged in agriculture. Settlements around paddy fields are highly concentrated, particularly in the south where water is scarce. In the north and in the hills, villages are smaller and more scattered. The only ports are Kee-Lung, serving Taipei the capital, Kao-Hsiung in the south-west and Hua-Lien in the east. Most of the industrial development is based around these towns.

Industry

Traditionally an agricultural community, Taiwan is gradually becoming industrialized, although only 12% of the population is engaged in manufacturing industries. Natural resources are limited, so manufacturing industries based on imported raw materials have grown up around Kee-Lung and Kao-Hsiung—the main ports. The textile industry is very important, accounting for 10% of Taiwan's exports. Other exports include chemical products, electrical appliances, cement, paper, sugar and machinery.

The Philippines
(Republika ng Pilipinas)

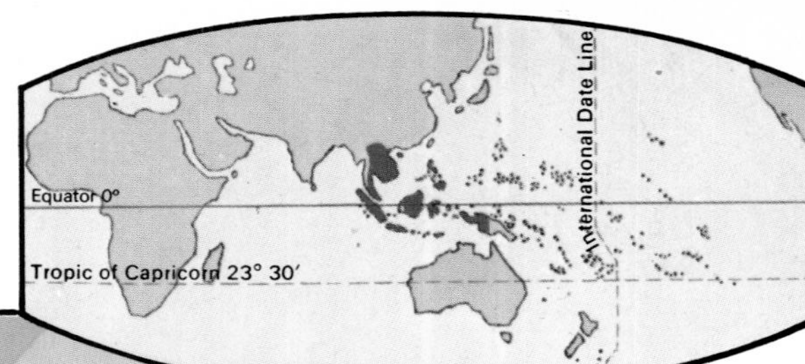

Statistics
Area
300,000km²/115,830 sq miles
Location
4°25′-21°20′N;
116°55′-126°40′E
Climate
tropical monsoon
Population
49,558,000 (1981)
Population density
165 per km²/428 per sq mile
Capital
Quezon city: 1,100,000 (1980)
Largest city
Manila: 1,600,000 (1980)
Languages
Filipino, English, Spanish
Gross National Product
5,355 million US dollars
Major imports
machinery, fuel, transport equipment, metals, foodstuffs, textiles
Major exports
timber, coconuts and coconut products, sugar, abaca (manila hemp) copper
Currency
peso (100 centavos = 1 peso)
Gross National Product
39,010 million US dollars (1981)
Status
independent republic
The Filipino people are basically Malay, but there has been extensive inter-marriage with Chinese and Spanish settlers.

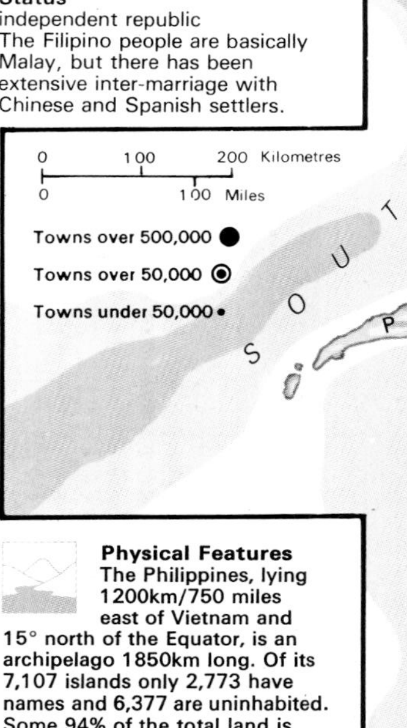

Physical Features
The Philippines, lying 1200km/750 miles east of Vietnam and 15° north of the Equator, is an archipelago 1850km long. Of its 7,107 islands only 2,773 have names and 6,377 are uninhabited. Some 94% of the total land is accounted for by the 11 major islands, each of which has an area exceeding 259 km². Luzon (108,380km²) and Mindanao (94,630km²) are the two largest; the others are Samar, Negros, Palawan, Panay, Mindoro, Leyte, Bohol and Masbate and Cebu—the most densely populated. A north-south mountain range of volcanic origin runs the length of the archipelago; its densely-forested slopes leave only narrow coastal plains. The rivers are fast-flowing and most drain north; the three longest, each over 320km, are the Cagayan, on Luzon, and the Agusan and Rio Grande on Mindanao. These two islands also have the most extensive lowland areas in the archipelago, and there are other large plains on Panay and Western Negros. Mt. Apo, a dormant volcano on Mindanao, is the country's highest peak: 2,954m. The coast is fringed with coral reefs. East of Surigao, on Mindanao, is the Philippine Deep, 10,973m, thought to be one of the world's deepest ocean troughs.

Energy
The Philippines' greatest engineering feat, the Pantabangan Dam in central Luzon, was completed in 1973. Adding to the country's hydro-electric output, it is also used for irrigation and flood control. A new project is geothermal power using underground steam. The first geothermal plant was set up at Tiwi, Luzon, and more geothermal wells are being dug. By 1990, Tiwi's estimated potential of 600 megawatts—enough to supply all Luzon, including Manila—should be realized. By that time, the total geothermal production is expected to cut the country's oil imports by 60%.

Climate
The Philippines are humid and warm. The average temperature at sea level is 27°C, but about 9°C lower in the mountains. Rainfall, varying from 102cm to 508cm, is heavy in the east particularly during the October-March north-east monsoon. At the same time it is dry in the west. From June to November, typhoons are a constant hazard, especially in Luzon and Samar, where high winds cause wide-spread damage and torrential rain leads to flooding and soil erosion.

Forestry
Nearly half of the total land area is covered with rain forests with over 3,000 tree species. About 60% of this forest, which is government-owned, is of commercial value—many of the hardwoods are especially suited to the furniture and construction industries—but is not yet fully exploited. Timber and wood veneers are the country's leading export making it the world's sixth largest lumber producer. Other forest products include gums, tan and dye barks, bamboo, rattan and vegetable oils.

Agriculture
Agriculture, employing 60% of the work force, dominates the economy. One half of all cultivated land is used for rice, Other domestic crops include maize, sweet potatoes and bananas. The main cash crops are coconuts, sugar and abaca (the fibre of this plant, Manila Hemp, is used in rope making). With 310 million coconut trees giving almost 10 billion nuts a year, the Philippines accounts for 44% of the world's coconut output and is its leading coconut producer. Some 12 million Filipinos are engaged in coconut growing or processing; coconuts and coconut products are the country's second largest export after timber The third major export is sugar, from Luzon, Negros and Panay, followed by abaca, grown on Luzon, Samar and Leyte. Other export crops are tobacco, coffee and pineapples.

Mining and industry
The Philippines is rich in minerals and ranks as a major world producer of gold, which is found on Luzon. Other important deposits being exploited on Luzon are copper, chromite, lead, zinc and iron; silver and manganese are also mined. Industrialization is slow and most of the country's factories process agricultural crops such as coconuts, sugar, rice and tobacco. Coconut-based manufactures, for example, inlcude margarine, soap, cosmetics, cattle-food and pesticides. Textile factories and cement works have been established recently.

Cities
The largest city and former capital is Manila, situated at the mouth of the Pasig river on the west coast of Luzon. Heavy industry is centred south of the river, while light industry lies to the north. The great urban concentration around Manila is known as Metro Manila and has a population of 7,000,000. Metro Manila comprises four cities and 17 municipalities; the largest of these, after Manila itself, is Quezon City, the capital. Lying to the north-east, Quezon is the seat of government offices and the University of the Philippines.

Communications
The road network is one of the best in Asia and is 60% hard-surfaced. Although trains run on Luzon and Panay, these are in competition with buses and planes. Altogether, four domestic airlines operate inter-island services between some 80 airports. Shipping is vitally important. Manila, handling 80% of all shipping, is the main port: its north harbour takes domestic traffic, the south harbour handles international trade. Other international ports are Cebu—more important than Manila for inter-island shipping—Iloilo, Davao, Zamboanga and Bacolod.

VIETNAM

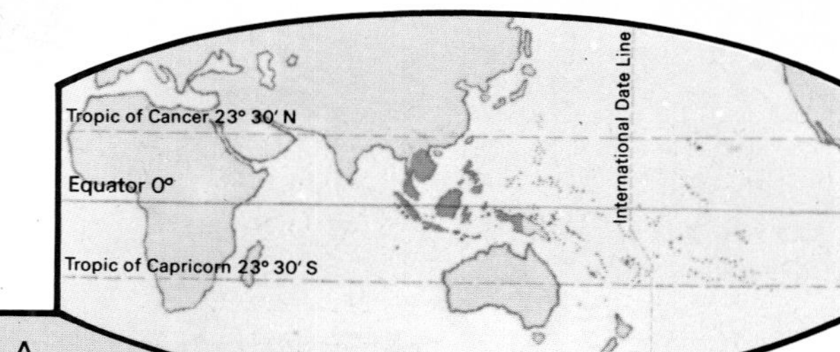

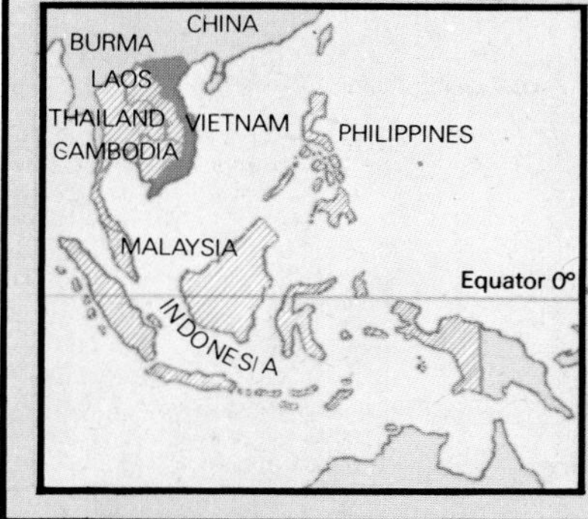

C H I N A
Ha Giang
Fan Si Pan 3142m
Lao Cai
Lai Chau
TONKIN MOUNTAINS
Da (Black)
Hong (Red)
Song Lo
Pon Loung 2985m
Langson
Thai Nguyen
Tonkin Lowland
Major centres
Large towns
Small towns
Viet Tri
Bac Ninh
HANOI
Hoa Binh
Hai Duong
Quang Yen
Haiphong
Nam Dinh
Ninh Binh
Gulf of Tonkin
VIETNAM
Phou Lai Leng 2711m
Vinh
LAOS
ANNAMESE CHAIN
Dong Hoi
Former demarcation line 22nd July 1954
m: 3000, 2000, 1500, 1000, 400, 200, 0, 200
f: 9000, 6000, 4500, 3000, 1200, 600, 0, 600
Quang Tri
Hue
Da Nang
Ngok Linh 2598m
Quang Ngai
An Nhon
Qui Nhon
Central Highlands
CAMBODIA
Nha Trang
Loc Ninh
Di Linh Plateau
Da Lat
Phan Rang
Saigon
Phan Thiet
Mekong
HO CHI MINH CITY
My Tho
Gô Công
Can Tho
Long Xuyen
Phu Quoc
Cochin China
Gulf of Siam
Quan Long
SOUTH CHINA SEA
Kilometres 0 50 100 150
0 50 100
Miles

Climate
Although both regions have a tropical monsoonal climate, the North has more pronounced seasons because of higher latitude. Average temperatures in Hanoi range from 16°C in January to 29°C in July, but in Saigon there is little variation: 27°C in January, 30°C in July. Most rain comes in summer with the SW monsoon: Hanoi receives an average of 177 cm, Ho Chi Minh City 203 cm, while parts of the Tonkin mountains and Annamese Chain receive over 406 cm. A feature of winter in the north is the 'crachin' or drizzle which permits the cultivation of an extra rice crop. Coastal areas in the south which are exposed to the NE monsoon, may receive up to 25 cm of rain in January.

Physical features
Vietnam is a mountainous country. The Annamese chain stretches almost the entire length of the country, with several peaks more than 2,000 m high. This range spreads eastwards to the sea, leaving only a narrow coastal plain. In the south, the mountains give way to the vast alluvial delta of the Mekong river, covering 37,814 km². Vietnam's other great lowland region is in the north: the Red River delta extending over 14,502 km². This area, liable to severe flooding, is bordered to the west by the rugged Tonkin mountains which rise to over 3,000 m in places. Some 80% of Vietnamese live on the deltas where population densities reach 1,525 per km². The Mekong delta has extensive swamps.

Agriculture
Vietnam is an agricultural or, more specifically, rice-growing country. In the north, 90% of cultivated land – mostly in the Tonkin lowlands—is devoted to rice, producing two or three crops a year. The remaining farmland is used chiefly for groundnuts, cotton, sugar and maize. South Vietnam's arable land, concentrated in the Mekong delta, yields only one crop of rice a year. Other major crops include rubber, sugar, tobacco, tea and cinnamon. Fish is the main source of protein: 250,000 South Vietnamese and twice as many North Vietnamese work as fishermen in the Gulf of Tonkin and the South China Sea. About two-thirds of Vietnam is forested. The tropical forests on the interior highlands mainly consist of valuable hardwoods such as teak, but the lumber industry is still underdeveloped.

The recent Vietnamese conflict seriously affected agriculture, industry, transport, trade, etc. As the immediate post-war period is one of confusion and change, the facts here relate to normal conditions. When the war between North and South Vietnam ended, the country was officially reunited in July 1976.

Vietnam
(Socialist Republic of Vietnam)
Area
329,566 km²/127,246 sq miles
Location
8°40′ – 23°15′ N
102°20′ – 109°30′ E
Population
55,707,000 (1981)
Population density
169 per km²/438 per sq mile
Capital
Hanoi: 2,000,000 (1981)
Largest City
Ho Chi Minh City: 3,500,000 (1981
Language
Vietnamese
Gross National Product
not available
Major imports
machinery, transport equipment, petroleum, foodstuffs, textiles
Major exports
coal, teak and forest products, rubber tea, groundnuts, copra
Currency
dong (100 hào = 1 dong)

Cities
Ho Chi Minh City, formerly called Saigon, has a greater urban population of 3.5 million. Its wide avenues, reflecting its French heritage, contrast sharply with the shanty towns developing round the perimeter. Built on the Saigon river, the city is a major port with 5 km of quays and an industrial centre. Hanoi, at the confluence of three rivers, is protected against floods by dikes 15 m high. A feature of the old city are its eleventh-century pagodas, while the modern sectors were built by the French in the nineteenth century. Hanoi is the industrial and commercial centre of the north.

Mining
At Quang Yen, north of the Red River, northern Vietnam has S.E. Asia's richest coal field; the 3 million tonnes mined annually meet domestic needs and provide 1 million tonnes for export. Iron ore is mined at Thai Nguyen – also the site of a major steel works, and of phosphate mines. The phosphate is used to manufacture fertilizer at Lao Cai. Other deposits include zinc, tin, antimony, bauxite and chromite. In contrast, southern Vietnam has few minerals apart from phosphate deposits on the Paracel islands, a small coal field near Da-Nang, and silica (used for glass-making), in coastal sands. There are also salt-beds along the coast from north to south.

Industry
North Vietnam is more industrialized than the south, largely because of its mineral wealth and investment from Russia and China. Hanoi is the main centre, with engineering and food processing plants, and a range of light industries. Haiphong, with shipyards, cement plants, engineering works and textile mills, comes second. Other developments include the steel complex at Thai Nguyen, a textile combine plants at Viet Tri. In southern Vietnam, industry – food processing and textiles – is concentrated in the Ho Chi Minh City area. Other manufacturers are glass, forest products, cement and cigarettes. In both countries handicrafts are important.

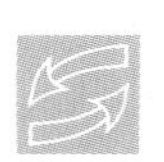

Transport
Inland waterways are vital in both North and South Vietnam. The south is served by the great Mekong River and its branches, when in the north the Red River, the Black River and the Song Lo are important. Hanoi stands at the confluence of these three rivers and is also the hub of the country's railways which link it with China, Dong Hoi and the sea port of Haiphong, the only port for ocean-going ships. The south has an equally sparse rail network – the main line runs from Ho Chi Minh City to Hue – but twice as many roads as the north. Internal air services are being developed and both Hanoi and Ho Chi Minh City have international airports.

Cambodia

Laos

Cambodia (Kampuchea) and Laos

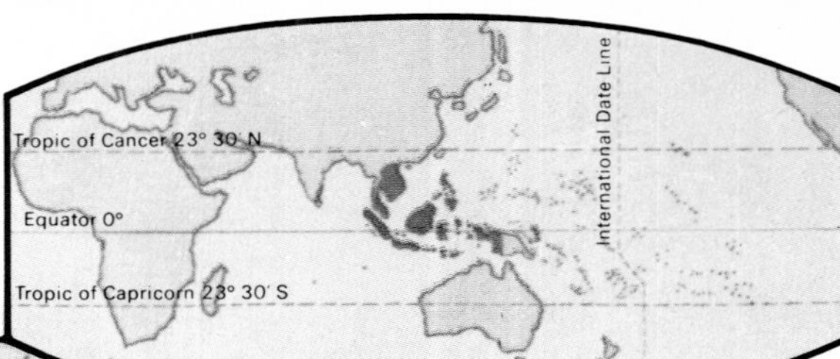

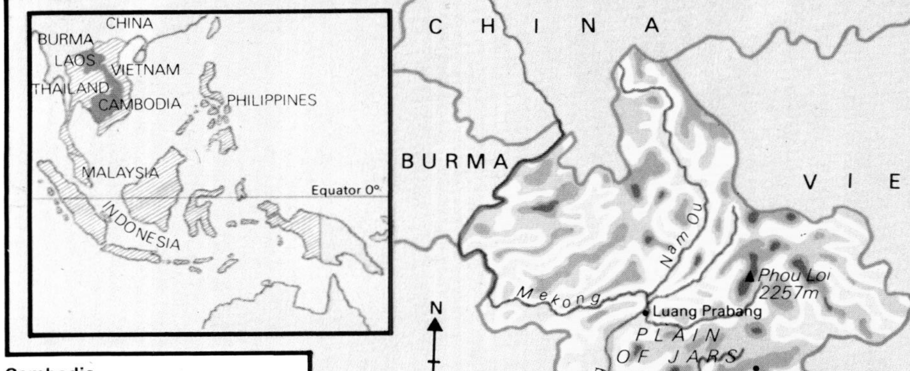

Cambodia
Area
181,033 km²/69,897 sq miles
Location
10°-14°55' N
103°-107°40' E
Population
7,090,000 (1981)
Population density
39 per km²/101 per sq mile
Capital and largest city
Phnom Penh: 500,000 (1981)
Language
Khmer
Major imports
petroleum, machinery, minerals, foodstuffs, chemicals, textiles
Major exports
rubber, rice, maize, forest products, pepper
Currency
riel (100 sen = 1 riel)
Gross National Product
not available
Status
independent republic

Laos
Area
236,800 km²/91,400 sq miles
Location
14°-22°40' N;
100°10'-107°50' E
Population
3,501,000 (1981)
Population density
15 per km²/38 per sq mile
Capital and largest city
Vientiane: 200,000 (1978)
Language
Lao
Major imports
petroleum, foodstuffs, machinery, transport equipment, textiles, chemicals
Major exports
tin, timber (teak), green coffee
Currency
kip (100 at = 10 bi = 1 kip)
Gross National Product
290 million US dollars (1981)
Status
constitutional monarchy

Climate
The climate in both Laos and Cambodia is tropical monsoonal with three seasons: a hot, wet season during the S-W monsoon, which lasts from June to October; a cool, dry season (November-February); and a hot, dry season (March-May). Some 80% of rain falls during the S-W monsoon period. In Cambodia, rainfall on the central plain is relatively low—127 cm a year—because of its sheltered position, but rises to over 508 cm in the Cardamon mountains. In Laos, most areas receive 178 cm of rain, with more than twice as much on high ground like the Bolovens Plateau. Temperatures in Cambodia range from 27°C in January, the coldest month, to 35°C in April. Corresponding temperatures in Laos are lower.

The information given here relates to normal conditions. Both Cambodia and Laos were involved in the recent Indochinese conflict with devastating consequences for agriculture, industry, communications, energy supplies, trade and population distribution.

Physical features
Laos and Cambodia have one major feature in common: the mighty Mekong River that rises in Tibet and flows 4,160 km to the South China Sea. In Laos, the Mekong forms the western boundary with Thailand. With its tributaries, it is bordered by lowlands hemmed in by the Annamese Chain along the Vietnam frontier, and by the north-eastern mountains which are over 2,500 m high. Cambodia is like a great saucer. The mountains of the Phanom Dang Raek range and the Cardamons, which rise to 914 m, edge the central lowland which has the Tonle Sap Lake and the Mekong river as its focal points. During the S-W monsoon, flood waters from the Mekong surge into the Tonle Sap: while in the dry season the lake covers 2,590 km² and is 1.5 m deep, in the rainy season its area increases to 10,360 km² and its depth to 15 m. This flooding is vital for rice growing.

Transport
Cambodia has some 19,312 km of navigable rivers and canals and Phnom Penh is an international port, able to take ships of up to 4,000 tonnes. These waterways are an indispensable means of transport, especially in the north and west, as roads mainly serve the south-east. The rail network consists of two lines linking Phnom Penh to Thailand and to the country's only ocean port, Kompong Som. In Laos, where there are no railways and few roads, the Mekong is the main highway. Away from the river and its tributaries, oxen are used. Elephants are also important as work animals—the country was once called Lanxang 'the land of a million elephants'. Both countries are developing domestic air services and Phnom Penh and Vientiane have international airports.

Fishing
In both countries, fish is the most important source of protein. Cambodia has the greatest freshwater fish resources in South-East Asia and 70% of the Cambodian catch comes from the Tonle Sap. Most fishermen are also farmers, except in the Tonle Sap. Nearly all the catch is used locally, half of it as dried fish. Marine fishing in the Gulf of Siam is of lesser importance. In Laos, the fish resources of the Mekong are not yet fully exploited.

Mining
Tin, from Phong Tiou, is Laos' leading export. Major reserves of iron ore in Xieng Khouang province have not yet been exploited; neither have smaller deposits of coal, lead and gold in the north, and copper in the south. In Cambodia, known mineral resources are few. Phosphate is mined near Kampot and a small quantity of gold and precious stones mined in the north-west. There is iron ore in the north but it remains unexploited.

Industry
Industry is primarily based on processing raw materials. In Cambodia most provincial capitals have rice mills, sugar refineries and textile mills. Other industries which have been established in major centres, notably Phnom Penh and Kompong Som, include vehicle-assembly plants, cement works and distilleries. In Laos, where large-scale operations are limited to rice-milling and saw-milling, cottage industries are important: hand-weaving, pottery, silver-engraving, leather-curing and wood-carving. Some light industries have also been introduced, producing cigarettes, soft drinks and shoes. In both countries, ambitious hydro-electric schemes are planned along the Mekong which should contribute to industrialization.

Agriculture
Both countries are agricultural with 80% of the population engaged in farming. The main areas under cultivation, where 9 out of 10 farmers grow rice, are the Mekong lowlands in Laos and the Cambodian central plain. Poor irrigation facilities mean that rice yields in both countries are among the lowest in monsoon Asia: Laos has to import rice although, in good years, Cambodia has a small surplus available for export. In Cambodia maize and rubber are grown in the south, and there are small pepper, tea and coffee plantations in the south-west. Other cash-crops include tobacco, cotton and kapok. Commercial crops grown in Laos are maize, tobacco, cotton, coffee and, in the north, opium. As most people in both countries are Buddhists and therefore vegetarians, animals such as water buffalo are mainly raised for work. The timber industry is more developed in Laos, where forests cover 70% of the area, than in Cambodia which is 50% forested.

People
In Cambodia, the majority of the people are Khmer. There are a number of urban minorities like the Chinese and Vietnamese, and other groups like the Cham, and highland peoples like the Jarai. In Laos, most of the population is Lao, but there are large minorities of other peoples like the Miao.

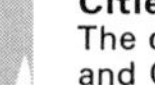

Cities
The capitals of Laos and Cambodia are both on the Mekong River. Vientiane, like Laos' other towns, is small: a famous sight is the That Luang, a 16th-century temple. Some 800 km further south, where the Mekong meets the Tonle Sap River, is Phnom Penh, the Cambodian capital. Although there are another 290 km/180 miles to the sea, Phnom Penh is a busy port. It is also the Republic's main industrial centre with food processing plants, rice mills, distilleries and textile factories. The other major towns in Cambodia are Battambang, Kompong Cham and Kampot. The ancient city of Angkor Wat was the capital of the Khmer empire (*c.*800-1430 AD).

Thailand

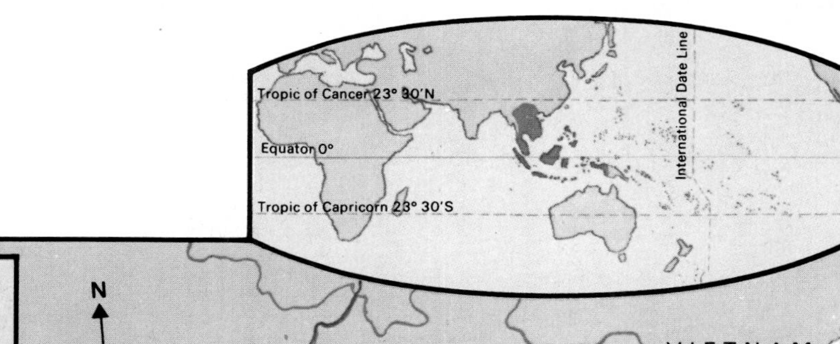

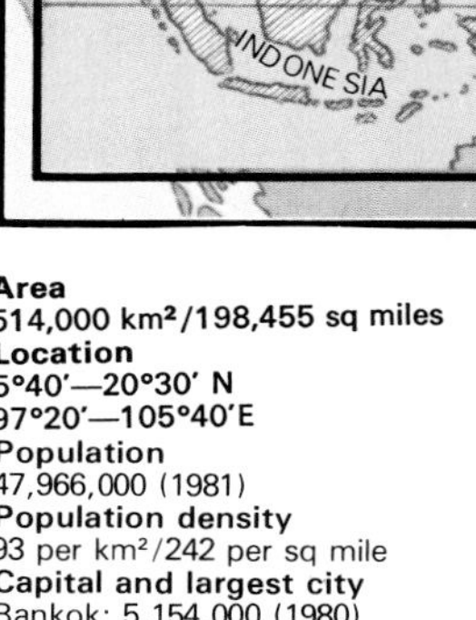

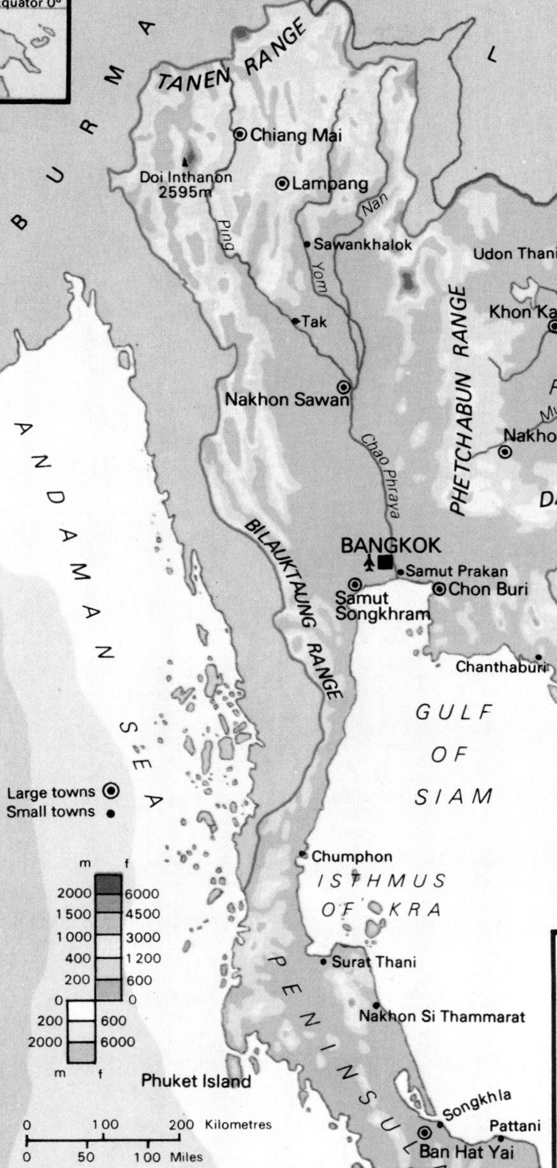

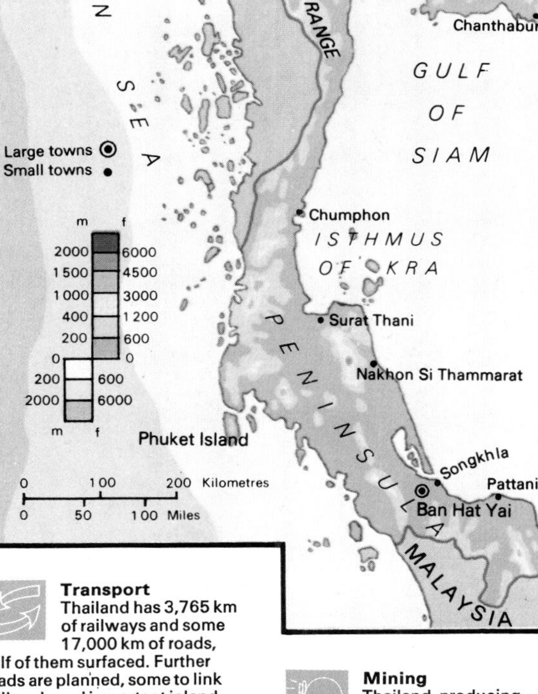

Physical features
The northern mountains which include Thailand's highest, Doi Inthanon, 2,595 metres high, give way to a central plain drained by tributaries of the Chao Phraya. The lower part of this plain corresponds to the Chao Phraya delta which has rich alluvial soil and is subject to seasonal flooding. This area is used almost entirely for rice and is the most densely settled. The Korat plateau, in the north-east, has an average height of 150 metres to the east, the low Phu Phan hills separate the lakes and swamps of the Mekong basin from the Chi-Mun rivers, while the mountains extend along the Burmese border and into the peninsula. The Chao Phraya is Thailand's principal river. One of its tributaries, the Nan, which flows 1,000 km before joining the Chao Phraya is the longest. The coasts are largely fringed with mangrove swamps and there are numerous offshore islands. The forests and river valleys of Thailand are alive with many kinds of wild animal such as the tiger, leopard and monkey, as well as exotic species of birds.

Forests
About 60% of Thailand is forested. Deciduous trees predominate in the north with tropical evergreen forests further south. The northern forests include teak which provides Thailand with its fifth most important export. Elephants and other animals are used for hauling the cut timber to extraction points—veneer quality logs are then transported by rail, but the majority go by water. The logs are drifted singly to the rafting stations at Tak and Sawankhalok where they are tied together in batches of 150 -350 before floating on to Bangkok. Rafting is confined to the early and late flood seasons: July-August, November-December. Other forest products are yangwood, firewood, charcoal, rattan, oil and bamboo. Extensive mangrove forests along the southern shores of the Gulf of Siam are now being exploited to produce timber and charcoal.

Industry
Industrial activity is basically related to processing raw materials such as sugar, tin, timber, tobacco and rice: there are, for instance, over 6,000 rice mills. In recent years, however, the government has established other industries. These include cement works, textile factories, paper mills, chemical plants, steel rolling mills and oil refineries. Energy requirements are partly met by hydro-electricity, but mostly by electricity generated in thermal plants using gas or solid fuel such as lignite. A nuclear power station is being built at Chon Buri. While major industries are concentrated in Bangkok, many world-famous Thai products are handmade in villages. These cottage industries include silk spinning and weaving, lacquer work, nielloware, silver and gold engraving, esparto grass weaving, wood carving, ceramics, jewelry and basketry.

Area
514,000 km²/198,455 sq miles
Location
5°40'—20°30' N
97°20'—105°40'E
Population
47,966,000 (1981)
Population density
93 per km²/242 per sq mile
Capital and largest city
Bankok: 5,154,000 (1980)
Language
Thai
GNP
9,369 million US dollars
Major imports
transport equipment, iron and steel, machinery, petroleum
Major exports
rice, maize, timber, tin, rubber
Currency
baht (100 satangs = 1 baht)
Gross National Product
36,900 million US dollars (1981)
Status
constitutional monarchy

Climate
Thailand, with a tropical monsoon climate, has three main seasons: dry, rainy and cool. The hottest and driest month is April, when Bangkok has temperatures of 33°C and in the north, Chiang Mai has 31°C. The cooler period lasts from November to February when temperatures in Bangkok fall to 24°C and in Chiang Mai to 19°C. The rainy season, caused by the southwest monsoon, extends from May to September and most areas receive three-quarters of their rainfall during these months. Amounts vary according to distance from the sea and exposure to the prevailing monsoon: Chiang Mai has 135 cm and Bangkok 88 cm of rain a year. The peninsular has less temperature variation and is generally wetter. Here, rainfall is recorded at Phuket as 228 cm a year.

Bangkok
In 1971, Bangkok and neighbouring Thon Buri were merged and became Bangkok metropolis. About half of Thailand's urban population lives in this metropolitan area which is the country's chief port and leading industrial city. Situated on the Chao Phraya river some 30 km inland, the city is known as the Venice of the East because of its many *khlongs* or canals. The administrative area is centred on the Grand Palace, while the commercial sector largely corresponds to the Chinese quarter, Sam Peng. Heavy industry is located near the port which handles nearly all Thailand's imports. Less than a third of these pass through the interior: most are either consumed or processed in the capital.

Transport
Thailand has 3,765 km of railways and some 17,000 km of roads, half of them surfaced. Further roads are planned, some to link railheads and important inland waterways with agricultural areas. There are 9,180 km of canals and rivers and over 10 million people live along waterways using boats for transport. Over 80% of rice produced is carried to mills by water and every year some 200,000 logs are floated down the rivers. Bulk cargoes, such as petroleum and building materials also move by water, both inland and along the coast. Bangkok is the main port, handling 85% of the country's foreign trade. There are several domestic air routes and Bangkok has an international airport.

Mining
Thailand, producing over 31,000 tonnes of tin a year, is the world's third largest supplier of this mineral. There are about 650 tin mines, mostly on the peninsula and Phuket island, and the ore goes to an oil-fired tin smelter on Phuket. Tin ranks as Thailand's fourth most important export. There are also extensive deposits of wolfram. Other mineral resources include small amounts of lead, antimony, iron ore, manganese, gypsum and fluorite. Lignite, a brown coal, is processed into solid fuel.

Agriculture
Thailand is a predominantly agricultural country. The main crop, covering three-quarters of all cultivated land, is rice. Most of the rice farms, which employ 72% of the population, are situated in the central lowland area. Annual production exceeds 13 million tonnes. Some two million tonnes are exported—mainly to Indonesia, Japan, Malaysia and India—and account for 36% of Thailand's export earnings. Other major export crops are maize and jute, grown in the northern uplands, and rubber, which comes from the southern region: Thailand is the world's third largest rubber producer. Coconuts, grown along the sandy coasts, are also important. Livestock farming—cattle and water-buffalo—is being developed in the north-east; poultry and eggs already form a significant export item. An annual fishing catch of 1.5 million tonnes exceeds domestic requirements so some, particularly shell-fish, is exported. The country's marine fishing grounds cover three-quarters of the shores on the Gulf of Thailand and the eastern shore between Burma and Malaysia.

Malaysia, Singapore and Brunei

(top left)
Malaysia
(top)
Singapore
Brunei (left)

Physical features
Malaysia consists of Peninsular or West Malaysia, which lies on mainland South-East Asia between Thailand and Singapore, and East Malaysia comprising Sabah and Sarawak on the north-west coast of Borneo (some 600 km lie between East and West Malaysia.) The peninsular has a series of central mountain ridges bordered by narrow coastal plains. More than 58% of West Malaysia is over 152m above sea level and the highest point is Gunong Tahan 2,189m. South of the Pahang, the largest river, are the Johore lowlands. Sabah and Sarawak are both mountainous (Mt Kinabalu is Malaysia's highest peak, 4,101m) with very narrow coastal belts. The two main rivers are the Rajang and the Kinabatangan. Brunei, which is divided into two by Sarawak, consists of a fertile coastal plain rising to a hilly interior. Singapore, made up of the main island and 54 islets, is low-lying and swampy (although many areas have been drained) with a central hill region. The island is criss-crossed by streams, yet the main river, Sungei Seletar, is only 14.5 km long.

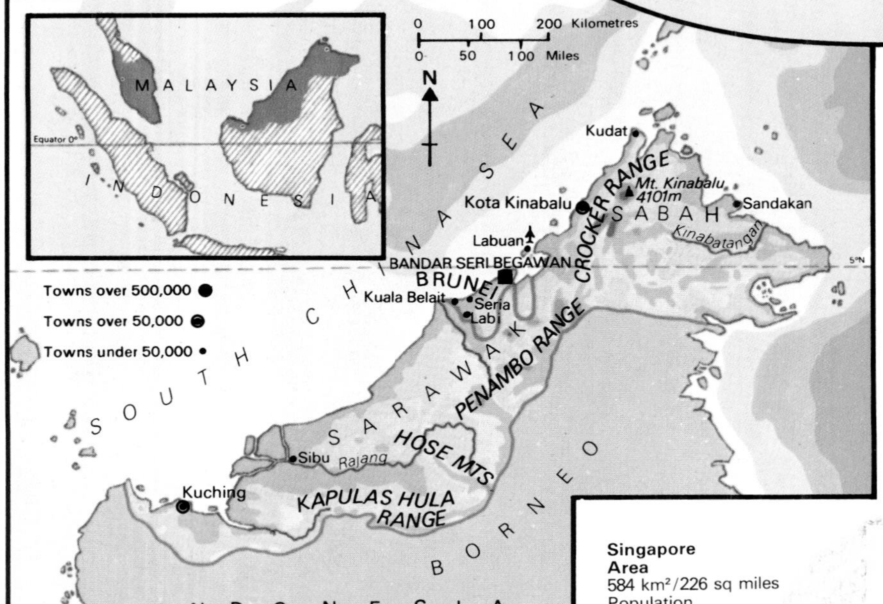

Malaysia
Area
333,403 km²/127,316 sq miles
Location
1° – 7° N ; 100° – 119° E
Climate
equatorial
Population
14,200,000 (1981)
Population density
43 per km²/112 per sq mile
Capital and largest city
Kuala Lumpur: 1,080,000 (1980)
Language
Bahasa Malaysia
Major imports
machinery and transport equipment, manufactured goods, foodstuffs
Major exports
rubber, timber, tin, palm oil, iron ore
Currency
Malaysian dollar (100 cents = 1 dollar)
Gross National Product
26,110 million US dollars (1981)
Status
independent constitutional monarchy

Singapore
Area
584 km²/226 sq miles
Population
2,444,000 (1981)
Population density
4,185 per km²/10,814 per sq mile
Capital and largest city
City of Singapore: 2,334,000 (1977)
Languages
Malay, Mandarin, Tamil, English
Major imports
foodstuffs, machinery, petroleum
Major exports
petroleum products, rubber, ships
Currency
Singapore dollar (100 cents = 1 dollar)
Gross National Product
12,800 million US dollars (1981)
Status
independent republic

Brunei
Area
5,765 km²/2,226 sq miles
Population
233,000 (1981)
Population density
40 per km²/105 per sq mile
Capital and largest city
Bandar Seri Begawan: 58,000
Language
Malay
Major imports
machinery, transport equipment, manufactured goods, foodstuffs, chemicals
Major exports
crude oil, natural gas, petroleum products
Currency
Brunei dollar (100 cents = 1 dollar)
Gross National Product
4,050 million US dollars (1981)
Status
independent sultanate

Climate
The climate is humid and hot. East Malaysia and Brunei are slightly hotter than the peninsular and Singapore. Rainfall is affected by the monsoons and is heaviest from November to March during the north-east monsoon ; the period from June to October is relatively dry except along the south-west coast of Sabah. But rainfall everywhere varies with altitude. In Brunei, for example, the coast receives 250 cm/100" a year, while parts of the interior receive 500 cm/200".

Forests
A quarter of the forest, which covers 70% of West Malaysia and 80% of East Malaysia, is commercially exploited, making timber the country's second largest export. In Brunei, three-quarters of which is forested, timber exports are restricted and the emphasis is on wood products : a new veneer and plywood factory at Muara will use timber. from the Temburong district and forests in the Kuala Belait and Labi areas will eventually supply a pulp mill at Kuala Belait.

Industry
Of the three countries, Singapore is the most industrialized. There are engineering works, shipyards, oil refineries, petrochemical plants, saw mills and textile, electrical and food-processing factories. In Malaysia, traditional industries are concerned with agricultural and mineral products : rubber-processing, saw milling, tin-smelting, copra-milling and, recently, oil-refining. New industries include steel, vehicle assembly, chemicals and the manufacture of consumer goods. Brunei is undergoing industrialization : there are plans for a glass factory using local silica, a petrochemical plant, a pulp mill, a plywood factory and a sago-processing plant.

Agriculture
Malaysia's economy is largely based on agriculture and this employs more than half the work force. The country is the world's largest producer of rubber—which accounts for 32% of export earnings—palm oil and pepper. Other cash crops are coconuts and, of lesser importance, sago and tea. After rubber the second main crop is rice, supplying 90% of domestic requirements. Rubber and pepper are also grown in Brunei but here, agricultural products make up less than 1% of exports. In an effort to reduce food imports, Brunei is trying to increase rice production and to develop livestock farming. Singapore also has a high level of food imports, but is self-sufficient in pork, poultry and eggs, while intensive market gardening meets half the state's vegetable needs. There are also rubber and coconut plantations. Fishing is growing in importance and both Brunei and Malaysia export prawns—some to Singapore which is not self-sufficient in fish.

Cities
In Singapore, 9 out of 10 people live in the capital. To combat overcrowding (in some areas there are over 40,000 people per km²/100,000 per sq mile) the government sponsors rehousing programmes. The city, which includes an industrial sector, is a free port and much of the cargo handled is in transit. The capital of Malaysia, Kuala Lumpur, is near the west coast of the peninsular on the Kelang and Gombak rivers. It is the country's major industrial city and is served by the port of Kelang. Brunei's capital, Bandar Seri Begawan, is an agricultural market town and river port.

Transport
A causeway links Singapore to Malaysia where there are good road and rail networks, especially in the rubber and tin belt. East Malaysia and Brunei have few roads ; the only railway is in Sabah, so river transport predominates. The main shipping ports are Singapore (the fourth largest in the world) ; Penang and Kelang in West Malaysia ; Kota Kinabalu, Sandakan and Kuching in East Malaysia ; Muara and Kuala Belait in Brunei. There are international airports at Kuala Lumpur, Kota Kinabalu, Penang, Singapore and Bandar Seri Begawan.

Mining
Over a third of the world's tin supply comes from Malaysia, making it the world's largest tin producer. Deposits are concentrated in Peninsular Malaysia and the most important are found in the western belt running from Perak to Negri Sembilan. Tin accounts for 13% of exports. Iron ore and bauxite are also exported. The petroleum industry is expanding : oil strikes have been made off eastern Peninsular Malaysia and off Sabah and Sarawak ; petroleum and petroleum products already make up 5% of total exports. In Brunei, a leading petroleum producer, oil and natural gas are essential to the economy and account for 99% of export earnings. Most of the output, coming from the onshore field at Seria and the offshore fields of Ampa, Fairley and Champion, goes by pipeline to refineries in Sarawak. Brunei also has the world's biggest liquefied natural gas plant.

Indonesia

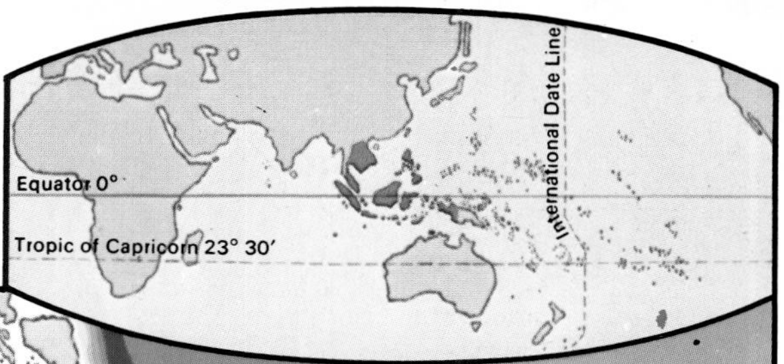

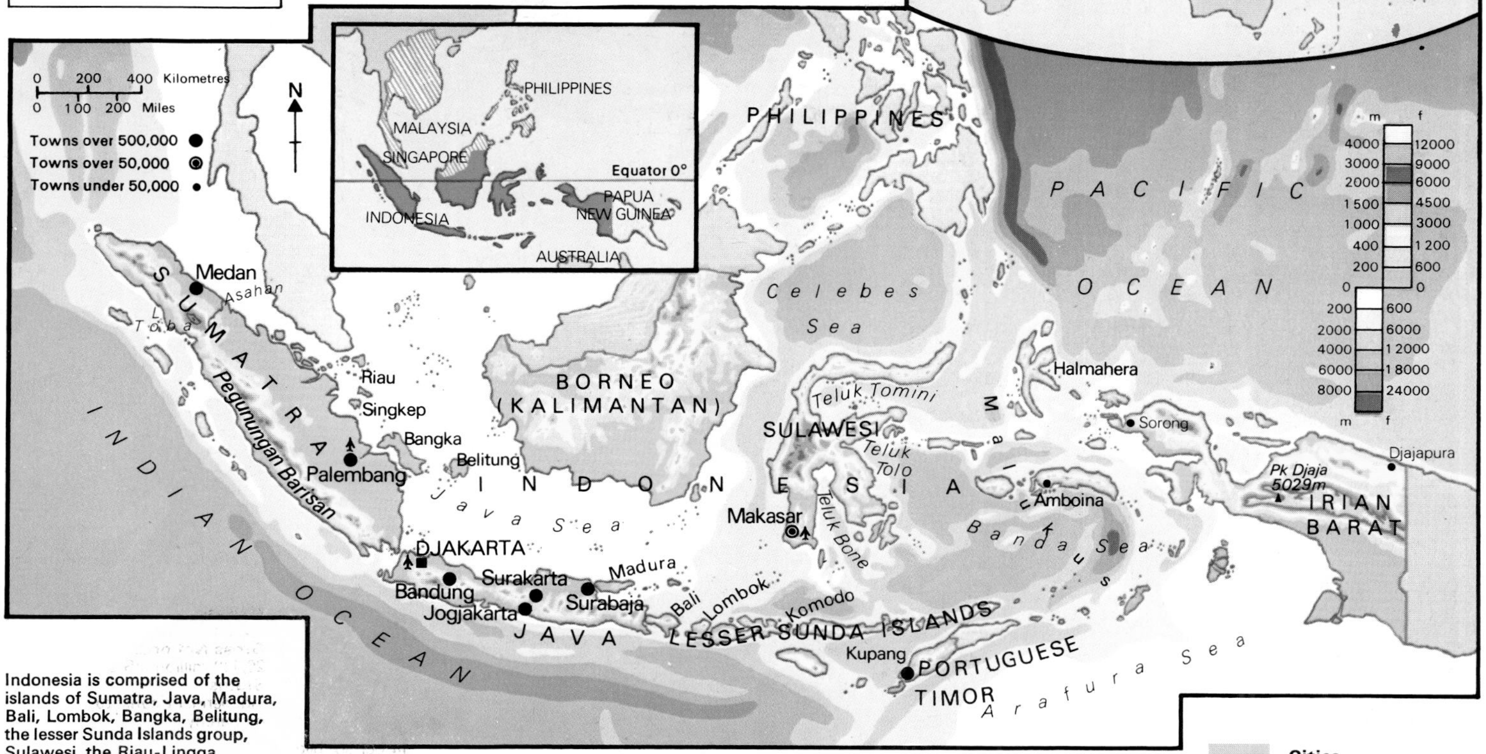

Indonesia is comprised of the islands of Sumatra, Java, Madura, Bali, Lombok, Bangka, Belitung, the lesser Sunda Islands group, Sulawesi, the Riau-Lingga Archipelago, the Maluku Islands, part of the islands of Borneo and Timor and the western half of the island of New Guinea (Irian Barat).

Land Area
1,904,344 km²/735,268 sq miles
Location
5°55'N-11°S; 95°-141°E
Population
149,451,000 (1981)
Population density
78 per km²/203 per sq mile
Capital and largest city
Djakarta: 5,500,000 (1981)
Language
Bahasa Indonesia
Major Imports
cotton, wheat flour, rice, machinery, fertilizers
Major Exports
oil, timber, rubber and latex products, tin, coffee
Currency
rupiah (100 sen=1 rupiah)
Gross National Product
78,750 million US dollars (1981)
Status
independent republic

Climate
Indonesia's position, straddling the equator, gives it a tropical climate. Temperatures range from 19°C to 36°C, with an average at sea level of 26°C. Humidity is high and rain is heavy throughout the year. In the very wet, mountainous zones, annual rainfall averages 609cm and Djakarta receives 203cm. In most areas rain is heaviest from November to March, the west monsoon season. In contrast, the east monsoon, coming from the dry interior of Australia from June to October, is not a major rainbearer and, in the extreme south-east, is even arid. Kupang, on Timor, for example, has only 3.7cm of rain during this five-month period and a few islands, like Komodo, are so parched that vegetation is very sparse.

Physical features
Indonesia, the largest country in South-East Asia, lies between the Indian and Pacific Oceans and occupies most of the Malay archipelago or East Indies. It consists of over 13,600 islands; the three largest—Kalimantan, Sumatra and Irian Barat—make up to 70% of the total land area. Nearly all the islands are mountainous. On some, like Sulawesi, the Malukus and the eastern Lesser Sundas, the land rises steeply straight from the sea; on others, there are lowland areas. Sumatra and Kalimantan have coastal swamps, while wide river valleys and alluvial plains characterize Java, Lombok and Bali. Indonesia's central mountain range reaches its highest point in Irian Barat at Mt Djaja (5029 m). The range includes over 400 volcanoes, 100 of which are active: on Bali, Gunung Agung, sacred as the home of the gods, last erupted in 1963.

Forests
About 60% of Indonesia is covered with dense forests. In coastal areas these forests are largely mangrove and nipa palm, while tropical rain forests grow in the interior. Timber production, which increases as new roads are built, is mainly carried out by men with the help of work animals, such as oxen and water buffaloes, rather than machines. Teak is the major timber export, followed by ebony, sandalwood and ironwood. Other important forest products are seeds used for drugs and dyes; mangrove bark for tannin; bamboo, rattan, resin; and cajuput oil, used in treating skin diseases. Tidal forests on Sumatra and Kalimantan are major sources of charcoal and fuel wood.

Agriculture
Indonesia is primarily agricultural; its rich lowlands and abundant rainfall create ideal conditions for farming, in which 80% of the population is engaged. The country is not, however, self-sufficient in the production of its staple food, rice, which is cultivated on both dry fields and terraced, wet fields. The latter, known as 'giant staircases to the heavens', are best because they yield two harvests a year. Other crops grown for domestic use include cassava, coconuts, peanuts, soya beans and sweet potatoes. The main cash crop is rubber. Other important exports are palm oil; coffee, which is grown on Java, Kalimantan, Bali and Sumatra; tea and tobacco, both produced on Java and Sumatra; sugar, mostly from Java; copra and spices. Recent projects affecting agriculture have included irrigation schemes—essential for rice—and transmigration, whereby Indonesians from overpopulated Java are moved to areas in need of workers

Crafts
Indonesia has many traditional crafts, but the most famous is batik, a method of hand-printing textiles. Starting with plain cloth, the batikmaker applies hot liquid wax to the areas he does not wish to dye, then dips the cloth into a vat of dye. The waxing and dyeing process is repeated for each colour, until the cloth is intricately patterned. Two other popular crafts are silver-work (practised in Jogjakarta on Java, Bali, South Sulawesi and Sumatra) and wood-carving. The best woodcarvers, who use modern themes influenced by the country's Hindu and Islamic heritage, are found on Bali and at Djapara.

Energy and industry
Indonesia has enough resources to provide for all her energy needs; wood, coal (which is mined in both Sumatra and Kalimantan) and oil are the major sources, but hydro-electricity is also important: three large plants are being built on the Asahan river in Sumatra and on the Djatiluhur and Brantas rivers in Java. Although Indonesia has industrial potential the economy is still basically agricultural, and less than 10% of the work force is engaged in manufacturing. Most major industries are connected with agriculture and mining: rubber-processing plants, rice and sugar mills, oil refineries, a fertilizer plant near the Palembang oil fields and a chemical works at Surabaja based on salt from Madura; the important textile industry uses yarns imported from overseas.

Mining
Indonesia's mineral wealth is vast. Petroleum and tin, mined on Bangka, Belitung and Singkep, are the most important. The republic is the largest oil producer in the Far East, production coming from Sumatra, Kalimantan and Java. Many of the oil fields are in dense jungle which makes drilling and transport difficult; helicopters are often used to bring men and equipment to the sites. About 15% of the crude oil produced is sufficient to supply domestic needs; the rest is exported. There is an important production of bauxite on the Riau islands, and nickel on Sulawesi and Halmahera. Other mineral deposits—not yet fully exploited, partly because of poor communications—include iron ore, manganese, copper, gold, silver, platinum and diamonds.

Cities
Although Java only comprises one-seventh of Indonesia's total land area, it is the most important island and the home of two out of three Indonesians. Djakarta, the country's capital, is on the island's north-west coast, built on swampy ground at the mouth of the Tji Liwung. The city, which has traditional bamboo-mat houses alongside concrete office blocks, is the republic's commercial and financial centre. Its port, Tandjung Priok, is the most important in Indonesia and handles nearly all imports which are then often re-shipped to other domestic ports. The republic's second and third largest cities are also on Java: Surabaja (2 million) is a major port and industrial centre; Bandung (1.4 million), on a volcanic plateau 610m/2,000 ft high, has many light industries. Other major cities are Medan (which has Indonesia's largest mosque) and Palembang, both on Sumatra, and Makasar.

Communications
Transport facilities vary from island to island. Java and Sumatra have adequate road networks, but in many other areas there may be no links between major settlements, and the local roads are unpaved. Rail transport is particularly important on Java, where the high population density makes it difficult to build new roads; Madura and Sumatra also have railways. Inter-island freight traffic moves by sea, while passenger traffic goes by air. The inter-island shipping fleet includes vessels from small barges to 500 tonne ships and serves some 300 ports; the three most important are Tandjung Priok, Surabaja and Belawan (Medan). A domestic air service, linking almost 40 towns, is provided.

Burma

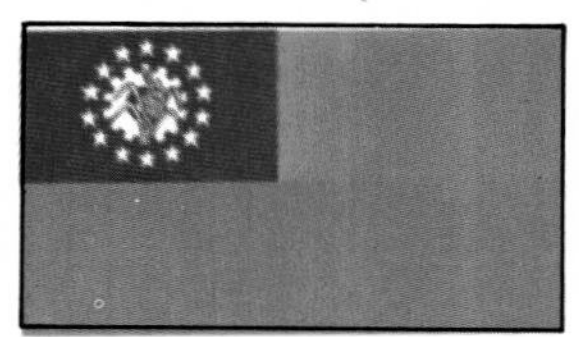

Area
676,580 km²/261,228 sq miles
Location
9°30'—28°35' N
92°10'—101°10' E
Population
34,109,000 (1981)
Population density
50 per km²/131 per sq mile
Capital and largest city
Rangoon: 2,186,000 (1980)
Language
Burmese
Major imports
machinery, transport equipment, textiles, metals
Major exports
rice, timber, rubber, minerals
Currency
kyat (1 kyat = 100 pyas)
Gross National Product
6,540 million US dollars (1981)
Status
independent republic

Physical features

Burma falls into three major regions: the western ranges, the central basin and the eastern plateaux. In the far north, mountains rise to 6,000 m: Hkakabo Ravi is the country's highest peak at 6,289 m. Running southwards are the western ranges. These stretch from the northern border with India to the Rangoon delta and include the Naga hills, the Letha Range, the Chin hills (Rongklang Range) and the Arakan Yoma. To the east is the 920 m high Shan plateau which becomes lower as it continues southwards into the Tenasserim peninsula. Between these two mountain systems is the central basin formed by the valleys of the Irrawaddy, Chindwin and Sittang rivers. The Irrawaddy and Sittang, divided in their middle courses by the Pegu Yoma, have adjoining deltas with a total area of 15,000 km². Although the 2,090 km long Irrawaddy is Burma's major river, the Salween is the longest. Rising in Tibet, it flows 2,815 km to the sea at Moulmein. Burma extends down the Tenasserim peninsula for over 300 km to Victoria Point—this is the narrowest region of the peninsula, only 50 km wide. The peninsula is a hilly region with peaks between 1,000 and 1,500 m while the west coast is studded with many islands.

Agriculture

Rice dominates the Burmese economy. Rice-fields, covering 70% of land under cultivation, are concentrated in the Irrawaddy delta. Although double-cropping is rare, Burma produces a surplus and is one of the world's leading exporters of rice. In drier areas—the middle Irrawaddy basin and the lower Cindwin valley—various crops are grown: maize, millet, sesame, tobacco, peanuts, cotton and pulses. There are sugar plantations in the Sittang valley and rubber is important on the Tenasserim peninsula. The government is developing jute cultivation in the delta so as to abolish the import of bags for rice. Other government schemes include irrigation projects and the increased use of fertilizers. Apart from rice, which accounts for 60% of total exports, rubber, pulses and oil-cake are exported. As Buddhists do not eat meat, cattle and buffalo are raised only for work. After rice, fish is the main food, coming mostly from rivers. Marine fishing is being developed.

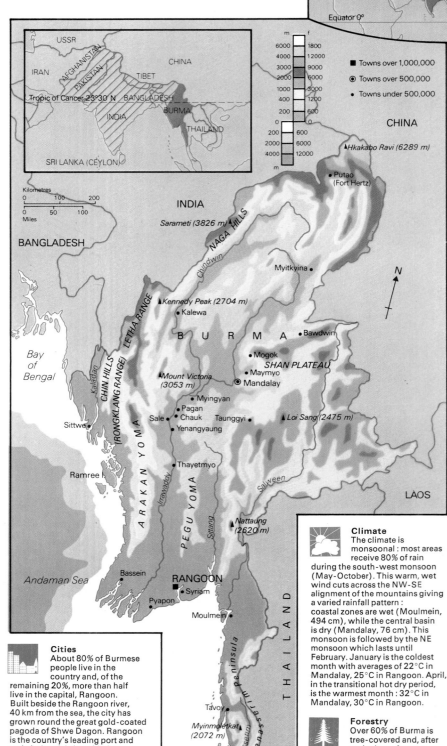

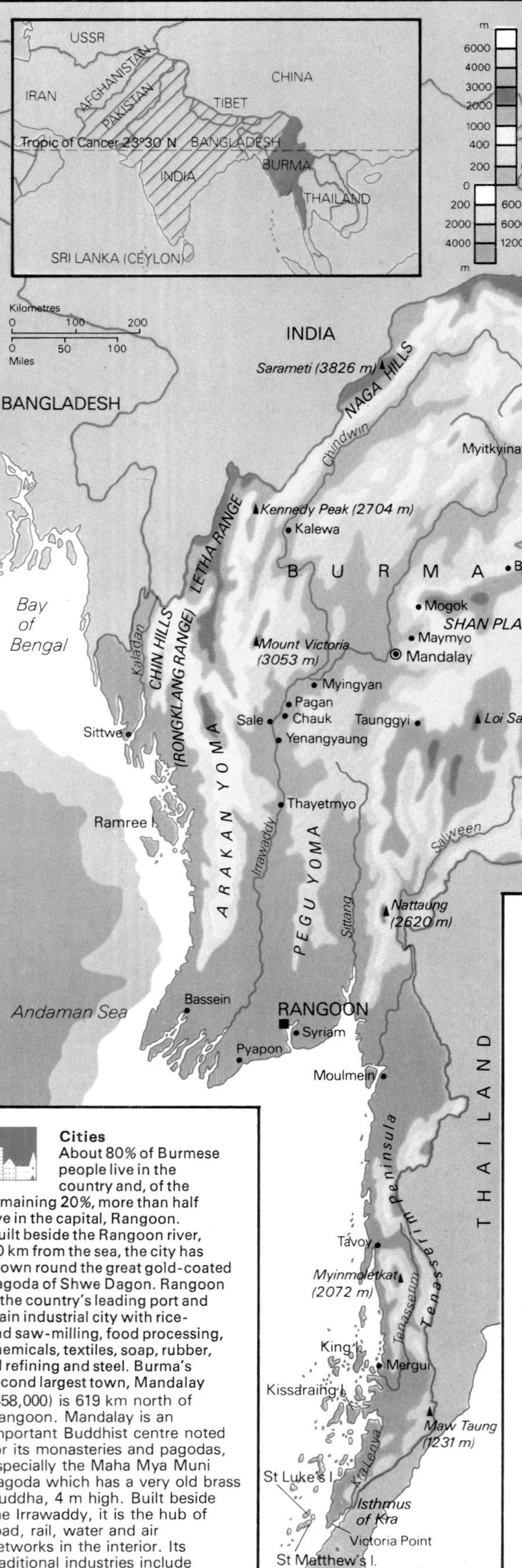

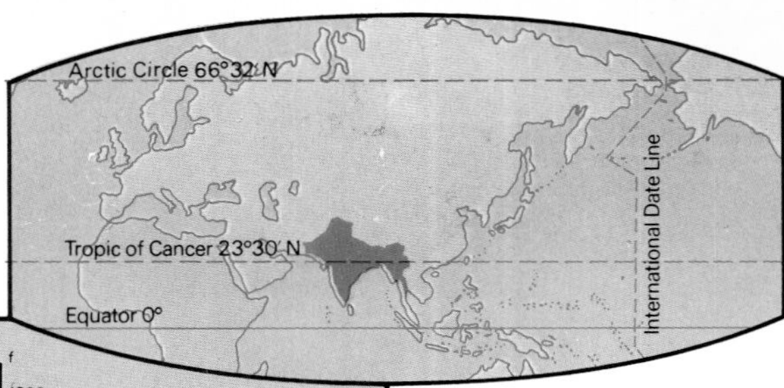

Cities

About 80% of Burmese people live in the country and, of the remaining 20%, more than half live in the capital, Rangoon. Built beside the Rangoon river, 40 km from the sea, the city has grown round the great gold-coated pagoda of Shwe Dagon. Rangoon is the country's leading port and main industrial city with rice- and saw-milling, food processing, chemicals, textiles, soap, rubber, oil refining and steel. Burma's second largest town, Mandalay (458,000) is 619 km north of Rangoon. Mandalay is an important Buddhist centre noted for its monasteries and pagodas, especially the Maha Mya Muni pagoda which has a very old brass Buddha, 4 m high. Built beside the Irrawaddy, it is the hub of road, rail, water and air networks in the interior. Its traditional industries include silk-weaving and jade-cutting. Other major towns include Moulmein and Mergui.

Climate

The climate is monsoonal: most areas receive 80% of rain during the south-west monsoon (May-October). This warm, wet wind cuts across the NW-SE alignment of the mountains giving a varied rainfall pattern: coastal zones are wet (Moulmein, 494 cm), while the central basin is dry (Mandalay, 76 cm). This monsoon is followed by the NE monsoon which lasts until February. January is the coldest month with averages of 22°C in Mandalay, 25°C in Rangoon. April, in the transitional hot dry period, is the warmest month: 32°C in Mandalay, 30°C in Rangoon.

Forestry

Over 60% of Burma is tree-covered and, after agriculture, forestry is the main occupation. Commercially, the most important forests grow in areas where rainfall is between 100 cm and 200 cm, especially on the Arakan Yoma, the Pegu Yoma and the Shan plateau. These monsoon forests produce teak, used for ships and furniture, also ironwood, used for railway sleepers. About 4,000 elephants are employed to haul logs to the river banks. The wood is then piled on bamboo rafts and floated downstream to the sawmills. Timber, mostly teak, accounts for 15% of exports. Swamps and mangroves cover the Irrawaddy delta.

Industry

Industrialization is still in its early stages. Traditional industries, rice-and saw-milling are based on the country's leading raw materials. New developments include textile factories at Rangoon, Myingyan and Paleik; fertilizer plants at Sale and Kynchaung; a steel works and a chemical plant at Rangoon and a cement works at Thayetmyo, fired by natural gas. Further industrialization partly depends on energy supplies. Current sources of power are a thermal plant at Rangoon and three hydro-electric stations. Larger supplies can undoubtedly be provided by an increased petroleum production and by harnessing the vast hydro-electric potential of Burma's rivers. About 1.5 million people are employed in the power, construction and manufacturing sectors. In rural areas, the state encourages the development of cottage industries such as ivory-carving, silver-work and weaving.

Mining

Burma's mineral wealth is largely under-exploited. The most important are petroleum, tin, tungsten and silver-lead. Oil-fields are situated along the valleys of the middle Irrawaddy and Chindwin with production centered on Chauk, Yenangyaung and Myingyan. The petroleum is refined at Chauk and Syriam, near Rangoon. Deposits of tin and tungsten occur in a belt running from the Shan plateau to the Tenasserim coast. The Bawdwin mines, also on the Shan plateau, yield lead, silver and zinc and, in smaller quantities, copper and nickel. Future mining developments could include coal found at Kalewa in the Chindwin valley and iron, at Taunggyi. More famous, though of less commercial value, are Burma's precious stones. Rubies, amethysts and sapphires, come from the mines at Mogok, in the Shan uplands; jade comes from Myitkyina in the extreme north, and gold from the banks of the Chindwin and Irrawaddy.

Transport

The Irrawaddy is the backbone of Burma's transport system. The river is navigable up to Myitkyina, 1,600 km from the sea, and its tributary, the Chindwin, is navigable for a further 650 km. The delta streams provide a 3,200 km network open to vessels and a canal, 96 km long, links the Sittang to the Irrawaddy. These inland waterways are essential to the rice trade: almost every ricefield is accessible by water and boats take the unhusked rice to the mills. Burma has four ports open to international shipping: Bassein, Moulmein, Sittwe and Rangoon—the country's main port, handling over 80% of exports. The waterway network is supplemented by rail. Branch lines spread out from the main line which runs from Rangoon to Myitkyina, via Mandalay. Roads are less important. Internal air services link 50 towns and both Rangoon and Mandalay have international airports.

Bangladesh

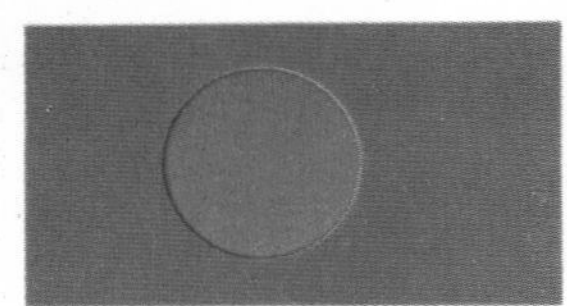

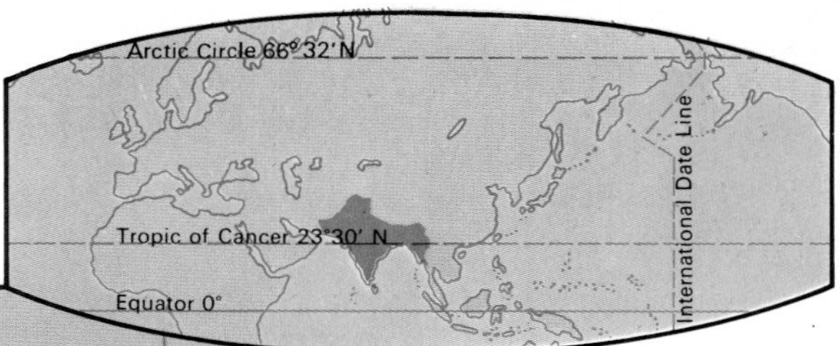

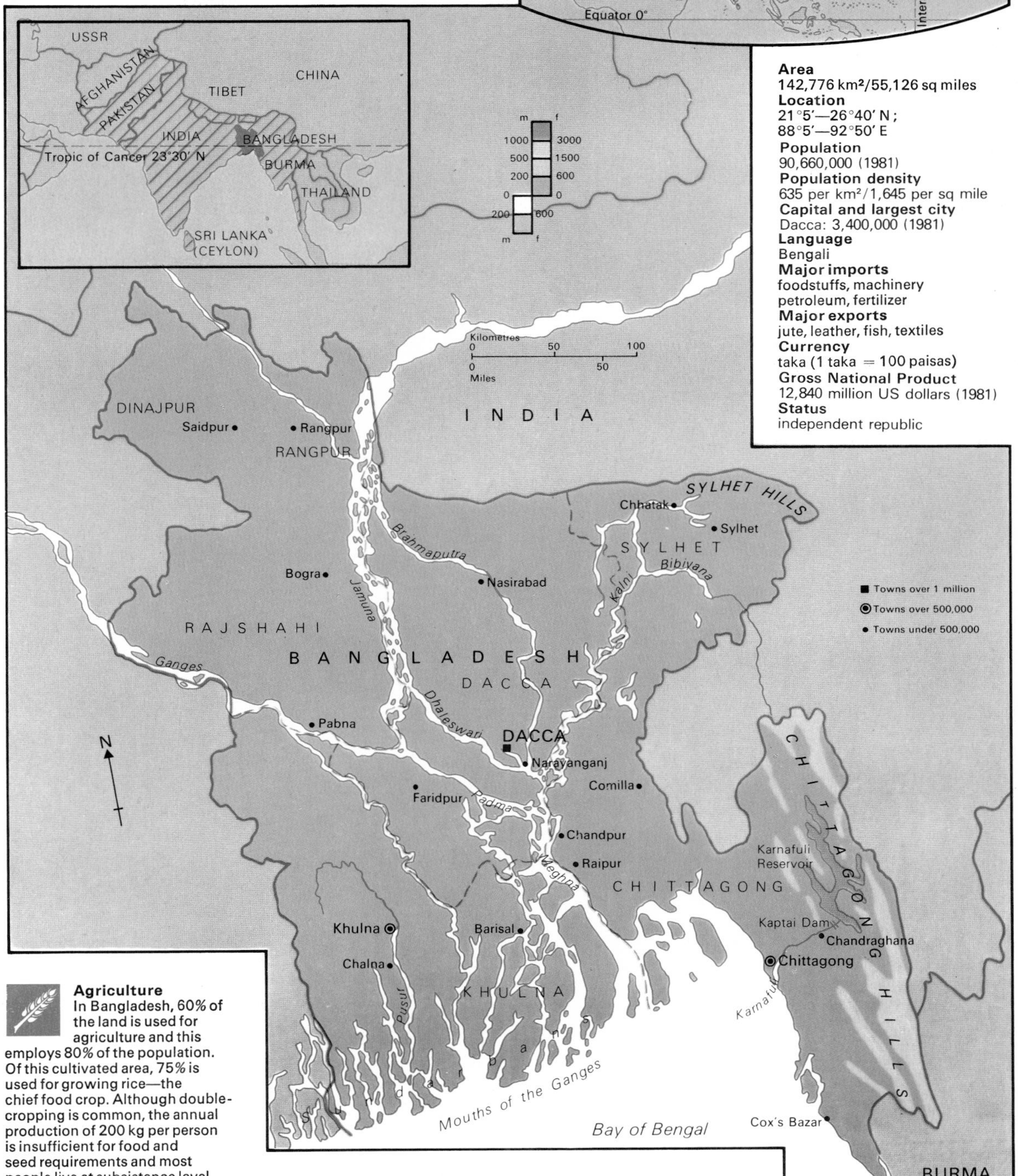

Area
142,776 km²/55,126 sq miles
Location
21°5′—26°40′ N;
88°5′—92°50′ E
Population
90,660,000 (1981)
Population density
635 per km²/1,645 per sq mile
Capital and largest city
Dacca: 3,400,000 (1981)
Language
Bengali
Major imports
foodstuffs, machinery
petroleum, fertilizer
Major exports
jute, leather, fish, textiles
Currency
taka (1 taka = 100 paisas)
Gross National Product
12,840 million US dollars (1981)
Status
independent republic

Forestry

Forests cover 15% of the country. Commercially, the most important areas are the Chittagong Hills and the delta mouth, the Sundarbans, home of the Bengal tiger. Covering an area of 5,960 km², the tidal Sundarbans forest is largely mangrove, but also contains gewa, a softwood used for newsprint, matches and boxes, and sundari, which gives the forest its name and is used for boat-building. The tropical rain forest on the Chittagong Hills yields teak, used for furniture, and bamboo, which is the basis of the country's paper industry. An associated forest product is honey with an annual yield of over 240,000 kg.

Physical features

Bangladesh is situated in the world's largest delta formed by the rivers Ganges, Brahmaputra and Meghna at the head of the Bay of Bengal. This vast alluvial plain, now extensively cleared for cultivation, was once completely covered with tropical rain forest. In places, it is less than 10 m above sea level and extremely vulnerable to flooding. Swampy islands, covered with mangrove forests known as the Sundarbans, fringe the coast. The delta is ever changing with the three main rivers and, more importantly, their many tributaries frequently altering course. Furthermore, the delta region is continually growing through the accretion of silt. The only major upland area in Bangladesh is in the southeast: the Chittagong Hills. These are a series of jungle-covered parallel ranges with an average height of 600 m. This densely forested region covers an area of over 3,000 km². There are also low hills, with a maximum height of 250 m, in the north-east near Sylhet. On the plain itself there are stretches of old alluvium which rise above the general level.

Industry

Bangladesh is still an agricultural country. The country has enormous resources such as peat, coal, oil and natural gas but these are, as yet, undeveloped. Although coal has been discovered, it is not yet mined and the country has to rely on imports. Petroleum also has to be imported as the production of oil from the Bay of Bengal is in its early stages. An oil refinery has, however, been built to exploit these oil reserves. On the other hand, natural gas, found in the Sylhet and Comilla districts, is fully exploited. In 1966, the first hydro-electric power station was installed. Situated by the Kaptai dam on the Karnafuli reservoir near Chittagong, this provides 80,000 kW of electricity. A nuclear power station is presently being built at Ruppur near the town of Pabna. Industry is concerned with the processing of raw materials. There are jute mills at Dacca, Narayanganj, Chittagong, and Khulna and a cement works at Chhatak which utilizes the country's limestone resources. Bamboo and softwoods supply paper mills at Chandraghana near Chittagong, Khulna and Pabna.

Agriculture

In Bangladesh, 60% of the land is used for agriculture and this employs 80% of the population. Of this cultivated area, 75% is used for growing rice—the chief food crop. Although double-cropping is common, the annual production of 200 kg per person is insufficient for food and seed requirements and most people live at subsistence level. The chief cash crop is jute and Bangladesh produces 50% of the world's supply. Like rice, jute requires standing water and high temperatures for ripening: the regularly flooded delta plain is therefore ideal for both crops. The country's second cash crop, tea, also requires heat and humidity but, as it does not grow in water, plantations are located on the Chittagong and Sylhet hills. Other products include sugar-cane, also grown in the Sylhet region, tobacco, cotton, wheat and oilseeds. The country's many rivers and streams are rich in fish, the main food after rice. The annual catch from inland waters is 50,000 tonnes and from the Bay of Bengal, 60,000 tonnes. More efficient farming is dependent on flood control and a number of drainage and storage schemes are being implemented.

Climate

The climate of Bangladesh is monsoonal. During the summer monsoon (May to October) the country receives 80% of its rainfall. The annual average on the plain is about 180 cm; high ground has up to twice this amount. Winter, which is warm and dry, lasts from November to March. The average temperature in Dacca for January the coldest month, is 21°C and for April, the hottest month, it is 27°C. The maritime influence causes high humidity which is over 90% during the wet season. There are frequent storms in May and October and winds of up to 150 km per hour rage over the Bay of Bengal, whipping up waves to as high as 7 m. These cause extensive flooding and often disastrous loss of life.

Cities

Only 5% of the population are urban-dwellers, and 80% of these live in either Dacca, Chittagong or Khulna. Dacca, the capital, is the country's largest and main industrial city. Traditionally, the city is famous for its muslin, embroidery and gold and silver-work. Current industrialization is based on jute-processing, rice-milling and cotton manufacture; the jute industry is centered on Narayanganj, a river port 16 km south of the capital and included in Greater Dacca. The second largest city, Chittagong (890,000), is also the country's leading port and handles nearly all jute, tea and leather exports. Khulna (437,000) is a commercial and industrial centre in the south-west.

Communications

The three main rivers, the Ganges, Brahmaputra and Meghna, and their many tributaries provide a comprehensive transport system. Nevertheless, these same rivers and the many other inland waterways that dissect the country, together with the persistent floods, have prevented the development of an extensive road and rail network. These are limited to some 2,800 km of railways and 5,800 km of roads. A domestic air service operates between major towns and there is an international airport north of the capital of Dacca.

The Himalayan States

Nepal

Bhutan

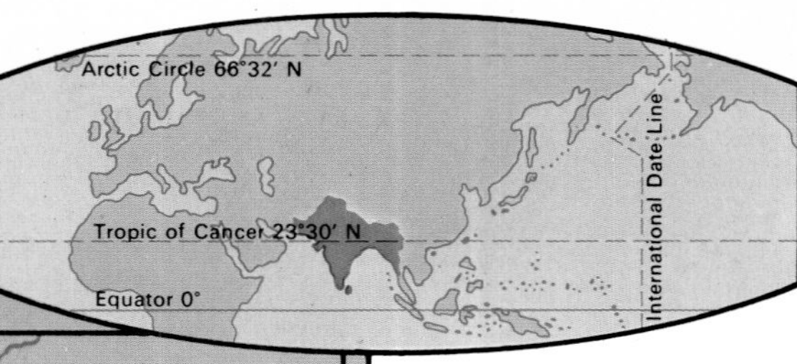

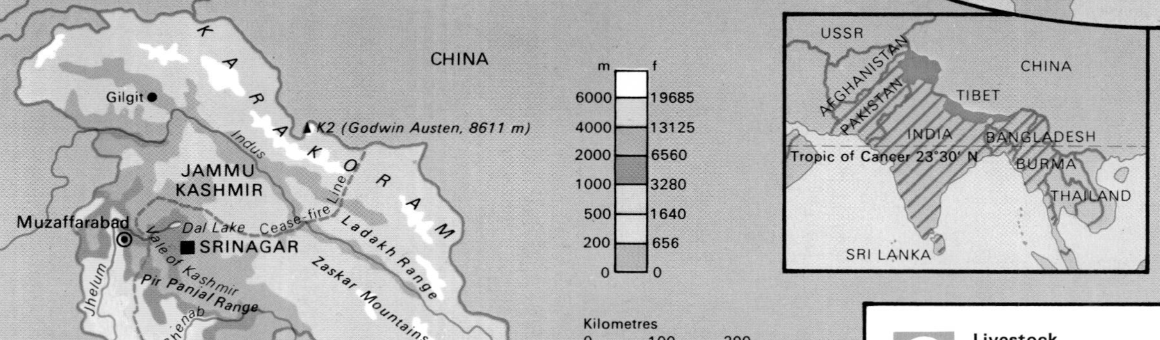

Nepal
Area
140,798 km²/54,362 sq miles
Location
26°20′—30°10′ N
80°15′—88°15′ E
Population
15,029,000 (1981)
Population density
107 per km²/276 per sq mile
Capital and largest city
Katmandu: 235,000 (1981)
Language
Nepali, but English, Hindi, Lepcha and Bhutanese also spoken
Major imports
manufactured goods, foodstuffs, minerals, fuels, machinery and chemicals
Major exports
food and live animals, jute, timber, medicinal herbs, hides
Currency
Nepalese rupee
(rupee = 100 paise)
Gross National Product
2,300 million US dollars (1981)
Status
constitutional monarchy

Bhutan
Area
46,600 km²/17,992 sq miles
Location
26°45′—28° N 89°—92° E
Population
1,300,000 (1981)
Population density
28 per km²/72 per sq mile
Capital and largest city
Thimphu: 10,000 (1980)
Language
Dzongkha
Major imports
textiles, machinery
Major exports
fruit, timber, jam, distillery products
Currency
Indian rupee (rupee = 100 paise)
Gross National Product
110 million US dollars (1981)
Status
democratic monarchy

Jammu and Kashmir
Area
101,283 km²/39,108 sq miles
Population
5,650,000 (1981)
Population density
56 per km²/145 per sq mile
Capital and largest city
Srinagar: 490,000 (1981)
Status
Jammu and Kashmir, the Indian part of Kashmir enjoys internal autonomy. It occupies about 70% of the total area of Kashmir, but there are frequent clashes on the disputed 'cease-fire' line.

Sikkim
Area
7,298 km²/2,818 sq miles
Location
27°—28° N
88°10′—89°5′ E
Population
315,000 (1981)
Population density
29 per km²/74 per sq mile
Capital and largest city
Gangtok: 15,000
Status
formerly an Indian protectorate with internal autonomy, Sikkim became part of the Indian republic in 1975

Cities

The capital of the Indian sector of Jammu and Kashmir is Srinagar, standing 1,600 m above sea level on the banks of the Jhelum river in the Vale of Kashmir. Canals, crossed by wooden bridges, flow through the picturesque city which has both Hindu temples and Moslem mosques. Srinagar is a major tourist centre and a leading attraction is the Dal Lake with its floating gardens. Bazaars display a wide range of Kashmiri crafts: carpets, embroidered silk, silverware, papier mâché and wood-carvings. Jammu, some 200 km south of Strinagar and over 1,000 m lower, is the winter capital and well-known for its traditional paintings. The chief town in the Pakistani sector is Muzaffarabad. Katmandu, the Nepalese capital, is situated at an altitude of 1,325 m near the confluence of the Baghmati and Vishnumati rivers. A city of palaces and temples, it is an important commercial centre at the heart of a densely populated farming region. Gangtok is the capital of Sikkim and an agricultural market town. With the royal palace as its focal point, Thimphu, the capital of Bhutan, is also a market town.

Minerals

The mineral wealth of the Himalayan states remains largely unexploited. In Kashmir, coal and bauxite deposits have yet to be developed but some lignite is mined in the Vale. Lignite is also worked locally in eastern Nepal; elsewhere in the country there is limited mining of copper, iron, dolomite and cobalt. Exploitation is more developed in Sikkim where lead, copper and zinc are mined at Rhotang. Graphite and gypsum have also been located. Bhutan is currently planning to develop its resources of coal, dolomite, graphite and gypsum.

Industry

Industry is generally limited to processing local produce and to traditional crafts. In Kashmir, the main industry after tourism is silkworm breeding which employs 8% of the population. Important crafts are wood-carving, carpet weaving, leather work and papier mâché. In Bhutan, sawmills, jam factories, distilleries and a furniture plant use local materials, and there are several craft industries including hand-weaving, embroidery, wood-carving and metalwork. As well as traditional manufactures and distilleries, Sikkim has a few small factories producing items such as nails and candles. In Nepal, factories process domestically produced jute, sugar, tobacco, timber and leather; new projects include a chemical works and an iron and steel complex. Hydroelectric plants are being constructed in all four states.

Livestock

With the exception of the Muslim population in Pakistani Kashmir, most of the Himalayan peoples are either Buddhists, and therefore vegetarians, or Hindus, who do not eat beef. Consequently, meat production is limited and animals are raised mainly for their hair, skin and milk. In the Nepalese valleys, cattle and buffaloes are often stall-fed as all available ground is cultivated. Goats and sheep graze in the mountains. In Kashmir and Sikkim, yaks and sheep provide hair and wool for woven goods.

Agriculture

Agriculture dominates the economy of all four states. In Bhutan, cultivation is concentrated in the central valleys. Rice and maize are grown on the valley floors while wheat and barley cover adjacent slopes. State orchards produce a variety of fruit, mostly for export. Sikkim is the world's leading producer of cardamom. Other cash crops include potatoes, apples, mandarin oranges, ginger and tea; principle food crops are rice and maize. In Nepal, 15% of land is under cultivation. Of this, 75% is in the Terai and the remainder is in the mid-Himalayan valleys. Half the arable land is used for rice; maize, millet and wheat are the other food crops. The two leading cash crops, jute and sugar, are grown in the Terai; fruit, tea and tobacco are being developed in the mid-Himalayas. In Kashmir, rice, maize and wheat are the main cereals. Fruit is the major cash crop and apples, apricots, peaches and plums are exported. Mulberry leaf production for silkworm breeding is important.

Physical features

Nepal, Sikkim and Bhutan lie between the Ganges Plain and the High Himalayas. Nepal has three zones. In the south is the Terai, a narrow, swampy malarial plain. North of this are the mid-Himalayas, a series of parallel ranges broken by transverse valleys. Beyond these ranges rise the snow-covered peaks of the High Himalayas, including Mount Everest (8,882 m) the world's highest mountain. Sikkim, drained by the Tista river, is very mountainous. Bhutan also has three zones: peaks of over 7,000 m in the north descend to a belt of low ranges crossed by valleys with the hot and steamy Duars plain in the extreme south. Kashmir is composed of a series of steps rising from 600 m to the great Karakoram range with the world's fourth highest peak, K2, at 8,951 m. The major flat area is the Vale of Kashmir, an alluvial basin drained by the Jhelum.

Climate

The average temperature for July in Srinagar is 23°C, in Katmandu it is 25°C. January figures are 0° and 10°C respectively. Altitude is an obvious influence and in the High Himalayas temperatures are always below freezing. In Bhutan, Nepal and Sikkim, most rain falls during June-September and is heaviest in the east: 760 cm a year in the Duars, 100 cm in western Nepal. In Kashmir, rain occurs mostly in the winter, averaging 66 cm per year.

Forestry

Forests, ranging from tropical hardwood to coniferous, cover 35% of Bhutan, Sikkim and Nepal, but only about 12% of Kashmir. Exploitation is very limited in Sikkim, but in Bhutan and Kashmir there is some production of timber, gums and resins. The industry is most developed in Nepal where hardwoods from the Terai and sal from the slopes are exported to India, and Terai softwoods are used for the manufacture of matches. In all four states, forests yield medicinal herbs.

Transport

Communications are poor and most people travel on foot or use animals, such as buffaloes. Nepal has the most developed transport system; there are about 3,000 km of roads mainly in the Terai and the Katmandu valley; railways link Raxaul (India) to Amlekhganj (48 km), and Jaynagar (India) to Bijalpura (53 km) while the Royal Nepal Airlines operate flights to some 35 Nepalese towns as well as to India, Bangladesh, Burma and Thailand. Sikkim has few roads and no railways or airports. Bhutan is also without railways but has an air service between Paro and Calcutta and 1,500 km of roads built with Indian aid. Kashmir is linked to the rest of India by road and rail from Jammu to Pathankot and by air from Srinagar and Jammu to Delhi. Internally, there are 5,600 km of roads.

Pakistan

Arctic Circle 66° 32' N
Tropic of Cancer 23° 30' N
Equator 0°
International Date Line

Area
801,408 km²/309,424 sq miles
Location
23°41'—36°50' N
60°55'—75°30' E
Population
84,501,000 (1981)
Population density
105 per km²/273 per sq mile
Capital
Islamabad: 201,000
Largest city
Karachi: 5,103,000
Language
Urdu
Major imports
transport equipment and machinery, iron and steel, chemicals and fertilizer
Major exports
raw cotton and cotton manufactures, rice, leather, fish
Currency
rupee (1 rupee = 100 paisa)
Gross National Product
29,800 million US dollars (1981)
Status
independent republic

Physical features

Pakistan divides into three geographical regions. Mountains dominate the north and north-west. These are highest in the north and situated there is Pakistan's highest peak, Tirichmir (7,694 m). In this area, the rivers Yarkhan, Swat, Chitral and Panjkora flow through deep gorges. Along the north-west frontier lie a series of lower ranges: Safed Koh, Sulaiman and Kirthar. The most famous pass across this mountain wall is the Khyber, linking Pakistan with Afghanistan. A second zone corresponds to the 900 m high desert plateau of Baluchistan, situated west of the Kirthar range. Finally, stretching from the Himalayan foothills and the Salt Range to the Arabian Sea is the alluvial plain formed by the Indus and its Punjab tributaries: Jhelum, Chenab, Ravi, Beas and Sutlej. The arid Thar desert lies east of the lower Indus.

Climate

Although classified as tropical monsoonal, the climate has continental characteristics. Winter (October to March) is dry and cold; in the mountains, temperatures are low (Lahore, 10°C) but increase southwards (Karachi, 16°C). Summer begins with a hot, dry season. Temperatures are highest inland: the May average is 33°C, (in Karachi, 28°C). Jacobabad has the highest temperatures—up to 50°C. Light rain, brought by the south-west monsoon, falls from June to September. The annual average is 50 cm in Lahore, 20 cm in Karachi and less than 10 cm in Baluchistan.

Communications

The 8,530 km rail network was once the key element of Pakistan's transport system, but roads (with a total length of over 40,000 km) are increasing in importance. Both road and rail link Karachi with Peshawar—the frontier town guarding the Khyber Pass. Karachi is the leading port and its natural harbour is visited by over 2,000 ships a year. There are international airports at Karachi and Lahore with domestic flights also operating from Peshawar and Rawalpindi.

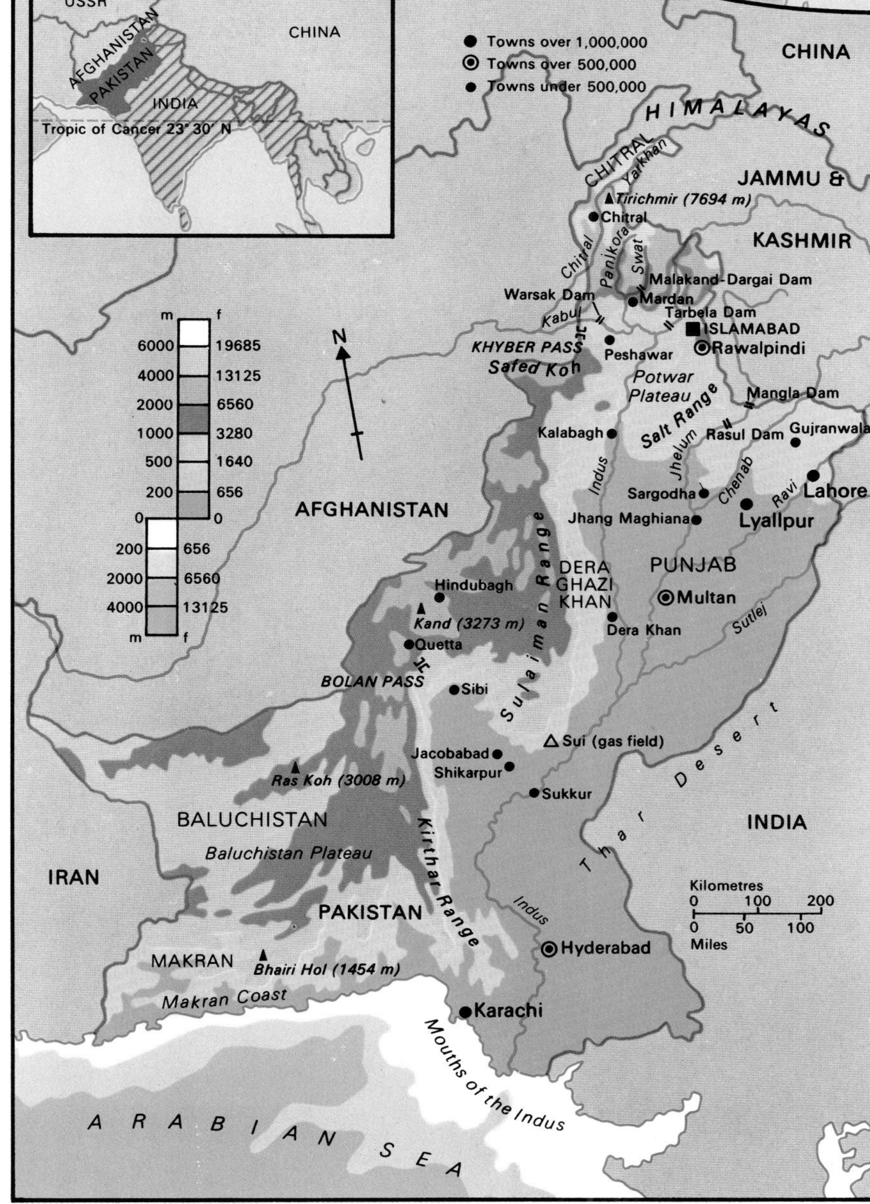

Cities

Only one Pakistani in five lives in a city and 25% of this urban population is concentrated in Karachi, the former capital and largest city. Situated west of the Indus delta, it is a leading industrial and commercial centre. It is also Pakistan's main port, handling 75% of foreign trade as well as serving landlocked Afghanistan. The new capital, Islamabad, is situated 14 km north-east of Rawalpindi at an altitude of 600 m. A blend of traditional Islamic and modern architecture, the city became operational on completion in 1965. The second largest city, Lahore (2,920,000) is situated on the left bank of the Ravi and is a major textile-manufacturing centre. Pakistan's third city is Lyallpur (1,016,000) which is an industrial centre and an agricultural market. Three other major towns are Hyderabad (785,000), Rawalpindi (615,000) and Multan.

Mining

Pakistan has limited mineral resources and those that do exist are not fully exploited. Low quality coal, mined in north-east Baluchistan and the Salt Range, meets half the country's requirements. Iron ore, worked at Kalabagh, is also low-grade; small higher-grade deposits are known to exist in the Chitral area but exploitation is hindered by inaccessibility. Chromite, extracted near Hindubagh, is largely exported to the US. Other minerals being exploited include limestone, quarried in the Salt Range; gypsum, mined at Sibi; rock salt from the Salt Range and uranium from the Dera Ghazi Khan region. Small oil fields on the Potwar plateau near Rawalpindi supply 10% of Pakistan's needs. The search for oil led to an important discovery: enormous reserves of natural gas. Gas is currently produced from Sui, which is one of the world's largest fields, and at Mari.

Energy

Until recently, most of Pakistan's energy needs were supplied by coal-fired thermal plants. The situation, however, is changing with the development of hydro-electric power and natural gas. In the last 20 years, great progress has been made in harnessing the country's hydro-electric potential—the biggest project being the Tarbela Dam on the Indus with a capacity of two million kilowatts. Other major plants include the Mangla Dam on the Jhelum, Warsak on the Kabul, Malakand-Dargai on the Swat canal and Rasul on the Jhelum canal. Since the late 1950s, natural gas has radically increased Pakistan's power output. Pipelines from the Sui field supply gas to homes and industry in Karachi, Multan, Lahore, Lyallpur, Rawalpindi and Islamabad. A nuclear power plant at Karachi which is currently using imported uranium will shortly switch to uranium from Dera Ghazi Khan.

Industry

Pakistan's first steps towards industrialization centred on the processing of its agricultural products. Cotton is the leading industry and employs 40% of industrial workers: cotton yarn and manufactures together make up 60% of exports. Hides and skins are the basis of the important leather industry: tanneries are widespread and there are several large shoe factories. Food-processing plants, found in most towns, include sugar, rice and oilseed mills; local tobacco is made into cigarettes. More recently, non-agricultural industries have been developed: the cement industry uses lime-stone; fertilizer manufacture and petro-chemical products are based on natural gas. Engineering industries, such as vehicle assembly and irrigation machinery, use imported materials. Apart from Karachi, Hyderabad and Sukkur, industry is concentrated in the zone between Multan, Lahore and Peshawar. Manufacturing employs less than 20% of the population; in rural areas a further 10% is engaged in handicrafts such as hand-woven fabrics, pottery, metalware and leather goods.

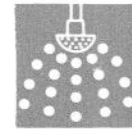

Irrigation

As rainfall is low, agriculture in Pakistan is dependent on irrigation and 70% of cultivated land is watered in this way. Most irrigation water flows through perennial canals: dams have been built across the Indus, Jhelum and Chenab and the water stored behind these dams is supplied to the plains by the largest network of irrigation canals in the world. Other more traditional systems include wells, underground water tunnels and flood irrigation. This last method is seasonal as canals, built above low-water level, only fill when rivers are in flood.

Agriculture

Agriculture is basic to the economy and employs about 80% of the population. The cultivated area, covering 25% of the country, largely corresponds to the irrigated Indus basin. The main cereals are wheat, grown as a winter crop, and rice and maize, both grown as summer crops. Rice surpluses are exported. The leading cash crop is cotton, valued not only for its fibre but also for its seed which is used for fodder and vegetable oil production. Other major cash crops include sugar cane, oilseeds and tobacco. Apricot, peach and apple orchards are sited on irrigated areas in Baluchistan, while dates are grown along the Makran coast. Livestock farming is important: oxen, mules and camels are used as work animals, sheep provide wool used for textiles and carpets in addition to meat and dairy produce. Cattle hides are the basis of leather manufacture. The fishing industry, located on the coast and lakes in the lower Indus basin, is expanding and part of the catch, principally tuna and shellfish, is exported. Many fish farms have been established around the lakes of Sind.

India 1

Area
3,159,530 km²/1,219,968 sq miles
Location
8°–33°15′ E
68°5′–97°25′ E
Population
690,183,000 (1981)
Population density
218 per km²/566 per sq mile
Capital
New Delhi: 5,200,000 (1980)
Largest city
Calcutta: 9,100,000 (1980)
Languages
Hindi, English, regional and tribal languages
Major imports
Machinery, steel, petroleum, raw cotton, fertilizers, chemicals
Major exports
jute products, leather tea, cotton textiles, iron ore
Currency
rupee (1 rupee = 100 paise)
Gross National Product
176,660 million US dollars (1981)
Status
federal republic

Physical features

India divides naturally into three regions: the Himalayas, the northern plain and the peninsula. The highest mountains in the world, the Himalayas, form a barrier across the north and although Mount Everest is actually in Nepal great peaks such as Nanda Devi (7,815 m) and Kamet (7,759 m) do lie in India itself. The Himalayas give way to the northern plain. This vast alluvial lowland, 350 km wide and stretching 4,000 km from east to west, is formed by the river basins of the Indus, Ganges and Brahmaputra. The peninsula plateau, the Deccan, lies south of the lowland and is separated from it by the Vindhya mountains. The Deccan is highest in the west where it rises to the Western Ghats with an average height of 1,200 m. Eastwards, it slopes down to the Eastern Ghats, 600 m. The Arabian Sea coastal strip is narrow, but between the Eastern Ghats and the Bay of Bengal there is a broad coastal plain crossed by the peninsula's main rivers: the Cauvery, Krishna, Godavari and Mahanadi.

Climate

India has four seasons: the cool season (December to February), the hot season (March-May), the S-W monsoon (June-October) and the retreating monsoon (November). The cool season is dry and sunny except in Madras where rainfall is heavy. In the coldest month, January, temperatures are 24°C in Madras and Bombay, 19°C in Calcutta and 14°C in Delhi. The hot season is dry and temperatures in May, the hottest month, are 33°C in Madras, 29°C in Bombay, 30°C in Calcutta and 32°C in Delhi. The southwest monsoon brings India 90% of its rain. One arm comes in over the Malabar coast depositing 500 cm on the Western Ghats. The other arms goes up the Bay of Bengal bringing rain to the north and east with the Khasi Hills, northeast of Bangladesh, receiving up to 2,000 cm. In contrast, the Thar desert on the borderland region with Pakistan receives as little as 12 cm.

Population

India is the world's second most populous country. The population is made up of many different peoples with distinct cultures. Communications are hampered by language problems: there are 15 major languages and 250 dialects. The official language, Hindi, is spoken by only 40% of the people, mostly in the north. India also has many religions: the main one, Hinduism, claims 85% of the population and has a profound influence on life in India. About 80% of the people live in rural areas where rainfall is sufficient for agriculture: the northern plain and the coasts of Kerala and Tamil Nadu.

Famine and food

In India, hunger is an everyday word. In the last 15 years, medical advances have caused a dramatic increase in population; the government responded by introducing a national birth-control campaign. Even if a lower birth-rate is achieved, food production must rise by at least 2% a year. Indian agriculture, however, is backward with small farms, primitive methods and only 20% of the land irrigated. Droughts and floods are common. Government projects to increase food production include fertilizer factories, irrigation and flood control schemes and improved seeds.

Agriculture: food crops

Agriculture employs 70% of the population and takes up 55% of the land. Most of this area is under cultivation and 30% of it is used for rice, the main food crop. Rice is grown in the Ganges basin (Bihar and parts of Uttar Pradesh and Madhya Pradesh) and along the east coast. These ricelands are densely populated, especially the Ganges basin where rich alluvial soil and adequate water for irrigation favour agriculture. The second staple food is wheat, grown as a winter crop in areas where rainfall is less than 100 cm such as the Punjab, Uttar Pradesh and Madhya Pradesh. Millets are grown mainly in regions with poor soil and where the rainfall is uncertain, notably on the Deccan.

Agriculture: cash crops

India is the world's leading tea producer and this crop accounts for 20% of exports. Tea plantations are situated on hillsides in Assam, West Bengal, Kerala and Tamil Nadu. India is also the world's leading producer of sugar (grown on the Deccan and the northern plain), of pepper (from Kerala) and of groundnuts (mainly from Tamil Nadu, Maharashtra and Gujarat). Groundnuts, as well as sesame, linseed and others produce oil for domestic and industrial use. Two other major crops are cotton and jute. Cotton is produced in the NW Deccan while jute is concentrated in West Bengal. Other important cash crops include coffee and rubber, both grown in the south.

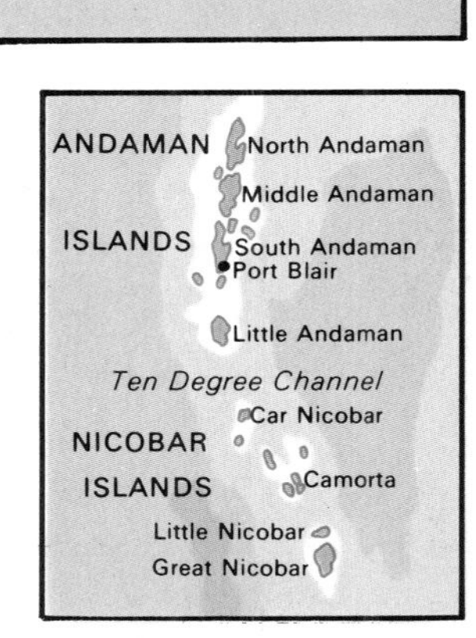

Livestock

India has 20% of the world's cattle, yet livestock is under-exploited. Only 5% of the land—usually arid scrub—is used for grazing so the country's 176 million cattle and 51 million buffaloes are kept for work and not for milk. As Hindus consider the cow sacred, it is not slaughtered and beef production is negligible. There are also 40 million sheep but the wool yield is low. Its coarse quality is best suited for carpets. Dung is dried and used as fuel rather than fertilizer.

Forestry and fishing

Originally, most of India was forested, but the land and fuel needs of the growing population led to deforestation. Today, forests cover only 21% of the country and play a minor role in the economy. Products include teak, from Madhya Pradesh and Mysore, sal from the north-east and softwoods from the Himalayas. Fishing also contributes little to the economy despite enormous potential. Kerala and Orisa are important for marine fishing, West Bengal for freshwater fish.

Island territories

Three island groups belong to India: the Andaman and Nicobar Islands and Lakshadweep. The Andaman and Nicobar Islands, administered jointly, are situated in the Bay of Bengal, 1,200 km east of Madras. They have a total area of 8,200 km² and a population of 115,000. The Andaman group consists of 204 islands, many of them forested. The main exports are Andaman redwood, gurjan (used for plywood) and softwoods which are used for matches. The Ten Degree Channel separates the Andaman Islands from the Nicobar group which consists of 19 islands. Coconuts are a staple food and also the chief export item. The capital of the joint territory is Port Blair on South Andaman Island. Lakshadweep lies 300 km west of Kerala in the Arabian Sea. Its 27 islands have an area of 32 km² comprising the Laccadives, Minicoy and Amindivis. They have a population of 32,000.

India 2

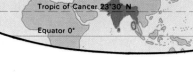

Minerals
With an annual production of 100 million tonnes, India is the world's sixth largest coal-producing country. Of this, 95% comes from West Bengal and Bihar. India is also rich in iron-ore and has about 20% of the world's reserves. The main deposits occur in the north-east Deccan and 75% of the output is exported. In contrast, the country is short of other metallic minerals and has to import copper, zinc and nickel. Manganese and bauxite are both found in the north-east Deccan and India is the world's third largest producer of manganese. Some gold is mined at Kolar in Karnataka. The chief non-metallic mineral is mica and 80% of the world's supply comes from India, mostly from mines in Bihar and Rajasthan. Also important is monazite, found in the Kerala beach sands. Salt is obtained by the evaporation process along the west and south-east coasts. India produces about 30% of its oil needs from fields in Gujarat and Assam. Drilling for more oil is in progress in the Gulf of Cambay.

Energy
More than half of India's electricity is generated by thermal plants, mostly coal-fired. Hydro-electricity is being developed but faces the problem of seasonal variations in river flow. So far, only 10% of the hydro-power potential has been harnessed, mainly in the Western Ghats, the Nilgiri Hills, the Damodar valley and the Himalayas. Nuclear power is also being developed, especially to serve industrial zones away from coalfields such as Madras, Bombay and Ahmadabad, and plants have been built in Tamil Nadu, Maharashtra and Rajasthan. Electricity production is increasing yearly and it is now estimated that 14% of villages are electrified. As yet, there is no national grid which means that there are power surpluses in some regions and shortages in others.

Industry
The introduction of heavy machinery dates from between 1907 and 1911 when the Jamshedpur steel-works, based on locally produced coal, iron, limestone and manganese, were established. Two other iron and steel complexes have been built west of Jamshedpur at Rourkela and Bhilai and two more in the Damodar valley at Durgapur and Bokaro. The Damodar valley, rich in coal and hydro-electricity, is a major industrial region. As well as steel, there are cement, chemical, aluminium, fertilizer and engineering works. Another great manufacturing zone is based around Calcutta, home of India's jute industry. Cotton textiles dominate the two industrial conurbations of Bombay and Ahmadabad and are important in the fifth industrial zone formed by Madras, Bangalore, Coimbatore and Madurai which is better known for its light- and electrical-engineering. Apart from these five major zones, most towns have factories which process local products such as cotton, leather, sugar, rice, wheat and salt.

Land transport:
Roads are a minor element in India's transport system: they total only 1,300,000 km and less than a third are surfaced. Road building is therefore a government priority and it is hoped that by 1981 no village will be more than 6 km from a surfaced road. There are 13 national highways, with a total length of 24,000 km, linking state capitals and major ports. In contrast to the inadequate roads, India's railways are important. The 60,130 km long network, which carries over 10,000 trains a day, is one of the world's longest. Although trains are slow, they are not expensive and 6 million people travel on them every day. Rail freight consists mainly of coal, ores and cereals.

Other transport:
Traffic on India's 14,400 km of navigable waterways is declining, except in West Bengal and Kerala. Marine shipping is, however, increasing. The country's leading ports are Calcutta, Bombay, Madras, Cochin, Marmagao, Kandla, Vishakhapatnam and Paradip. The two main ship-yards, equipped to build ocean-going vessels are at Vishakhapatnam and Cochin. Air transport is developing rapidly. There are two corporations: Indian Airlines, which flies to over 80 towns within India and to adjacent countries such as Sri Lanka, Burma and Nepal; and Air India, which operates overseas flights from international airports at Delhi (Palam), Bombay (Santa Cruz), Calcutta (Dum Dum) and Madras.

Cottage industry
Although not as profitable as factory production, cottage industries are encouraged by the government as they provide employment in rural areas. These are often organized on a co-operative basis. Of the 25 million people working in village industries, a quarter are handloom operators engaged in making khadi (a hand-spun and hand-woven cotton cloth). Other home industries include hand-woven silk, particularly in Karnataka and Assam, filigree work in Orissa and Andhra Pradesh, brass and copper ware, carved ivory and leather goods, and bicycle assembly.

Irrigation
In a country where rainfall is seasonal, unreliable and, in places, almost non-existent, irrigation is essential to agriculture. Traditional methods are wells, tanks and canals. Wells are most common in the northern plain; water is brought to the surface in a variety of ways, often by animals hauling up skin buckets or turning a wheel composed of scoops. Tanks, formed by low earth walls, predominate in the south. The government has included irrigation schemes in all of its five-year plans and most of the projects involve multi-purpose storage dams providing power as well.

Cities
Six Indian cities have a population of over two million. The largest is Calcutta (9.1 million). Situated 140 km upstream from the River Hooghly estuary, Calcutta is a major port and handles 40% of the country's exports, notably jute and tea. The city has a wide range of manufactures; the most important is jute-processing. Overcrowding is a serious problem and there are innumerable slum and street dwellers. The second largest city is Bombay (8,200,000), the main port on the Arabian Sea and the country's financial centre. Cotton dominates the city's industry with raw cotton and cotton textiles as major export items. Delhi (5,200,000) is the third largest city and includes the nation's capital, New Delhi, which lies 5 km to the south. Old Delhi, on the Jumna river, is noted for its traditional metalwork, embroidery and ivory carvings. New Delhi's modern government buildings (built in 1912) contrast with the old city's monuments such as the 17th century Red Fort and Jami Masjid mosque. Madras (4,300,000) is the cultural and commercial centre on the east coast of southern India. Inland from Madras is Bangalore (2.9 m), an industrial centre. Ahmedabad (2.5 m) is an important railway junction and cultural centre in Givarat.

Trade
Traditionally, India is a major exporter of jute products, cotton textiles and tea; these are still the main exports together with hides and iron ore. In spite of the increasing production of other commodities such as sugar and steel, the value of exports is well below that of imports. This is partly explained by a series of poor harvests which have made large imports of food necessary. Raw materials, such as chemicals and petroleum, for India's expanding industry are another major import item. India's main trading partners are the USSR, USA, UK and Japan.

Caste system
One feature of Hinduism which has greatly influenced the structure of Indian society is the caste system. This divides Hindus into several thousand classes, or castes. A Hindu is born into a certain caste and can never leave it. His caste invariably determines his social status, his occupation (some jobs are traditionally associated with specific castes) and his choice of wife (it is rare to marry outside one's caste). This rigid social order has often checked economic progress: high-caste individuals consider it their right to own land but not to work it; low-caste persons are condemned to menial jobs. Recent laws, however, have been introduced against caste discrimination and the barriers between castes are slowly being broken down, especially in cities.

Sri Lanka (Ceylon) and the Maldive Islands

Sri Lanka **Maldives**

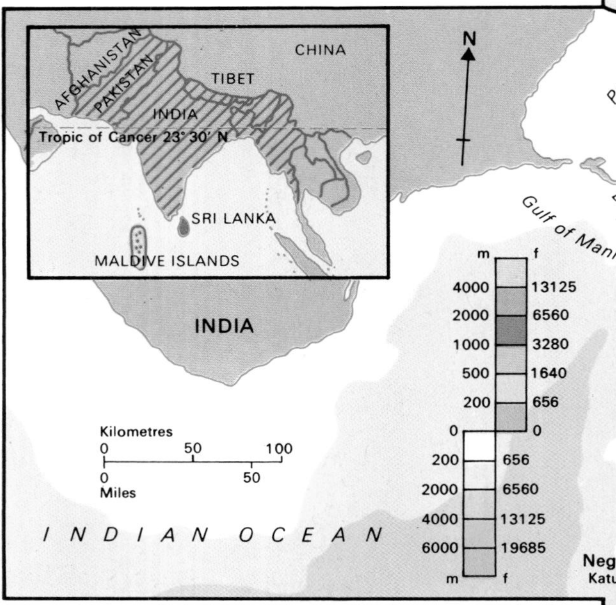

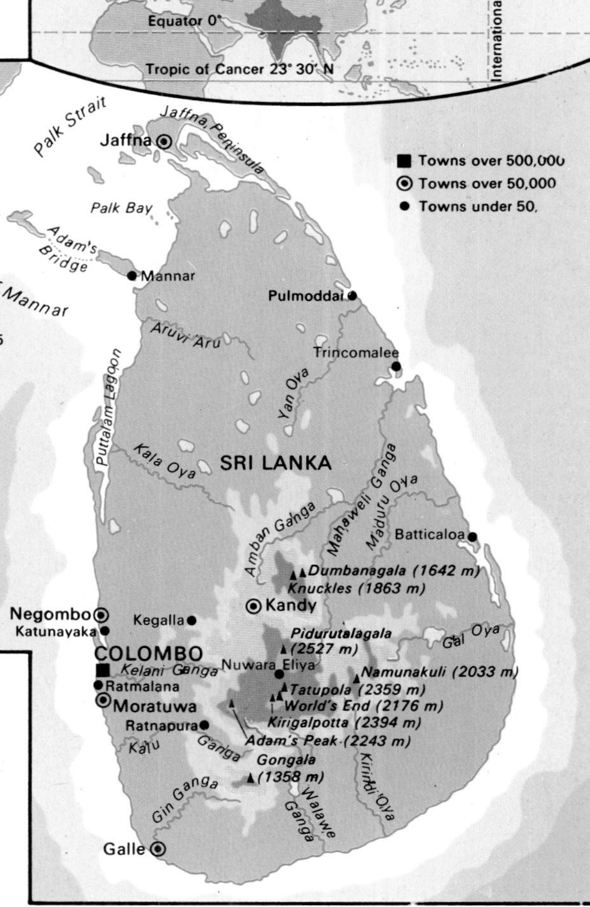

Agriculture

Sri Lanka is essentially agricultural and 25% of the country is farmed. Rice, which occupies about 40% of the cultivated area, is the main food crop. With the aim of achieving self-sufficiency in rice, more land is being made available through irrigation schemes such as those on the Gal Oya, Mahaweli and Walawe. The three leading cash crops—tea, rubber and coconut—make up 90% of exports; tea alone accounts for 55%. They are mostly grown in the wet zone: tea plantations are located mostly in the hills up to heights of 1,800 m; rubber covers the lower slopes and coconuts grow on the plains. In world production, Sri Lanka holds second place for tea and fourth for rubber. Coconut products include timber, palms, arak, coir, copra and oil. Other cash crops are cocoa and citronella.

The main crop grown in the Maldives, both for domestic consumption and export, is coconut.

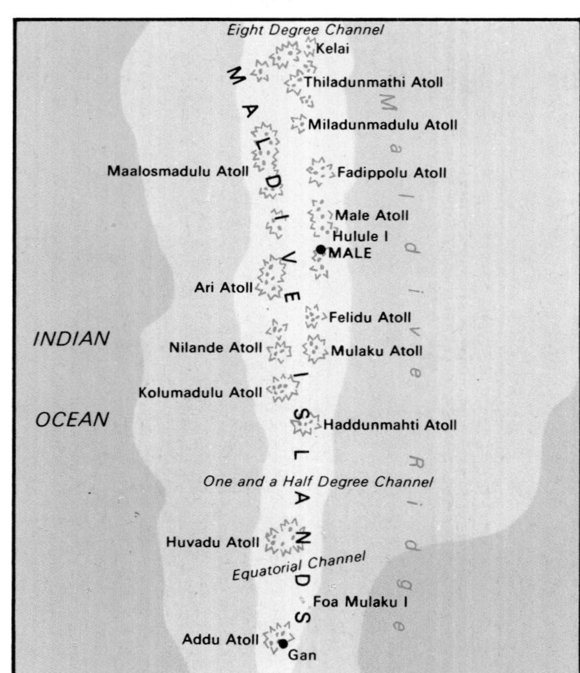

Sri Lanka
Area
65,610 km²/25,332 sq miles
Location
5°55'—9°50' N
79°42'—81°52' E
Population
14,988,000 (1981)
Population density
228 per km²/592 per sq mile
Capital and largest city
Colombo: 586,000 (1981)
Language
Sinhala, Tamil and English
Major imports
foodstuffs, fuels, machinery and textiles
Major exports
tea, rubber, coconut products, cocoa and cinnamon, gems
Currency
Sri Lanka rupee (1 Sri Lanka rupee = 100 cents)
Gross National Product
4,460 million US dollars (1981)
Status
independent republic

Maldive Islands
Area
298 km²/115 sq miles
Location
3°15'—8° N
73°—74°20' E
Population
155,000 (1981)
Population density
520 per km²/1,348 per sq mile
Capital and largest city
Male: 32,000 (1980)
Language
Divehi (a dialect of Sinhala), Arabic is widely read
Major imports
rice, textiles, chemicals
Major exports
fish (especially dried bonito), copra, shells, millet, coconut products such as coir (a coconut fibre)
Currency
Maldivian rupee (1 Maldivian rupee = 100 larees)
Status
independent republic

Physical features

Sri Lanka is linked to India by a line of sandy islands known as Adam's Bridge. The island is 432 km long and 224 km at its widest point. There is a mountainous zone in the south with peaks rising to over 2,000 m: the highest point being Pidurutalagala (2,527 m). These mountains are flanked by hilly uplands which give way to an alluvial coastal plain, broadest in the north and narrowest in the west and south. In the far north is the limestone Jaffna peninsular. The coast is fringed with sand dunes and lagoons. Sri Lanka's rivers radiate from the hilly interior: the longest is the Mahaweli Ganga (332 km). The Maldives, located 640 km south-west of Sri Lanka, consist of some 2,000 coral islands covered with grass, scrub and coconut palms—only 215 are inhabited.

Climate

Both countries are affected by the south-west and north-east monsoons. These bring an average rainfall of 150 cm to the Maldives. In Sri Lanka, the south-west (the wet zone) has up to 500 cm of rain a year but the rest of the island has less than 120 cm a year. Sri Lanka's high temperatures are modified by sea breezes and altitude. At Colombo the January temperature is 25°C, at Nuwara Eliya (1,890 m) 14°C; in May it is 28°C and 16°C respectively. The Maldives are hot and humid (av. temp: 27°C).

Transport

Sri Lanka's roads (about 19,000 km total length) cover the island adequately and are supplemented by 1,450 km of railways. Colombo is the principal port and handles nearly all exports, except tea which is shipped mainly from Trincomalee—one of the world's finest natural harbours. Galle and Jaffna are also major ports. There are several airports including Ratmalana (domestic) and Katunayaka (international) near Colombo. Steamers link Sri Lanka with the Maldives. Under construction is an airport on Hulule, an island 2 km from Male.

Fishing

The Maldivian economy is dominated by fishing which employs over 50% of the population. Every day several thousand sailing boats made of coconut wood make for the fishing grounds—up to 30 km away. The catch, mainly bonito and tuna, is cooked, cured and dried then exported to Sri Lanka. While the men are fishing the women are collecting shells, entirely for export. Some of the rarest shells come from the Maldives. In Sri Lanka, both island and sea-water fishing are being developed. Pearl fishing, once important in the shallow waters of the Gulf of Mannar, is in decline because of poor yields.

Minerals & energy

Sri Lanka has a limited range of minerals. High-grade graphite is the most important and 80% of production is exported. Other commercially valuable minerals include ilmenite (extracted at Pulmoddai and mainly exported to Japan) and monazite, rutile and zircon (all found in beach sands). High-quality iron ore occurs in the centre and south of the island. There are also deposits of phosphates, china clay, quartz (used in glass) and, in the north, limestone. Sri Lanka is famous for its gemstones found in the Ratnapura region. These include ruby, sapphire, aquamarine garnet, moonstone, topaz and chrysoberyl. Salt production, by evaporation, is centred on the islands' lagoons. There is no coal or oil and power is supplied either by thermal stations using imported fuels or by hydroelectric plants, often linked to irrigation and flood-control schemes.

Industry

Partly because of Sri Lanka's limited mineral and power resources, industrialization is still in its early stages. The processing of tea, rubber and coconuts is important and industries using domestic raw materials include cement (limestone), bricks and ceramics (clay), paper (rice straw), tyres (rubber) and leather goods. Imported materials are the basis of industries such as oil and sugar production, textile manufacture and steel-rolling. Handicraft production is considerable: wood and ivory carving, basketry, handloom weaving, lace, jewellry and tortoise-shell ware. Maldivian industry deals with processing fish and coconuts; copra is an important export. Coconuts are also the basis of two cottage manufactures produced almost exclusively by women: coir (fibre) and cadjan (palm) weaving. Two other traditional island crafts are reedware and lacquer work. Tourism is being developed in both countries.

Towns

Sri Lanka's capital, Colombo, is on the west coast near the mouth of the Kelani river. The port has one of the world's largest artificial harbours and, with its central position in the Indian Ocean, is an important supply and refuelling base. Industries in Colombo are concerned with processing imports. The second largest town is Jaffna (107,800), a leading port in the north, followed by Kandy (93,600), a former capital and a tea and rubber centre. The Maldivian capital, Male, handles most of the islands' trade.

Afghanistan

Area
647,500 km²/250,000 sq miles
Location
29°30′—38°35′ N
60°50′—75° E
Population
16,349,000 (1981)
Population density
25 per km²/65 per sq mile
Capital and largest city
Kabul: 970,000 (1980)
Languages
Pushtu (or Pashto), Dari
Major imports
foodstuffs, machinery, petroleum products, chemicals
Major exports
hides and skins, fruit (fresh, preserved and dried), nuts, cotton, carpets, natural gas
Currency
afghani (1 afghani = 100 puls)
Gross National Product
not available
Status
independent republic

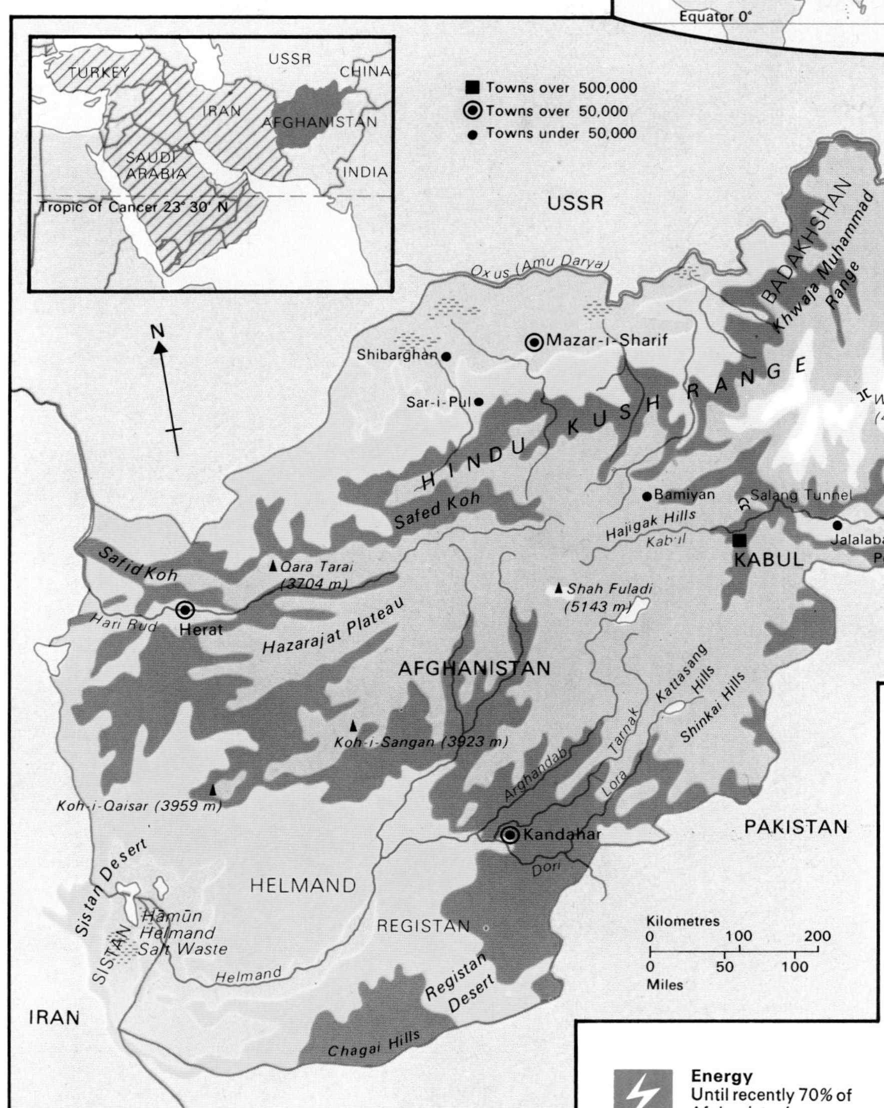

Physical features

The mountainous, landlocked country of Afghanistan has a minimum height of 1,200 m and is dominated by the Hindu Kush mountains. This great range which has an average altitude of 4,000 m is highest in the north-east: some of the peaks in the Wakhan district rise to over 6,500 m. Lowland areas include the region between the Hindu Kush and the river Oxus (Amu Darya), the south-western deserts of Sistan and Registan and the fertile valleys around Kabul, Bamiyan and Jalalabad. Four major rivers flow out of the Hindu Kush watershed: the Oxus (which forms the northern border with the USSR) the Hari Rud (ending in a closed salt basin on the Iranian frontier), the Helmand (which drains the south-west—ending in the Hamun Helmand salt waste in Iran) and the Kabul in the east, eventually joining the Indus.

Climate

The climate of Afghanistan is characterized by extreme temperatures, dryness and strong winds. Summer is hot and arid: in Jalalabad, July temperatures rise to over 45°C; the highland areas are cooler—Kabul (at 1,800 m), 38°C. Between June and September the strong north-west 'wind of 120 days' blows across the Iranian plateau at speeds of up to 160 km per hour. Winter is cold. January temperatures on the central Hazarajat plateau fall to —26°C, at Jalalabad to —4°C. A little rain falls between November and May with up to 15 cm in the north and west and about 30 cm in the east. Perpetual snow lies on mountains over 4,000 m.

Forestry and fishing

Following widespread deforestation (mostly for fuel) forests now cover less than 3% of the country. Mainly located in the east and on the northern slopes of the Hindu Kush, they include both coniferous and deciduous trees. They provide timber for construction and furniture-making nuts such as pine kernels and pistachios, resins, tan and dye barks. Replanting has begun in some places. To combat protein deficiency in the national diet, fishing is being developed in the country's rivers and lakes.

Agriculture

Farming is the main economic activity in Afghanistan. About 20% of the land (corresponding to fertile valleys and plains) is cultivable although only half of this is currently in use. Inadequate rainfall makes irrigation vital. This ranges from wells to major schemes such as the Helmand valley project. In this way, 70% of the cultivated land is watered. Wheat is the staple food crop followed by barley, maize and rice. Sugar-beet and cane, and oilseeds are also important, but production is low and imports are necessary. The two major cash crops are cotton (grown near Mazar-i-Sharif, Herat and in the Helmand valley) and fruit. Grapes account for 50% of fruit production and raisins are exported to Europe, USSR and China. Afghanistan is essentially a pastoral country. Its 10 million sheep provide meat, grease (used as a butter substitute) and wool. Around 70% of the wool is exported, the rest is woven into carpets. In the northern provinces there are also 4 million Karakul sheep; their valuable skins, made into fur coats, are a leading export.

Mining

Afghanistan's mineral resources are, for the most part, unexploited. At present, the most important asset is natural gas found in the north near Shibarghan and Sar-i-Pul. Over half the output is piped direct to the USSR, accounting for 15% of exports. Coal has been located in the northern slopes of the Hindu Kush but, so far, extraction is confined to mines at Dara-i-Suf, Karkar and Ishpushta. Mines are, however, being prepared for production near Herat. Afghanistan is the world's leading producer of lapis lazuli; this semi-precious stone has been mined in Badakhshan province for thousands of years. Gypsum, limestone, salt, talc and chromite are also currently worked. Deposits not yet exploited include copper, lead, zinc, beryl, mica, manganese, baryte, gold, silver, asbestos and sulphur; petroleum exists in the north. There are also important high-grade iron-ore reserves in the Hajigak hills, 100 km north-west of Kabul. The use of natural gas as an energy source for the reduction of this ore is being studied.

Energy

Until recently 70% of Afghanistan's energy needs were supplied by imported petroleum. This was supplemented by domestically produced coal and wood. With the development of natural gas and hydro-electric power, however, the pattern is changing. Although much natural gas is exported, some is retained for domestic consumption and the first gas-fired thermal station is in operation at Mazar-i-Sharif. With its major rivers rushing down through the mountains, the country has great hydro-electric potential yet to be harnessed.

Cities

The capital, Kabul, which is situated by the Kabul river at an altitude of 1,800 m, is over 3,000 years old. A former trading centre between East and West, the city is still the country's major market place. Industrial developments include food-processing plants and textile mills. Kandahar (230,000), the second largest town, was built 200 years ago by Ahmad Shah Durrani—the founder of the state of Afghanistan. It is a commercial and industrial centre in the agricultural south-west. Other towns include Herat (150,000) in the west and Mazar-i-Sharif (100,000) in Karakul sheep country near the gas reserves.

Transport

In the last 10 years Afghanistan, with Soviet and American aid, has built a network of trunk roads linking Kabul to all leading towns. An outstanding feature of this network is the high-altitude Salang tunnel in the Hindu Kush. There are no railways but a regular internal air-service is operated by Bakhtar Afghan Airlines to 14 provincial centres. The international Ariana Afghan Airlines flies from Kabul airport. A few waterways are navigable. There is some barge traffic on the Oxus (Amu Darya) and, in the east, rivers are used for floating logs. As the country is landlocked, Afghanistan has transit rights with its neighbours: Iran, the USSR and Pakistan. The bulk of foreign trade is taken by truck over the Khyber Pass to Peshawar, then by train to Karachi.

Industry

Industry employs less than 1% of the working population and is primarily concerned with processing domestic raw materials. Afghanistan's first established industry was cotton textile manufacture and today there are six major spinning and weaving plants. Cloth production, however, still accounts for only 75% of national requirements. There are also factories manufacturing woolen and rayon textiles. Other industries based on agricultural produce include sugar-refining, leather-tanning, fruit-preservation, raisin-cleaning and oilseed crushing. Other industries include cement (from limestone) and nitrogen fertilizers (from natural gas). A copper-smelting plant is planned. Industry still contributes less to the national income than traditional handicrafts which include metalware, leather work, jewellry, tiles and especially carpets and rugs. These carpets and rugs, hand-woven in rural areas, are a major export item and are particularly popular in West Germany and the UK.

Iran

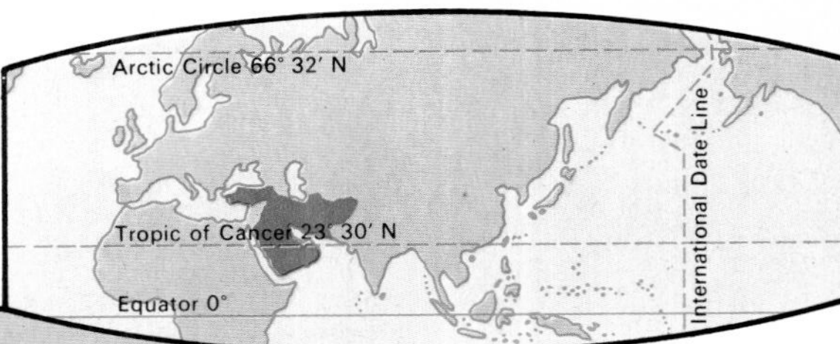

Area
1,648,000 km²/636,290 sq miles
Location
25°—39°45′ N
44°—63°30′ E
Population
40,095,000 (1981)
Population density
24 per km²/63 per sq mile
Capital and largest city
Tehran: 6,200,000
Language
Farsi
Major imports
machinery and transport equipment, iron and steel, foodstuffs, chemicals, textiles
Major exports
petroleum and petroleum products carpets, fruit (fresh and dried) hides, leather, mineral ores
Currency
Rial (1 Rial = 100 dinars)
Gross National Product
not available
Status
Islamic republic

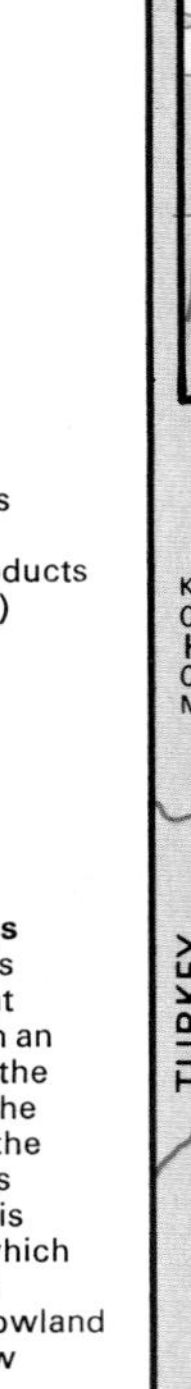

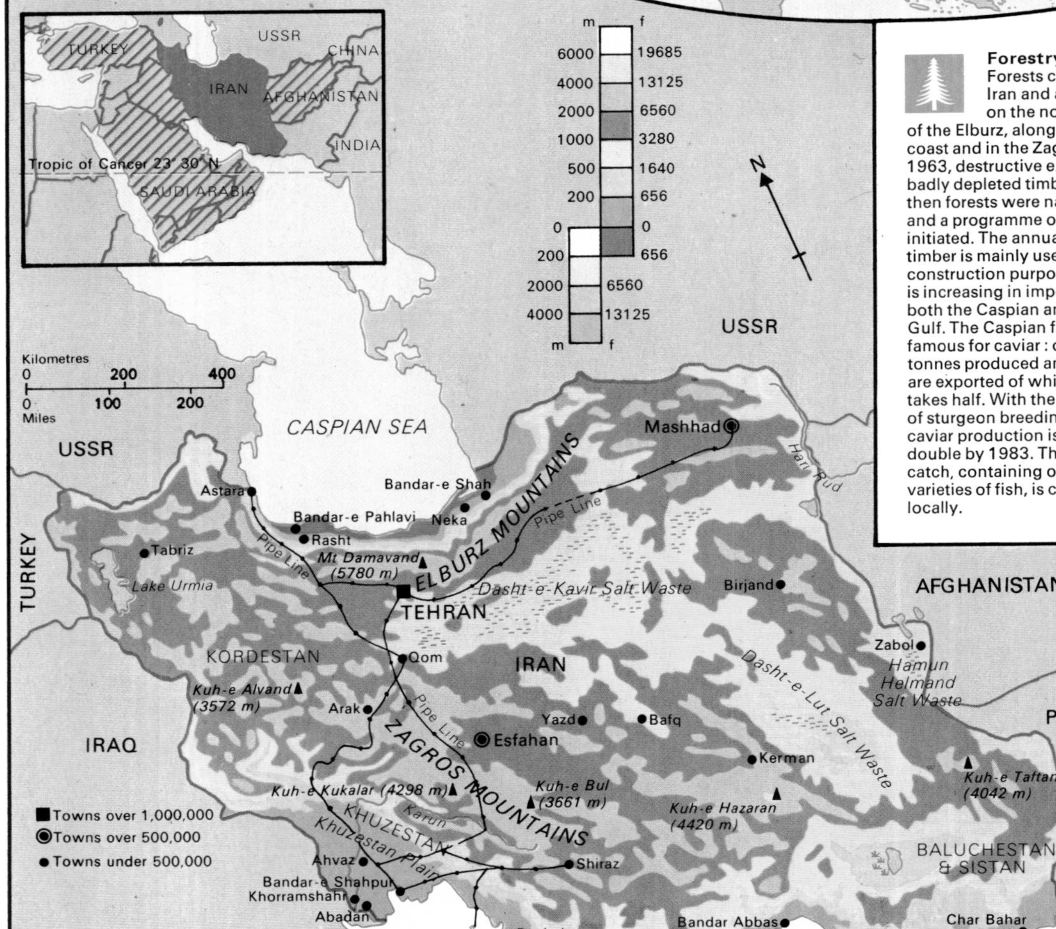

Forestry and fishing

Forests cover 11% of Iran and are concentrated on the northern slopes of the Elburz, along the Caspian coast and in the Zagros. Before 1963, destructive exploitation badly depleted timber resources, then forests were nationalized and a programme of afforestation initiated. The annual yield of timber is mainly used for construction purposes. Fishing is increasing in importance in both the Caspian and the Persian Gulf. The Caspian fisheries are famous for caviar: of the 200 tonnes produced annually, 195 are exported of which the USSR takes half. With the introduction of sturgeon breeding stations, caviar production is expected to double by 1983. The Persian Gulf catch, containing over 100 varieties of fish, is consumed locally.

Physical features

The centre of Iran is occupied by a great desert plateau with an average height of 1,500 m in the west and 900 m in the east. The southern and western rim of the plateau consists of the Zagros mountains. The northern rim is formed by the Elburz range which rises to 5,780 m at its highest point—Mount Damavand. Lowland areas are limited to the narrow coastal strip bordering the Caspian Sea and the Khuzestan plain at the head of the Persian Gulf. The most important river is the Karun which is 800 km long. On the plateau, most rivers flow inland from the mountain rim and terminate in closed basins which dry out into salt marshes in summer. Westwards, near the Turkish border, many rivers drain into Lake Urmia, a salt lake.

Climate

The central plateau has a climate of extremes. Summer is characterized by high temperatures (rising to 50°C), dryness and the scorching 'wind of 120 days'. Winter is cold with temperatures below —20°C and snow on high ground. Most of the plateau receives less than 25 cm of rain a year, coming mainly in winter. Tehran has temperatures of 37°C in July and —3°C in January. The Caspian lowlands are warm and humid with 125 cm of rain a year, mostly in summer. The Khuzestan plain is also humid with milder winters: in Abadan, temperatures are 45°C in August and 7°C in January.

Transport

The basis of Iran's transport system is a 40,000 km network of roads. Railways are less extensive. There is a 1,400 km long main line which goes from Bandar-e Shahpur via Tehran to Bandar-e Shah. Principal branches from this serve Tabriz, Mashhad and the steelworks at Esfahan. Iran National Airlines fly to 15 Iranian cities, to neighbouring countries and to Europe. Tehran and Abadan have international airports. The main port is Khorramshahr, handling 50% of Iran's non-oil cargo, followed by Bandar-e Shahpur, Bandar Abbas, Bushehr, Lengeh and Chah Bahar. Bandar-e Pahlavi and Bandar-e Shah trade with the USSR.

Oil

Iran has an oil-based economy. Petroleum and petroleum products account for 89% of exports. It is the world's fourth largest oil-producer and 90% of the production comes from fields lying between the Iraqi border and Shiraz. Crude oil is exported via Kharg Island, the world's largest oil terminal. The world's biggest oil refinery at Abadan has an output of 500,000 barrels a day. There is another refinery at Shiraz and two more are under construction at Tabriz and Neka. The oil industry which, in spite of its importance, employs under 1% of the population is nationalized.

Mining

The steel plant at Esfahan uses iron ore from Bafq near Yazd and coal from Kerman. Coal is also mined in the Elburz mountains. Lead and zinc are mined at Bafq and near Qom. Chrome and turquoise are produced for export and other important deposits include sulphur, salt, limestone, ochre and kaolin. In the last 10 years, substantial copper deposits have been located, especially near Kerman and Iran could soon be a leading producer of copper. Iran also has the world's second largest reserves of natural gas, found in the south and in the Elburz mountains. Some of the gas is piped direct to the USSR. Iran's mineral wealth is rapidly being developed.

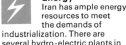

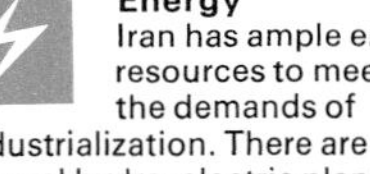

Energy

Iran has ample energy resources to meet the demands of industrialization. There are several hydro-electric plants in operation and thermal stations are fired by oil or gas. Gas is increasingly important. The 1,140 km long pipeline taking gas from Ahvaz to Astara on the Soviet border is known as IGAT (Iranian Gas Trunkline). Gas from IGAT is distributed via spur lines to major centres (Tehran Esfahan and Shiraz). This pipeline network is being extended and by 1978 should provide 30% of Iran's power needs.

Cities

Tehran is situated on the southern slopes of the Elburz at an altitude of 1,200 m. The bazaars and narrow streets of the old city contrast with the modern sector lying to the north. Over 50% of Iran's manufactured goods, ranging from cigarettes and shoes to textiles and china, are produced in Tehran. Esfahan (700,000) is the second largest city and the country's textile centre. This town now has Iran's first steel mill. Mashhad (600,000) is a commercial centre for the north-east.

Agriculture

Agriculture is the main economic activity and employs over 50% of Iranians. About 25% of the country is cultivable but less than half of this is under cultivation. The main cereal crops are wheat and barley, grown on the Gulf coastlands and the southern Elburz slopes. Rice is cultivated in the Caspian lowlands. Two of the main cash crops, cotton and sugarbeet, are extensively grown; a third, tobacco, is limited to the Caspian area. Other crops produced commercially include tea, olives, nuts, fruit (grapes, citrus, melons, apricots) and, in the extreme south, dates. About 25% of the cultivated area is irrigated, mainly from traditional underground water ducts; modern water storage projects are being developed. Along the Turkish and Iraqi borders, agriculture is rain-fed. Output is being increased by mechanization, fertilizers and the establishment of farming co-operatives in most villages. Livestock is important: the wool provided by some 30 million sheep, principally grazed in the Zagros mountains, is the basis of the carpet industry. Many of the herds belong to nomadic tribesmen who bring them to the coastlands in winter.

Industry

In the last 10 years Iran has concentrated on industrialization in an effort to reduce its dependence on oil and agriculture. Traditional industries have been expanded; for example, the processing of local raw materials such as cotton at Esfahan, silk in the Caspian area, sugar refining, rice milling, fruit canning, flour milling, tanning, cement and construction materials and cigarette manufacture. New industries have been introduced. In exchange for Iranian natural gas, the Russians helped build a steelmill at Esfahan, a machine plant at Arak and a machine tool factory at Tabriz. Foreign capital has also contributed to an aluminium smelter at Arak and a petrochemical complex at Bandar-e Shahpur. Many European vehicle manufacturers have production plants in Iran. The main industrial centres are Tehran, Esfahan, Tabriz, Arak, Mashhad, Shiraz and Rasht. Handicrafts are widespread and include pottery, metalware, jewellery, leatherwork and, most important, carpet-weaving. Hand-woven carpets are Iran's chief non-oil export which is expected to earn 500 million US dollars by 1978.

Iraq and Kuwait

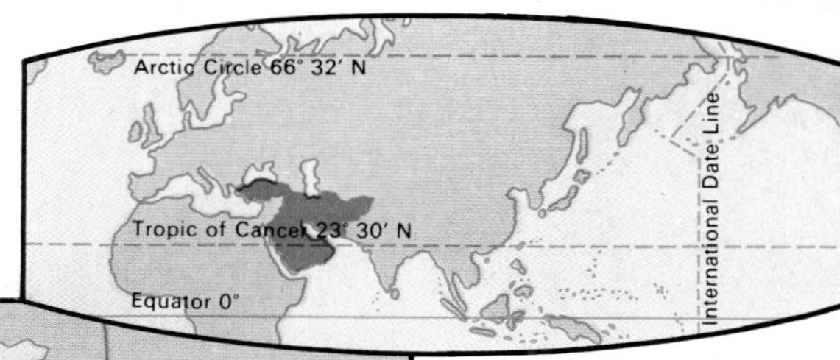

Iraq
Area
438,446 km²/169,284 sq miles
Location
29°—37°20′ N
38°45′—48°30′ E
Population
13,541,000 (1981)
Population density
31 per km²/80 per sq mile
Capital and largest city
Baghdad: 3,206,000 (1977)
Language
Arabic
Major imports
machinery and transport equipment, iron and steel, sugar, textiles
Major exports
crude oil, dates, wool, skins and hides, cement
Currency
dinar (1 dinar = 1,000 fils)
Gross National Product
not available
Status
independent republic

Kuwait
Area
17,818 km²/6,880 sq miles
Location
28°30′—30° N
46°30′—48°40′ E
Population
1,464,000 (1981)
Population density
82 per km²/213 per sq mile
Capital
Kuwait City: 60,000 (1980)
Largest city
Hawalli: 152,000 (1980)
Language
Arabic
Major imports
machinery, transport equipment, manufactured goods, foodstuffs
Major exports
petroleum and petroleum products, fertilizers, fish
Currency
dinar (1 dinar = 1,000 fils)
Gross National Product
30,600 million US dollars (1981)
Status
constitutional emirate

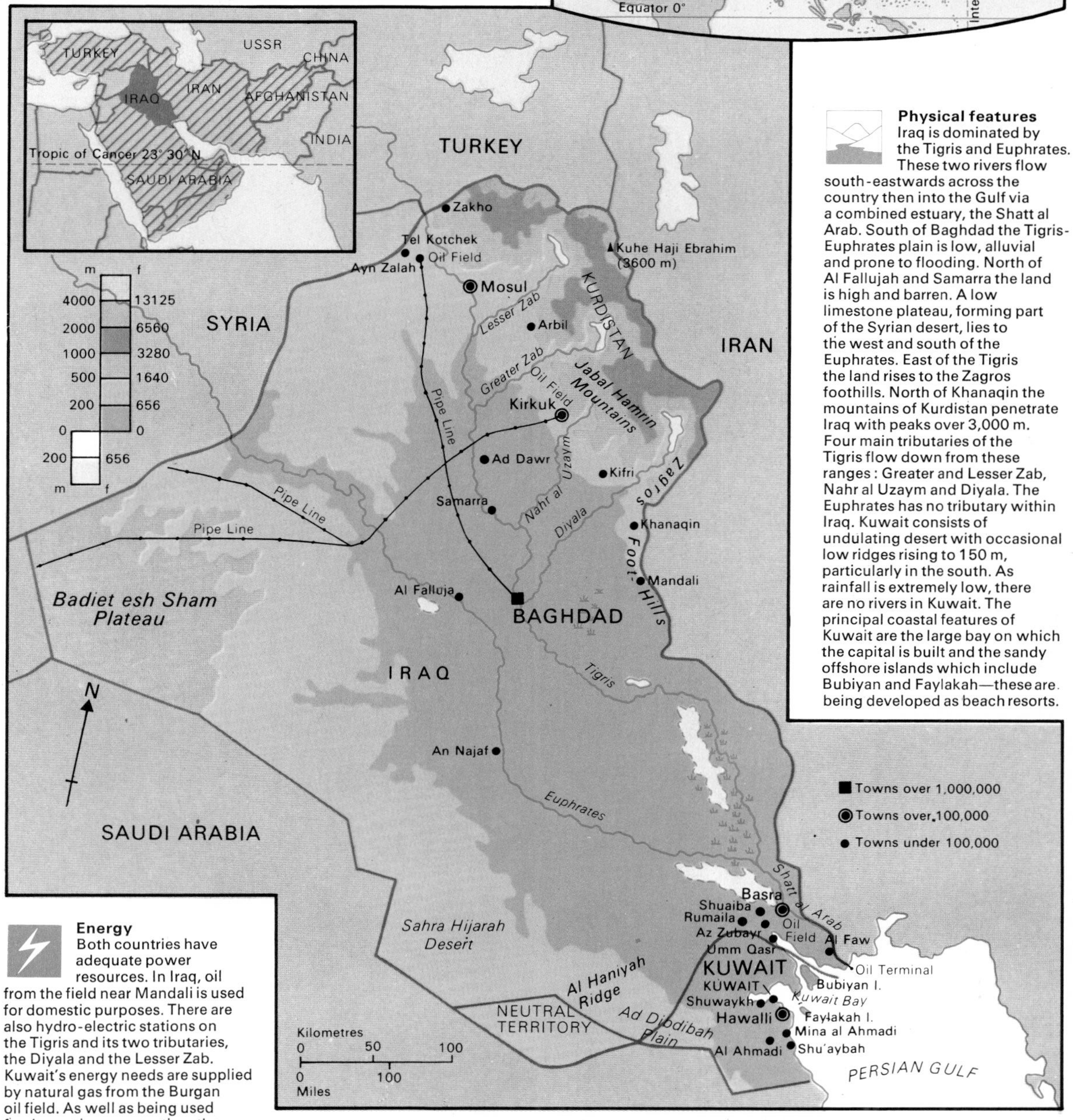

Cities

The capital of Iraq, Baghdad, is situated on the Tigris 560 km from the Persian Gulf. Flooding was once common but the city is now protected by the Samarra barrage. The greater part of Iraqi industry, ranging from steel and bricks to leather and cigarettes, is located in the capital. Iraq's second city, Basra (371,000), is 112 km inland on the west bank of the Shatt al Arab and is the country's leading port. The Kuwaiti capital, situated on the south side of Kuwait Bay, developed as a trading centre and today is a major Gulf port. One of its suburbs, Hawalli, has become the state's largest city.

Climate

Both countries have hot, arid summers. In July and August day temperatures, normally 50°C, rise to 70°C. Sandstorms are common in June and July. Winter is cold and damp. In January the average temperature in the capital of Kuwait is 20°C, in Mosul in the north of Iraq it is 8°C. Rain occurs between November and April and is heaviest in north-east Iraq. Kuwait has about 10 cm a year, Basra 15 cm, Mosul 40 cm and in the north-east mountains up to 100 cm—falling mainly as snow. In April and May, melting snow causes the Tigris and Euphrates to flood.

Energy

Both countries have adequate power resources. In Iraq, oil from the field near Mandali is used for domestic purposes. There are also hydro-electric stations on the Tigris and its two tributaries, the Diyala and the Lesser Zab. Kuwait's energy needs are supplied by natural gas from the Burgan oil field. As well as being used for domestic consumption, the gas also powers the state's electricity generating stations.

Transport

In Iraq, a main road runs from the Jordanian frontier through Baghdad to Basra. Other major routes link Baghdad to Zakho, Khanaqin and An Najaf. The main railway goes from Basra via Baghdad and Kirkuk to Arbil. A line from Baghdad to Tel Kotchek connects with the Syrian network and provides a through service from the Gulf to Europe. Inland waterways are important locally. Basra is the leading port but Umm Qasr is being developed. The state airline, Iraqi Airways, operates international services from Baghdad and Basra. Kuwait has no railway, but an efficient 1,600 km road system links the capital to Al Ahmadi, other oil-producing zones, and the Iraqi and Saudi borders. Kuwait is the chief port followed by Shuwaykh and Shu'aybah. Some 20 airlines, including Kuwait Airlines, serve the one international airport.

Agriculture

Just ove 25% of Iraq is cultivable and half that area is now under cultivation. In the north-east, where agriculture is rain-fed, wheat, barley, tobacco and fruit are the main crops. On the plains, the growing of wheat, barley, maize, millet, sesame and cotton relies on irrigation. About half of the land under cultivation is irrigated. In the Hawr al Hammar lake area, rice and dates are grown. Iraq produces over 300,000 tonnes of dates a year and, together with Egypt, ranks as the world's leading date exporter. Livestock, in particular sheep, are reared and wool is exported. Forests in the north-east yield timber for construction as well as licorice, dye-barks and gum tragacanth. In Kuwait, less than 0.1% of the total area is cultivated. Of this, two-thirds is used for vegetables such as tomatoes, radishes, melons and cucumbers. Fishing is a traditional Kuwaiti activity; prawns and shrimps are exported.

Mining

The major mineral resource in both countries is oil. Crude oil accounts for over 90% of Iraq's exports. The three main production areas are at Kirkuk, at Ayn Zalah (north-west of Mosul) and at Rumaila and Az Zubayr, south of Basra. Oil from the northern fields is taken by pipelines to Mediterranean ports in Lebanon and Syria. Output from the south is exported via Al Faw. The main refinery is at Ad Dawr. Kuwait is the world's seventh largest oil producer. The Burgan oilfields are the most important. These are situated on the Ahmadi ridge and gravity takes the oil down to the two coastal terminals and offshore-tanker terminal. The world's first all-hydrogen refinery at Shuaiba supplies petroleum products for domestic consumption and export. No other mineral resources have been located in Kuwait but, in Iraq, deposits of iron, chrome, copper, lead and zinc have been found.

Physical features

Iraq is dominated by the Tigris and Euphrates. These two rivers flow south-eastwards across the country then into the Gulf via a combined estuary, the Shatt al Arab. South of Baghdad the Tigris-Euphrates plain is low, alluvial and prone to flooding. North of Al Fallujah and Samarra the land is high and barren. A low limestone plateau, forming part of the Syrian desert, lies to the west and south of the Euphrates. East of the Tigris the land rises to the Zagros foothills. North of Khanaqin the mountains of Kurdistan penetrate Iraq with peaks over 3,000 m. Four main tributaries of the Tigris flow down from these ranges: Greater and Lesser Zab, Nahr al Uzaym and Diyala. The Euphrates has no tributary within Iraq. Kuwait consists of undulating desert with occasional low ridges rising to 150 m, particularly in the south. As rainfall is extremely low, there are no rivers in Kuwait. The principal coastal features of Kuwait are the large bay on which the capital is built and the sandy offshore islands which include Bubiyan and Faylakah—these are being developed as beach resorts.

Industry

In Iraq, all leading industries are nationalized. These include cement, asbestos, bricks, steel, textiles, flour, sugar, leather-tanning, cigarettes and paper. A smaller but equally important activity is date-packing. The current five-year plan aims at developing the petrochemical electrical and food-processing industries. Baghdad, Basra and Mosul are the principal manufacturing centres. With a view to diversifying its economy, Kuwait has embarked on a major industrialization programme. The three main development areas, in addition to petrochemicals, are chemical fertilizers (accounting for 62% of Kuwait's non-oil exports), building materials (such as cement and bricks) and flour production (including biscuits and pasta). Two industries connected with traditional activities are boat-building and fish-freezing. At Shuwaykh, Kuwait has the world's largest desalination plant.

Turkey

Climate

The west and south coasts of Turkey have a Mediterranean climate with hot summers and mild, rainy winters. The average temperature in July is 28°C, in January it is 11°C and annual rainfall, occurring between September and May, is about 75 cm. The Black Sea coast and Istanbul have slightly lower temperatures: 23°C in July, 7°C in January and rain in all seasons. The central plateau has hot summers with temperatures up to 33°C and severe winters with temperatures dropping to —12°C (snow is common). South-eastern Turkey has a semi-arid desert climate: hot summers, cool, damp winters.

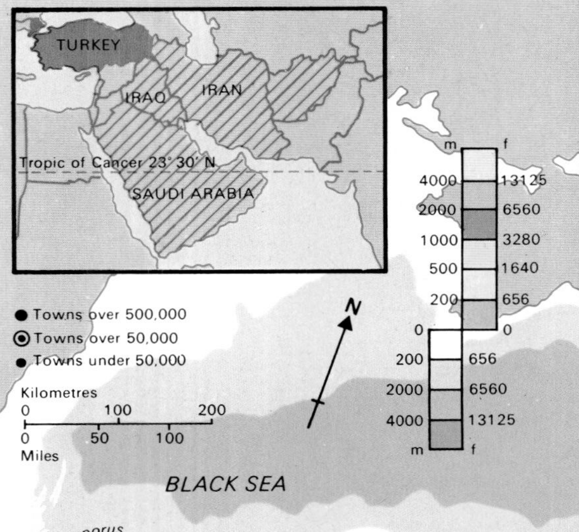

Mining

There are important chrome deposits near Maras and Fethiye and Turkey is one of the world's four leading chrome producers. Other mineral exports include copper (from Murgul and Ergani) and, in smaller quantities, zinc, manganese, mercury, borax and antimony. At Konya there is an aluminium plant using local bauxite. The output of iron ore, mined at Divrigi, does not meet the increasing domestic demand. Lignite and coal are mined in small quantities and the main coalfields are at Eregli and Zonguldak. Oil, coming mostly from the Siirt region, provides 30% of the throughput of the country's four refineries.

Transport

The government is taking steps to improve Turkey's road and rail system. There are 35,000 km of state highways (50% of which is hard-surfaced) and a further 186,500 km of minor roads. In 1973 the world's fourth longest bridge, linking Europe and Asia, was opened at Istanbul. Work has begun on a highway running from Greece, via Istanbul and Ankara, to Syria. New stock is being built for the 8,200 km rail network. Of the country's 18 airports, two (Ankara and Istanbul) are international. The two main ports are Istanbul, which handles over 50% of Turkish imports, and Izmir. Other leading ports include Samsun and Mersin.

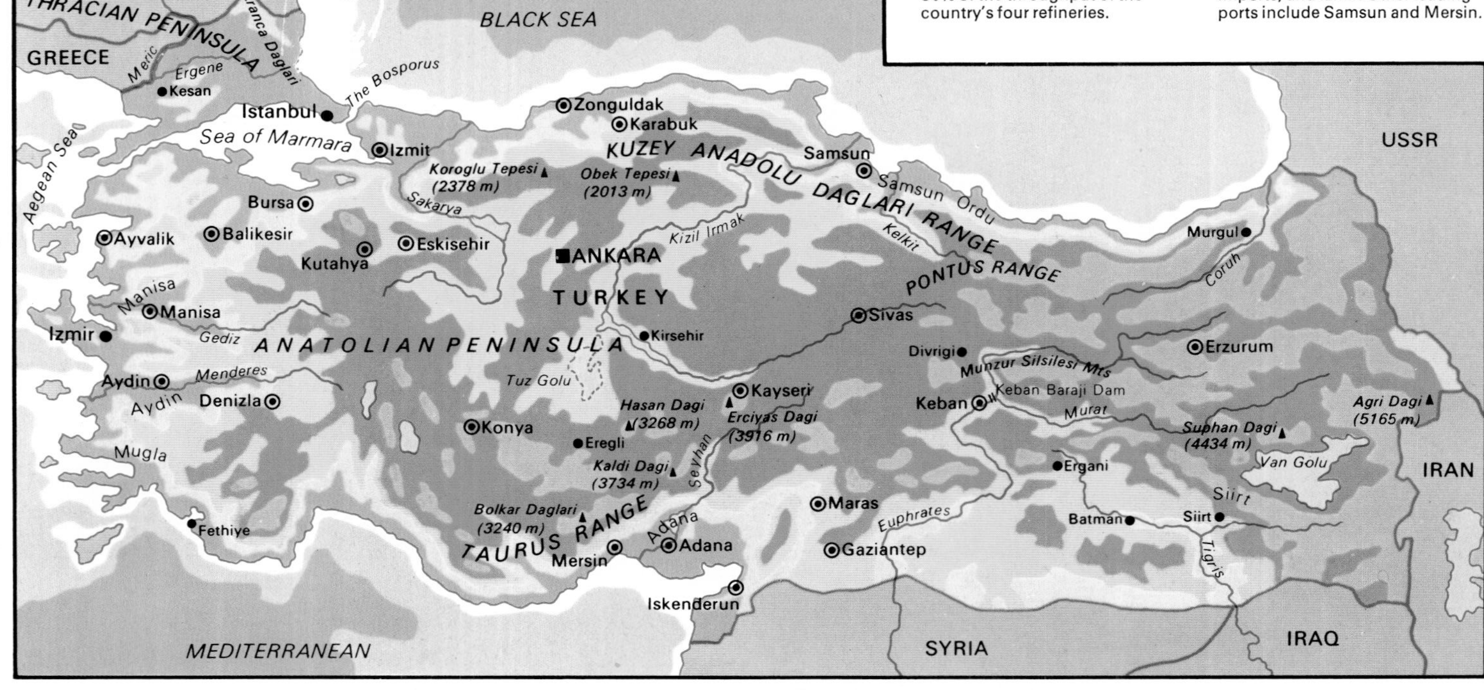

Area
779,452 km²/300,950 sq miles
Location
35°50'—42°5' N
25°40'—44°50' E
Population
45,529,000 (1981)
Population density
58 per km²/151 per sq mile
Capital
Ankara: 1,878,000 (1980)
Largest city
Istanbul: 2,773,000 (1980)
Language
Turkish
Major imports
machinery, iron and steel, oil, transport equipment
Major exports
cotton, fruit and nuts, tobacco, cereals, minerals, livestock
Currency
lira (1 lira = 100 kurus)
Gross National Product
70,210 million US dollars (1981)
Status
independent republic

Tourism

Tourism is a major growth industry. In the last five years the number of visitors to Turkey has trebled and the income from tourism has increased six-fold.

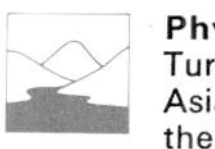

Physical features

Turkey links Europe and Asia. European Turkey, the Thracian peninsular, has an area of only 23,764 km². Thrace is a land of wide, undulating plains, with highlands in the north-east and south-west. Asian Turkey, the Anatolian peninsular, is much bigger. Central Anatolia consists of a vast plateau with an average height of 1,200 m, broken by ridges and volcanic outcrops. In the extreme east is Turkey's highest peak, Agri Dagi (Mt Ararat): 5,165 m. This central plateau is bordered to the north by the Kuzey Anadolu Daglar Range which extends eastwards into the Pontus range. In the south, the plateau is bordered by the Taurus range which extends north-eastwards to the Munzur Silsilesi mountains and the higher mountains in the east. The main rivers draining off the plateau are the Tigris, Euphrates, Seyhan, Menderes, Gediz and Kizil Irmak. There are about 65 lakes: the largest is Van Golu, 3,738 km² in area and 1,800 m deep, followed by Tuz Golu which has an area of 1,642 km² and is over 800 m deep.

Agriculture

Agriculture employs 60% of the population and accounts for 65% of exports. About 60% of the land is under cultivation. On the Anatolian plateau the cultivated area is used for cereals: wheat and barley are the main crops. Cash crops are concentrated on the fertile coastal plains. These include sugarbeet, cotton (grown in the Adana, Manisa and Mugla regions) and tobacco (from the Ordu, Samsun, Manisa and Aydin districts). Citrus fruits, grapes, figs and hazelnuts are extensively grown and dried fruit is exported through Izmir. Olives, used mainly to produce oil, are cultivated in the west. Silk production is centred at Bursa. Animals, principally sheep and goats, are important and livestock is exported. Forests cover 25% of the country. Half of this is of low commercial value but Turkey is self-sufficient in timber, firewood, resin and turpentine. Fishing is being developed, but at present only 20% of the potential catch is landed. Recent measures to assist agriculture include irrigation and machinery.

Industry

Although Turkish industry is expanding, it is still primarily concerned with supplying the domestic market and few manufactures are exported. The textile industry, centred at Istanbul, Aydin, Denizli, Adana, Gaziantep and Kayseri, is the most important: output is 80% cotton, 20% woollen. Iron and steel production was formerly confined to the Black Sea coalfield with works at Eregli and Karabuk but, with Soviet aid, a third steel mill has been built at Iskenderun. Another major industrial activity is petroleum refining: crude oil is imported from Iran and Iraq and refined at Izmit, Mersin, Batman and Izmir. Other industries include paper manufacture, flour-milling, sugar-refining, cement production, vehicle assembly and fertilizers; a petro-chemical plant was opened at Izmir in 1971. Traditional crafts are important and some products, such as woven carpets from Siirt, Kirsehir and Sivas, are exported. Turkish ceramics are also known internationally; the two main centres are Istanbul and Kutahya.

Energy

Although the output of power has quadrupled in the last ten years, 60% of the population is still without electricity and wood and dried dung are widely used for domestic purposes. Thermal stations generate 80% of the energy supply and these use oil and lignite. The remainder is from hydro-electric stations: there is a major dam at Keban and another hydro-electric station is under construction at Ayvalik.

Cities

Ankara, which lies 200 km south of the Black Sea on the edge of the Anatolian plateau, has been the capital since 1923. About 350 km to the west is Istanbul, the country's largest city. This was the former capital of the Byzantine Empire, then of the Ottoman Empire and, finally, of Turkey. It is built on a peninsular surrounded on three sides by water: the Sea of Marmara, the Bosphorus and the Golden Horn. Istanbul's historic monuments, which include many mosques, have made it an important tourist centre.

Saudi Arabia

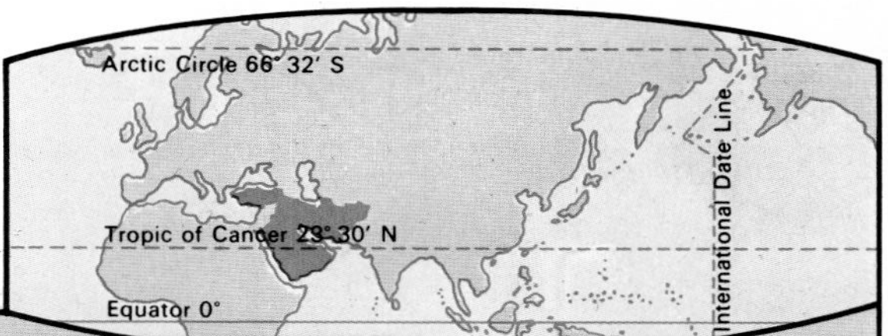

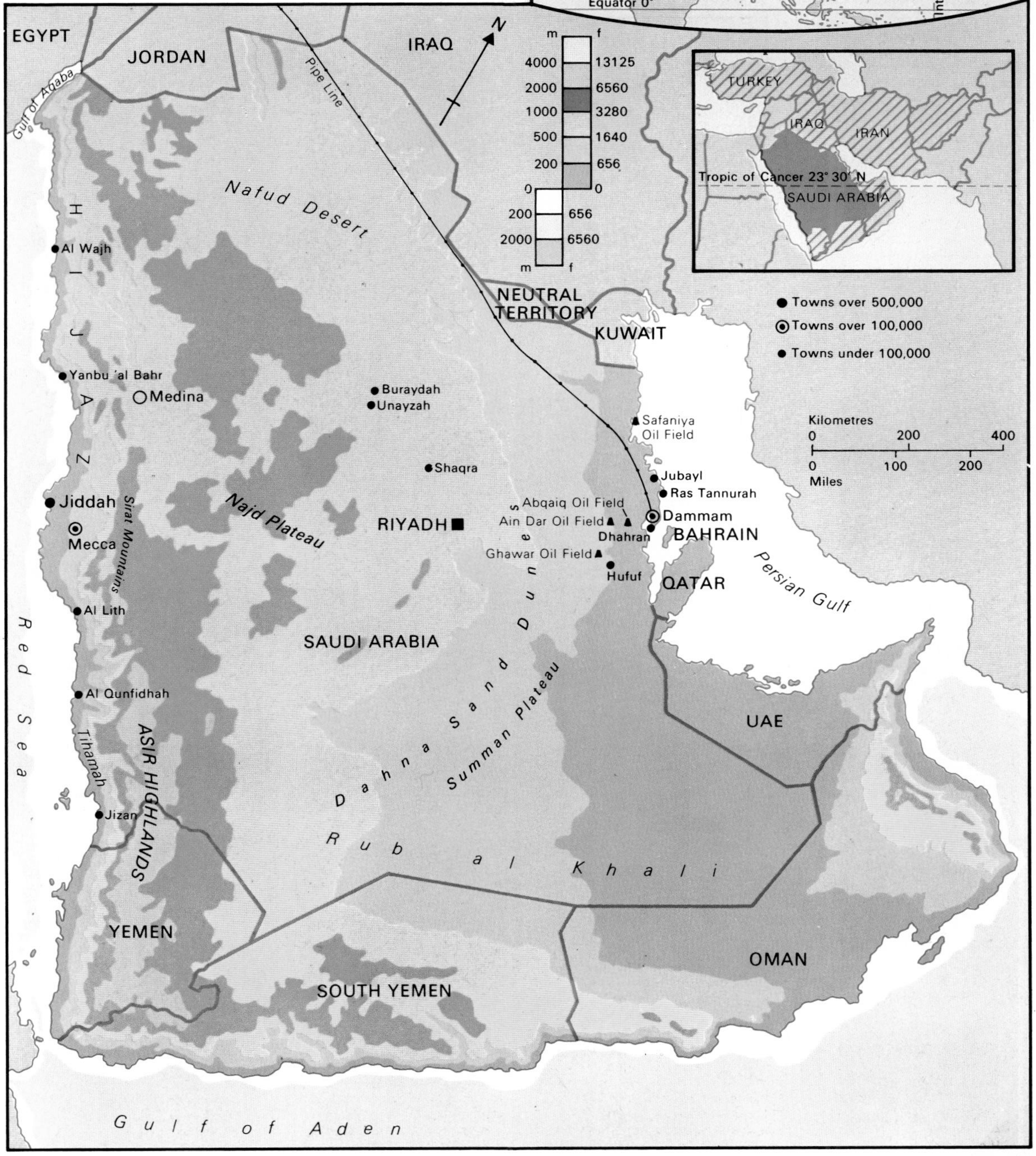

Area
2,300,000 km²/888,000 sq miles
Location
16°—32°10′ N
34°30′—56° E
Population
9,305,000 (1981)
Population density
4 per km²/10 per sq mile
Capital and largest city
Riyadh: 1,790,000 (1981)
Language
Arabic
Major imports
foodstuffs, machinery, transport equipment, building materials, textiles
Major exports
petroleum and petroleum products
Currency
rial (1 rial = 20 qurush)
Gross National Product
117,240 million US dollars (1981)
Status
absolute monarchy

Physical features
Saudi Arabia is situated between the Red Sea and the Persian Gulf and occupies 80% of the Arabian peninsular. It consists of a block of old, hard rock, highest along the Red Sea and tilted downwards towards the north-east. A narrow coastal plain, the Tihamah, borders the Red Sea. This is paralleled by steep ranges varying in height from 1,500 m in Hijaz to 2,500 m in the Asir highlands. East of these mountains lies the arid Najd plateau. A sandy strip 1,300 km long links the Nafud desert in the northwest to the uninhabited 'empty quarter', the Rub 'al Khali desert in the south. The barren Summan plateau separates the Dahna sand dunes from the low plains adjoining the Persian Gulf. Surface water is rare and there are no permanent rivers—seasonal streams evaporate into wadis (dry valleys). There is, however, abundant underground water which provides numerous oases and wells.

Climate
Saudi Arabia has one of the hottest summer climates in the world. Inland, July and August temperatures often rise to 50°C. The coasts are slightly cooler—Jiddah 32°C, Dammam 35°C—but the humidity, which can be as high as 90%, is intolerable. Winter temperatures are 23°C in Jiddah, 17°C in Dammam and 14°C in Riyadh. It is coldest in the Asir highlands where frost and snow occasionally occur. Rainfall is slight: Dammam and Riyadh have about 10 cm a year, Jiddah 6 cm while the Rub 'al Khali frequently has none. In contrast, the Asir mountains receive over 35 cm.

Transport
Roads are a government priority in Saudi Arabia. These now total over 16,000 km and a further 1,000 km are being built annually. A major achievement is the coast-to-coast route which runs from Jiddah via Riyadh to Dammam. There is only one railway, the 575 km line between Dammam and Riyadh. The state-owned Saudi Arabian Airlines operates scheduled internal and overseas services as well as special flights for pilgrims. There are international airports at Jiddah, Dhahran and Riyadh. The main ports are Jiddah and Dammam.

Cities
Although Riyadh is the administrative capital, Jiddah (983,000), with the Saudi Ministry of Foreign Affairs and embassies, is the diplomatic centre. Jiddah, which originated as a meeting place for pilgrims on their way to Mecca, is now Saudi Arabia's leading industrial city and chief Red Sea port. The country's third largest town is Mecca (463,000), the birthplace of Mohammed. Built around an oasis on a caravan route in the Sirat mountains, Islam's holy city is visited by a million pilgrims each year. Non-Muslims are not allowed inside the city; they are also barred from Medina (100,000), 523 km north of Mecca. Medina, where Mohammed governed and died, is Islam's second most sacred city and also a place of pilgrimage.

Agriculture
About 25% of the population is employed in arable farming. The cultivated areas, representing 0.2% of the total land surface, are concentrated in the Asir (where agriculture is rain-fed) and in the east (which is irrigated). The main cereals are wheat, millet and maize; other crops include fruit, melons, coffee and dates. Although output has increased, particularly of fruit and vegetables, food is still imported. A further 50% of the population is engaged in herding. Camels, sheep and goats are raised for their milk, meat, wool, hair and skins. Half of these pastoralists are nomadic Bedou who roam the deserts with their camels. Desalination plants, irrigation and desert reclamation schemes are being developed to improve agriculture.

Industry
Industrialization is still in its early stages and production is aimed at the domestic market. Major projects currently in operation are petrol refineries at Ras Tannurah and Jiddah, cement plants at Jiddah, Riyadh and Hufuf, a steel-rolling mill at Jiddah, a fertilizer factory at Dammam and three desalination plants. Industrial estates have been set up at Jiddah, Riyadh and Dammam and a fourth is planned for Jubayl. A refinery at Riyadh, flour and sugar mills, vehicle assembly works as well as additional fertilizer factories and cement plants are all under construction. There are plans for the further diversification of industry including aluminium manufacture, iron and steel production, mining and the liquefaction of gas.

Mining
Saudi Arabia, with almost 20% of the world's oil, has the largest reserves in the world. It is also the world's leading oil exporter and, after the USA and the USSR, holds third place for production. The oil industry is centred at Dhahran; the main fields are Ghawar, Abqaiq, Ain Dar and Dammam, all in the east, and offshore, Safaniya. About 75% of the crude oil is shipped from the Ras Tannurah terminal, mainly to Europe and Japan; 15% goes through Tapline (the Trans-Arabian Pipeline) to the Mediterranean port of Saida in the Lebanon; the rest is piped to refineries on Bahrain Island and at Ras Tannurah and Jiddah. Deposits of copper, zinc, iron, phosphates and uranium have been located but are not exploited commercially.

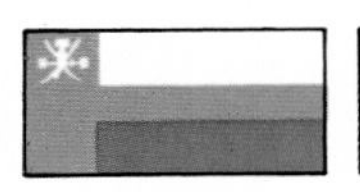

Oman and Yemen

People's Democratic Republic of Yemen (PDR)

Yemen Arab Republic (YAR)

Oman (top left)
PDR (top)
YAR (left)

Physical features
Oman, the second largest state in the Arabian peninsula, is a land of desert broken in the north by the barren Hajar mountains which rise to over 3,000 m. The Jabal Qara mountains lie to the south. The coastal strips fringing both ranges are relatively densely populated. Offshore are the five Kuria Muria islands and, further north, Masirah island. In the PDR, the long coastal belt varies in width from 6 to 60 km. This is backed by a mountain range which rises to a plateau over 1,800 m high. Socotra (3,100 km²) is the largest island in the Gulf of Aden. The YAR's coastal plain, the Tihamah, is an arid strip of sand dunes. About 50 km inland, the plain rises to the Upper Tihamah, a foothill zone flanked by rugged mountains rising to heights of over 3,000 m—75% of the population is concentrated in this highland region. The Rub al Khali (Empty Quarter) lies further inland.

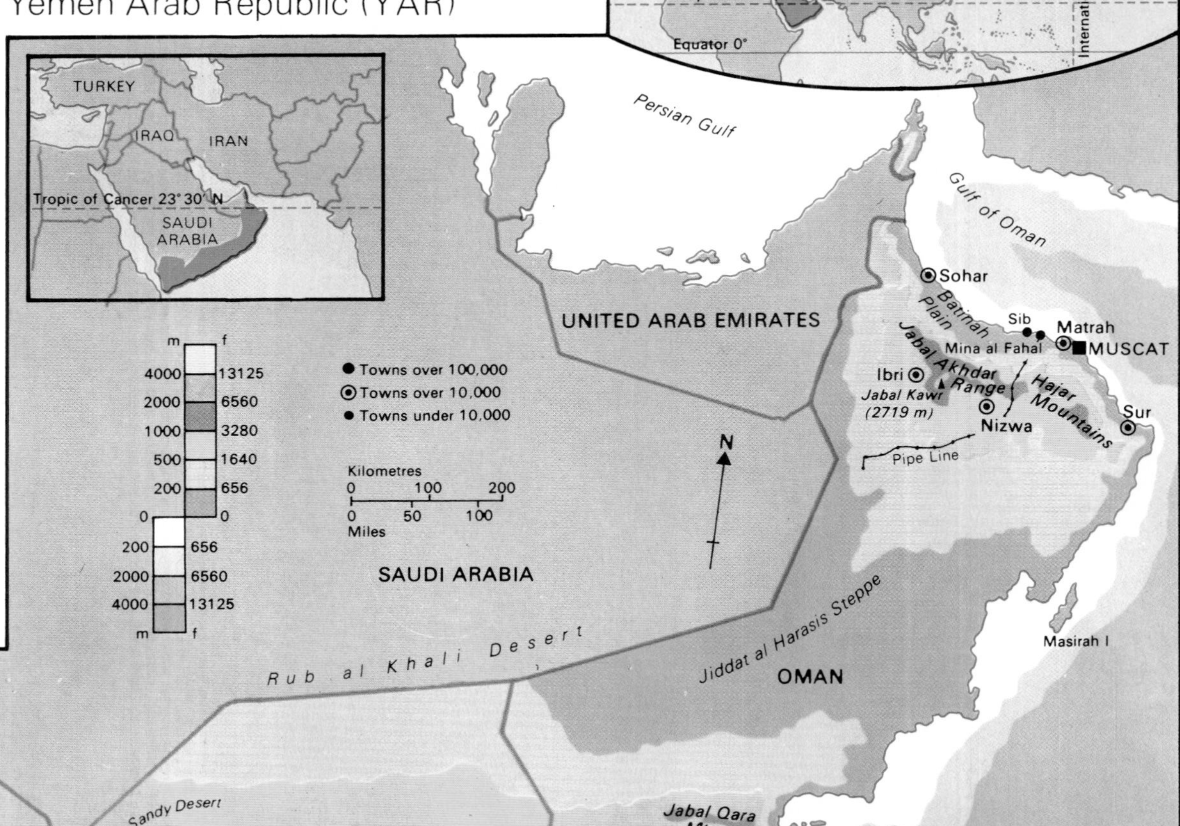

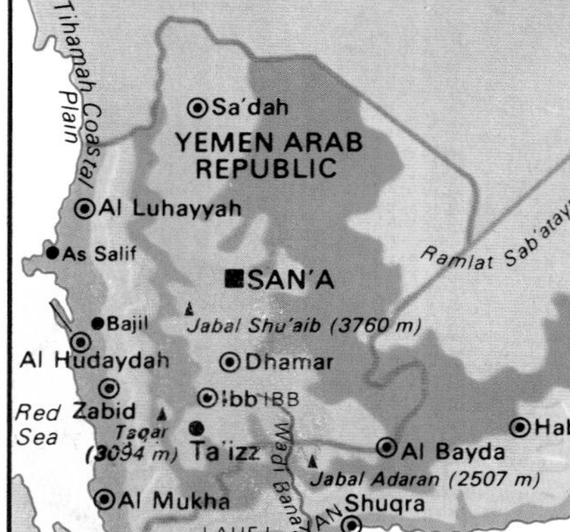

Oman
Area
212,400 km²/82,000 sq miles
Population
919,000 (1981)
Population density
4 per km²/11 per sq mile
Capital and largest city
Muscat: 50,000 (1981)
Language
Arabic
Major imports
foodstuffs, machinery and transport equipment, cement
Major exports
crude oil, limes, dates, fish
Gross National Product
5,440 million US dollars (1981)
Currency
Rial (1 rial = 1,000 baiza)

Climate
In the three states, coastal areas are humid (over 80%), hot and arid. In January, Aden has an average temperature of 25°C, in June it is 33°C—annual rainfall, which occurs in winter, is under 10 cm. In Oman and the PDR rainfall increases in the mountains to 25 cm. It is even heavier in the YAR highlands: the Upper Tihamah receives up to 50 cm and the main ranges about 100 cm—falling mostly in summer. The YAR highlands are cooler—average annual temperature is 18°C.

Democratic Republic of Yemen
Area
293,000 km²/113,130 sq miles
Population
1,957,000 (1981)
Population density
7 per km²/17 per sq mile
Capital and largest city
Aden: 264,000 (1980)
Language
Arabic
Major imports
crude oil, foodstuffs, textiles
Major exports
refined petroleum, cotton, dried fish, coffee
Gross National Product
910 million US dollars (1981)
Currency
Dinar (1 dinar = 1,000 fils)

Mining
Oil dominates the Omani economy. Production began in 1967 and has increased as new fields, all in the interior, have been developed. The oil is piped to the terminal at Mina al Fahal, near Matrah. Important copper deposits have been discovered in the north, but so far remain unexploited. In the PDR salt is mined in the north-east. About a million tonnes a year are also mined at As Salif in the YAR. Other minerals known to exist include coal, iron, sulphur, uranium, gold and silver.

Yemen Arab Republic
Area
200,000 km²/77,220 sq miles
Population
7,251,000 (1981)
Population density
36 per km²/94 per sq mile
Capital and largest city
San'a: 278,000 (1981)
Language
Arabic
Major imports
foodstuffs, machinery and transport equipment, chemicals
Major exports
cotton, coffee, hides, skins, salt
Gross National Product
3,310 million US dollars (1981)
Currency
Riyal (1 riyal = 40 bugshas)

Transport
In Oman, new roads, an international airport at Sib and a deep-water port at Matrah have all been financed by oil revenues. Two other major ports are at Raysut and Sur. In the PDR most roads are unsurfaced except near Aden. The port of Aden handles nearly all the PDR's trade and is a re-fuelling stop for international shipping. In the YAR, main roads connect San'a, Ta'izz and Al Hudaydah, the chief port. As Salif port is used for the salt trade. None of the states has a railway.

Agriculture
In all three states, agriculture employs over 70% of the population. In Oman, the main cultivated areas are the Batinah plain, the Jabal Akhdar and parts of the Hajar range. About 50% of the land under cultivation is used for dates; other crops include limes, coconuts and bananas. The staple food, rice, has to be imported. There are beef and dairy herds in the Qara mountains. In the PDR, the main cash crop is cotton, grown intensively in Abyan and Lahej, followed by coffee and tobacco. The main food crops, sorghum, millet and sesame, have to be supplemented by imports. Agriculture is the basis of the YAR's economy. The main export crops are cotton (grown on the humid Tihamah) and coffee: this is grown in the highlands and known as mocha as it was formerly exported via the port of Mocha (Al Mukha). Qat (a narcotic); dates and tobacco are also cash crops. Cereals, fruit and vegetables are grown in the highlands where sheep, goats and cattle are also raised. Fishing is important in Oman and the PDR. In the PDR, the industry is centred on Aden and Al Mukalla; anchovy, tuna and sardine are dried and exported. Some Omani ports have cold store facilities.

Industry
Industry is undeveloped in the three states and handicrafts, such as weaving, pottery and leatherwork, are still important. In Oman, the income from oil has stimulated industrialization: a cement plant is under construction near Muscat and future projects include a flour mill, a fertilizer complex using natural gas and a desalination plant. The oil refinery at Little Aden accounts for 80% of the PDR's industrial output. Other activities include fish-processing, ship-building and repair and cotton textiles. In the YAR, industry is based on local raw materials. There are cotton mills at San'a and Bajil, a rock salt factory at Salif and a fish-canning plant at Al Hudaydah.

Cities
Matrah (15,000), a suburb of Muscat, is Oman's chief port and a departure point for caravans taking goods to the interior. About 2,000 km south-west is Aden, the biggest port between Suez and India. Its role as a trading centre has been seriously affected by the closure of the Suez canal. The YAR capital, San'a, situated in the mountains about 130 km inland, is a noted Moslem centre with over 40 mosques.

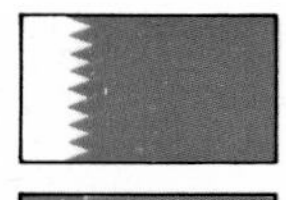

Bahrain, Qatar, United Arab Emirates (UAE)

Bahrain (top left)
Qatar (top)
UAE (left)

Bahrain
Area
662 km²/256 sq miles
Location
25°45′—26°27′ N
50°25′—50°54′ E
Population
362,000 (1981)
Population density
547 per km²/1,414 per sq mile
Capital and largest city
Al Manamah: 300,000 (1980)
Language
Arabic
Major imports
Machinery and transport equipment, textiles, foodstuffs
Major exports
refined petroleum, aluminium, fish
Currency
Dinar (1 dinar = 1,000 fils)
Gross National Product
3,240 million US dollars (1981)
Status
independent emirate

Qatar
Area
11,400 km²/4,400 sq miles
Location
24°35′—26°30′ N
50°45′—51°30′ E
Population
236,000 (1981)
Population density
21 per km²/54 per sq mile
Capital and largest city
Doha: 190,000 (1982)
Language
Arabic
Major imports
machinery and transport equipment, foodstuffs, textiles
Major exports
petroleum and petroleum products
Currency
Riyal (1 riyal = 100 dirhams)
Gross National Product
6,540 million US dollars (1981)
Status
independent sheikdom

United Arab Emirates
Area
83,655 km²/32,300 sq miles
Location
23°—25°52′ N
51°—56°23′ E
Population
1,091,000 (1981)
Population density
13 per km²/34 per sq mile
Capital
Abu Dhabi: 449,000 (1980)
Language
Arabic
Major imports
foodstuffs, transport equipment, manufactured goods
Major exports
petroleum
Currency
Dirham (1 dirham = 100 fils)
Gross National Product
26,910 million US dollars (1981)
Status
independent federation

Transport
Of the three territories, Bahrain has the best road network. The international airport on Muharraq (a stopping-point for long distance flights to the Far East and Australia) was the first in the world to be purpose built for Jumbos. There are steamer services from the main port, Mina Sulman, to destinations in the Gulf, India and Pakistan. In Qatar, the interior network is poor; the state is linked to other countries by an airport at Doha, ports at Doha and Umm Said and a road to Saudi Arabia. In the UAE, the main road runs along the coast. The chief ports are Dubai, Abu Dhabi and Khor Fakkan and there are international airports at Abu Dhabi, Dubai and Sharjah.

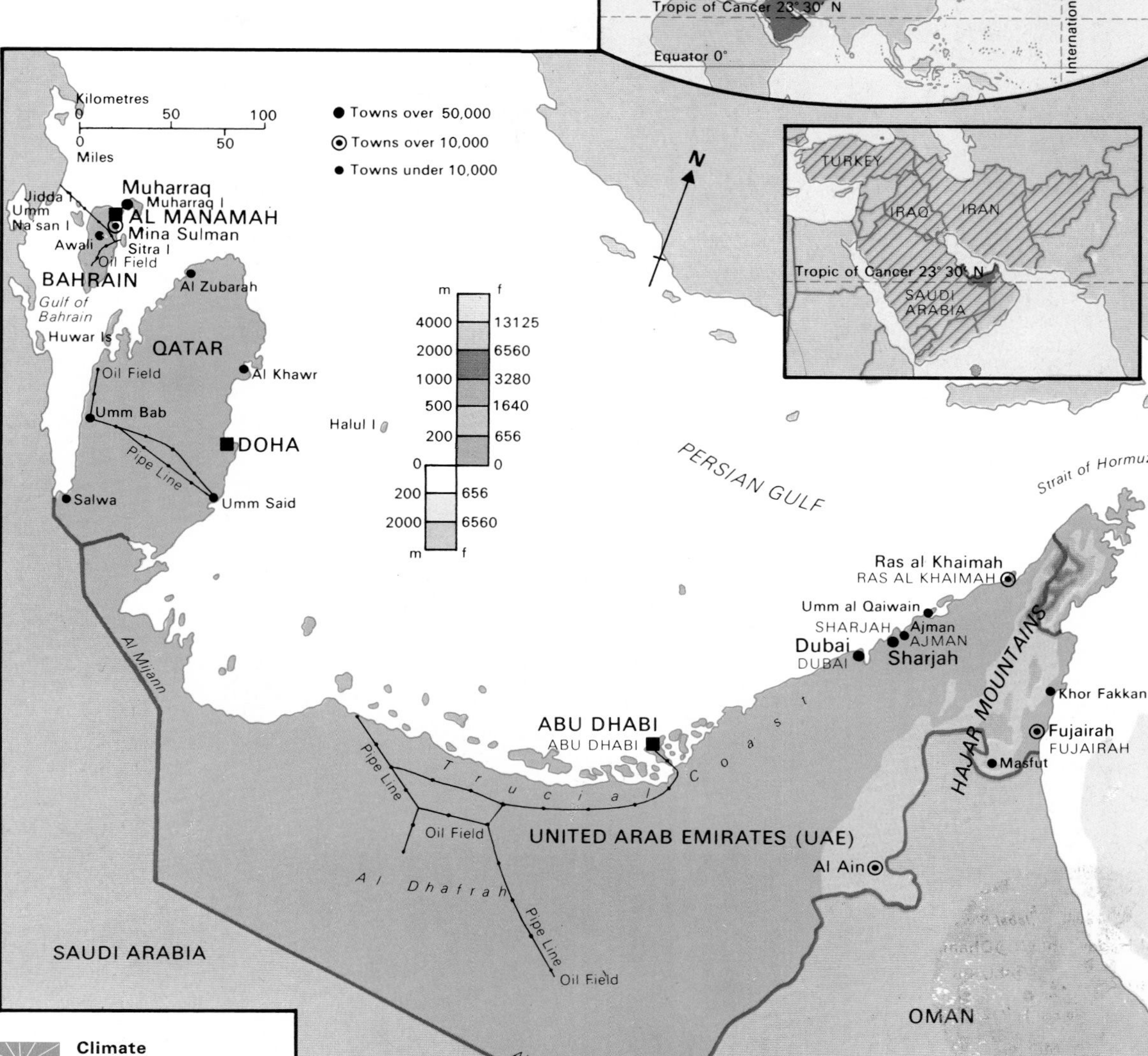

Climate
Most of the region has a hot, dry, desert climate. Summer temperatures range from 30° to 50°C, but drop in winter to 20°C. Rainfall occurs between December and March and is very light. The annual average is under 10 cm except in the Hajar mountains which may have up to 45 cm. In Bahrain, humidity is high.

Physical features
Bahrain consists of 33 islands in the Persian Gulf. The biggest island, Bahrain, is 48 km long and 16 km wide and fringed with coral reefs. The other main islands are Muharraq, Sitrah (both linked to Bahrain by causeway), Umm Na'san and Jidda. Nearer Qatar are the Huwar islands which are inhabited only by a few fishermen. All the islands are low-lying—the highest point being Jabal ad Dukhan (135 m) on Bahrain. The Qatar peninsula is also low-lying, rising to a maximum height of 75 m. The country is largely arid with sand dunes predominating in the south. The shallow coastal waters are dotted with islets and coral reefs. Five of the seven states comprising the UAE have similar features: desert, salt flats and populations centred on coastal towns. The exceptions are Ras al Khaimah and Fujairah, which both have fertile zones situated in the northern fringes of the Hajar mountains.

Agriculture
In Bahrain, agriculture is limited to the north of the main island where springs and artesian wells make irrigation possible. Dates are grown on two-thirds of the cultivated area with the rest used for vegetables, fruit (mango, banana, citrus, pomegranate) and dairy farming (which is being developed). Prawn fishing is important with production exported to Japan, Europe and the USA. As a result of poor soils and lack of water, Qatar has little agriculture. It is, however, self-sufficient in vegetables and even exports melons, tomatoes, marrows, aubergines and cucumbers. Orchards have been planted. Fishing is important and 7 tonnes of shrimps are caught each day—mostly for export. Agriculture is also restricted in the UAE. The main cultivated areas are found in Ras al Khaimah, Fujairah and at Al Ain, an oasis. Dates, wheat, barley, millet and fruit are grown and Al Ain is famous for its mangoes. Fishing for mackerel and tuna is traditional, particularly at Sharjah, Ajman and Umm al Qaiwain and at Fujairah on the Gulf of Oman.

Industry
All three countries are using their oil revenues to develop industry. Bahrain's first major project was an aluminium smelter. Other industries include ship repair and prawn processing. Mina Sulman is a free port with a thriving entrepôt trade. Traditional activities such as building dhows (sailboats), weaving and pearl fishing are in decline. In the last five years there has been considerable industrial expansion in Qatar with a fertilizer factory, flour mill, cement works and a shrimp processing plant. An iron and steel mill, a petrochemical complex and an aluminium smelter are being planned. A similar industrialization programme is being implemented in the UAE, particularly at Abu Dhabi and Dubai (278,000). Dubai is a free port and has become the federation's commercial centre. In all three countries, water for industry is supplied by desalination plants.

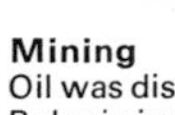

Mining
Oil was discovered in Bahrain in 1932, making it the first oil-producing state in the Gulf. Production from the field at Jabal ad Dukhan is relatively low—about 3 million tonnes a year. This crude oil, plus a further 9 million tonnes piped from the Dammam field in Saudi Arabia, is refined at Sitrah where there is also a 5 km long tanker terminal. Natural gas reserves have recently been exploited and are used to power the refinery, aluminium smelter and a thermal power station. About 11 million tonnes of oil (50% of Qatar's production) comes from the Dukhan field on the west coast; the other half coming from offshore fields. A pipeline runs from Dukhan to the tanker terminal at Umm Said. Natural gas powers thermal stations and desalination plants. The leading UAE oil producer is Abu Dhabi with onshore and off-shore fields: oil revenues make Abu Dhabi, per capita, the world's richest state. Oil is also produced from offshore fields in Dubai and Sharjah. In the federation, mineral surveys are being made. It is thought that asbestos exists in Ras al Khaimah, and chrome and copper in Ajman. Marble is quarried at Masfut.

Syria

Area
185,180 km²/71,500 sq miles
Location
32°20′—37°15′ N
35°35′—42°20′ E
Population
9,314,000 (1975 estimated)
Population density
50 per km²/130 per sq mile
Capital and largest city
Damascus: 2,250,000 (1980)
Language
Arabic
Major imports
machines, metals, foodstuffs, chemicals, transport equipment
Major exports
cotton and cotton textiles, crude oil, wool, livestock, wheat
Currency
pound (1 pound = 100 piastres)
Gross National Product
14,660 million US dollars (1981)
Status
independent republic

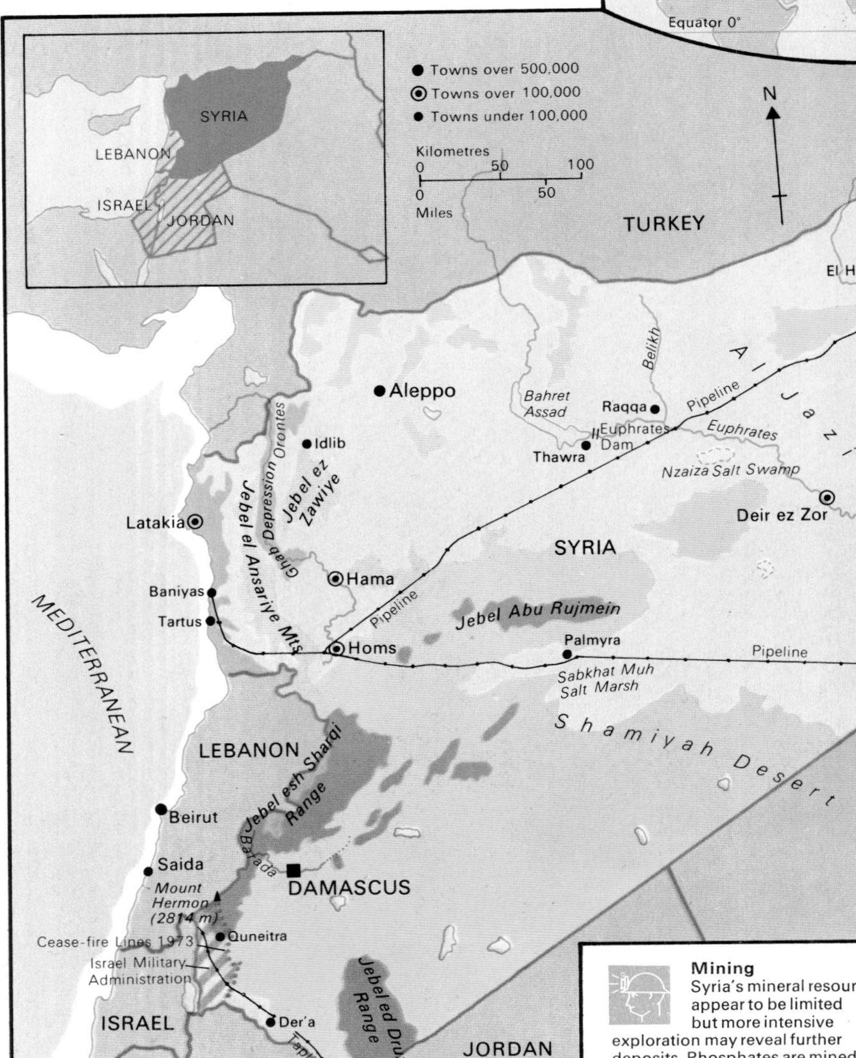

Physical features
A narrow coastal plain separates the Mediterranean from the Jebel el Ansariye mountains. This range stretches from the Turkish border in the north to the Lebanon mountains in the south. East of the Jebel el Ansariye is the swampy Ghab depression—part of the Great Rift Valley that continues through the Red Sea and into East Africa. The Orontes river, which rises in Lebanon, flows 325 km northwards to Turkey through the Ghab. South of Homs, the Lebanese border follows the Jebel esh Sharqi and Mount Hermon ranges. Mount Hermon itself is Syria's highest peak at 2,814 m. The remainder of the country is largely desert steppe extending eastwards to the Euphrates. The most important features of the steppe are low ridges near Palmyra, the volcanic Jebel ed Druz range in the south and the plateau's western rim, the Jebel ez Zawiye. The région north-east of the Euphrates, the Al Jazirah, is drained by the Belikh and the Khabur. The Euphrates, which flows across Syria for 600 km, is the longest river. The source of the Euphrates is in Turkey and its total length is 2,330 km.

Climate
Inland Syria has a more extreme climate than on the coast and in the western mountains. In the desert, summer temperatures rise to over 40°C, but can fall to 0°C in winter. Rainfall, occurring in winter, is very low: less than 12 cm a year. Along the coast, summer temperatures range from 25°C to 32°C. Winters are mild (about 10°C) and wet. The coastal belt and mountains receive over 75 cm of rain between October and May. On the mountain peaks this often falls as snow: Mount Hermon is snow-covered until June or July.

Flora and fauna
The desert plateau is barren except for patches of sparse grazing. In spring, however, the fringes of the plateau are bright with colourful wild flowers. The western mountains were once thickly forested, but are now mostly scrub-covered. Thin forests (mainly oak and pine) remain in the Jebel el Ansariye. Gazelles and foxes are found in the desert, while wolves, wild boar and bears live in the mountains.

Agriculture
Agriculture plays a major role in the Syrian economy and agricultural products account for over 60% of exports. Rain-fed farming is practised on the western margins of the steppe (where precipitation reaches 50 cm a year), along the coast and on the mountain slopes. Other areas under cultivation are irrigated: the Euphrates and Khabur valleys, the Damascus oasis and parts of the Ghab where swamp land has been reclaimed. Wheat, barley, millet and maize are mainly grown in the unirrigated steppe regions. In good years, Syria exports up to one million tonnes of cereals. Cotton, providing 30% of total exports, is the chief cash crop. Other crops include rice (in the Euphrates valley), tobacco (from the Latakia district), citrus fruits (grown along the coast) and, at higher altitudes, olives, grapes and deciduous fruits. Modernization schemes include mechanization, co-operatives, fertilizer production and irrigation projects. Sheep, goats and cattle are important and the region north of the Euphrates is a major stock-raising area. Forests cover only 5% of Syria. Fishing is also under-developed and catches are consumed locally.

Euphrates dam
The key to Syria's economic future is the Euphrates dam situated at Thawra. This giant project is now nearing completion. The dam will revolutionize Syrian agriculture by doubling the area under irrigation. A further 360,000 hectares will be reclaimed when a subsidiary scheme, harnessing the river Khabour, is completed. The dam will also promote industrial growth: its hydro-electric power station, with a capacity of 1,200 MW, is scheduled to meet the future energy needs of Syrian industry.

Oil
Crude oil accounts for 35% of Syrian exports. Production comes from the fields at Qarachuk, Rumailan and Suwaydiyah in the north-east. The oil is piped to the port of Tartus for export and to Homs for refining. A second refinery at Baniyas on the Mediterranean coast is near completion. The Syrian oil industry is nationalized. Three oil pipelines cross Syria. Two Iraqi pipelines cut through from Kirkuk to Baniyas and Tartus and, in the extreme south-west, the Tapline from Saudi Arabia crosses Jordan and Syria to Saida in Lebanon.

Mining
Syria's mineral resources appear to be limited but more intensive exploration may reveal further deposits. Phosphates are mined in the Jebel esh Sharqi. Other minerals worked include sandstone (found near Palmyra and used in glass manufacture), asphalt (used in road construction), limestone (quarried near Aleppo) and marl (used in cement production). Rock salt is exploited in the Deir ez Zor and salt is also produced from the salt lakes. Iron ore deposits have been discovered near Palmyra, Aleppo, Homs and Damascus. Lignite, manganese, chromite and asbestos exist and natural gas has been located in Al Jazirah.

Transport
Damascus and Aleppo are the focal points of Syria's transport system. The 17,000 km of roads radiate from these two centres. New highways are being built linking Damacus with Aleppo, Beirut (Lebanon) and Amman (Jordan). Three railways of varying gauges serve the main towns in the west and there are also rail links with Iraq, Lebanon, and Turkey. Two new links under construction are El Qamishliye to Latakia and Damascus to Aleppo. Latakia is the main port but there are oil-tanker terminals at Tartus and Baniyas. El Qamishliye, Aleppo, Latakia and Damascus have airports. The communications network was badly damaged by the war in October 1973.

Industry
The textile industry is the most developed. The production of cotton, wool, silk and artificial fabrics is centred on Damascus, Aleppo, Homs and Hama. Cement production is next in importance: there are currently seven plants in operation and a further four are planned for 1977. Other leading industries include flour, sugar, vegetable oils, soap, shoes, glass and refrigerator assembly. Two major projects have recently been completed: a nitrous fertilizer plant near Homs with an annual capacity of 250,000 tonnes and a metallic bar factory near Hama. The latter is to be part of a giant metallurgical complex which will manufacture sheet-iron, iron-wire, steel and which will be powered by electricity from the Euphrates dam. At present, the metallic bar factory uses imported materials, but it is hoped that the needs of the new complex will, in part, be supplied by the iron-ore discovered in Syria.

Cities
Damascus, situated on the Barada River at the desert's edge, is one of the world's oldest cities and has been inhabited for over 4,000 years. Biblical Damascus stands side by side with the modern city which was planned in 1929. It is a centre of light industry—particularly textiles and leathergoods—and is an important link in trade between Baghdad, Beirut and Amman. The capital is also noted for its handicrafts which include ceramics, glassware and mother-of-pearl work. Aleppo (1,863,000) is Syria's second city. It is an industrial centre manufacturing textiles (especially silk) and processing food. Homs (822,000) is the next largest city and is also a manufacturing and trading centre.

Lebanon

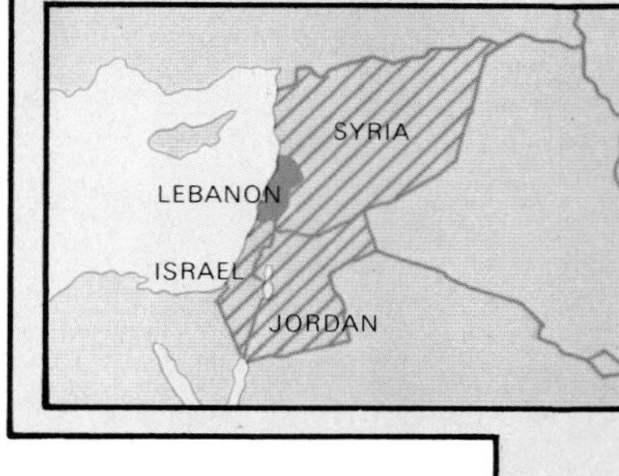

Area
10,400 km²/4,000 sq miles
Location
33°04′—34°40′ N
35°05′—36°40′ E
Population
2,716,000 (1981)
Population density
261 per km²/679 per sq mile
Capital and largest city
Beirut: 1,100,000 (1982)
Language
Arabic
Major imports
machinery, textiles, foodstuffs, transport equipment, chemicals, precious stones and metals, base metals
Major exports (& re-exports)
fruit and vegetable products, machinery, textiles, precious stones and metals
Currency
pound (1 pound = 100 piastres)
Gross National Product
not available
Status
independent republic

Physical features

Lebanon is a mountainous land about 220 km long and varying between 30 and 60 km wide. The fertile coastal belt is very narrow and rises abruptly to the Lebanon mountains. This range, which is highest in the north, runs parallel to the coast: its main peaks are Qornet es Saouda (3,088 m) and Sannin (2,628 m). The country's eastern border is formed by the Anti-Lebanon (Jebel esh Sharqi) and Hermon ranges rising to 2,814 m (Mt Hermon). Between the Lebanon and Anti-Lebanon ranges lies the El Beqa'a valley, a flat alluvial plain some 150 km long and 16 km wide. This depression is part of the Great Rift Valley. Lebanon's two main rivers rise in the El Beqa'a near Ba'albek: the Orontes flows north into Syria but the Litani (145 km long) remains in Lebanon, entering the Mediterranean north of Tyr. A third river, the Kebir, flows along the northern border between Lebanon and Syria. The remainder of the country's drainage is seasonal with winter torrents rushing down mountain slopes.

Climate

On the coast, summers are hot and humid and winters mild. The average temperature is 32°C in July and 16°C in January. In the El Beqa'a valley, away from the sea, temperatures are slightly more extreme: 35°C in July and 10°C in January. The mountains are cooler and at an altitude of 1,500 m temperatures are 8°C cooler than on the coast. Rain occurs between October and May —ranging between 30 cm in the El Beqa'a and 150 cm in the mountains with 80 cm on the coast. The mountains are snow-covered from December to May, hence the origin of the country's name from laban which is Aramaic for 'white'.

Tourism

Each year some two million people visit Lebanon attracted by its scenery, climate, biblical sites, history (which goes back beyond the Phoenicians) and its beach and ski resorts. In recent years, however, the Arab-Israeli conflict and internal disturbances have adversely affected the industry.

Flora and fauna

Lebanon once had extensive forests of cedar, pine and oak, but these have largely been destroyed. The famous Lebanese cedars, formerly a major export, are now almost extinct and only a few small groves remain in the mountains. The western slopes of this range are scrub-covered, with scattered clumps of pine, evergreen oak, cypress and wild olive. In spring, the El Beqa'a valley is bright with wild flowers. A few wolves and bears are known to exist in remote areas of the Lebanon.

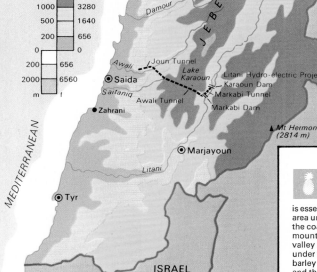

Mining and energy

Lebanon has limited mineral resources. Small deposits of iron-ore, lignite and phosphates are worked but these have no commercial significance. On the other hand, large quantities of building stone are quarried and salt is extracted from sea-water. Other deposits include copper, oil-shale, asphalt, glass-sand and clay (suitable for ceramic manufactures). The output of fuel from the Saida and Tripoli refineries is sufficient for domestic needs. There is a surplus of electricity (augmented by the Litani hydro-electric project) which is exported to Syria.

Transport

Beirut international airport, one of the busiest in the Middle East, is used by over 30 airlines, including the two national carriers: Middle East Airlines and Trans Mediterranean Airways. The leading port, Beirut, handles over 3,000 vessels a year. There are oil terminals at Tripoli and Zahrani, while Jubail, Saida and Tyr are used by local steamers and fishing boats. The road network is good and 75% of roads are paved. Bus and long distance taxi services cover the country. There are three railway lines: Saida-Tripoli, Beirut-Rayak-Damascus, Tripoli-Homs.

Agriculture

Although over 50% of the country is uncultivated, Lebanon is essentially agricultural. The area under cultivation comprises the coastal strip, terraced mountain slopes and the El Beqa'a valley but only half of this is under full irrigation. Wheat and barley are the chief cereal crops and these are grown mainly in the El Beqa'a but, as only 20% of total farmland is used for cereals, flour imports are necessary. The leading cash crops, forming Lebanon's main export, are fruit and vegetables. Citrus fruits (oranges, lemons and limes) are the most important, followed by apples. Other export crops include grapes, bananas, olives, figs, onions, tomatoes, potatoes and cucumbers. Cotton and tobacco are also grown, mainly for local consumption. Livestock is limited as grazing is scarce, but about 600,000 goats, sheep and cattle are raised, primarily for dairy purposes. Poultry is being developed and about 60% of the total 600 million eggs which are produced annually is exported.

Industry

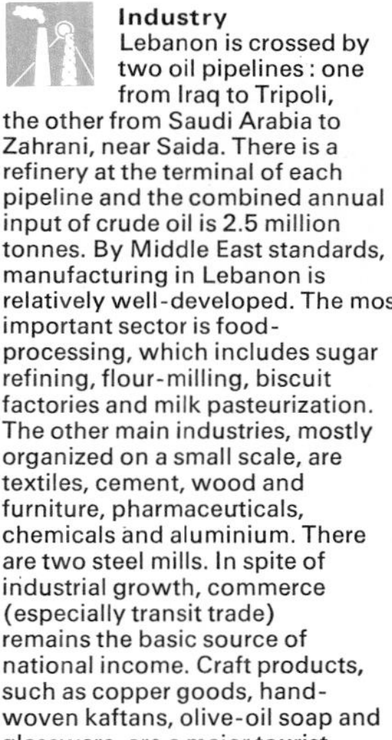

Lebanon is crossed by two oil pipelines: one from Iraq to Tripoli, the other from Saudi Arabia to Zahrani, near Saida. There is a refinery at the terminal of each pipeline and the combined annual input of crude oil is 2.5 million tonnes. By Middle East standards, manufacturing in Lebanon is relatively well-developed. The most important sector is food-processing, which includes sugar refining, flour-milling, biscuit factories and milk pasteurization. The other main industries, mostly organized on a small scale, are textiles, cement, wood and furniture, pharmaceuticals, chemicals and aluminium. There are two steel mills. In spite of industrial growth, commerce (especially transit trade) remains the basic source of national income. Craft products, such as copper goods, hand-woven kaftans, olive-oil soap and glassware, are a major tourist attraction.

Cities

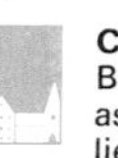

Beirut, which originated as a Phoenician city, lies at the crossroads of Asia, Europe and Africa. It is Lebanon's leading commercial city with a stock exchange, free port facilities and a free money market. The capital is also the major industrial centre and 80% of Lebanese industry is located in the Beirut region. The cosmopolitan city, which houses 40% of the country's urban population, is divided into distinct communities—for example, there are separate Christian and Moslem sectors. Lebanon's second largest city, Tripoli (240,000), is also a major port and industrial centre. It has Byzantine remains but many buildings are medieval.

Jordan

Area
96,188 km²/37,140 sq miles
East Bank : 89,555 km²
West Bank : 6,633 km²
Location
29°20′—33°25′ N
34°55′—39° E
Population
3,370,000 (1981)
Population density
35 per km²/91 per sq mile
Capital and largest city
Amman: 750,000 (1980)
Language
Arabic
Major imports
machinery, foodstuffs, textiles, minerals, chemicals
Major exports
phosphates, fruit and vegetables, cement, cigarettes
Currency
dinar (1 dinar = 1,000 fils)
Gross National Product
3,880 million US dollars (1981)
Status
constitutional monarchy

As a result of the Arab-Israeli war in 1967, the territory lying west of the River Jordan—known as the West Bank and representing 6% of the total area—came under the control of Israel. The information here refers mainly to the East Bank.

Physical features
About 80% of Jordan is desert. The fertile area is located in the west—mainly in the Jordan river valley. In the Israeli-occupied zone west of the river, limestone hills rise to over 900 m. In the north-west, the border with Syria and the Israeli-held Golan Heights is formed by the River Yarmuk, a tributary of the Jordan. The 250 km-long Jordan valley, part of the Great Rift Valley, lies below sea level. The river flows into the Dead Sea which has no outlet; the rift valley, however, continues to the Gulf of Aqaba where Jordan has 20 km of coastline. To the east, the mountains rise steeply from the narrow fertile belt. Beyond these mountains, which are highest in the south (Jebel Ram: 1,754 m), the land descends gradually to the arid, stony desert.

Climate
In Amman, 720 m above sea level, the average temperature in summer is 28°C, in winter, 10°C. The climate is more extreme in the desert and the Jordan valley where August temperatures frequently reach 40°C. Rainfall occurs during winter: the hills on the West Bank receive 80 cm a year, the Aqaba region, 10 cm and the desert has less than 4 cm.

Cities
The ancient Graeco-Roman city of Amman has recently expanded to become the country's main industrial centre. Leading manufactures include food-processing, tobacco, textiles, plastics, cement, electrical goods and paper products. Amman is also the hub of Jordan's transport system. Other East Bank towns which have developed rapidly are Zarqa (265,000) and Irbid (140,000), both in the north.

Transport
As economic development in Jordan is hindered by poor communications, transport is a current government priority. The 9,000 km road network (75% surfaced) links Amman to all main towns. Major highways connect the capital with Aqaba, Syria (via Jarash) and Iraq (via Mafraq). There is only one railway: a single line track running from Der'a (Syria) via Amman to Naqb Ishtar. This is now being extended to Aqaba. Aqaba is the only port and phosphate exports account for over 50% of the trade handled there. Alia (Royal Jordanian Airlines) operates a domestic service between Amman, Aqaba and Ma'an and overseas flights from Amman. A new international airport is being built near the capital.

Mining
Phosphates are the most important of Jordan's mineral resources and make up 25% of total exports. Over one million tonnes a year are produced from rich deposits at Er Ruseifa and near the Wadi el Hasa. Two other minerals exploited commercially are marble (near Amman) and potash (from the Dead Sea). Clay and feldspar deposits are also worked and a ceramics industry is based on local materials. Copper has been discovered in Wadi Araba and excavation is due to begin in 1976. Other minerals known to exist include iron ore, nickel, manganese, quartzite and barite. The country's one oil refinery at Zarqa is supplied by Tapline (the Trans-Arabian Pipeline) which crosses Jordan.

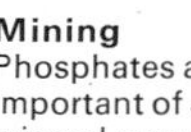

Agriculture
Agriculture is the most important sector of the economy and employs 40% of the working population. Most farms, however, are small, irrigation is limited and soils are badly eroded with the result that farming is often at subsistence level. The main cereals are wheat and barley, grown in unirrigated areas. Production therefore varies according to rainfall, but even in good years the bulk of Jordan's grain requirements has to be imported. Tomatoes are the leading export crop; other exports include citrus, grapes, melons, aubergines, cucumbers and cauliflowers. Tobacco is also a major industrial crop. The output of fruit and vegetables was severely affected by the loss of the West Bank: 80% of the fruit growing area and 45% of the vegetable growing area are under Israeli administration. The Bedou graze sheep, goats and camels on the sparse desert pasture. There is some fishing in the rivers Jordan and Yarmuk and in the Gulf of Aqaba.

Industry
The three principal industries are phosphate extraction, cement manufacture and oil-refining. Cement production is increasing and now accounts for 15% of total exports. Output from the oil refinery at Zarqa meets domestic requirements; the two main electricity generating plants, fired by oil, are at Amman and Zarqa. In recent years, a range of small industries, based on local raw materials, has been established including cigarette manufacture, fruit and vegetable canning, olive oil refining and soap manufacture. With the loss of the West Bank, Jordan's growing tourist industry suffered a major setback: nearly all the Holy Places, including Jerusalem and Bethlehem, are under Israeli control. However, Jordan still has some outstanding tourist attractions, such as the ancient rose-red rock city of Petra, 40 km west of Ma'an. The tourist trade stimulates handicrafts such as mother-of-pearl work, wool and goat-hair rugs, tapestries and ceramics.

Flora and fauna
Much of the country has no vegetation other than desert scrub. The main forested regions are in the highlands near Ajlun, Jarash and Ma'an where evergreen oak and Aleppo pine predominate. Junipers and wild olives are found in areas with less rainfall. Ibex, panther, wolf, gazelle and wild boar still exist in remote areas, particularly the southern uplands.

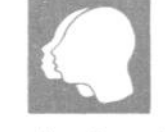

Peoples
The Arab-Israeli conflict has created population problems for Jordan. In 1948, and again in 1967, Palestinian refugees, fled to Jordan from Israeli-occupied territory. There are some 750,000 refugees, accounting for 33% of the total population. The economic difficulties of absorbing the Palestinians into Jordan are heightened by racial, cultural and religious differences.

Israel

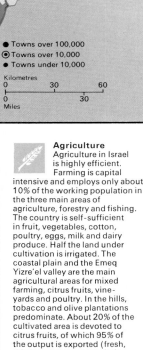

Area
21,287 km²/8,219 sq miles
Population
3,954,000 (1981)
Population density
186 per km²/481 per sq mile
Capital
Jerusalem: 398,000 (1980)
Largest City
Tel Aviv-Yafo: 336,300 (1980)
Language
Hebrew, Arabic
Major imports
rough diamonds, machinery, iron and steel, ships, aircraft, foodstuffs
Major exports
polished diamonds, citrus fruits, textiles, minerals
Currency
shekel (1 shekel = 100 new agora)
Gross National Product
20,420 million US dollars (1981)
Status
independent republic

As a result of the 6-day war in June 1967, the following areas came under Israeli administration: Gaza Strip, Sinai peninsula, West Jordan and the Golan Heights. Sinai was returned to Egypt in 1982. The administered areas are included in the information given here.

Physical features
Israel divides into four regions. The Mediterranean coastal plain, fringed with sand dunes, has an average width of 4 km and is split into two by Mt Carmel, a limestone ridge of 546 m high. This alluvial lowland is flanked by the central mountain zone—the hills of Galilee, Samaria and Judea—which has its highest point in Galilee: Mt Meron (1,208 m) Galilee is separated from Samaria by the Emeq Yizre'el valley, a traditional route from the Mediterranean to Jordan. South of this valley, the Samarian and Judean hills (with an average height of 600 m) slope eastwards to the deep Jordan Rift Valley—the third region. The Jordan river links two internal seas: the Sea of Galilee (Lake Kinneret) and the Dead Sea (the lowest point in the world at 392 m below sea level). The Dead Sea has no outlet and evaporation balances inflow, but the Rift Valley continues to the Red Sea and is known as the Araba. The fourth zone corresponds to the Negev desert.

Climate
On the coast, winters are mild, summers hot. In Tel Aviv, the average temperature in January is 20°C, in August 30°C. The mountains are cooler: in Jerusalem, the January temperature is 15°C and in August, 28°C. The hottest parts of the country are the Rift Valley and the desert. The January and June temperatures for Kefar Blum are 21 and 34°C and for Elat, 23 and 33°C. Rainfall, occurring mainly in winter, is heaviest in the northern mountains (where it sometimes falls as snow) and lowest in the desert. Tel Aviv receives about 72 cm a year, Beersheba has about 53 cm a year, while Elat has only 2 cm.

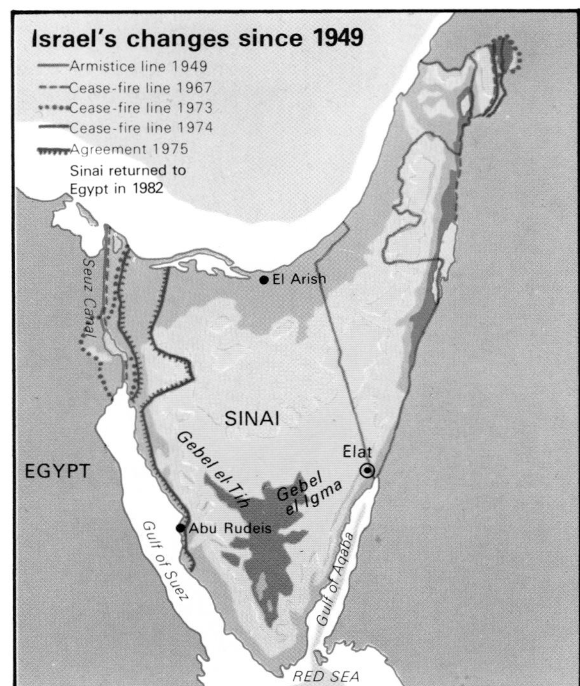

Agriculture
Agriculture in Israel is highly efficient. Farming is capital intensive and employs only about 10% of the working population in the three main areas of agriculture, forestry and fishing. The country is self-sufficient in fruit, vegetables, cotton, poultry, eggs, milk and dairy produce. Half the land under cultivation is irrigated. The coastal plain and the Emeq Yizre'el valley are the main agricultural areas for mixed farming, citrus fruits, vine-yards and poultry. In the hills, tobacco and olive plantations predominate. About 20% of the cultivated area is devoted to citrus fruits, of which 95% of the output is exported (fresh, dried or processed into fruit juices). Poultry and dairy cattle are important in the lowlands, while sheep and goats are mainly grazed in the Galilee hills and the Negev. On the West Bank, vegetables are the main export crop. With Israel's modern fleets, most marine fishing takes place in the Atlantic and Indian Oceans.

Irrigation
As Israel lives on the edge of a desert the supply of water is vital. The principal sources of water—Lake Kinneret and the Jordan—are in the north, while the areas most in need of irrigation are in the south. To overcome this problem the National Water Carrier was devised. The NWC pumps water via canal and tunnel, mainly by gravitation, to the Negev. There are also desalination plants at Elat and Ashdod.

Mining
A major part of Israel's mineral resources is found in the Dead Sea: potash and bromine are extracted from its waters. The only other deposits of commercial significance are copper, mined near Elat, and phosphate, at Oron in the Negev. Natural gas and oil are produced in the northern Negev. (Control of the Abu Rudeis oilfield in the Gulf of Suez was relinquished by Israel after the 1975 agreement with Egypt.)

Industry
Although most raw materials have to be imported, industry has developed rapidly and industrial products (excluding diamonds) now make up 35% of all exports. The main industries produce electrical and electronic goods, textiles, processed food, chemicals and vehicles. Israel is also one of the world's major diamond-polishing centres: the worked diamonds are almost all marketed abroad and account for 40% of total exports. Heavy industry, such as steel, engineering, cement and oil-refining is largely concentrated at Haifa, the main port. The other leading industrial area is Tel Aviv-Yafo.

Transport
An extensive road network is the principal feature of the Israeli transport system and buses are the main form of public transport; railways are less important. A domestic air service links major towns; overseas flights are operated by El Al from Lod airport, 14 km from Tel Aviv. In the last 20 years, the Israeli merchant fleet has quadrupled. Haifa is the largest port, handling over 50% of total cargo; Ashdod, the second port, came into operation in 1965 and replaced facilities at Tel Aviv and Jaffa. Israel's third port, Elat, is on the gulf of Aqaba which runs into the Red Sea and is used to offload oil for trans-shipment to Ashdod, via pipeline.

Cities
Jerusalem, situated in the Judean hills, 27 km west of the Dead Sea, first became the capital of the Jewish nation 3,000 years ago under King David. Known as the Holy City, it is a place of pilgrimage for Jews, Moslems and Christians. Between 1949 and 1967 the city was divided between Israel and Jordan. The largest city was formed in 1950 when the old port of Jaffa merged with its modern suburb of Tel Aviv. Tel Aviv-Yafo is Israel's cultural, commercial and industrial centre.

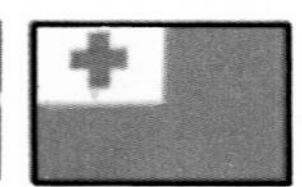

Nauru (top left)
Tonga (top)
Samoa

Micronesia and Polynesia

Micronesia ("tiny islands") consists of the Caroline, Mariana, Marshall and Gilbert archipelagos, Nauru and Ocean Island
Land area
2,800 km²/1,100 sq miles
Largest islands
Guam (Marianas) : 541 km²/209 sq miles ; Babelthuap and Ponape (Carolines) : each 339 km²/130 sq miles
Population
303,000 (1981)
Population density
108 per km²/275 per sq mile
Major imports
foodstuffs, fuels, machinery, textiles
Major exports
copra, phosphate, handicrafts
Status
Trust Territory of the Pacific Islands (Carolines, Marshalls, Marianas except Guam) : UN trust territory administered by USA ; Guam : US territory ; Kiribati (Gilberts and Ocean Island): independent republic; Nauru: independent republic

Polynesia ("many islands") includes Samoa; Ellice Islands; Tokelau Islands; Wallis and Futuna Islands; Tonga; Cook Islands and Nieu; French Polynesia; Pitcairn Island and Easter Island
Land area
9,507 km²/3,741 sq miles
Largest islands
Savai'i (W. Samoa) : 1,657 km²/703 sq miles ; Upolu (W. Samoa) : 1,191 km²/430 sq miles; Tahiti : 1,042 km²/400 sq miles
Population
480,000 (1981)
Population density
50 per km²/128 per sq mile
Major imports
foodstuffs, fuels, machinery, textiles
Major exports
copra, bananas, handicrafts
Status
Tonga : independent state ; W. Samoa ; independent state ; American Samoa : US territory ; Cook, Tokelau and Nieu Islands : NZ territories; Turalu (Ellice Island): independent state; Pitcairn Island: UK colony; French Polynesia, Wallis and Futuna: French territories; Easter Island: Chilean dependency.

Physical features
The islands are generally classified as high or low. The high islands are the summits of ocean-floor volcanic mountain ranges. Mount Silisili on Savai'i rises to 1,858 m. These volcanic islands have a jagged landscape : cliffs, canyons, peaks and ridges. As the mountains are high enough to trap rain, the surface is often forested like the wooded Wallis and Futuna Islands. The low islands are coral atolls : a chain of islands enclosing a lagoon. In the Carolines, for example, many of the atolls are only 2.5 m above sea-level, while some of the Tongan islands have been uplifted to 18 m The Kwajalein atoll in the Marshalls is the world's largest : 38 islands surround a lagoon of 2,202 km² Many archipelagos include both high and low, such as the Cook Islands : in the south these are high volcanic, further north they are low atolls.

Scattered across the Pacific Ocean, between 130°E and 130°W—a distance of 11,265 km —are thousands of islands with a total land area of 260,000 km², excluding New Zealand and New Guinea. These islands fall into three great divisions : Melanesia, Micronesia and Polynesia.

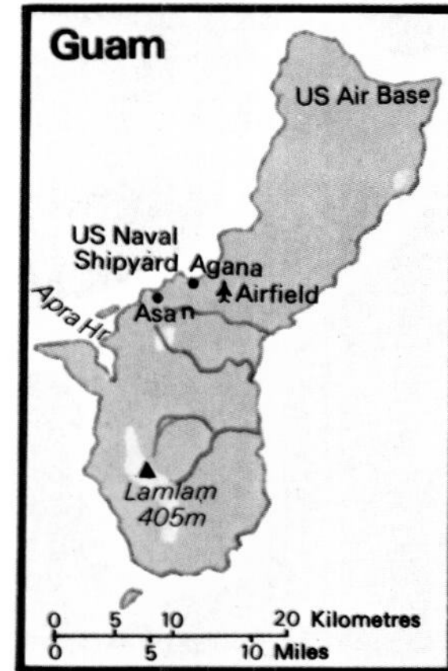

Climate
The climate, influenced by latitude and sea, is both tropical and oceanic. Humidity is high : on average 80%. Temperatures are also high and mostly uniform throughout the year. On Guam, the average annual temperature is 27°C with a mean annual range of less than 2 degrees. Even on remote Easter Island, temperatures only range from 16°C to 23°C and, although the nights are cold, humidity remains high. Rainfall is less uniform. Across the east and central Pacific the N.E. and S.E. tradewinds bring rain to windward coasts, while western Micronesia is subject to year-round monsoons and, from July to November, typhoons. Relief greatly affects rainfall : the high islands of the Carolines receive as much as 1,016 cm a year, but the neighbouring low atolls of the northern Marshalls receive only 50 cm. In some places rainfall is very uncertain. Nauru, for example, has to import 165 million litres of water a year.

Agriculture
On all the islands subsistance agriculture provides the islanders' food. Main root crops include taro, yam and sweet potato ; principal tree crops are coconut, bananas and breadfruit. The volcanic islands have a greater range of crops than the coral atolls, but on both farming methods are traditional and production is in the hands of individual families. In many places the islanders' farming and fishing rights are carefully guaranteed. In Tonga, for instance, where all land belongs to the Crown, each male over the age of 16 is granted an allotment amounting to 3.3 hectares. On the island of Nauru, the Baudu lagoon is divided between families, each family having exclusive fishing rights in its area. The one product grown for export in nearly every territory is copra. Bananas are also important, and cacao, pepper and coffee are being introduced as prospective cash crops.

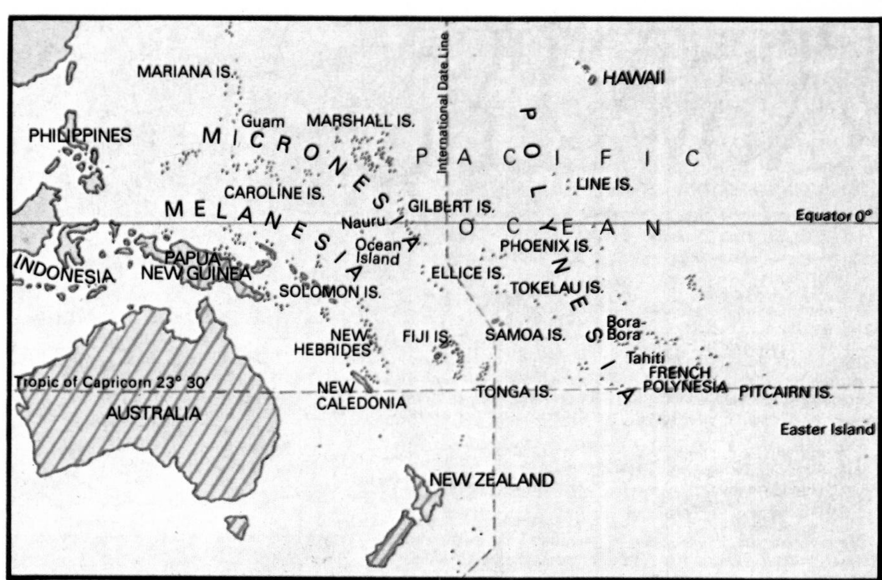

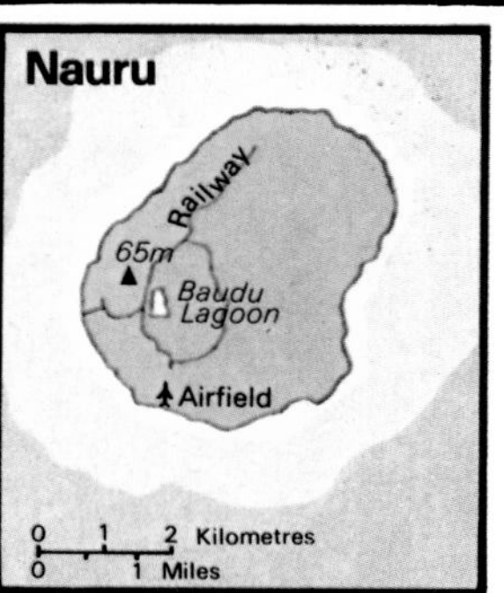

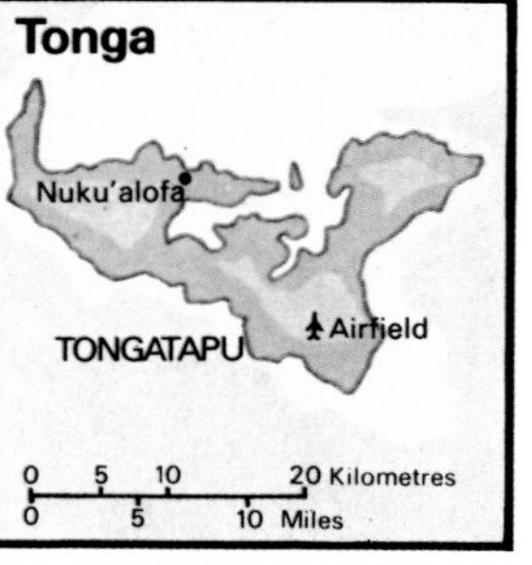

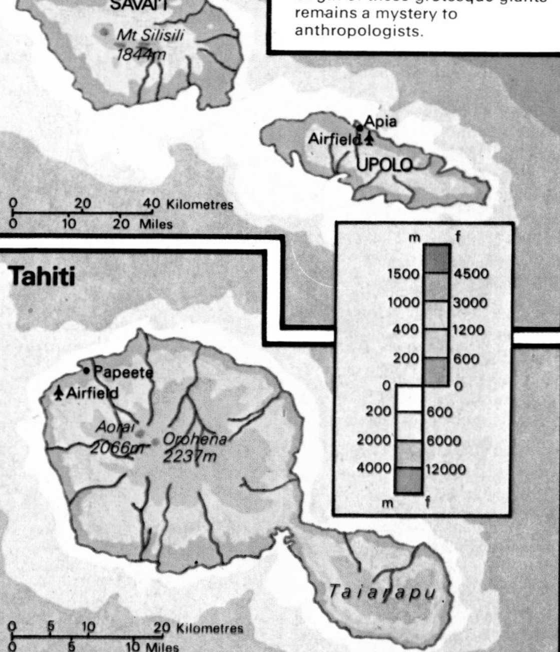

Communications
In most territories, the traditional forms of inter-island transport —canoes and schooners—have been supplemented by air services. There are internal flights within French Polynesia for instance, and remote islands, such as Nieu near the Cook Islands, have air links with important centres like Tonga. Regular air and shipping services operate between the major island groups and New Zealand, Australia and Japan. The transpacific flights of international lines use Easter Island, Tahiti and Guam as stopovers. Transport on larger islands is usually by bus or taxi.

Easter Island
The most isolated Polynesian island is the most famous : Easter Island. The island is known for its colossal statues of the 'big-eared' men. These statues, from 3.6 m to 10 m high and weighing up to 100 tonnes, are carved out of volcanic rock from the Rano-raraku crater in the north-east of the island. Each statue represents the upper half of a body with an upturned head and long ears. These figures, facing inland, fringed the island and were supported by great burial terraces. The origin of these grotesque giants remains a mystery to anthropologists.

Industry
Industry is very sparsely developed and is invariably connected with processing local produce. In many places, the islanders are engaged in handicrafts. On Pitcairn, for instance, they sell woodcarvings and baskets woven from pandanus palm leaves to passing ships. Visitors to Tonga may buy tapa cloth, grass skirts and tortoise-shell ornaments. In addition to handicrafts, Tonga has a dried coconut works, a tobacco factory and a rope works. Western Samoa also has several factories : wood veneer, soap and soft drinks. American Samoa and the Carolines both have tuna-canneries, while fruit and fruit juices are tinned in the Cook Islands. In Guam, a factory assembles watches from Swiss-made components but most activity is centred on the US naval shipyard and air base. Several islands are developing a tourist industry. Nearly all islands issue exotic postage stamps, prized by philatelists all over the world.

Mining
The economies of Ocean Island and Nauru are both based entirely on phosphate industry. On Ocean Island, the land is leased by the British Phosphate Commission and the phosphate—about 600,000 tonnes a year—is shipped overseas for processing. It is estimated that the phosphate deposits will be exhausted by 1980 and, as nearly all the 2,192 inhabitants are employed by the BPC, alternative industries such as fishing and tourism are being explored. The phosphate deposits on Nauru, producing some 2 million tonnes a year, are expected to last another 25 years. 50% of the production—used for fertilizer—is exported to Australia and 25% each to New Zealand and Japan. 75% of the revenue from exports is being invested to produce an income for the Nauruans when the phosphate is exhausted. Extra labour is hired from the Gilbert and Ellice Islands and Hong Kong.

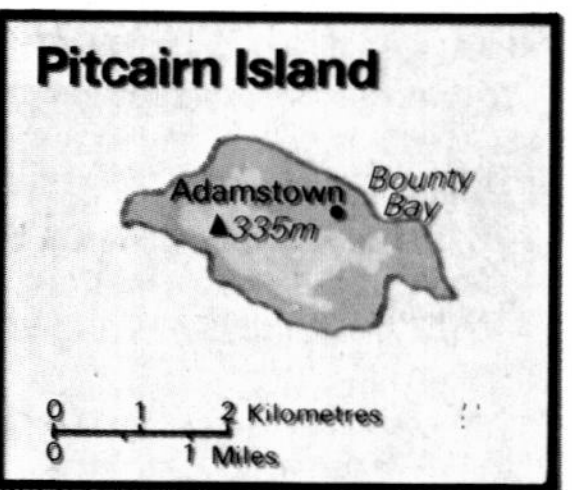

Papua New Guinea

Fiji

Papua New Guinea and Melanesia

Melanesia ('black islands') is the most westerly Pacific island group. Lying between the equator and the Tropic of Capricorn, it includes New Guinea—divided politically into Irian Barat and Papua New Guinea—the Bismarks, Solomons, New Hebrides, New Caledonia and Fiji.

Land Area
552,675 km²/213,389 sq miles

Largest Islands
Papua New Guinea: 461,700 km²/178,260 sq miles (the whole of New Guinea covers 876,100 km²/338, 260 sq miles); New Caledonia: 19,100 km²/7,374 sq miles; Bouganville (Solomons): 10,620 km²/4,100 sq miles; Viti Levu (Fiji): 10,390 km²/4,011 sq miles

Population
4,212,000 (1981)

Population density
8 per km²/20 per sq mile

Major imports
machinery, foodstuffs, fuels

Major exports
copra, timber, cocoa, coffee, minerals, bananas, sugar

Status
Papua New Guinea: independent state; Solomon Islands: independent state; Vanuatu (New Hebrides): independent republic; New Caledonia: French territory; Fiji: independent state

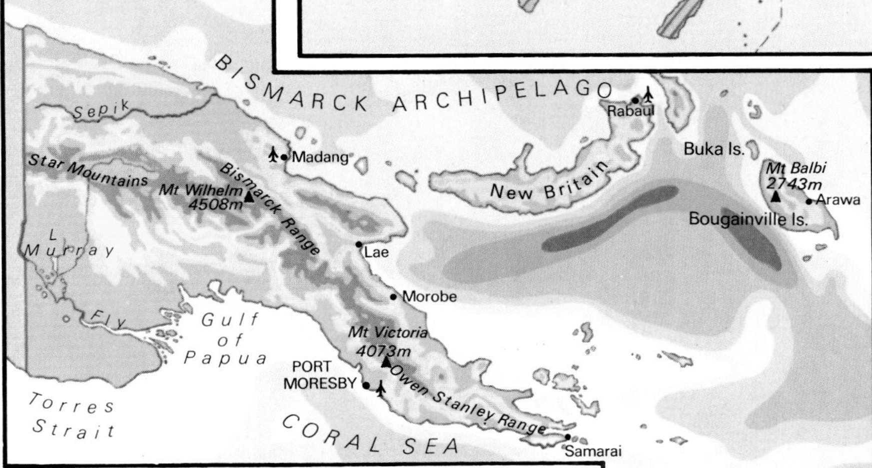

Physical features

Many Melanesian islands are continental: they are associated with the submerged margins of Asia and Australia and are generally mountainous. The highest peak in the New Guinea Trust Territory is Mt. Wilhelm 4,508 m and, in Papua, Mt. Victoria 4073 m in the Owen Stanley Range. These are occasionally snow-covered. Two of the island's main rivers are in the eastern half: the Sepik drains north, and the Fly, south. Both have swampy lowland plains, huge deltas and are liable to flood. Off the north-east coast, especially near the Huon peninsula, there are coral reefs rising more than 610 m above sea level. The remaining territories comprise mountainous volcanic islands such as Espiritu Santo (New Hebrides), Choiseul (Solomons), New Britain and Vanua Levu, and low-lying coral atolls, like the Fijian Lau group and the Loyalty Islands (New Caledonia). Several islands in the New Hebrides, including Ambrym, Lopevi and Tanna, have active volcanoes; New Caledonia has the world's second longest coral reef.

Communications

A traditional form of transport, the canoe, is still widely used, especially along reef-bound coasts and on narrow rivers. As roads are generally scarce waterways are necessary. In Fiji, for example, bananas are floated on rafts downstream to the coast. Fiji has Melanesia's only railway, built to meet the needs of the sugar-refining industry. Links between the islands and beyond are by sea and air. Nandi airport on Viti Levu is a recognized stopover for transpacific flights. Air Melanesia and Air Pacific operate regional services and, for internal flights, many islands have their own airline, like Air Niuguini on Papua New Guinea, Solomon Islands Airways and Fiji Air Services.

Mining

The island richest in minerals is New Caledonia where ores and semi-processed metals account for over 90% of exports. Nickel, chrome and iron are the most important, but cobalt and manganese are also mined. Other manganese deposits being exploited are on Efate and on Fiji. Fiji also has small amounts of silver and copper, but its main mineral resource, and third largest export, is gold mined at Vatukoula on Viti Levu. Gold is also mined in the Marobe district of Papua and on Guadalcanal. Bougainville's main mineral wealth lies in the copper at Panguna: a special town, Arawa, is being built to service the mine and deposits are expected to last 30 years. A smaller output of copper comes from the Star Mountains in Papua.

Climate

The climate is basically hot and humid with a wet season from November to April and a slightly drier, less humid period from May to October when the cooler south-east trade winds prevail. In New Guinea and the Solomons, rainfall is heavy: high ground in New Guinea receives 750 cm of rain a year. Both the New Hebrides and New Caledonia are subject to violent storms and rainfall is unevenly spread: in the New Hebrides, annual rainfall averages well over 200 cm; in New Caledonia, it ranges from 200 cm in the east to 100 cm in the west. In Fiji rainfall also varies from 300 cm in the east to 175 cm in the west, and average temperatures range from 20°C in July to 30°C in February.

Agriculture

With the exception of New Caledonia, the Melanesian economy is dependent on agriculture. The most important cash crop is copra, followed by coffee and cocoa. In Papua these three products make up 50% of exports and in the Solomons, copra alone brings in half the overseas earnings. In Fiji, sugar dominates. Other crops grown in smaller quantities throughout the region are rubber, tea, oil-palm and spices. Subsistence farming includes yams (on dry ground), taro (in heavy rainfall areas) and bananas, maize, cassava, breadfruit and pineapples. The staple food grown by the Solomon islanders is rice. Livestock farming is limited to cattle in Papua, New Caledonia and Fiji, and pigs in the New Hebrides, but there are also goats. A further 45% of Papua's exports consists of forest products. Timber, mostly mahogany and kauri pine, is also grown commercially in New Caledonia, the Solomons and the New Hebrides. Fishing is also important: shellfish, octopus and tuna are caught offshore, while lagoons yield mullet, bream and turtles.

Industry

Although secondary manufactures, such as packaging materials, fibreglass products and footwear are being developed, industry is essentially based on primary products. New Caledonia, for instance, has nickel-processing plants, sawmills, meat-preserving factories and coffee-barking mills while Fiji's main industries are centred on cane-crushing, gold-refining, processing copra into coconut oil and meal, pineapple-canning and timber-processing. Other leading Fijian manufactures are cement and biscuits. Biscuits, as well as twist tobacco and baskets, are made in the Solomons—among the least developed of the Pacific islands. Baskets, and other traditional crafts are also characteristic of the New Hebrides where industrial activity is based on meat-canneries, a fish-freezing plant, soft-drink factories, a cement works and a shipyard. Tourism, currently being developed in the New Hebrides and New Caledonia, is of major importance in New Guinea as well as in Fiji where it has surpassed sugar as the major foreign exchange earner.

Cities

The largest city in Melanesia is Suva (66,000), the capital of Fiji. On the south-east coast of Viti Levu, Suva is the country's light industrial centre and leading port, handling over 800 ships a year in its natural deep-water harbour. Noumea (74,000) in the south-west of New Caledonia is the territory's capital and only port. The capital and commercial centre of Vanuatu, Vila (15,000) is also a port with a new deep-water quay completed in 1972. Honiara (15,000) on the north coast of Guadalcanal is the capital of the Solomons and handles most of the territory's overseas trade. Papua New Guinea is administered from Port Moresby (131,000).

Australia-West

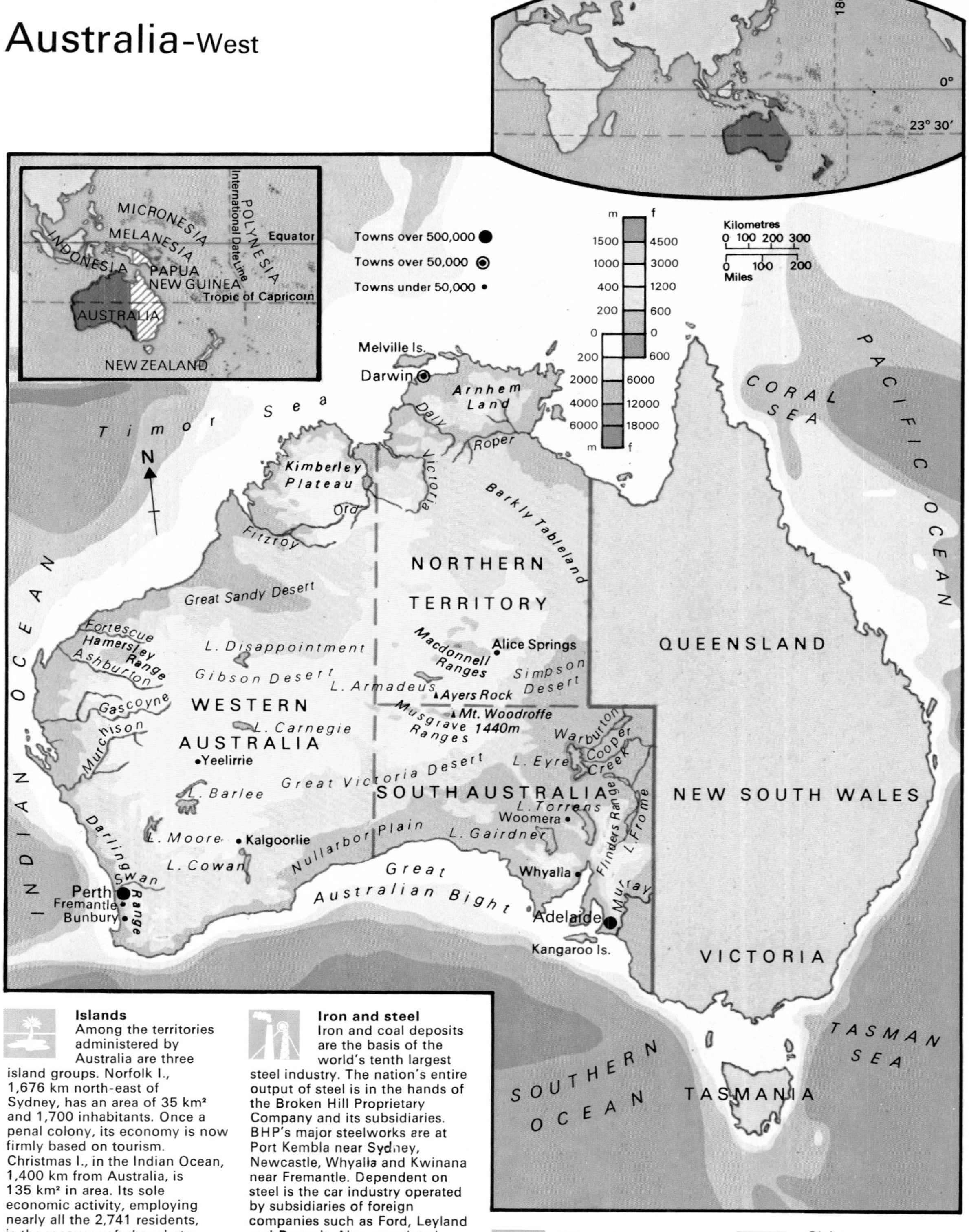

Area
7,686,884 km²/2,967,909 sq miles
Location
10°40′ – 43°40′S.
113°10′ – 153° 40′ E
Population
14,927,000 (1981)
Population density
2 per km²/5 per sq mile
Capital
Canberra: 228,000 (1980)
Largest City
Sydney: 3,232,000 (1980)
Language
English
Gross National Product
165,460 million US dollars (1981)
Major imports
machinery, transport equipment, textiles, petroleum, chemicals
Major exports
wool, meat, ores, cereals, sugar, coal, dairy products
Currency
Australian dollar (100 cents = 1 dollar)
Status
The Commonwealth of Australia is a federal state and constituent member of the Commonwealth of Nations.

Physical features

Australia, the only continent occupied by a single nation, is the world's sixth largest country. It is also the world's lowest and flattest land mass. Almost 75% of the continent is a vast, ancient plateau, formed more than 3,000 million years ago, with an average height of 300 m. To the east of this is lowland of less than 150 m, followed by a highland belt stretching along the coast. The dominating structure, the Great Western Plateau, emerges from the Indian Ocean coastal plain to cover almost the whole of Western Australia (the largest state, occupying one third of the continent), much of the Northern Territory, South Australia and a part of Queensland. The monotony of the plateau, largely desert, is broken by the Kimberley, Hamersley, Macdonnell and Musgrave ranges and by isolated outcrops such as Ayers Rock, a giant red rock 335 m tall.

Climate

As Australia covers more than 30° of latitude—the distance from Switzerland to Ghana—the climate is varied, but it is modified by the oceans and the absence of high mountains. The north lies within the tropics and has high temperatures, heavy rain and cyclones. In Darwin, annual temperature range is from 23°C to 32°C and the average annual rainfall, coming in the January–March wet season, is 154 cm. 60% of the country is in the temperate zone with warm summers and mild winters. January and July temperatures in Sydney are 26°C and 16°C, and in Perth, 29°C and 17°C. Winter, however, does bring snow to the Alps in the south-east. Rainfall is uneven. S.E. trade winds carry rain to the east coast: for example, 120 cm a year in Sydney. Westerly winds bring light rain to the south, but the interior around Lake Eyre receives less than 15 cm a year.

Islands

Among the territories administered by Australia are three island groups. Norfolk I., 1,676 km north-east of Sydney, has an area of 35 km² and 1,700 inhabitants. Once a penal colony, its economy is now firmly based on tourism. Christmas I., in the Indian Ocean, 1,400 km from Australia, is 135 km² in area. Its sole economic activity, employing nearly all the 2,741 residents, is the recovery of phosphate. The Cocos (Keeling) Is., 27 coral islands in the Indian Ocean, are 2,767 km north-west of Perth and 14 km² in total area. The population of 640 is engaged in copra production.

Communications

Transport in Australia faces the problem of distance—4,000 km separate east from west, and 3,500 km north from south. Distance is made worse by the distribution of population—6 out of 10 Australians live in a city, mostly in one of the state capitals which are all on the coast and at least 640 km apart. A transport system has evolved which includes 880,000 km of roads, 50% unpaved; 40,000 km of government railways; and 120,000 km of air routes travelled by 8 million passengers a year.

Iron and steel

Iron and coal deposits are the basis of the world's tenth largest steel industry. The nation's entire output of steel is in the hands of the Broken Hill Proprietary Company and its subsidiaries. BHP's major steelworks are at Port Kembla near Sydney, Newcastle, Whyalla and Kwinana near Fremantle. Dependent on steel is the car industry operated by subsidiaries of foreign companies such as Ford, Leyland and Renault. Also associated with steel is a shipbuilding industry.

Sheep

64% of the continent is farmland but, because of low rainfall, 90% of this is only rough grazing for sheep. The country's 148 million sheep, mostly merinos, constitute 15% of the world's sheep and produce 33% of the world's wool, making Australia the world's leading wool producer and exporter. Sheep are found in all states. In arid areas, where drought can halve sheep numbers, merinos are grazed exclusively. In high rainfall zones, like Tasmania, different breeds are raised to give super-fine wools. The main markets for Australian wool—its leading export—are Japan, the USSR and EEC countries.

Minerals

Australia is rich in minerals. Iron, mainly from the Hamersley Range, is the most important and is Australia's biggest mineral export. Australia is the world's largest bauxite producer. Other major deposits exploited are nickel at Kalgoorlie, manganese, found in Western Australia and in the Northern Territory, and copper, occuring throughout the continent. Australia is fourth in the world production of lead and zinc, mined at Broken Hill, Mount Isa and Read-Roseberry, and sixth in gold production. Recently, uranium has been discovered in the Northern Territory and at Yeelirrie. Mines at Lightning Ridge are the world's major source of opals. Australia now produces 70% of its crude oil requirements, mostly from fields in the Bass Strait which also have natural gas.

Cities

Adelaide is the capital of South Australia and the continent's fourth largest city (1,035,000) Ringed by fertile plains, the city was originally a market for agricultural produce, but has now become industrialized and specializes in engineering, textiles and chemicals. Australia's fifth largest city, Perth (926,000), on the Swan River 19 km from the sea, is the capital of Western Australia. Half the state's population lives there. Heavy industry is concentrated in the suburbs of Perth and Fremantle which, situated at the mouth of the Swan River, is Australia's third largest port. The capital of the Northern Territory, Darwin, is smaller (43,000) and is closely associated with the Territory's two main economic activities: mining and beef cattle.

Australia-East

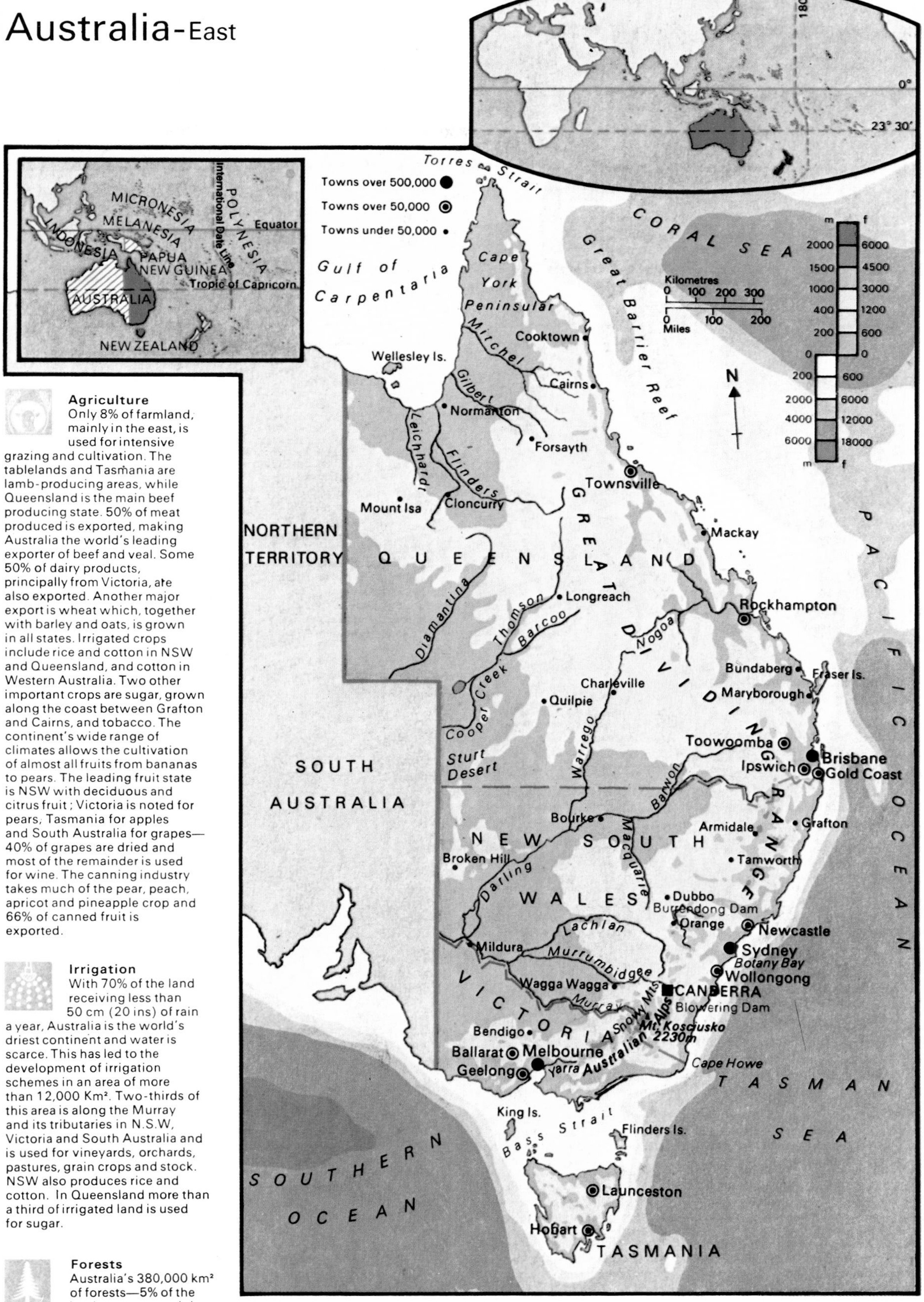

Physical features

East of the western plateau, and stretching from the Gulf of Carpentaria to South Australia, are lowlands. On average, these are less than 150 m high and Lake Eyre is nearly 12 m below sea level. Following the coast from Cape York to south Tasmania is a 3,200 km long chain of highlands, the Great Dividing Range. Most Australians live east of this on the coastal plain, which ranges from 50 to 400 km wide. The Great Divide mountains are faily low except for the Australian Alps in the south-east, which include the continent's highest peak, Mount Kosciusko, 2,228 m (7,300 ft). The seaboard from Tasmania to Brisbane is a succession of rocky headlands and sandy beaches. North of Brisbane, the coast is in the lee of the Great Barrier Reef, a belt of coral reefs and islands extending 2,000 km up to New Guinea. Australia lacks the big river systems of mountainous continents and many of its rivers only flow after heavy rain. Its largest system is the Murray and its tributaries, Darling, Murrumbidgee, Lachlan, which drain 1,057,000 km². But even the Murray takes a year to empty into the sea what the Amazon River in South America discharges in 36 hours.

Industry

Since the Second World War, Australian industry has greatly expanded. In addition to steel, engineering and paper, main industries include foodstuffs, chemicals and textiles. Australia produces a lot of surplus food, and exports of raw and processed food bring in a third of the nation's export income. The chemical industry, from local resources such as coal, molasses, salt and sulphur, produces basic chemicals used for explosives, plastics, fertilizers, cosmetics, etc. The rapid growth of oil refining has given an impetus to petro-chemicals and the textile industry is able to rely on local resources.

Cities

The national capital, Canberra, situated in the Australian Capital Territory 310 km from Sydney, is mainly administrative but has some light industry. Australia's oldest and largest city, Sydney, is built on low hills by the south Pacific. Capital of New South Wales (NSW), Sydney is Australia's financial centre and major port. Its most famous structure is the single span steel harbour bridge, the second longest in the world: 503 m (1,650 ft). The nation's second largest city and former capital is Melbourne (2,995,000). Capital of Victoria, the city houses 75% of the state's industry—metals, textiles, foodstuffs, paper. Brisbane (1,102,000), Queensland's capital and Australia's third city, has shipyards, engineering works, oil refineries, food-processing factories and sawmills. The most southerly city is Hobart (162,000), capital of Tasmania, and mainly concerned with fruit. Its port is most active during the apple season and fruit-processing is a major industry.

Agriculture

Only 8% of farmland, mainly in the east, is used for intensive grazing and cultivation. The tablelands and Tasmania are lamb-producing areas, while Queensland is the main beef producing state. 50% of meat produced is exported, making Australia the world's leading exporter of beef and veal. Some 50% of dairy products, principally from Victoria, are also exported. Another major export is wheat which, together with barley and oats, is grown in all states. Irrigated crops include rice and cotton in NSW and Queensland, and cotton in Western Australia. Two other important crops are sugar, grown along the coast between Grafton and Cairns, and tobacco. The continent's wide range of climates allows the cultivation of almost all fruits from bananas to pears. The leading fruit state is NSW with deciduous and citrus fruit; Victoria is noted for pears, Tasmania for apples and South Australia for grapes—40% of grapes are dried and most of the remainder is used for wine. The canning industry takes much of the pear, peach, apricot and pineapple crop and 66% of canned fruit is exported.

Irrigation

With 70% of the land receiving less than 50 cm (20 ins) of rain a year, Australia is the world's driest continent and water is scarce. This has led to the development of irrigation schemes in an area of more than 12,000 Km². Two-thirds of this area is along the Murray and its tributaries in N.S.W, Victoria and South Australia and is used for vineyards, orchards, pastures, grain crops and stock. NSW also produces rice and cotton. In Queensland more than a third of irrigated land is used for sugar.

Forests

Australia's 380,000 km² of forests—5% of the land area—are mainly found in the wetter zones near the east and south-east coasts and in Tasmania. Most of this is eucalyptus forest which fills all the country's hardwood requirements and most of its paper needs. The nation's 16 pulp and paper mills are concentrated mainly in Victoria, Tasmania and NSW. Australia exports veneers, sleepers and woodchips but, because conifers are deficient, has to import softwoods. To tackle this deficiency, softwood has been planted over 4,000 Km².

Flora and fauna

About 50 million years ago, links with other land masses disappeared, cutting off Australia and its plant and animal life from the rest of the world. Species evolved that are unknown elsewhere, such as the emu—a flightless bird—and the kangaroo, which can bound at 40 kph (25 mph). Like the koala, it is a marsupial: it rears its young in a pouch. Best known native trees are the acacia and eucalyptus, in which the koala lives.

Energy

Australia's greatest engineering project is the Snowy Mountains Hydro-Electric Scheme in NSW. The scheme provides about 2,344 million m³ of irrigation water a year and its total generating capacity is almost 4,000 megawatts. Another major hydro-electric scheme in Tasmania supplies nearly all that state's electricity. Taking the continent as a whole, however, over 70% of electricity comes from thermal plants fuelled by coal.

Aboriginals

The Aboriginals are thought to have arrived in Australia some 30,000 years ago. In a difficult environment they lived as semi-nomadic hunters and food-gatherers. When European settlement began almost 200 years ago, conflict and disease reduced their numbers drastically. Today the Aboriginal population is about 140,000. Many still live a traditional life in the 350 Aboriginal reserves, but others are moving to cities.

New Zealand

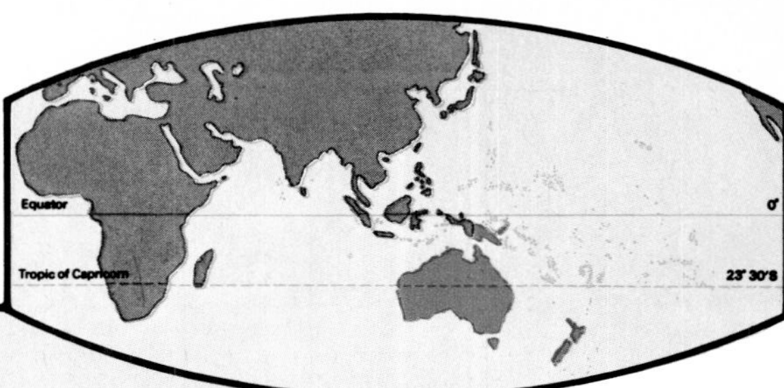

Maoris
The first Polynesians probably arrived in New Zealand in 800AD. They were the Maoris—hunters of the now extinct moa bird. More arrived in the great migration of 1350 and these original settlers, fishermen and farmers, were undisturbed until European colonization in the 1800s caused bitter conflict in some areas. Today, however, the Maoris—about 8% of the population—are an integral part of New Zealand society, proud of their culture and active in politics. Many now live and work in cities. Auckland is the world's largest Polynesian city.

Cities
The country's capital, Wellington, is on the southern tip of the North Island and is partly built on reclaimed land. It is New Zealand's political and commercial hub, but the biggest city is Auckland. On an isthmus between the Waitemata and Manukau harbours, Auckland is also the largest port. It handles 33% of exports and 50% of imports, and is the main industrial complex, producing one third of the country's manufactured goods. These include machinery, timber products, chemicals, processed food, textiles, plastics and cement. The second largest industrial centre is Christchurch (321,000).

Climate
Although New Zealand's climate ranges from subtropical in the north to almost continental in the central South Island, conditions are not extreme: winters are mild, summers warm. In the coldest month (July) minimum temperatures are 3°C in Dunedin and 8°C in Auckland. In January, summer maximums range from 19°C to 23°C. Prevailing westerly winds bring rain to the west coast all year, but the areas east of the ranges are drier, especially in summer and autumn, when hot, arid north-westerlies blow. In winter, snow covers the mountains and, in bad years, settles on the lowlands south of Christchurch.

Area
268,675 km²/103,736 sq miles (excluding the Pacific island territories of Tokelau and Niue)
Location
34°05′–47°20′ S
166°10′–178°20′ E
Population
3,305,000 (1981)
Population density
12 per km²/32 per sq mile
Capital
Wellington: 342,000 (1981)
Largest city
Auckland: 818,000 (1981)
Language
English
Major imports
machinery, transport equipment, metals, textiles, fuels, foodstuffs, fertilizers
Major exports
dairy produce, meat, wool
Currency
NZ dollar (100 cents = 1 dollar)
Gross National Product
25,460 million US dollars (1981)
Status
independent monarchical state and constituent member of the Commonwealth of Nations
National bird
kiwi

Energy
New Zealand's energy needs are largely supplied by hydro-electricity. In the North Island, stations are concentrated on the Waikato river. The newest stations are in the South Island, where the major Clutha and Waitaki river schemes offer great potential. Electricity also comes from thermal plants using coal, oil, natural gas and geothermal steam. The Kapuni field near New Plymouth produces natural gas and a larger field, off the Taranaki coast, is being developed. Of lesser importance is coal, mined in Westland and Waikato valley.

Physical features
The three islands of New Zealand lie 2,000 km south-east of Australia and 10,000 km west of Chile. The two larger islands, North (114,453 km²) and South (150,718 km²), are long and narrow: no point is further than 110 km from the sea. The third, Stewart Island, is smaller (1746 km²). The mountains in the South Island, the Southern Alps, include the country's highest peak, Mount Cook (3,764 m), and a network of lakes and glaciers. In places, glaciers spread down to 300 m above sea level. In the centre of the North Island is a volcanic plateau, dominated by the volcanic peaks of Ruapehu, Ngauruhoe and Tongariro, by geysers and hot springs and by New Zealand's largest lake, Lake Taupo (606 km²). Although 75% of New Zealand is more than 200 m above sea level, there are lowland areas. The most extensive are on the Canterbury Plains, crossed by rivers, which cover 12,500 km² of the South Island's east coast. The North Island has rich grasslands round the Waikato.

Transport
The road and rail networks on both islands are linked by ferries from Wellington to Lyttelton (the port of Christchurch) and across Cook Strait to Picton. An internal airline, the National Airways Corporation, operates services from 24 airports. Three of these airports—Auckland, Wellington, Christchurch—are also used by Air New Zealand for international flights. The country's seaports handle more than 13 million tonnes of foreign trade cargo a year. The chief ports are Auckland, Wellington, Lyttelton and Tauranga, with oil imports coming in at Whangarei.

Industry
In the last 20 years, New Zealand's industry has grown dramatically. Apart from the expansion of industries based on agricultural and forest products—timber, pulp and newsprint are now major exports—other domestic raw materials are being exploited. These include clay for bricks, limestone for cement, and ironsands, found along the west coast of the North Island and used in the Glenbrook steel plant near Auckland. Wax is also extracted from peat for use in paints and explosives. Essential to New Zealand's industrialization is cheap hydro-electricity. This led to the siting of a giant aluminium smelter at Bluff which uses imported Australian bauxite.

Agriculture
Although only 12% of the population works in farming, New Zealand's foreign trade depends on agricultural products which make up 80% of exports. It is the world's largest exporter of dairy products and lamb, and second largest exporter of wool. 22,000 dairy farms produce 6,000 million litres of milk a year. The milk is taken to co-operatives where it is processed into more than 100 products including butter and cheese. Between them, the country's 40,000 sheep farmers own 60 million sheep producing 315,000 tonnes of wool a year. Britain takes 19% and other major customers are the USA, Belgium, France, Japan and the USSR. Sheep rearing gives rise to New Zealand's other major export, lamb, which is sent to more than 100 countries. Beef is also produced and other associated exports are sausage casings, tallow, hides and skins. The country's success in livestock farming lies in its ability to grow good grass and clovers (seeds are exported world-wide) thanks to even rainfall, plentiful sunshine and fertilizers. The other factor is mechanization: aircraft, for instance, are used for top-dressing, spraying and sowing. Arable farming is equally successful and New Zealand is self-sufficient in wheat and in hops. Fruit growing has also become important and apples and pears and exotic local fruits are air-freighted abroad.

The Antarctic

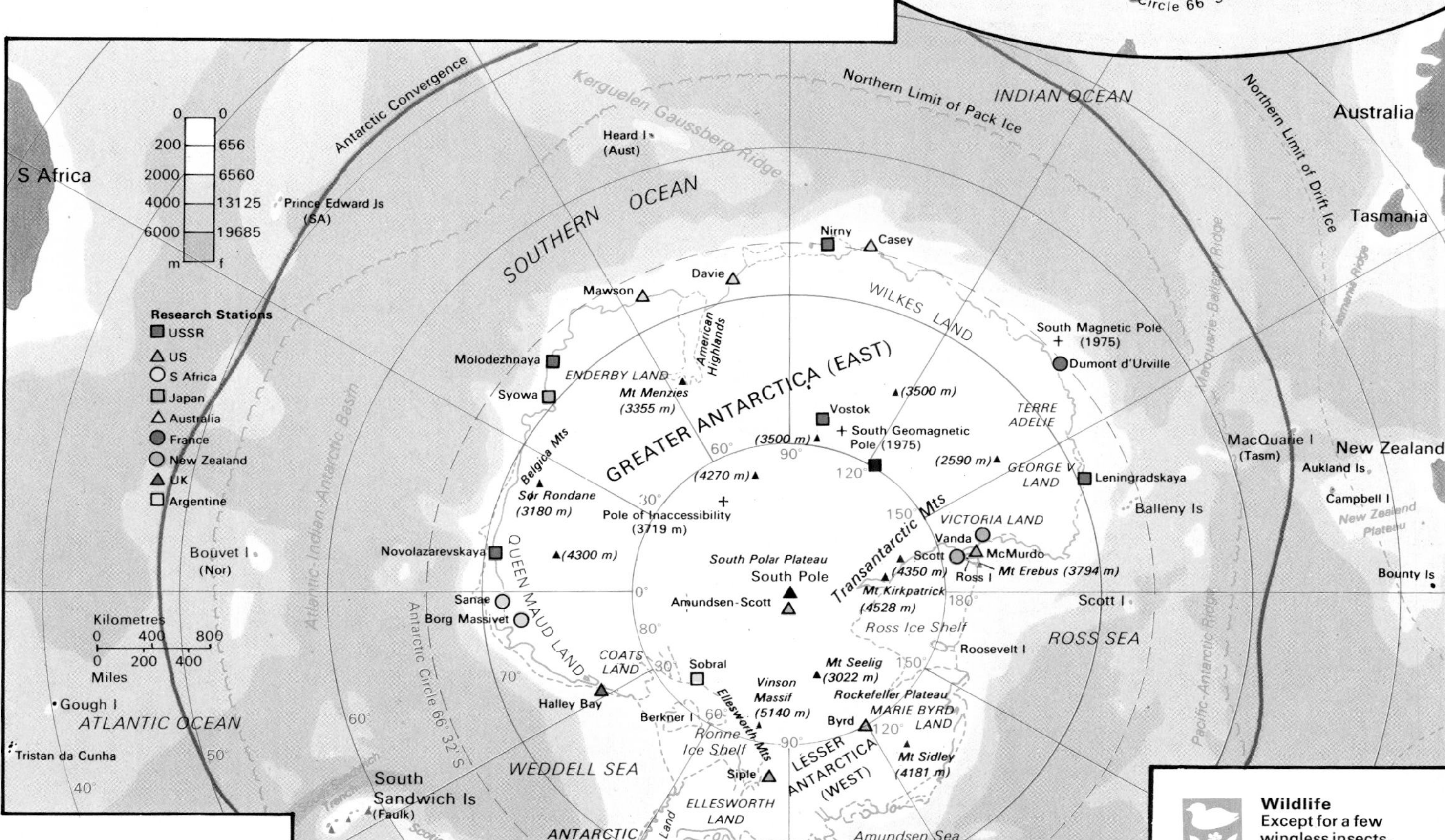

The Antarctic

The Antarctic comprises the continent of Antarctica and its surrounding seas and numerous islands; these include the South Shetlands, the South Sandwich Islands, the South Orkneys, South Georgia, Bouvet Island, Heard Island, the Balleny Islands, Scott Island and Peter I Island. Various boundaries are used to define the region: the Antarctic Circle at 66°32'S; the political limit corresponding to latitude 60°S; and the Antarctic convergence—the border generally accepted for geographical and scientific purposes. This oceanographic boundary, a belt of water 30 to 50 km wide, lies between latitudes 50° and 62°S—the zone where cold northward-moving antarctic surface water sinks below warmer subantarctic water.

Antarctica

Antarctica, centred on the South Pole, is the world's coldest and most desolate continent. It is also unique in its isolation, situated 960 km from South America, 2,700 km from Australia and 4,000 km from South Africa. Except for the deep indentations of the Ross and Weddell seas and the projecting Antarctic peninsula, the continent is roughly circular in shape and lies almost wholly within the Antarctic Circle. With a total area of 13.8 million km² it is the world's fifth largest continent, nearly equal in size to the US and Europe combined. Antarctica is surrounded by the Southern or Antarctic Ocean, formed from the southern waters of the Pacific, Indian and Atlantic oceans and extending northwards to the tips of the neighbouring continents.

Climate

Antarctica has a far harsher climate than the Arctic, largely because of its average altitude but also because the ocean, frozen in winter, insulates the continent from the warming influence of open water. Inland temperatures often drop to –56°C and the world's lowest recorded temperature of –88°C was at the Soviet station, Vostok. The coast is milder but even in summer no point has a monthly mean above freezing. Bitter winds, rushing seawards, are a constant feature of Antarctic weather; speeds average 80 kph but gusts exceed 300 kph. Loose snow, driven by these winds, causes dense blizzards. Precipitation, in the form of snow, is very low (equal to 5 cm of rain) making Antarctica one of the Earth's great deserts.

Vegetation

The continent's severe temperatures and extreme aridity are hostile to plant life except for algae, mosses, lichens and, in the northern part of the Antarctic Peninsula, some small flowering plants.

The land

Ice covers 95% of Antarctica; exposed areas comprise sections of mountain ranges, projecting peaks and, along the coast, dry valleys known as 'oases'. Most ice-free zones occur in Victoria Land and the Antarctic Peninsula. The principal mountain chain is the Transantarctic range which rises to over 4,500 m and extends from Victoria Land to Coats Land. Other ranges fringe the coast: the Ellsworth mountains contain Antarctica's highest peak, the Vinson Massif (5,140 m). The Transantarctic chain divides the continent into two parts. The larger part, East Antarctica, is a continental shield composed of old, hard rocks. The smaller section, West Antarctica, is more recent in origin and consists of folded ranges and plateaux; Mt Erebus, on Ross Island, is an active volcano. The Antarctic Peninsula, with its magnificent ice-capped plateau and fjord-indented coast, is probably an extension of the Andes; it is linked to Tierra del Fuego by the submarine Scotia Ridge of which the South Shetlands, the South Orkneys and the South Sandwich Islands are outcrops.

Land ice

Antarctica is a vast dome of ice formed by the snows of past millennia. At the dome's summit, near the Pole of Inaccessibility (800 km from the South Pole), the ice is about 4,000 m thick; its average thickness of 2,000 m makes Antarctica the highest continent. This enormous ice-sheet, representing 90% of the world's ice, is in constant motion: under its own pressure the ice flows slowly outwards and downwards to the sea. Surface features include giant terraced steps, wave-like dunes and crevasses up to 40 m deep and 20 m wide. Most of the glacier sheet terminates at the coast but some of the ice spills out over the sea as floating ice-shelves; the largest is the Ross Ice Shelf, covering 806,000 km².

Sea ice

Antarctica is surrounded by pack-ice that ranges from huge flat-topped icebergs (160 km long and 50 m high) to small fragments only a few centimetres across. Wind and currents keep the ice moving and, in summer, create a maze of lanes through which ships can pass. Access is easiest via the Ross Sea which is almost ice-free in February and March; in contrast, navigation on the Weddell Sea is difficult as the ice jams against the peninsula. In winter, the pack-ice extends northwards for hundred of kilometres and effectively doubles the area of the continent.

Wildlife

Except for a few wingless insects, Antarctica has no land animals, but marine and bird life are more plentiful. The ocean floor abounds with molluscs and small creatures such as sponges, sea-urchins and starfish while seals and whales swim in the Antarctic waters; the various species include the blue whale weighing up to 150 tonnes. Gulls, petrels and penguins are the most common birds; the emperor penguin is the only one that winters on shore; the others migrate to the edge of the pack-ice.

Man in Antarctica

The rigorous climate is inhospitable and dangerous to man. As a result, Antarctica is the only continent with no permanent human inhabitants. The current population (about 1,000) consists mostly of scientists engaged in research. Various countries maintain research stations in Antarctica and seven of them (Norway, Australia, France, New Zealand, Chile, the United Kingdom and Argentina) claim territory. The claimed sectors are segments running from the coast to the South Pole; only one zone, Marie Byrd Land, remains unclaimed. In 1959 an international treaty was signed suspending all territorial claims for 30 years and guaranteeing the free use of the continent for peaceful purposes only.

Usefulness

Primarily, Antarctica is a great scientific laboratory. In addition, there are valuable minerals in Greater Antarctica but the high costs involved make exploitation uneconomic: some whaling and sealing occur in the Southern Ocean.

Zefa (UK) Ltd.

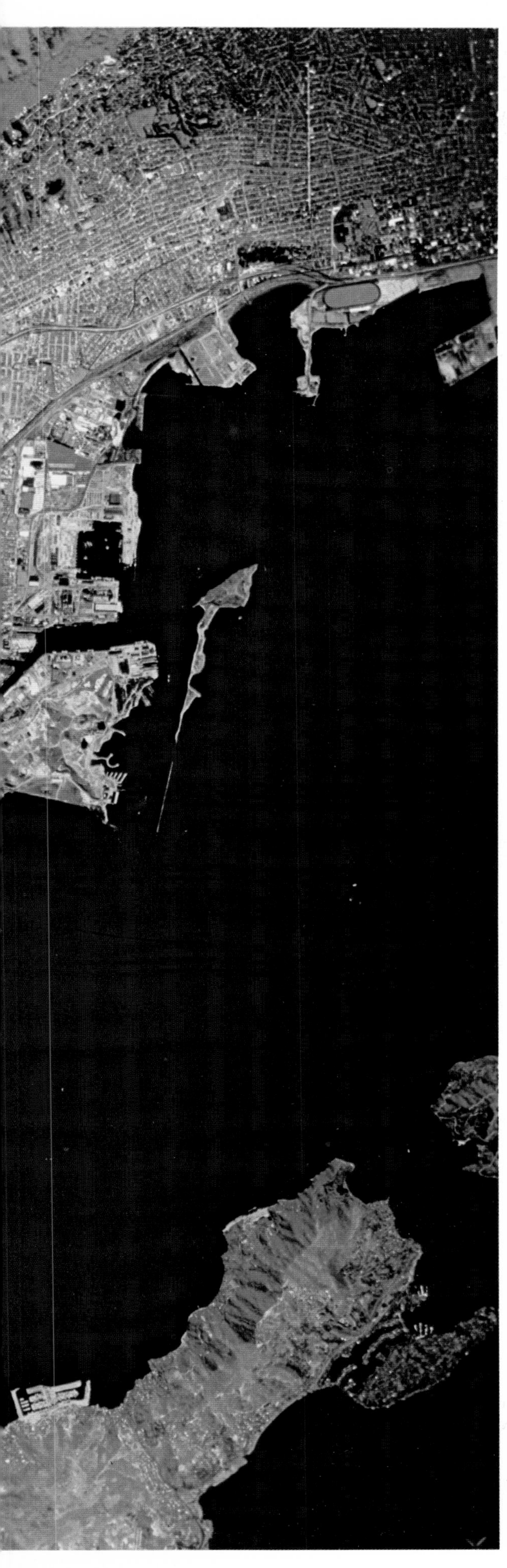

Mapping the Earth

Large scale maps can be produced with a photographic base. This photograph of San Francisco is taken on infra red film, which will penetrate mist – the wavelength of infra red light being greater than the diameter of dust and air molecules.

Mapping the Globe

Scala

Left, right and far right: Depiction of the Greek mathematician and geographer Claudius Ptolemy (left), who lived during the second century AD. His great work, *Geographia*, discusses the making of a world map based on a conical projection, estimates the latitude and longitude of some 8,000 places and has instructions for 26 regional maps. During the Dark Ages, classical advances, including the notion of a spherical Earth, were lost. Instead, the world was thought of as a flat disc. Mapping was based on Christian doctrine rather than on geographical fact, as the map (far right) shows. Dated around 1300, this has Jerusalem at the world's centre and includes many biblical references. With the Renaissance, great advances were made in cartography, Ptolemy's scholarship was discovered and his world map, together with its inaccuracies, was copied. By the sixteenth century terrestrial globes (such as the one seen right, dated 1541) were made, indicating a return to maps suited to practical needs.

Many people, asked to describe an area, would give a purely verbal outline based on the relative positions of various landmarks. But any two maps of the same area based on such a description would probably be quite different. True map making depends on the setting up of some system of co-ordinates.

Everyone has seen street maps with square grids superimposed, so that a particular street can be found in, say, square B3. This system is called *Cartesian:* there is a starting point, called the *origin*, for the two scales, which are at right angles to each other.

Such a two dimensional system works well over small areas and on flat ground. If the Earth were flat, a simple Cartesian system would be quite satisfactory. Since the Earth is a globe, however, another system has to be used. Each place is located by its *latitude* and *longitude*. The zero value for latitude, corresponding to the origin, is the equator. Lines of latitude are then imaginary circles parallel to the equator and called *parallels*. These circles get smaller towards the poles, and are numbered according to their angle from the equator as seen from the Earth's centre. The equator is then 0° and the poles 90°N and 90°S.

The circles of longitude, on the other hand, are not parallels but are all *great circles*—that is, circles of the same diameter as the Earth. Each one passes through both poles, and is called a *meridian*, running from north to south. The zero point of the longitude system is internationally agreed to be at Greenwich, England. All other lines of longitude are described as either east or west of Greenwich.

The position of any place on Earth, therefore, is given by two co-ordinates. Each can be measured as accurately as required, using degrees, minutes (sixtieths of a degree) and seconds (sixtieths of a minute). A second of latitude is just under 31 m (102 ft); for greater accuracy than that, decimals of a second are used. The size of a second of longitude varies between the equator and the poles.

Latitude and longitude can be measured using a sextant to observe the positions of astronomical bodies. In theory a complete map of the world could be built up by measuring the latitude and longitude of each place individually, and this is indeed how explorers made maps of the territories they visited. A few places would be located accurately and the rest filled in by eye. But to make a detailed map in this way would be very time-consuming. Instead, the mapping of an area is based (on a nationwide basis, for example) on triangulation control.

Triangulation

The first stage in surveying a previously unmapped area is to establish a *ground control*—the relative positions of a few easily-visible points. To do this the process of *triangulation* is carried out. This hinges upon the proposition that, if the length of one side of a triangle and the three angles within the triangle are

Mansell Collection

GERHARD MERCATOR

Left: Mercator, the 16th century geographer. His 1569 map projection has become world famous.

Below: Mercator's cylindrical projection is one of the most commonly used. If a light is projected through a glass globe. it throws shadows of the parallels and meridians on to the surrounding cylinder. This projection distorts rapidly towards the poles. If the cylinder is placed horizontally (as in the small diagram), a *transverse* Mercator projection results, in which the line of zero distortion runs from north to south, not east to west.

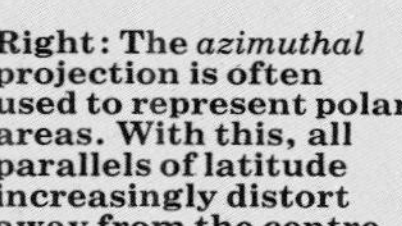

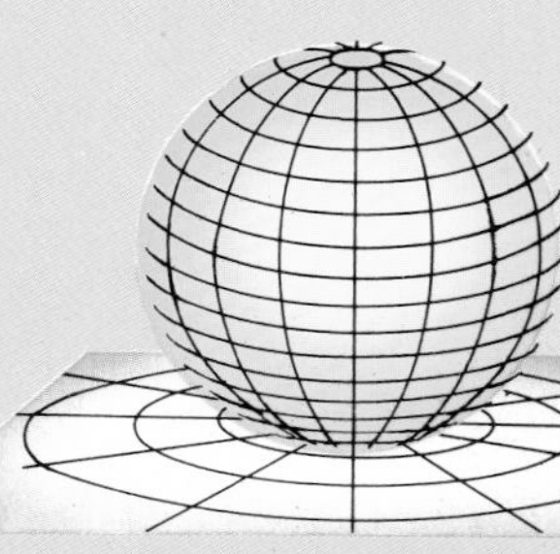

Right: The *azimuthal* projection is often used to represent polar areas. With this, all parallels of latitude increasingly distort away from the centre.

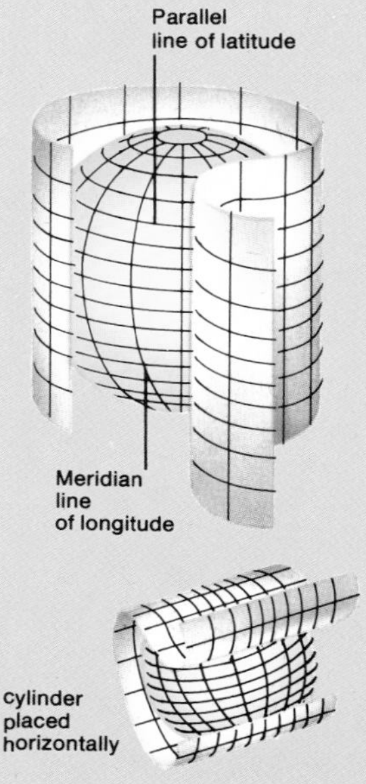

CYLINDRICAL PROJECTION

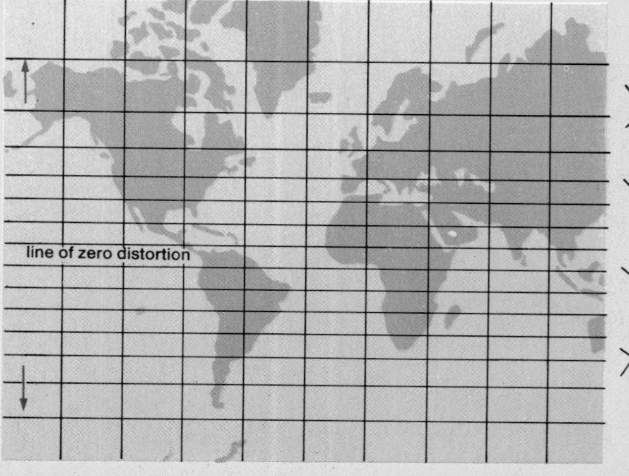

Michael Holford/National Maritime Museum

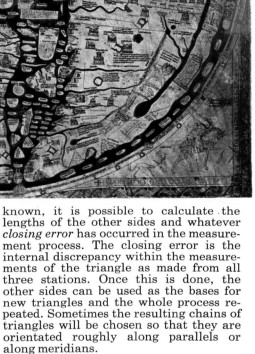

Woodmanstone Colour Slides

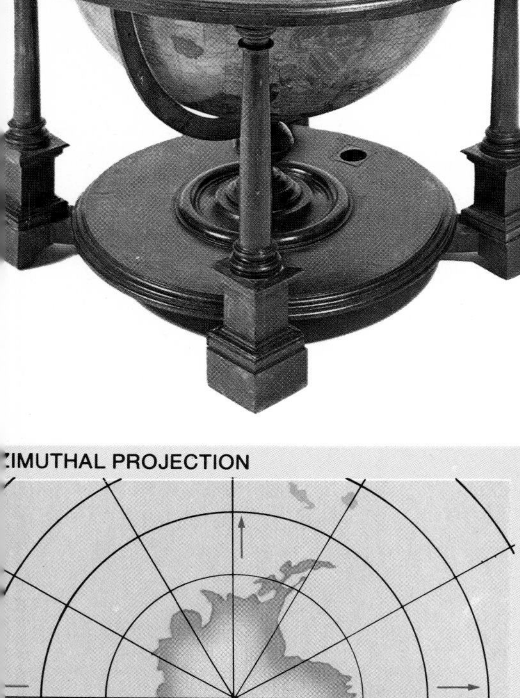

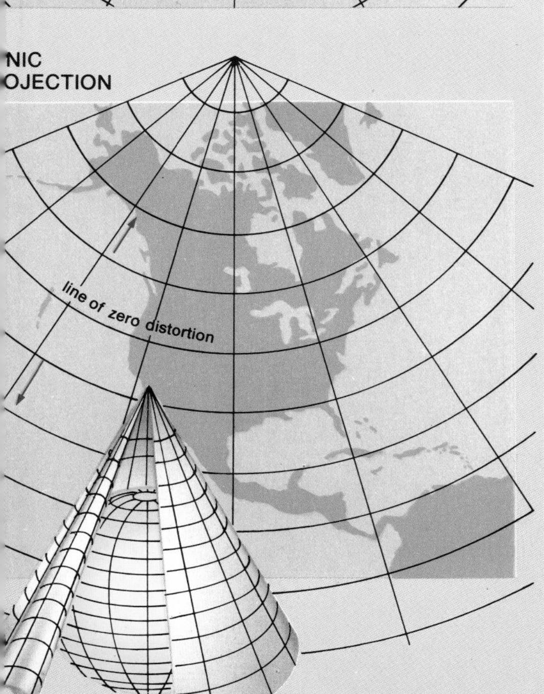

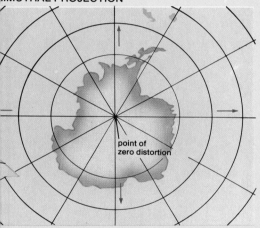

Below left: In the *conic* type of map projection all meridians (lines of longitude) are projected as straight lines and the parallels of latitude are arcs of concentric circles. The line of zero distortion is the circular arc where paper and globe meet. Mapping parts of the US was based upon local versions of this.

Below: Much topographic survey is now carried out by *photogrammetry*. This involves collecting aerial photographs of the area and correcting these by plotting the true relative positions of certain points on the ground by field survey. Overlaps in adjacent photographs must occur to provide the necessary stereoscopic image.

Aerofilms

known, it is possible to calculate the lengths of the other sides and whatever *closing error* has occurred in the measurement process. The closing error is the internal discrepancy within the measurements of the triangle as made from all three stations. Once this is done, the other sides can be used as the bases for new triangles and the whole process repeated. Sometimes the resulting chains of triangles will be chosen so that they are orientated roughly along parallels or along meridians.

Triangulation involves measuring a baseline, then taking observations of the angles between other points which can be seen from each end of this line. The 'altitude' of the other points is also observed from the baseline by measuring their position above or below the horizontal.

Generally speaking, a country is first covered by a primary triangulation in which the sides of the triangles average about 50 km in length. Once this has been established and the average closing error for any triangle is no more than about 3 cm, secondary triangulation is carried out within the primary triangles, followed by tertiary triangulation within each of the secondary triangles. Closing errors in the tertiary triangles are not so critical since they do not accumulate throughout the whole survey, but they are normally less than 30 cm in about 4 km.

Until the 1960s almost all triangulation measurements were made with optical instruments such as *theodolites*, which measure angles, and *tacheometers*, which measure the size of a staff of known height, thus giving its distance. Since then, triangulation has been increasingly carried out with electronic distance-measuring devices; these measure the lengths of the sides of the triangle directly and, in favourable conditions, provide an accuracy of a centimetre or less over two kilometres.

Filling in the details

Once the ground has been established by triangulation, most large and medium scale (say 1:50,000 scale or larger) mapping is now carried out by *photogrammetry*. The scale of a map gives its size in relation to the land it represents. Thus a distance on a 1:50,000 map is 50,000 times shorter than the real thing. Such a map has a scale of 2 cm to 1 km.

Photogrammetry involves taking overlapping air photographs, so that each point on the ground is seen from two positions. Once processed, the photographs can be used to give stereoscopic images, so that the height of the ground, as well as surface details, can be measured.

Ordnance Survey

Above right: The first triangulation, carried out by Sir William Roy from Hounslow to Paris (1784-1790). It established the relative position of Great Britain and Europe.

Right: *Theodolites* used in a survey of Bahrain. Theodolites are used to measure angles between survey points in conspicuous locations such as hill tops. The angles are measured in both the horizontal and the vertical planes. If the distance between any two stations and the height of one is known, the distance between all others and the height of all survey points may be calculated through a triangulation network. Triangulations often span distances of over 50 km (30 miles).

Fairey Surveys

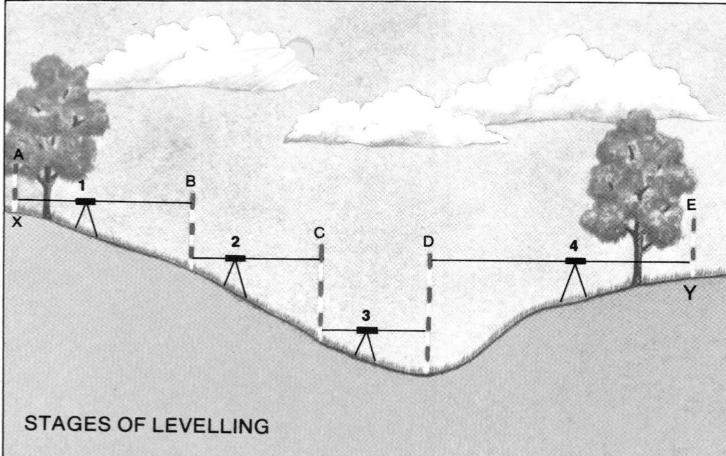

Left: A simple and accurate way of measuring height differences between two points (X and Y) is provided by levelling. In principle, the operator sets up his telescope to be horizontal at position 1. He then looks back to a calibrated staff A, reads off the height on the staff and repeats this with the staff at B, C and so on.

Below: Satellites are now used as survey beacons. A satellite observed simultaneously from three triangulation points on Earth appears against a different star background in each case. By knowing exact star positions, the locations of the Earth stations can be traced back.

An alternative method is to carry out a levelling survey on the ground. This gives accurate height values over short distances and uses a levelling telescope which can accurately be made horizontal. The procedure is to observe a calibrated staff (that is, a staff with heights marked off in bands) through the telescope, so that the height difference between the two stations can be measured directly. This process is repeated with the staff and telescope in different positions.

Representing position

Once the basic survey measurements of relative position have been made and checked, they need to be represented in a convenient form. Much the simplest way is to plot them on a globe, a model of the world, since this gets over the problems of transferring information collected on a near-spherical world to a flat sheet of paper. Globes, however, are inconvenient to use in many situations and numerous map *projections* have been devised to permit the convenient representation of all or part of the spherical world on flat paper.

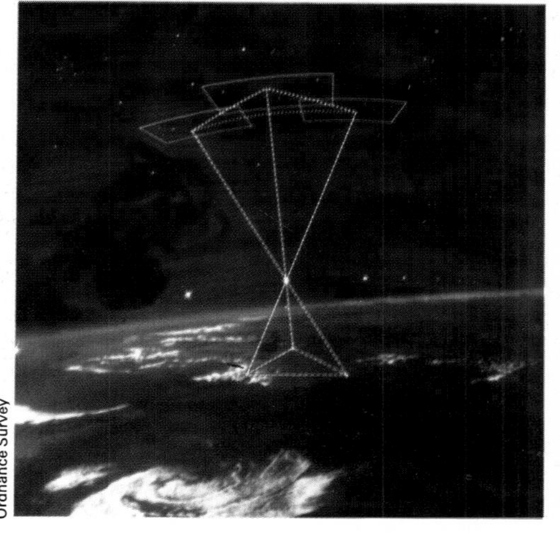
Ordnance Survey

The simplest form of map projection is to 'peel the skin' off a globe. This gives a series of *gores*, strips of paper joined at the equator and tapering to points at the poles. In effect, this produces a form of *interrupted* map projection but its very fragmentary nature makes it difficult to use: oceans and continents are frequently split into two or more parts.

Geographers have suggested that there are four vitally important properties of a map projection. These are that the resulting map should accurately reproduce correct areas, correct shape, correct angular relationships and correct distances between points. Unfortunately it is totally impossible to have all these properties in any projection for a flat sheet of paper and the map maker therefore has to select the projection according to which property is most important for the purpose of the map.

The representation of *conformality* is one in which all angles and shapes over small areas are correctly reproduced: because of these properties, such projections are normally used for topograhic maps (that is, the familiar straightforward maps of an area), navigation charts and military maps. A consequence of the correct angular representation is that parallels and meridians meet at right angles. Equal area projections, on the other hand, often give extremely distorted shapes to countries but represent the area of one correctly in regard to all the others shown. Because of this property, they are commonly used in mapping distributions, such as of population density, of agricultural produce and output. If an equal area projection were not used in these circumstances, the same values for two equally sized countries, one at the equator and one near the pole, would look very different indeed. It can be shown by simple algebra that no map projection can be both conformed and equal area, though there are many which are neither but are created as a compromise between these two extremes.

Map of Europe and the Atlantic from the 1513 edition of Ptolemy's *Geographia*. It shows how the distance from Europe to America had been underestimated since the second century, thus misleading Columbus and other explorers. The criss-cross lines mark compass points.

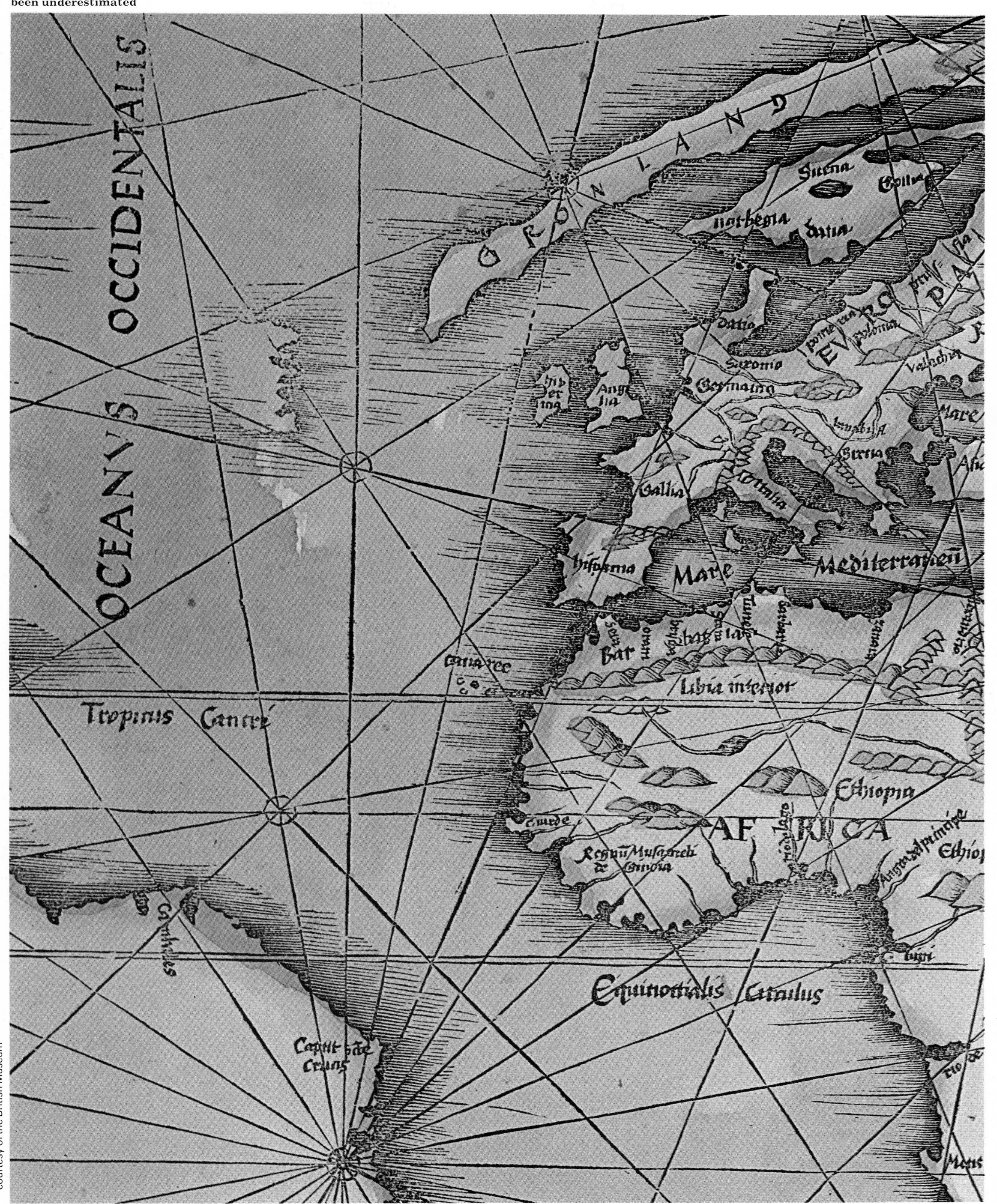

courtesy of the British Museum

Making Maps

Leonie Finlay

Maps have been made for at least 4,500 years. However, the manner in which they have been made has changed dramatically over the last few hundred years. The change has been from individually constructed manuscript maps to maps reproduced in quantity on a printing press though now, in certain respects, there is a return to the production of single maps suited to a particular purpose. All of these changes have been largely brought about by changes in technology.

Before a map is made, the map-maker or *cartographer* must make certain decisions which determine the form of the map, bearing in mind its purpose. There will of course be great differences between maps intended for trained map users, for tourists, for display purposes and so on, and the design must be appropriate to each. What the particular map needs to show determines to some extent the scale which is used. Small scale maps, which can cover a large area such as a whole country, usually show major details—rivers, cities, towns, roads—only. For greater local detail, large scale maps covering a smaller area are used.

Collecting information

When the information for a map is constructed from original survey measurements the product is called a basic map. For this, the cartographer will plot the relative positions of the survey points and the detail of the landscape in between these will either be provided for him by a trained user of air photographs—a photogrammetrist—or will be sketched in using whatever other information is at hand.

When an overlapping pair of aerial photographs is mounted in a *stereoscope*, the photogrammetrist sees a three-dimensional view of the ground to be mapped. First the two photographs are tilted if necessary to correct for the tilt of the aircraft and so on when the photographs were taken. The operator can now recognize variations in height in the stereoscopic view. The machine he uses may have, for example, a small dot or bar in the optical system. This dot can be moved around by the operator. The procedure may then be to move the dot across the surface keeping it at the same apparent height as judged in the stereo view. The dot's movements then trace out a *contour*—a line of constant height. Quite often the dot controls are linked to a pen mechanism which draws a map directly. Such devices are called *stereoplotters*.

Up to 80 per cent of the survey information comes from air photographs. The remaining information must be collected by observers on the ground, who check and correct the material provided by the photogrammetrist and stereoplotter and who add details which might have been obscured in an aerial photograph. These details, necessary for large scale maps such as those produced by the British Ordnance Survey, include the accurate naming of features, the type of vegetation, buildings which are covered by trees or otherwise not visible in an aerial view, the ground measurements of buildings, house numbers, boundaries and divisions under roofed areas.

Leonie Finlay

Above and left: Stereoplotters, such as the high precision version shown here, are used to create corrected images of three-dimensional models of the terrain from aerial photographs. On this, the operator follows 'lines of interest' such as field boundaries. Imaginary lines, such as contours, may also be followed. Some stereoplotters can produce a map directly as a result of this process by being linked to a pen mechanism, or co-ordinatograph. This instrument, a detail of which is seen left, is tracing the lines of buildings, fields and paths followed by the operator onto a stable base plastic material.

Compilation

It is probably more common, however, for the cartographer to create a 'derived' map, that is, a new map from several existing ones, especially when he is mapping to a small scale. These, however, may be at different scales and on different projections, and only certain parts of the information on each may be required. The conversion of all the information to a common scale is normally carried out by photographic enlargement or reduction. Alternatively another simple, if tedious, process can be carried out by overlaying grids of appropriate sizes on the old and new maps—the location of the features on the old are transposed to the new using the grid lines as guides. If the grids are replaced by graticules, that is, lines of longitude and latitude as depicted on the

Ordnance Survey

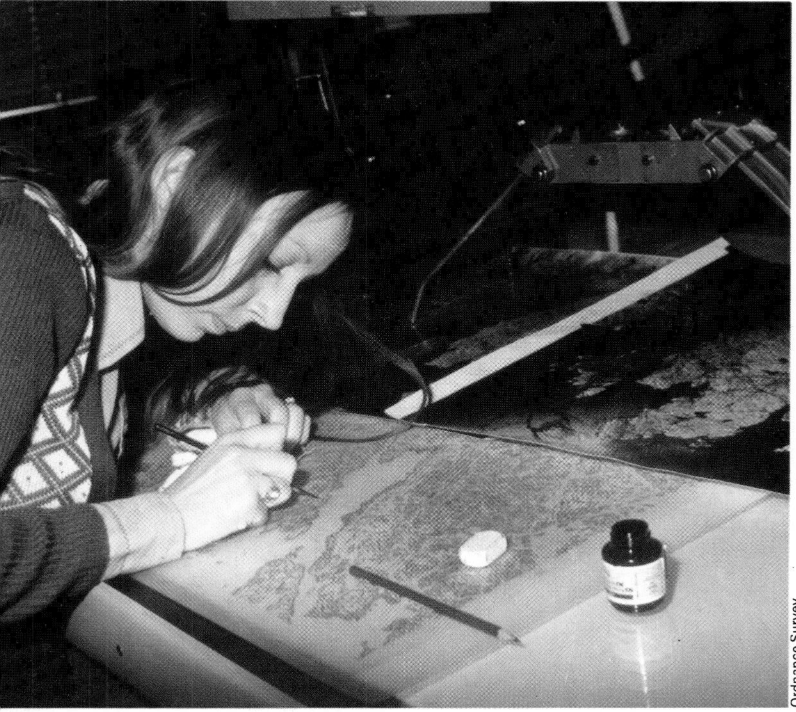

Ordnance Survey

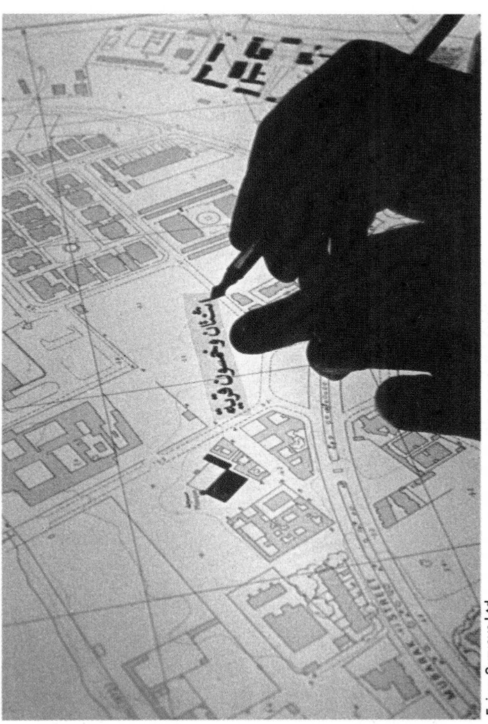

Fairey Surveys Ltd.

Left: Altitude is often shown on British maps by the use of contours—imaginary lines joining all places of the same height. Where very steep slopes occur, however, the contour lines on the map are so close together that they coalesce. In such places they are often removed and a drawing of a steep rock face inserted by hand.

Right: A minimum of overlap must occur between the names and other details on a map. Most names are now set on a phototypesetter in the size and language required—in this case Arabic. The self-adhesive film can be stuck down in the appropriate place. When photographed, it will appear as part of the original map.

Below: This camera is designed to reproduce lines and other cartographic details of consistent width and clarity over an area of more than one metre square. The map or section of a map being photographed is held in a glass frame by a vacuum. It can be accurately reduced or enlarged in scale.

Below: Map making is becoming increasingly automated. Here a girl is digitizing an Ordnance Surveyor's map; she is following the lines of the map and these are being stored by the computer as repeated pairs of co-ordinates. Labels are then added to indicate the meaning of each line. Once this is complete, the same data may be used to produce a wide variety of maps with different scales, symbols and projections. Alterations need simply to be digitized and the old parts deleted within the computer. Ordnance Survey cartographers were pioneers in this field; by the end of 1976 they had digitized about 4,000 maps.

Leonie Finlay

old and the new maps, then conversion from one map projection to the other may be carried out in addition to the change of map scale; it is not simple to change map projection by photographic means.

Once the scale and projection of all the source maps have been brought to a single, common standard, the features which are required are traced off by the cartographer and then re-drawn. Only rarely can satisfactory maps be made by merely assembling pieces of existing maps and reproducing these without re-drawing. Because the original maps may have been drawn differently and at different scales, the photographic process produces lines of different thickness and symbols of different types representing the same feature within the composite map. In addition, the cartographer normally brings the mapped features into a conformity to suit his own process.

In a description of the map-making process, the amount of information carried in the margin of the map is easily overlooked. But these margins often contain valuable information such as the date of survey and of any revisions; the name of the publisher; information on latitude and longitude; the variation between true north and magnetic north; the type of projection used; and the key, the scale and the grid system.

Until the 1960s, the map image was normally created by drawing on paper or on film with a dense black ink. High quality maps of certain types were still made in some places by direct engraving and etching of a copper plate which was subsequently used for printing. Now the majority of high quality maps available are drawn using a *scriber*. With this, the cartographer in effect chisels lines in a coating on plastic material. This coating, often red or yellow, is transparent so that the cartographer can see the base map below, but is opaque when seen by the blue-sensitive emulsions on the films used for copying.

Dotted and pecked lines are achieved by scribing continuous lines and then filling in alternate sections with an opaque liquid; double lines, such as those used to show roads, are drawn with a special double headed scribing tool.

Scribing gives much higher and more consistent quality of linework than does the use of pen and ink and is much easier than engraving. The use of plastic-based materials avoids the problems of shrinkage which occur with paper when the temperature and humidity of the air change. Before the ready availability of easily-handled plastics, very high quality maps had to be drawn on glass.

Though lines are usually now scribed, a different approach is taken in depicting symbols and in shading or colouring areas. If a cartographer makes frequent use of a particular small symbol—say for a telephone box—he will draw it at perhaps twenty times its final size, then have it photographically reduced and reproduced many times on 'stripper film'. The mini-symbols on this may then be stuck down in the correct position on a positive copy of the map. Place names are commonly set in this way though the originals are produced by machine rather than via an enlarged drawing. The use of stripper film ensures that different type styles and

Fairey Surveys Ltd.

Above: 3-dimensional models of terrain are an easily understood form of mapping. They are usually cut by hand from expanded polystyrene but can be cut under computer control from a map stored in digital form. Normally, terrain models must use a greatly exaggerated vertical scale before the relief is noticeable.

Below: Air photograph and details from two maps of Hatfield, Hertfordshire, England. The larger scale map (1:10,000, that is, one unit on the map represents 10,000 units on the ground), top, shows details such as individual houses. The small scale (1:50,000) map, lower, is heavily generalized. Symbols rather than drawings of features are used and roads have exaggerated widths so they can be coloured, important to road classification. Colour is used more extensively in this map. The air photograph resembles the larger scale map in some respects, but is on a different scale and needs skilled interpretation.

Below right: Infra-red photograph of part of the Blackwater estuary, Essex, England. Since World War II, infra-red (or *false*) colour film has been used in mapping to distinguish areas of healthy (red) and diseased (blue) vegetation and to show up the depth of water (seen here as light and dark blue areas).

Aerofilms

Crown Copyright Reserved

weights may be used, the names can be set at any angle and may easily be positioned so as not to overlap important crossroads and other features in the map.

If the map is to be produced in colour, each colour is prepared separately as a black and white overlay. The colour only appears when the final plate is printed using the chosen ink colour. Up to 10 colours are common, each one having its own plate.

Automated cartography

Since the late 1950s, attempts have been made to introduce computers into the map-making process. The reasons for this are the speed and flexibility of their operation and the basic repetitiveness of some parts of map-making. Many organizations now use computing, but a milestone was the production in Britain in 1971 of the Abingdon geology map by the Experimental Cartography Unit: this was the first map to be made by automated means and published as one of a conventional map series.

The essence of map-making by computer is similar to manual cartography. Compilation of the materials, however, is done inside the computer. The most common method of obtaining information is to digitize (convert into numbers) the location of roads and other features from existing maps. In this process lines are stored as repeated co-ordinate pairs, each pair giving a measure of so many millimetres to the east and so many to the north of the south-west corner of the map.

The greatest advantage of computer cartography is that it greatly simplifies selection of an area of interest, of features of interest within that area, of the projection on which the results are to be produced and the graphic symbols used to show them. A change of features of interest, for example, does not involve the cartographer in manual re-drawing: he specifies which ones he wants and the machine will draw them on film or paper, often to very high accuracy indeed.

Different machines use different means of drawing such as pens, beams of light and laser beams. The use of cathode ray tubes is becoming much more common—these appear like televisions and *ephemeral* maps may be drawn on them if no *hard copy* map is needed. Some of these can draw at speeds of more than 100 metres per second. In addition to this speed and flexibility, the basic cartographic information can often be used for other tasks. A suitably programmed computer, for example, will be able to draw sections through the topography along a given road or find the answers to such questions as 'how many buildings lie within this area?' Though a very important and far-reaching development, the use of computers in mapping still necessitates the cartographer's design skills to produce maps which can be used by the average person.

Photomapping

A number of maps, particularly in Sweden and the US and at large scales, are now produced with a photographic base rather than the normal line depiction of the topography. This is particularly useful in areas which do not already have accurate maps or in areas of rapid change, such as in cities.

Often these maps consist of mosaics of air photographs. Since each photograph is distorted because of the variations in the height and orientation of the survey aircraft and because of variation in ground height, they often have to be *rectified* before being pieced together. Such rectification can remove all of the distortions apart from those due to variations in ground altitude. To get rid of this, a special electronic or optical process termed *orthophotography* has been devised. It produces planimetrically correct photographs, that is, photographs which are as free of geometric distortion as the best maps.

Whatever the sophistication of the rectification carried out, the photographs have to be converted from their continuous tone nature (in which all shades of grey are present in the film) into a half-tone before they can be printed. This involves breaking up the original into dots of different sizes, the larger dots representing the darker areas: the coarse half-toning in newspaper pictures illustrates the end result. The infills for roads, lakes and so on are printed, often in different colours, on top of the half-tone image to enhance the appearance and to make the map easier to use. The more annotation, the more the photomap comes to resemble the conventional map, but it retains one important difference—all the features of the landscape are on it, not merely ones selected and interpreted by the cartographer. Some training is usually necessary before photomaps can be used successfully, since the user must be able to interpret air photographs as well as map-read.

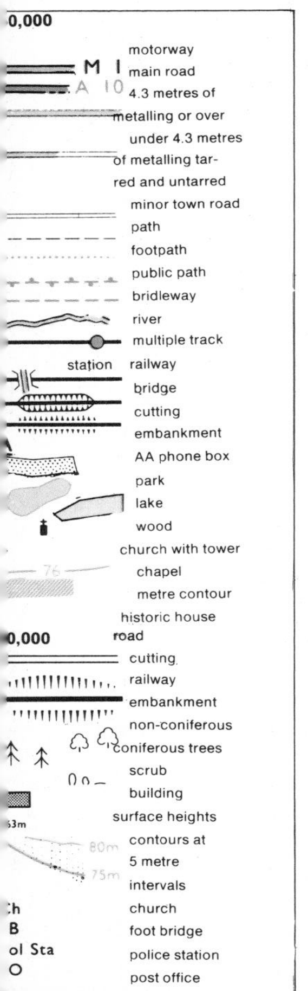

Ordnance Survey

Using Maps

Maps are a familiar feature of modern life: they are seen everywhere. On television the weather forecast is explained with the help of a map, in town centres the road systems and important local buildings, like the hospital and police station, are displayed on a map, and on railway stations maps show how to travel from one place to another. The appearance of maps varies enormously. Just how a particular map is designed depends on its intended use, and a map designed for one purpose may be quite useless for another: there is, for example, no need for a map of a railway system to be geographically accurate.

Maps are basically of two kinds: *topographic* and *thematic*. The first shows the form of the landscape and the man-made features upon it, while the second shows the distribution of particular phenomena such as the spread of Dutch Elm disease through England in 1976.

The most common use of topographic maps is for route finding by motorists at both very large (town plan) and very small (1:250,000 to 1:1,000,000) scales. In between these two extremes, a variety of other uses, such as for walking and cycling, predominate.

Even if motoring information is the most common use for many maps, other very different kinds of route finding needs exist. Military uses for maps include finding routes where all movements will be out of sight of an observer on a particular hilltop and planning routes for armoured vehicles that avoid valleys in which they might get bogged down. Both military and civilian aircraft have special requirements for route-finding maps. One type of screen display sometimes provided in modern aircraft is the *moving map:* a background map moves continuously to maintain the aircraft's current position at the centre of the screen.

On a more individual level, the Scandinavian sport of orienteering—running in races through forested terrain with the aid of a map and compass—is becoming widespread in Europe and new large scale maps are in continuous production to meet the needs for maps of terrain unfamiliar to all the contestants. Other leisure maps are also now widely available, often tailored to one particular user: in Britain, for example, a special series of maps is available to dinghy sailors.

In most countries, the planning departments of both central and local government are major map users. Central government is chiefly interested in strategic planning, and so most of their maps tend to be small scale, covering the whole of the country. A good example is the *Atlas of the Environment* produced by the Department of the Environment in Britain. This contains about 50 maps of England and Wales and the major conurbations: most are derived from the census of population carried out every ten years and show such features as 'percentage of homes lacking all standard amenities' (inside toilet, bath and hot water). Such maps very quickly show which areas of the country are more 'deprived' than

Cooper-Bridgeman Library

Left: This topographic map of Chelmsford in England was made by John Walker in 1591. Maps like this provide historians with information that would be extremely hard to obtain from any other source: for example, an accurate measure of the extent, and therefore an estimate of the town's population.

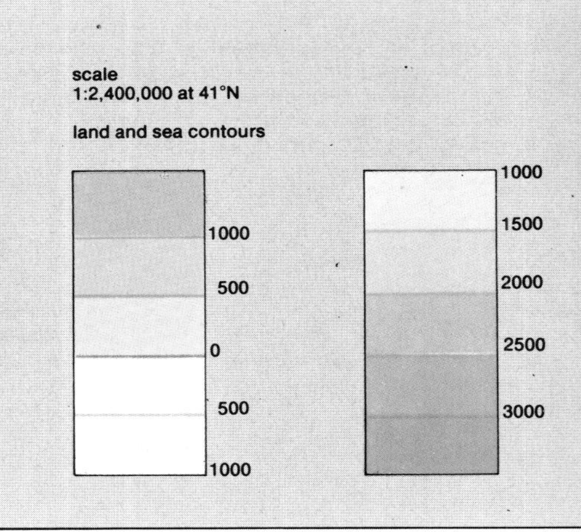

Right: Part of a contour map and key (above) of the east Atlantic. The map is based on many thousands of soundings each checked for consistency by an oceanographer. The position of each sounding is shown as a black dot. Maps of this type are important for navigation and studies of the sea bed.

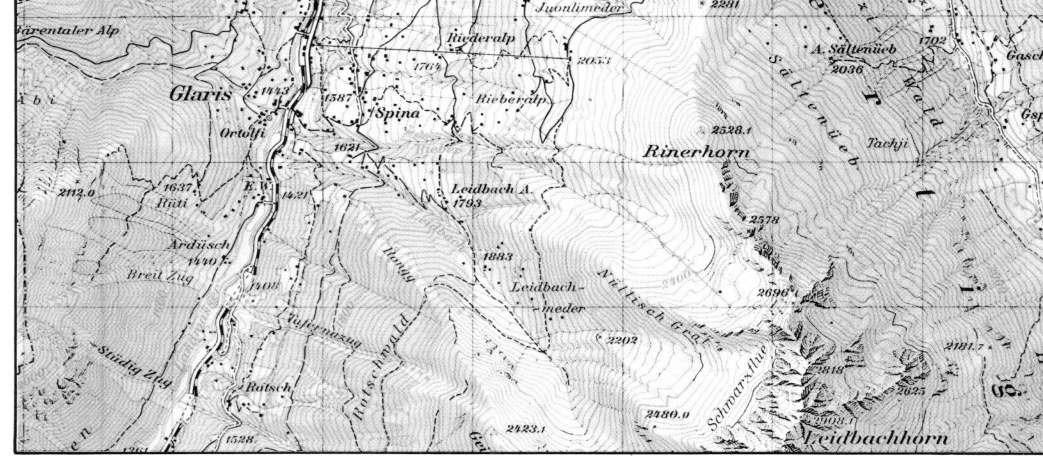

Above: On this Swiss topographic map, relief is shown by contours, by rock drawing and by shading of east and south-facing slopes. Although the scale is only 1:50,000 individual houses are shown. The map provides an enormous amount of detail of the topography of the area.

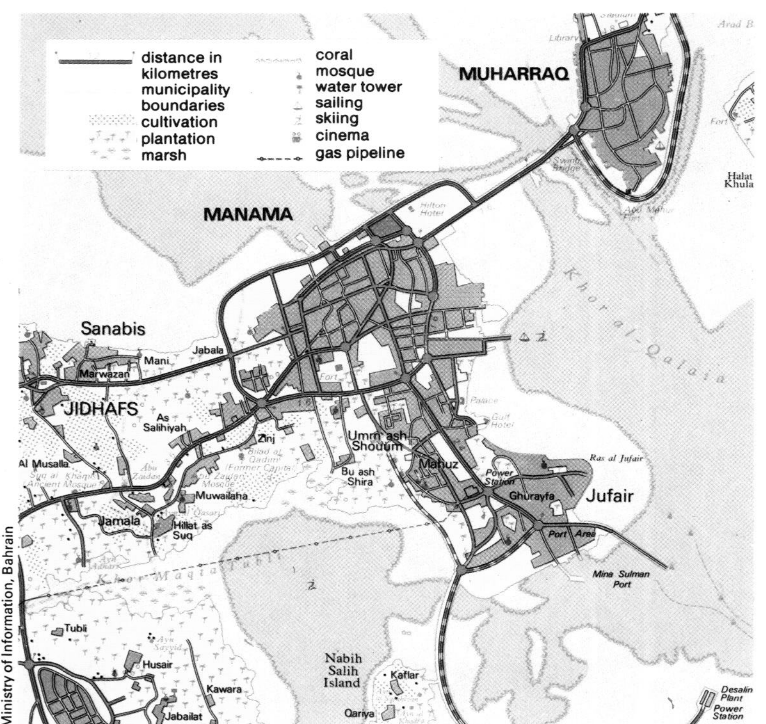

Ministry of Information, Bahrain

Left: The features shown on this map of the northern part of Bahrain have been selected to be of interest to visitors. The map is shown at about half the scale of the Swiss map (above) and the amount of detail is much less. The sizes of certain features on the map (such as the widths of some roads) have been exaggerated for clarity.

Right: A navigational chart showing the arc of visibility of the light on the Needles Rocks at the western tip of the Isle of Wight, England. The chart also shows depths (in fathoms), the type of sea bottom (such as shingle, weed or mud), the direction of magnetic north and the positions of anchorages, radio beacons, radar reflectors and wrecks.

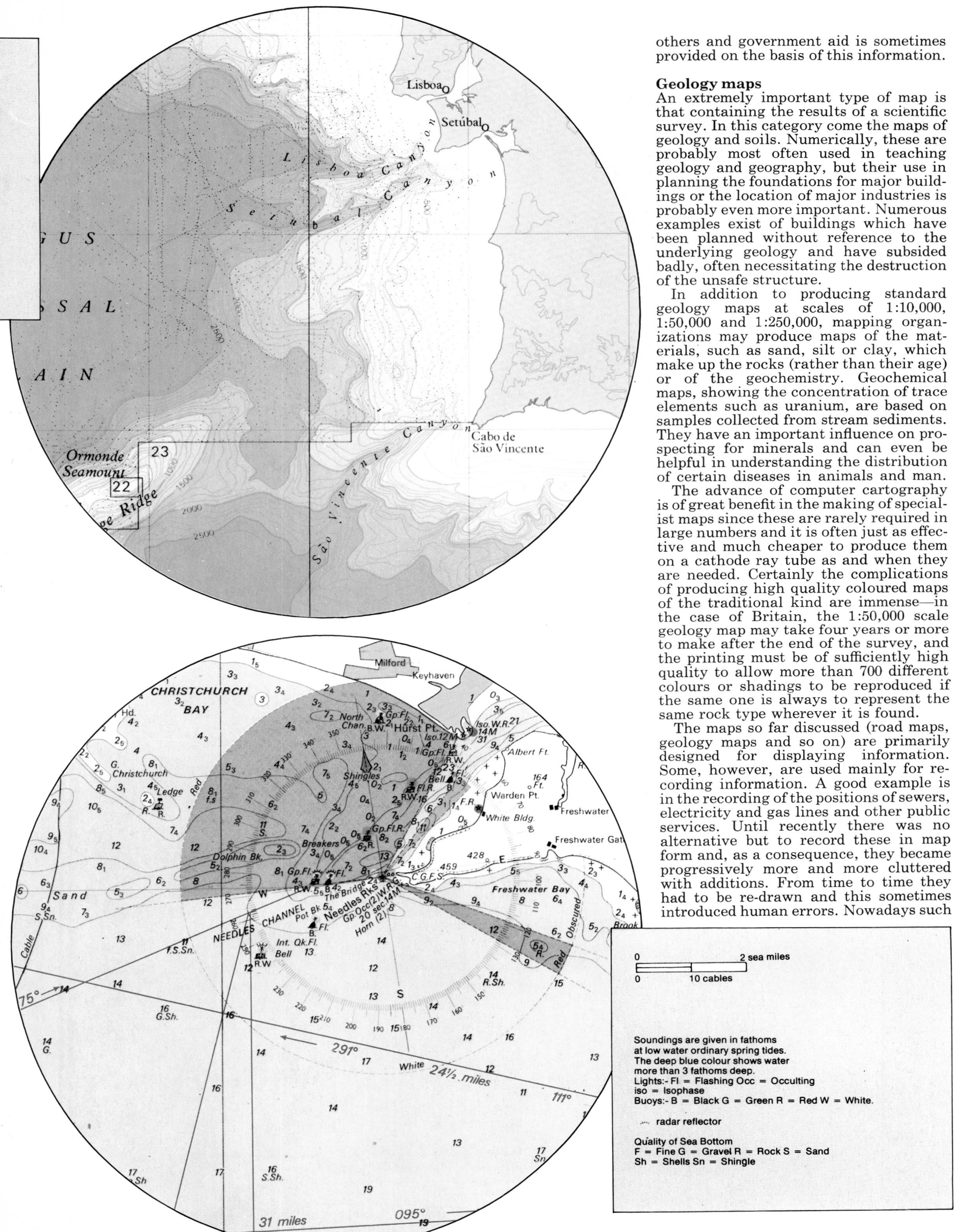

others and government aid is sometimes provided on the basis of this information.

Geology maps

An extremely important type of map is that containing the results of a scientific survey. In this category come the maps of geology and soils. Numerically, these are probably most often used in teaching geology and geography, but their use in planning the foundations for major buildings or the location of major industries is probably even more important. Numerous examples exist of buildings which have been planned without reference to the underlying geology and have subsided badly, often necessitating the destruction of the unsafe structure.

In addition to producing standard geology maps at scales of 1:10,000, 1:50,000 and 1:250,000, mapping organizations may produce maps of the materials, such as sand, silt or clay, which make up the rocks (rather than their age) or of the geochemistry. Geochemical maps, showing the concentration of trace elements such as uranium, are based on samples collected from stream sediments. They have an important influence on prospecting for minerals and can even be helpful in understanding the distribution of certain diseases in animals and man.

The advance of computer cartography is of great benefit in the making of specialist maps since these are rarely required in large numbers and it is often just as effective and much cheaper to produce them on a cathode ray tube as and when they are needed. Certainly the complications of producing high quality coloured maps of the traditional kind are immense—in the case of Britain, the 1:50,000 scale geology map may take four years or more to make after the end of the survey, and the printing must be of sufficiently high quality to allow more than 700 different colours or shadings to be reproduced if the same one is always to represent the same rock type wherever it is found.

The maps so far discussed (road maps, geology maps and so on) are primarily designed for displaying information. Some, however, are used mainly for recording information. A good example is in the recording of the positions of sewers, electricity and gas lines and other public services. Until recently there was no alternative but to record these in map form and, as a consequence, they became progressively more and more cluttered with additions. From time to time they had to be re-drawn and this sometimes introduced human errors. Nowadays such

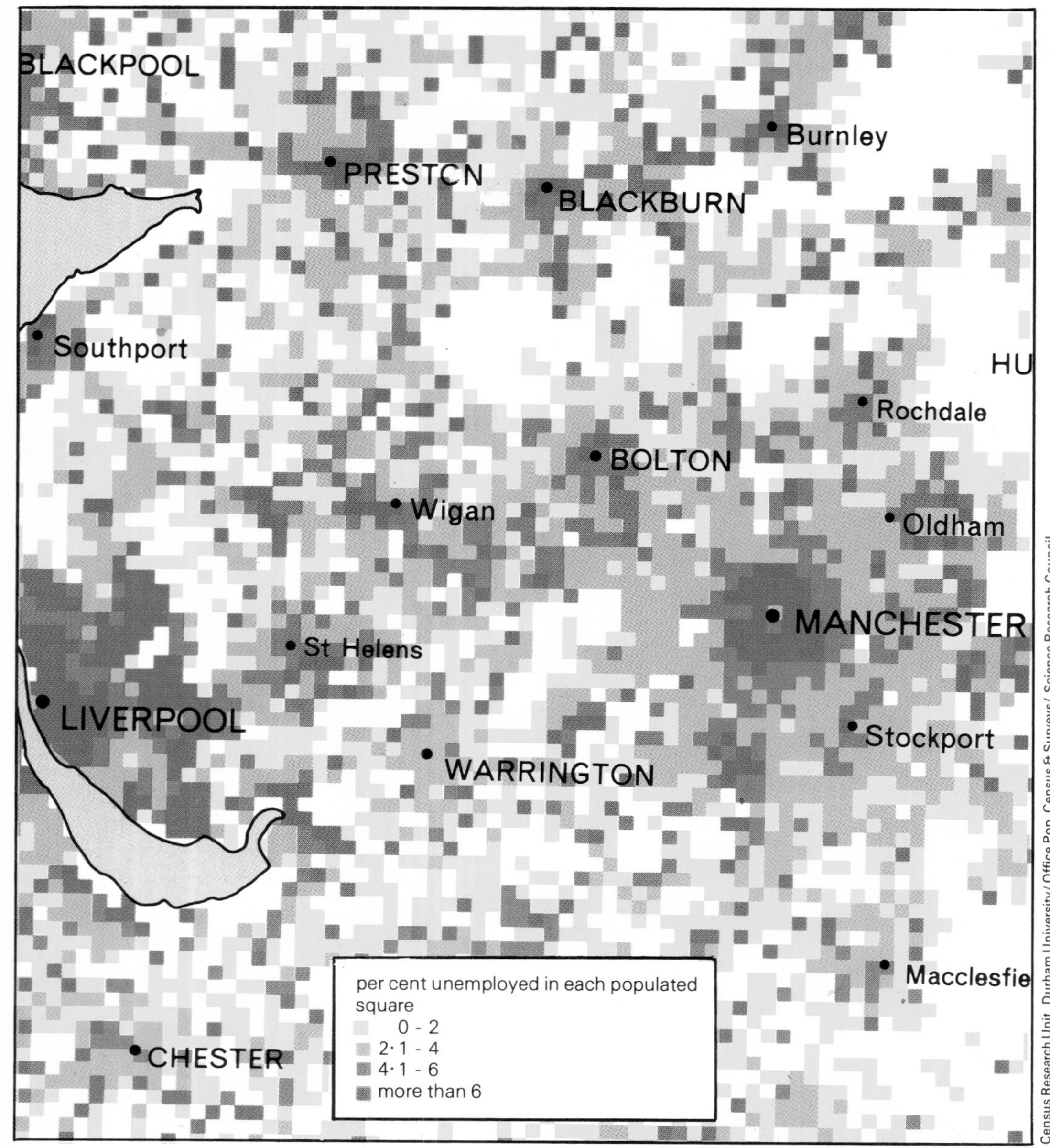

Census Research Unit, Durham University/ Office Pop. Census & Surveys/ Science Research Council

information is often digitized from maps and stored on magnetic tape; a computer can then draw out maps of selected portions of the network at a given scale or can be instructed to correct any mistakes which have been discovered.

Another important use of maps is to link the real world to some other store of information. Perhaps the best example of this is the soil map which normally contains coloured areas, each with a symbol indicating the soil type or, in technical terms, the *soil series*. The characteristics such as depth, colour, stoniness, acidity and so on, of any particular soil series may be found in an accompanying *memoir*. This combined use of map and memoir is necessary to interpret soils or plan their future use.

Using maps

Whatever the task the map reader must be familiar with the conventions and limitations of the map. Perhaps the most common conventions are those of having north at the top of a published map and using colours similar to those of the features in the real world, such as blue for sea and green for grass. The limitations of the map are quite another matter and most of these stem from the question of map scale. A simple example illustrates this: on a 1:10,000 scale map (one unit of length on the map represents 10,000 of the same units on the ground) a road represented as 2 mm wide would be 20 m wide in reality. On a 1:50,000 scale map, the same 2 mm would represent a road 100 m wide and on a 1:250,000 scale map, it would represent a width of no less than 500 m.

Such scale considerations ensure that the cartographer must adapt the way he shows the world to what is possible on a relatively small piece of paper. As a result, he will often show some features on small scale maps by caricatures—twisting alpine roads have many individual bends missed out but are still shown as being very sinuous to maintain the impression of their character. In topographic maps, this sort of generalization normally begins at scales of about 1:50,000 and smaller: at larger scales most features can be represented without significant distortion.

A second limitation of any map is in what it shows. The conventional line map, like the British Ordnance Survey maps, show only a selection of what might have been put on the map. Relatively little, for example, is shown of land use except for the location of wooded areas, and nothing is shown of underground features such as subways or sewers. Maps in different countries, even if they are drawn to the same scale, will show different things, as can be seen by comparing maps of adjacent areas on either side of an international boundary.

Sometimes, however, a map shows more than is apparent. A good example of this is seen in a geology map now published in Britain at 1:50,000 scale. This shows the age and, to some extent, the physical character of the rocks making up the landscape by different colours and by symbols. Underneath the colours, however, is an Ordnance Survey topographic map printed in grey. By comparing the Ordnance Survey contours and the position of the boundaries of the rocks on the geology map, the geologist can tell not only where the rocks appear on the ground but also whether they are tilted underground and, if so, where the boundary between any two strata is to be found at all depths. Thus the amount of information that can be derived from the whole map is more than can be obtained from all the parts considered separately.

Map reading

An essential ability in using maps is to be able to think spatially: to be able to establish a mental picture of the mapped area by translating the symbols on the map into real features. Until relatively recently it was thought that such spatial abilities were not acquired until the age of six or seven, but experiments have shown that children as young as three years can occasionally think in this way, though they are incapable of sophisticated work, such as working out whether one point can be seen from another, until they are eight or nine.

It is clear from everyday experience that some people can understand and read maps much better than others. To improve map design, geographers need to understand the mechanisms by which the map user finds and selects the information he is seeking on the map. Many studies have been carried out—some as long ago as the 1920s—but the majority of these were inconclusive and more recent studies have only served to illuminate the difficulty of carrying out perception tests on map users.

In standard tests maps with only slight differences are given to different users who are then assessed for speed and accuracy in carrying out tasks such as finding the most direct route from place A to place B. In theory, with a well-designed experiment and with careful use of statistics, it should be possible to determine just which difference has had the greatest effect on the usefulness of the map. Unfortunately, however, it is virtually impossible to change an item in a map design without changing many others: changing scale without altering the map size or the area displayed is, for example, quite impossible. Some findings of value have come out of these studies. For example, map users regularly underestimate the values represented by the circular symbols commonly used to indicate the sizes of towns on maps. The larger these are, the larger the towns they represent, but the increase is usually underestimated: the problem is easily solved by making the symbols larger still. Perhaps the most important finding, however, is that individuals can vary hourly in their accuracy and speed of map reading.

Index

Page numbers in *italics* indicate illustrations in addition to text matter on the subject.

A

B

C

D

E

F